Modern Methods of Plant Analysis

New Series Volume 9

Editors

H.F. Linskens, Erlangen/Nijmegen

J.F. Jackson, Adelaide

Volumes Already Published in this Series:

Volume 1: Cell Components
1985, ISBN 3-540-15822-7

Volume 2: Nuclear Magnetic Resonance
1986, ISBN 3-540-15910-X

Volume 3: Gas Chromatography/
Mass Spectrometry
1986, ISBN 3-540-15911-8

Volume 4: Immunology in Plant Sciences
1986, ISBN 3-540-16842-7

Volume 5: High Performance Liquid Chromatography
in Plant Sciences
1987, ISBN 3-540-17243-2

Volume 6: Wine Analysis
1988, ISBN 3-540-18819-3

Volume 7: Beer Analysis
1988, ISBN 3-540-18308-6

Volume 8: Analysis of Nonalcoholic Beverages
1988, ISBN 3-540-18820-7

Volume 9: Gases in Plant and Microbial Cells
1989, ISBN 3-540-18821-5

Forthcoming:

Volume 10: Plant Fibers
ISBN 3-540-18822-3

Volume 11: Physical Methods in Plant Sciences
ISBN 3-540-50332-3

Gases in Plant and Microbial Cells

Edited by
H.F. Linskens and J.F. Jackson

Contributors

D.J. Arp L. Baresi P.K. Bassi S. Ben-Yehoshua A.C. Cameron
J.V. Dean H.P. Fock R. Hampp J.E. Harper U. Heber Y. Inoue
J.F. Jackson A.M. Johnson-Flanagan B.H. Marie W. Mehrle
D.J.D. Nicholas D.M. Oosterhuis D.P. Ormrod H. Pfanz G. Sarath
N.L. Schaefer T.D. Sharkey M.R. Smith M.S. Spencer H.S. Srivastava
D.F. Sültemeyer S. Swenson W. Vidaver F.W. Wagner S.D. Wullschleger

With 88 Figures and 29 Tables

Springer-Verlag
Berlin Heidelberg New York
London Paris Tokyo

Professor Dr. HANS-FERDINAND LINSKENS
Goldberglein 7
D-8520 Erlangen

Professor Dr. JOHN F. JACKSON
Department of Biochemistry
Waite Agricultural Research Institute
University of Adelaide
Glen Osmond, S.A. 5064
Australia

ISBN 3-540-18821-5 Springer-Verlag Berlin Heidelberg New York
ISBN 0-387-18821-5 Springer-Verlag New York Berlin Heidelberg

Library of Congress Cataloging-in-Publication Data. Gases in plant and microbial cells/edited by H. F. Linskens and J. F. Jackson; contributors, D. J. Arp ... [et al.]. p. cm. – (Modern methods of plant analysis; new ser., v. 9) Includes bibliographies and index. ISBN 3-540-18821-5. ISBN 0-387-18821-5 (U.S.) 1. Gases in plants – Analysis. 2. Plant cells and tissues – Analysis. 3. Gases in microorganisms – Analysis. I. Linskens, H. F. (Hans F.), 1921– . 2. Jackson, J. F. (John F.), 1935– . QK875.G38 1989 581.1-dc19

Typesetting, printing and bookbinding: Brühlsche Universitätsdruckerei, Giessen
2131/3130-543210 – Printed on acid-free paper

Introduction

Modern Methods of Plant Analysis

When the handbook *Modern Methods of Plant Analysis* was first introduced in 1954 the considerations were:

1. the dependence of scientific progress in biology on the improvement of existing and the introduction of new methods;
2. the difficulty in finding many new analytical methods in specialized journals which are normally not accessible to experimental plant biologists;
3. the fact that in the methods sections of papers the description of methods is frequently so compact, or even sometimes so incomplete that it is difficult to reproduce experiments.

These considerations still stand today.

The series was highly successful, seven volumes appearing between 1956 and 1964. Since there is still today a demand for the old series, the publisher has decided to resume publication of *Modern Methods of Plant Analysis*. It is hoped that the New Series will be just as acceptable to those working in plant sciences and related fields as the early volumes undoubtedly were. It is difficult to single out the major reasons for success of any publication, but we believe that the methods published in the first series were up-to-date at the time and presented in a way that made description, as applied to plant material, complete in itself with little need to consult other publications.

Contributing authors have attempted to follow these guidelines in this New Series of volumes.

Editorial

The earlier series *Modern Methods of Plant Analysis* was initiated by Michel V. Tracey, at that time in Rothamsted, later in Sydney, and by the late Karl Paech (1910–1955), at that time at Tübingen. The New Series will be edited by Paech's successor H.F. Linskens (Nijmegen, The Netherlands) and John F. Jackson (Adelaide, South Australia). As were the earlier editors, we are convinced "that there is a real need for a collection of reliable up-to-date methods for plant analysis in large areas of applied biology ranging from agriculture and horticultural experiment stations to pharmaceutical and technical institutes concerned with raw material of plant origin". The recent developments in the fields of plant biotechnology and genetic engineering make it even more important for workers in the plant sciences to become acquainted with the more sophisticated methods, which sometimes come from biochemistry and biophysics, but which also have been developed in commercial firms, space science laboratories, non-university research institutes, and medical establishments.

Concept of the New Series

Many methods described in the biochemical, biophysical, and medical literature cannot be applied directly to plant material because of the special cell structure, surrounded by a tough cell wall, and the general lack of knowledge of the specific behavior of plant raw material during extraction procedures. Therefore all authors of this New Series have been chosen because of their special experience with handling plant material, resulting in the adaptation of methods to problems of plant metabolism. Nevertheless, each particular material from a plant species may require some modification of described methods and usual techniques. The methods are described critically, with hints as to their limitations. In general it will be possible to adapt the methods described to the specific needs of the users of this series, but nevertheless references have been made to the original papers and authors. While the editors have worked to plan in this New Series and made efforts to ensure that the aims and general layout of the contributions are within the general guidelines indicated above, we have tried not to interfere too much with the personal style of each author.

There are several ways of classifying the methods used in modern plant analysis. The first is according to the technological and instrumental progress made over recent years. These aspects were used for the first five volumes in this series describing methods in a systematic way according to the basic principles of the methods.

A second classification is according to the plant material that has to undergo analysis. The specific application of the analytical method is determined by the special anatomical, physiological, and biochemical properties of the raw material and the technology used in processing. This classification will be used in Volumes 6 to 8, and for some later volumes in the series. A third way of arranging a description of methods is according to the classes of substances present in the plant material and the subject of analytic methods. The latter will be used for later volumes of the series, which will describe modern analytical methods for alkaloids, drugs, hormones, etc.

Naturally, these three approaches to developments in analytical techniques for plant materials cannot exclude some small overlap and repetition; but careful selection of the authors of individual chapters, according to their expertise and experience with the specific methodological technique, the group of substances to be analyzed, or the plant material which is the subject of chemical and physical analysis, guarantees that recent developments in analytical methodology are described in an optimal way.

Volume Nine – Gases in Plant and Microbial Cells

This volume is the first work in recent times to contain an authoritative compilation of methods for the analysis of a comprehensive range of gases interacting with plant cells. In view of the importance of gaseous components to plant life, the editors have had much satisfaction in bringing together the work of authors, each of whom is an expert on certain gases or plant cells interacting with gases. For not only are gases essential for plant metabolism and development, but conversely plant life itself has been one of the major factors in the development of the present-day gaseous composition of the earth's atmosphere. While there is some controversy about the composition of the earth's primitive atmosphere, it is thought to have been rich in carbon dioxide and water vapor, and in addition to contain such gases as methane, ammonia and hydrogen. Notably oxygen is not considered to have been present at the earliest times, and at the start of life approximately 4000 million years ago, carbon dioxide may have made up as much as 30% of the atmosphere (Charlson et al. 1987; Lovelock and Whitfield 1982).

It is appropriate here to consider further the role plants are throught to have played in the development of the composition of the atmosphere and through this our climate. Examination of Precambrian fig tree sediments in South Africa thought to be 3200 million years old, has revealed the presence of chlorophyll breakdown products in algallike remains. It is thought that Ecobacteria and Cyanophyceae carried out a photosynthesis-like reaction, perhaps without producing oxygen in these early times. It is likely that the process of photosynthesis began in these early epochs, utilizing the rich source of the atmosphere for carbon dioxide needed in the process and later producing oxygen which thus began accumulating. There is evidence from fossil remains in the 1000-million-year-old Bitter Springs sediments in Australia of aerobic life. In the Cambrian period about 600 million years ago, it is likely that atmospheric oxygen had built up to significant proportions due to photosynthetic bacteria, blue-green algae and aquatic fungi. By Carboniferous times (300 million years ago) there had developed huge forests of psilopsids in Europe and North America, and with photosynthesis steadily consuming carbon dioxide and giving up oxygen, the earth's atmosphere gradually came to approach that of the present day. Oxygen-breathing fish and amphibians had meanwhile developed as a consequence, followed by warm-blooded mammals breathing oxygen some 200 million years ago in Triassic times. It is likely that the oxygen given off by plants may have been deadly to many organisms at that time, while allowing the development of oxygen-breathing mammals.

While oxygen was accumulating, carbon dioxide was reduced by a factor of 1000 or so to the level we have today, approximately 350 ppm by volume. According to Charlson et al. (1987) a level of about 150 ppm carbon dioxide can be tolerated before impairment of plant growth occurs, a level not so far below current values. However, it seems that carbon dioxide in the atmosphere is again increasing at the rate of 1.5 ppm $year^{-1}$ (Woodward 1987) from the present 350 ppm, probably for the most part due to the release of carbon dioxide as a result of industrial and other activities of man from coal deposits laid down from Carboniferous-Triassic times. Indeed, it is possible that temperate arboreal plant species are reacting to this increase, since Woodward (1987) presents evidence to suggests that there has been a 50% decrease in stomatal density in leaves of certain species over the last 200 years, when over the same period there has been an increase from 280 to 350 ppm atmospheric carbon dioxide. This may also mean an increased efficiency in water use through reduced escape of water vapor. It can be seen from the above that the gases of the atmosphere and plant life are indeed closely linked. The gas consumed by photosynthesis, carbon dioxide, is a very important component of the atmosphere in terms of climate. Thus, the Vostoc ice cores provide us with a 160000-year record of temperature and atmospheric carbon dioxide content. Barnola et al. (1987) have reported on their findings from these cores, and come to the conclusion that carbon dioxide could well have been a dominant forcing factor in climate over this period. They found a close correlation between temperature and carbon dioxide; thus, the ice ages some 160000 and 18000 years ago were times of lower (approximately 200 ppm) carbon dioxide and lower temperature (some 8 °C colder than now).

It is evident then that the plants not only depend on the gases of the atmosphere for their very existence, but also influence its composition. Analysis of gases is therefore of utmost important in the study of plant cells. Oxygen evolution and uptake occupy crucial roles in plant metabolism, and so analysis of both are dealt with in this volume. Carbon dioxide assimilation for photosynthesis similarly finds an important place, while nitrogen fixation, immunological detection of nitrogenase and analysis of the nitrogen oxides are all covered, a consequence of the fact that nitrogen is today a major component of our atmosphere. Analysis of nitrogen fixation is important since here again nitrogen is an essential part of the make up of all living matter, and plants harness this gaseous raw material raw and make it available for other living matter. It is considered that nitrogen fixation by bacteria in symbiotic relationship with plants are responsible for 90% of nitrogen turnover in the biosphere, fixing approximately 10^9 t $year^{-1}$. According to Nicholas (this Vol.), fertilizers produced by man harness only 5% of the annual amount of nitrogen fixed for cell metabolism.

The measurement of gases resulting in acid rain and their effects on plant life are another important aspect of gases interacting with plant cells. No treatment of gases and plant cells today would be complete without mention of the so-called greenhouse gases. As a result of human activity there has been an input into the atmosphere of carbon dioxide as discussed above, but also nitrous oxide, methane, synthetic halogen compounds and ozone, collectively known as the greenhouse gases. These gases allow sunlight through the atmosphere but trap longer wavelength emission from the earth with resultant warming and shifts in temperature and rainfall. Wigley and Raper (1987) have suggested that global warming as a result of these greenhouse gases building up will mean a temperature rise of 0.6° to 1.0 °C between now and the year 2025 A.D., with a rise of 4 to 5 cm in sea level.

Whether or not this warming takes place, in many parts of the world plant crops suffer water stress due to drought and/or normal summer conditions, resulting in loss of production. For this reason measurement of water vapor loss in vegetative and reproductive (or seed-producing) parts of plants is considered in this volume, together with methods used in the analysis of the effects of water vapor loss and cells most affected. Ozone is also known to cause reductions in crop yield and it seems that formation of ethylene in plants due to stress determines plant sensitivity to ozone (Mehlorn and Wellburn 1987). In addition, the very existence of such a gaseous growth hormone has changed man's understanding of fruit ripening and interaction over short distances between plant parts and plant species. The consideration of ethylene analysis and ethylene effects therefore occupies an important place in this volume.

Plant cells truly hold the key to the gaseous composition of the biosphere and the many conversions of gases to and from important metabolites of living cells.

References

Barnola JM, Raynaud D, Korotkevich YS, Loris C (1987) Vostoc ice core provides, 160000-year record of atmospheric CO_2. Nature 329:408–414

Charlson RJ, Lovelock JE, Andreae MO, Warren SG (1987) Oceanic phytoplankton, atmospheric sulphur, cloud albedo and climate. Nature 326: 655–661

Lovelock JE, Whitfield M (1982) Life span of the biosphere. Nature 296: 561–563

Mehlorn H, Wellburn AR (1987) Stress ethylene formation determines plant sensitivity to ozone. Nature 327:417–418

Wigley TML, Raper SCB (1987) Thermal expansion of sea water associated with global warming. Nature 330:127–131

Woodward FI (1987) Stomatal numbers are sensitive to increase in CO_2 from pre-industrial levels. Nature 327:617–618

Acknowledgements. The editors express their thanks to all contributors for their efforts in keeping to production schedules, and to Dr. Dieter Czeschlik, Ms. K. Gödel, Ms. J. v. d. Bussche and Ms. E. Göhringer of Springer-Verlag for their co-operation with this and other volumes in Modern Methods of Plant Analysis. The constant help of José Broekmans is gratefully acknowledged.

Nijmegen and Adelaide, Winter 1988/1989

H. F. Linskens
J. F. Jackson

Contents

Oxygen

O_2 Evolution and Uptake Measurements in Plant Cells by Mass Spectrometry
H. P. FOCK and D. F. SÜLTEMEYER (With 8 Figures)

Microassay of O_2 Evolution from Single Plant Cells
R. HAMPP and W. MEHRLE (With 14 Figures)

Measurement of O_2 Evolution in Chloroplasts
Y. INOUE (With 5 Figures)

Carbon Dioxide

Analytical Gas Exchange Measurements of Photosynthetic CO_2 Assimilation
T. D. SHARKEY (With 3 Figures)

Other Gases

Hydrogen-Oxidizing Bacteria: Methods Used in Their Investigation

D. J. Arp (With 3 Figures)

Methane Estimation for Methanogenic and Methanotropic Bacteria

M. R. Smith and L. Baresi (With 3 Figures)

Methods for the Quantification of Ethylene Produced by Plants
P. K. BASSI and M. S. SPENCER (With 6 Figures)

Determination of Extra- and Intracellular pH Values in Relation to the Action of Acidic Gases on Cells
H. PFANZ and U. HEBER (With 7 Figures)

List of Contributors

ARP, DANIEL J., Biochemistry Department, University of California, Riverside, CA 92521, USA

BARESI, LARRY, Jet Propulsion Laboratory, California Institute of Technology, Mailstop 125–112, 4800 Oak Grove Drive, Pasadena, CA 91109, USA

BASSI, PAWAN K., Ortho Agricultural Chemicals Division, Chevron Chemical Company, P.O. Box 4010, Richmond, CA 94804, USA

BEN-YEHOSHUA, SHIMSHON, Department of Fruit & Vegetable Storage, Agricultural Research Organization, Volcani Center, P.O. Box 6, Bet – Dagan 50250, Israel

CAMERON, ARTHUR C., Department of Horticulture, Michigan State University, East Lansing, MI 48824, USA

DEAN, JOHN V., University of Minnesota, 1991 Buford Circle, St. Paul, MN 55108, USA

FOCK, HEINRICH P., Fachbereich Biologie, Universität Kaiserslautern, Postfach 3049, 6750 Kaiserslautern, FRG

HAMPP, RÜDIGER, Universität Tübingen, Institut für Biologie I, Biochemie der Pflanzen, Auf der Morgenstelle 1, 7400 Tübingen, FRG

HARPER, JAMES E., USDA/ARS, Department of Agronomy, University of Illinois, 1102 S. Goodwin Ave., Urbana, IL 61801, USA

HEBER, ULRICH, Institut für Botanik und Pharmazeutische Biologie der Universität Würzburg, Mittlerer Dallenbergweg 64, 8700 Würzburg, FRG

INOUE, YORINAO, Solar Energy Research Group, The Institute of Physical and Chemical Research (RIKEN), Wako, Saitama 351-01, Japan

JACKSON, JOHN F., Department of Agricultural Biochemistry, Waite Agricultural Research Institute, University of Adelaide, Glen Osmond, S.A. 5064, Australia

JOHNSON-FLANAGAN, ANNE M., Department of Plant Science, University of Alberta, Edmonton Alberta, Canada T6G 2P5

MARIE, BEVERLEY H., Department of Horticultural Sciences, University of Guelph, Guelph, Ontario, Canada N1G 2W1

MEHRLE, WERNER, Universität Tübingen, Biologie I, Abt. Biochemie, Auf der Morgenstelle 1, 7400 Tübingen, FRG

NICHOLAS, DAVID J. D., Department of Agricultural Biochemistry, Waite Agricultural Research Institute, University of Adelaide, Glen Osmond, S.A. 5064, Australia

OOSTERHUIS, DERRICK M., Altheimer Laboratory, Department of Agronomy, University of Arkansas, Fayetteville, AR 72703, USA

ORMROD, DOUGLAS P., Office of Graduate Studies, University of Guelph, Guelph, Ontario, Canada N1G 2W1

PFANZ, HARDY, Institut für Botanik und Pharmazeutische Biologie der Universität Würzburg, Mittlerer Dallenbergweg 64, 8700 Würzburg, FRG

SARATH, GAUTAM, Department of Biochemistry, University of Nebraska-Lincoln, Lincoln, NE 68583-0718, USA

SCHAEFER, NICHOLAS L., CSIRO, Division of Water Resources, PMB Griffith, N.S.W. 2680, Australia

SHARKEY, THOMAS D., Department of Botany, University of Wisconsin, Madison, WI 53706, USA

SMITH, MICHAEL R., Western Regional Research Center, U.S. Department of Agriculture, 800 Buchanan Street, Albany, CA 94710, USA

SPENCER, MARY S., Department of Plant Science, University of Alberta, Edmonton, Alberta, Canada T6G 2N2

SRIVASTAVA, H. S., Department of Plant Science, Faculty of Life Sciences, Rohilkhand University, Bareilly, U.P. 243005, India

SÜLTEMEYER, DIETER F., Fachbereich Biologie, Universität Kaiserslautern, Postfach 3049, 6750 Kaiserslautern, FRG

SWENSON, SARA, Department of Biological Sciences, Simon Fraser University, Burnaby, B.C., Canada V5A 1S6

VIDAVER, WILLIAM, Department of Biological Sciences, Simon Fraser University, Burnaby, B.C., Canada V5A 1S6

WAGNER, FREDERICK W., Department of Biochemistry, University of Nebraska-Lincoln, Lincoln, NE 68583-0718, USA

WULLSCHLEGER, STAN D., Altheimer Laboratory, Department of Agronomy, University of Arkansas, Fayetteville, AR 72703, USA

Oxygen

O_2 Evolution and Uptake Measurements in Plant Cells by Mass Spectrometry

H. P. FOCK and D. F. SÜLTEMEYER

1 Introduction

Among the different devices to study plant gas exchange, the mass spectrometer is the most universal detector. With the aid of mass spectrometers the concentrations of several gases ($^{16}O_2$, $^{18}O_2$, $^{12}CO_2$, $^{13}CO_2$, $^{14}CO_2$, $^{14}NH_3$, $^{15}NH_3$ and others) in the atmosphere or in the liquid medium surrounding terrestrial or aquatic plants can be simultaneously and continuously measured.

O_2 gas exchange has been extensively studied by mass spectrometry (MS) in a number of photosynthesizing organisms, including blue-green algae (Hoch et al. 1963; Sültemeyer et al. 1987b), green and macroalgae (Glidewell and Raven 1975; Radmer and Kok 1976; Bréchignac and André 1984; Sültemeyer et al. 1986; Bate et al. 1988), mosses and higher plants (Canvin et al. 1980; Gerbaud and André 1980; Furbank and Badger 1982; Ishii and Schmid 1982; Aro et al. 1984; André et al. 1985) and isolated chloroplasts (Egneus et al. 1975; Radmer 1979; Furbank et al. 1983). In labelling experiments with oxygen-18 ($H_2{}^{18}O$, $^{18}O_2$) it became obvious that O_2 exchange in the light is composed of the rate of gross O_2 evolution (E_0) which is generated by photolysis of water and the rate of gross O_2 uptake (U_0; Hoch and Kok 1963; Canvin et al. 1980; Bader et al. 1987). Several O_2-consuming reactions may contribute to U_0 (Fig. 1) among which O_2 reduction by light-generated electrons (Mehler-type reaction), reactions in photorespiration and mitochondrial O_2 uptake in the light may physiologically be important (Berry et al. 1978; Fock et al. 1981; Peltier and Thibault 1985b; Sültemeyer and Fock 1986; Sültemeyer et al. 1986; Bate et al. 1988).

Furthermore, by monitoring the O_2 ($^{16}O_2$, $^{18}O_2$) exchange of photosynthesizing systems (Fig. 7) significant progress has been achieved in understanding the role of some of the reactions which furnish U_0 and effect E_0 (Canvin et al. 1980; Furbank and Badger 1982, 1983; Furbank et al. 1983; Sültemeyer et al. 1987a, b; Bader et al. 1983, 1987). These studies require specially designed gas-exchange systems for the different organisms under investigation with special adaptors to the measuring MS suitable for short- or long-term experiments. It is the aim of this chapter to describe and discuss these methods together with some applications of mass spectrometric O_2 gas-exchange measurements.

2 Theory

2.1 Determination of U_0

The determinations of the opposite O_2 fluxes by photosynthesizing cells require a different isotope composition of molecular oxygen which flows into and out of photosynthesizing cells (Fig. 1). Since no radioactive oxygen isotope is available for labelling experiments, the stable isotopes of oxygen in their molecular forms, $^{18}O_2$ and $^{16}O_2$, are generally used for monitoring O_2 gas exchange. Whereas the

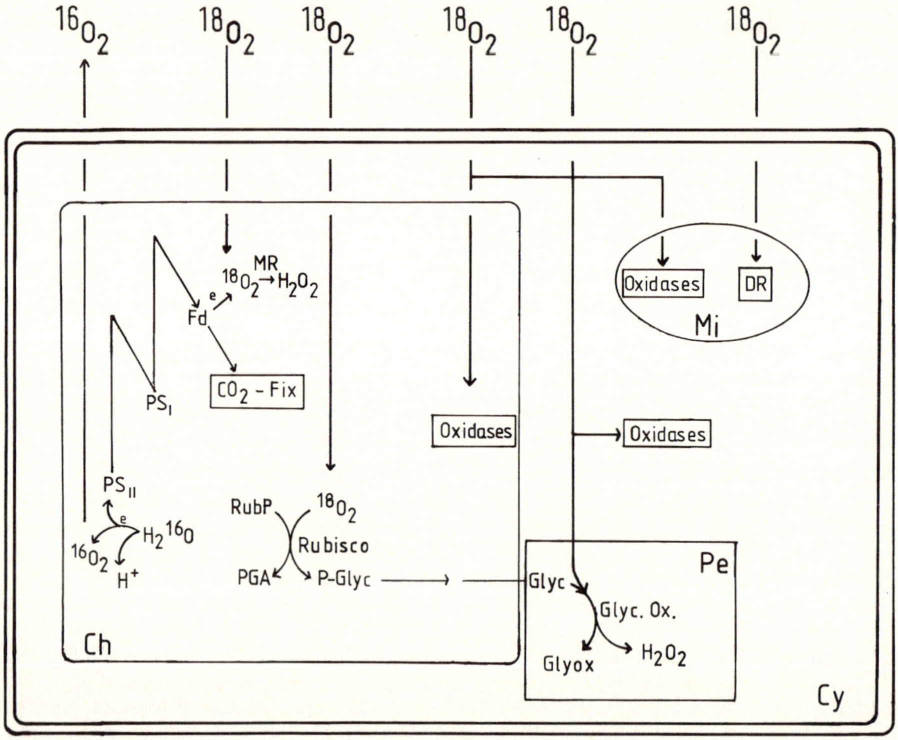

Fig. 1. Scheme of reactions which may be involved in gross O_2 evolution and uptake of a photosynthesizing cell. *Ch* chloroplast; *Cy* cytoplasm; *DR* dark respiration; *Fd* ferredoxin; *Glyc* glycolate; *Glyc. Ox.* glycolate oxidase: *MR* Mehler reaction; *Mi* mitochondria; *Pe* perotisome; *PGA* 3-phosphoglyceric acid; *P-Glyc* phosphoglycolate; $PS_{I(II)}$ photosystem I(II); *RubP* ribulose-1,5-bisphosphate; *Rubisco* RubP carboxylase/oxygenase

natural abundance of $^{16}O_2$ gas is about 99.6% of total O_2, the molecular percentage of $^{18}O_2$ is about 4×10^{-4}% (Radmer and Ollinger 1980).

If the surrounding medium (atmosphere or liquid phase) of a photosynthesizing organism has been enriched with $^{18}O_2$ gas, commercially available from several suppliers at low $^{16}O_2$ concentration, then mainly $^{18}O_2$ is taken up by the O_2-consuming mechanisms, while $^{16}O_2$ is simultaneously evolved by photolysis of $H_2{}^{16}O$ (Figs. 1, 7). This leads to a dilution of the $^{18}O_2$ concentration and an increase in the $^{16}O_2$ concentration during photosynthesis with the result that no longer $^{18}O_2$ alone but also $^{16}O_2$ is taken up by the cells. The rate of total O_2 uptake in the light (U_0) is, therefore, composed of the individual rates of $^{18}O_2$ ($\Delta U^{18}O_2$) and $^{16}O_2$ ($\Delta U^{16}O_2$) uptake:

$$U_0 = \Delta U^{18}O_2 + \Delta U^{16}O_2\ . \qquad (1)$$

During a light period $\Delta U^{18}O_2$ may be directly obtained from the changes in $^{18}O_2$ concentration recorded by MS, while the rate of $^{16}O_2$ uptake has to be calculated. This is possible by assuming that the ratio at which both isotopes are taken up from the medium is directly proportional to the ratio of their individual concentrations (Radmer and Ollinger 1980):

$$\frac{[^{16}O_2]}{[^{18}O_2]} = \frac{\Delta U^{16}O_2}{\Delta U^{18}O_2}. \tag{2}$$

With Eq. (2) $\Delta U^{16}O_2$ can be expressed as:

$$\Delta U^{16}O_2 = \Delta U^{18}O_2 \times \frac{[^{16}O_2]}{[^{18}O_2]}. \tag{3}$$

By substituting $\Delta U^{16}O_2$ in Eq. (1) by Eq. (3) the rate of gross O_2 uptake (U_0) is derived as:

$$U_0 = \Delta U^{18}O_2 \times \left(1 + \frac{[^{16}O_2]}{[^{18}O_2]}\right). \tag{4}$$

2.2 Determination of E_0

The isotope composition of molecular oxygen (O_2) evolved by photolysis of water may be estimated from the isotope composition of oxygen in water which consists of 99.8 at% ^{16}O, 0.2 at% ^{18}O and 0.04 at% ^{17}O (Radmer and Ollinger 1980). Since the abundance of ^{17}O is too small to be of any significance in these measurements, the evolved O_2 carries the masses 32, 34, and 36 and statistically shows the isotope concentrations:

$$100 \times (0.998)^2\%\ ^{16}O_2 = 99.60\%\ ^{16}O_2; \tag{5}$$

$$100 \times 2 \times 0.002 \times 0.998\%\ ^{16}O^{18}O = 0.40\%\ ^{16}O^{18}O; \tag{6}$$

$$100 \times (0.002)^2\%\ ^{18}O_2 = 4 \times 10^{-4}\%\ ^{18}O_2. \tag{7}$$

The rate of gross O_2 evolution in the light (E_0) will thus equal the sum of the rates of $^{16}O_2$ ($\Delta E^{16}O_2$), $^{16}O^{18}O$ ($\Delta E^{(16+18)}O_2$) and $^{18}O_2$ evolution ($\Delta E^{18}O_2$):

$$E_0 = \Delta E^{16}O_2 + \Delta E^{(16+18)}O_2 + \Delta E^{18}O_2. \tag{8}$$

With a percentage of 4×10^{-4} of the gross O_2 evolution, $\Delta E^{18}O_2$ can be safely omitted and Eq. (8) changes to:

$$E_0 = \Delta E^{16}O_2 + \Delta E^{(16+18)}O_2. \tag{9}$$

Then $\Delta E^{(16+18)}O_2$ becomes:

$$\Delta E^{(16+18)}O_2 = 0.004 \times \Delta E^{16}O_2 \tag{10}$$

and Eq. (9) changes to:

$$E_0 = \Delta E^{16}O_2 + 0.004 \times \Delta E^{16}O_2 = 1.004 \times \Delta E^{16}O_2. \tag{11}$$

Consequently, O_2 evolved during photosynthesis is almost completely composed of $^{16}O_2$ and in most experiments the small (0.4%) contribution by $^{16}O^{18}O$ to E_0 can be neglected without losing accuracy:

$$E_0 = \Delta E^{16}O_2 \ . \tag{12}$$

Equation (12) will be valid as long as the isotope composition of oxygen in water as the substrate of O_2 evolution does not change and $^{16}O_2$ is not taken up by the cells. At least in short-term experiments the oxygen isotope composition of cell water is stable. But $^{16}O_2$ (together with $^{18}O_2$) consumption by the cells may be high. For realistic determinations of E_0, the measured rate of $^{16}O_2$ evolution ($\Delta E^{16}O_2$) has to be corrected against the rate of $^{16}O_2$ taken up [$\Delta U^{16}O_2$ in Eq. (1)]:

$$E_0 = \Delta E^{16}O_2 + \Delta U^{16}O_2 \ . \tag{13}$$

$\Delta U^{16}O_2$ can be substituted by Eq. (3):

$$E_0 = \Delta E^{16}O_2 + \Delta U^{18}O_2 \frac{[^{16}O_2]}{[^{18}O_2]} \ . \tag{14}$$

The calculation of the rate of $^{16}O_2$ uptake ($\Delta U^{16}O_2$) is mainly influenced by the changes in the concentration ratio of both O_2 isotopes [Eq. (3)]. However, one should prevent that the changes of this ratio become too high. Otherwise, the accuracy of the determination of U_0 will be reduced. This could be done by using small amounts of photosynthesizing material. For example, measurements should not be used to determine U_0 when the difference between the initial and the final $[^{16}O_2]/[^{18}O_2]$ ratio exeeds 1.5 (Sültemeyer and Fock 1986; Sültemeyer et al. 1986; Bate et al. 1988).

2.3 Determination of DR

Determination of the rate of dark respiration (DR) in the presence of both isotopes, $^{16}O_2$ and $^{18}O_2$, is simplified by the fact that only O_2 uptake proceeds in the dark and, therefore, it is the sum of $^{18}O_2$ and $^{16}O_2$ uptake:

$$DR = \Delta U^{18}O_2 + \Delta U^{16}O_2 \ . \tag{15}$$

2.4 Correction of E_0 and U_0 Against Withdrawal of Gas

Equations (4), (14), and (15) are valid under conditions, when the rate of gas lost from the system (through leaks and to the MS) is negligible in comparison to the rate of O_2 uptake by the cells. However, if the withdrawal of gas from the system is significant, it has to be corrected according to Peltier and Thibault (1985b):

$$U_0 = (\Delta U^{18}O_2 - K \times [^{18}O_2]) \times \left(\frac{[^{18}O_2]+[^{16}O_2]}{[^{18}O_2]}\right), \quad (16)$$

$$E_0 = (\Delta E^{16}O_2 - K \times [^{16}O_2]) + (\Delta U^{18}O_2 - K \times [^{18}O_2]) \frac{[^{16}O_2]}{[^{18}O_2]}, \quad (17a)$$

$$E_0 = (\Delta E^{16}O_2 - K \times [^{16}O_2]) + U_0 \times \left(\frac{[^{16}O_2]}{[^{16}O_2]+[^{18}O_2]}\right), \quad (17b)$$

where K is the rate constant of O_2 consumed by the MS and lost through leaks. It can be measured in the absence of photosynthesizing material.

If the rate of gas lost from the cuvette is significant in comparison to O_2 uptake by the cells in the dark, then Eq. (15) is changed to:

$$DR = \Delta U^{18}O_2 - K \times [^{18}O_2] + \Delta U^{16}O_2 - K \times [^{16}O_2]. \quad (18)$$

3 Equipment

3.1 Mass Spectrometers

According to the principle of mass spectrometry gas samples are introduced into the analyzer and ionized at low partial pressure (about 10^{-8} to 10^{-5} Torr) by bombardment with accelerated electrons (usually 70–90 eV), thermionically generated from a durable filament. The resulting ions are then separated by electric and/or magnetic fields or by other ion separation (e.g. resonance) procedures on the basis of their mass (m) to charge (e) ratios (m/e) and quantitatively analyzed.

For O_2 and CO_2 isotopes and most common gases the predominant peak corresponds to the ions which have been formed by removal of a single electron, e.g. $^{16}O_2^+$ (m/e = 32) from $^{16}O_2$; $^{18}O_2^+$ (m/e = 36) from $^{18}O_2$; $^{12}CO_2$ (m/e = 44) from $^{12}CO_2$, etc. Single ionizations of molecules cause an electric current, when the ions impinge on an ion multiplier or a collector plate connected to ground. Simultaneously unfocussed ions of different mass are diverted to the detector ground. The collector current is proportional to the number of ionized as well as original neutral molecules of the same mass over several orders of magnitude.

The analyzers currently being utilized for the simultaneous determination of several isotopes in gas-exchange studies are magnetic mass spectrometers (Berry et al. 1978; Radmer 1979; Fock et al. 1981; Furbank and Badger 1982, 1983; Sültemeyer and Fock 1986) and scanning quadrupole mass spectrometers (Radmer and Kok 1976; Aro et al. 1984; Bréchignac and André 1984; André et al. 1985). The magnetic mass spectrometers are either run with several fixed collectors (Canvin et al. 1980; Furbank et al. 1982, 1983; Sültemeyer et al. 1986,

1987 a, b; Bader et al. 1987; Bate et al. 1988) or operated with one collector in the scanning mode (Egneus et al. 1975; Radmer 1979; Radmer et al. 1986).

In general, the measured currents are low. Therefore, electrical signal stability by electronic and/or by computer procedures that remove the "noise" is crucial for reliable gas concentration measurements. In our experiments the signal to noise ratio for $^{16}O_2$ dissolved in water and in equilibrium with 21% $^{16}O_2$ in the atmosphere was about 80–100. These values, which are usually sufficient for the measurement of O_2 evolution and uptake, may have to be improved for studies on CO_2 gas exchange. For the determination of O_2 evolution and uptake by cells a simple analyzer with only a small mass range and a resolution of one mass unit is required. If simultaneously CO_2 exchange by cell suspensions is to be measured, particularly at high pH values (pH $\geqq$ 8.0), then a medium to high sensitivity MS may be necessary (Miller et al. 1988). Masses of interest are selected by the position of fixed collectors or electronic peak selector stepper units which are required in the scanning mode. The output signals are then cyclically measured, recorded and possibly stored in a computer attached to the MS. From the recordings or from the stored signals the rates of E_0, U_0, NET (rate of net O_2 evolution in the light) and DR are calculated by the aid of computer facilities.

3.2 Inlet Systems

The inlet system connects the plant chamber to the analyzer of the MS. In principle, two different inlet systems are being utilized: the membrane inlet and the solenoid valve-controlled inlet system.

Figure 2 shows a diagram of the thermostated membrane inlet system used in our experiments (Sültemeyer and Fock 1986; Sültemeyer et al. 1986, 1987 a b; Bate et al. 1988). It is a modification of the system earlier described by Hoch and

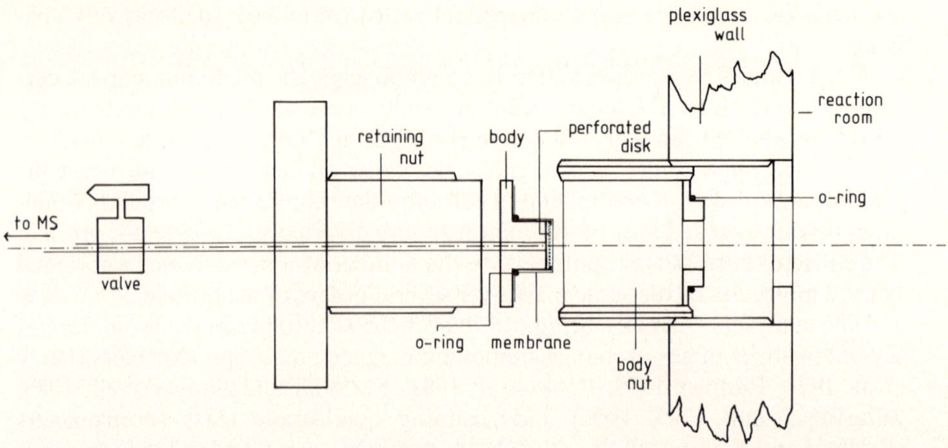

Fig. 2. Schematic diagram of the membrane inlet system used in the authors' experiments (Sültemeyer et al. 1986)

Kok (1963). Similar equipment has been used in other studies (Berry et al. 1978; Canvin et al. 1980; Radmer and Ollinger 1980; Fock et al. 1981; Furbank et al. 1982). The suspending medium is separated from the high vacuum side of the analyzer by a semipermeable membrane which allows the permeation of free gases only but not of water. The choice of the proper membrane material should depend on the gases of interest and the expected kinetics under investigation. For CO_2 and O_2 exchange studies Teflon, polyethylene, polypropylene and silicon rubber films have been used (Furbank et al. 1982; Sültemeyer et al. 1986; Bader et al. 1987; Radmer et al. 1986). Furthermore, the membrane should be thick enough (5–100 μm) to allow a continuous flow of gas into the MS without destabilizing the vacuum.

The membrane is fastened by an O-ring on a perforated stainless steel disk which provides mechanical support for the film (Fig. 2). This O-ring forms the seal between the atmosphere and the membrane. The active area of the membrane is 28 mm^2. After crossing the membrane the gas mixture is introduced into the analyzer through a thermostated stainless steel capillary (0.3 mm in diameter). An on/off valve allows or prevents the flow of gas into the MS. With this valve open, the time delay between fast changes in the O_2 concentration of the medium from 250 to 0 μM O_2 and a 60% response by the MS is about 3 s.

In other systems the gas flow into the MS is controlled by restriction capillaries and solenoid valves instead of a membrane (Gerbaud and André 1980; Ishii and Schmid 1982, 1983; Bréchignac et al. 1983; Aro et al. 1984; Bréchignac and André 1984; André et al. 1985; Peltier and Thibault 1985a). For each analysis a small volume of gas is periodically allowed to enter the MS. Because of the necessary vacuum periods required for the measurements, this inlet system is particularly suitable for long-term experiments. Thus, in connection with plant chambers (see Sect. 4.1) the gas-exchange behaviour of whole plants during development may be analyzed.

4 O_2 Exchange of Higher Plants (Whole Plants, Single Leaves)

4.1 Determination of U_0 and E_0 over Long Periods of Time

The general concept of these investigations is to grow one or several whole plants in almost gas-tight plant chamber(s) in a controlled environment and to study physiological activities of the plant(s) during development (Gerbaud and André 1979; André et al. 1985). In this connection the plants' gas exchange is measured and the data are compiled, stored and recalled from the computer when required (André et al. 1979, 1985).

From the temperature, light and humidity controlled plant growth chamber a manifold of inert gas lines leads to a MS, to a CO_2 IRGA and to other analyzers (Fig. 3; André et al. 1985). For analysis a small fraction (<0.5 ml) of gas is periodically withdrawn from the plant chamber via computer-operated solenoid values, introduced into the MS and other analyzers, and vented to air. However,

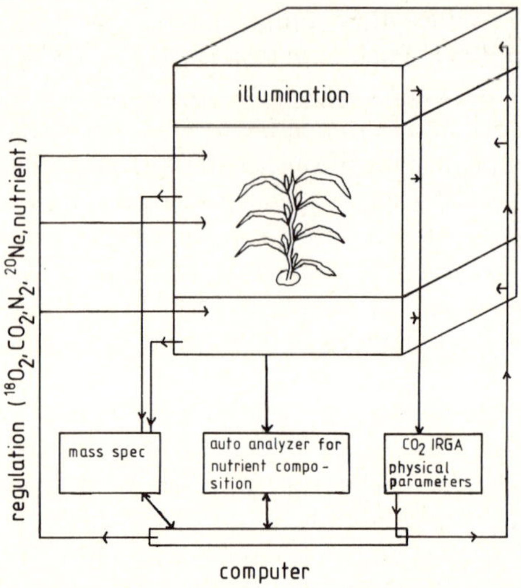

Fig. 3. Scheme of the computerized system for measuring O_2 and CO_2 gas exchange by whole plants over long periods of time. (After André et al. 1979)

the CO_2 IRGA has to be supplied with more gas for the measurements. Therefore, after infrared gas analysis the test gas may be discharged to air only with large plant chambers, while with small chambers the test gas, as a significant proportion of the total gas volume, must be recycled into the plant chamber.

Gas concentrations are measured periodically (every 10–20 min) with the MS and continuously with the CO_2 IRGA. The time required for one MS analysis is about 15 s. Before and after sample analysis from the plant chamber(s) a standard gas mixture (control, from a pressurized cylinder) is measured. Calibration of the MS and quantitative measurements are then achieved by relating the readings of the samples to those of the controls.

The CO_2 IRGA is set at the desired CO_2 concentration in the plant chamber. It serves as the controlling instrument that triggers the valve for (CO_2+N_2) pulse injections into the chamber in the light as long as the measured CO_2 concentration is below the set value. If the CO_2 concentration increases above the set value in the dark, then the IRGA initiates CO_2 trapping. The average rates of net CO_2 uptake in the light and CO_2 evolution in the dark are determined by the number of CO_2 pulses into the plant chamber or by CO_2 trapping at almost constant CO_2 concentration in the chamber.

In order to avoid significant changes in the O_2 concentration in the chamber during the plants' life cycle, the evolved O_2 in photosynthesis has to be diluted by N_2. Therefore, the CO_2 injected into the chamber, which is almost equal to the O_2 produced during photosynthesis, is diluted in approximately 4 vol. N_2. This (CO_2+N_2) mixture is stored in a pressurized gas cylinder (Gerbaud and André 1979).

The average rate of O_2 uptake in the light (U_0, over hours or a day) is determined with only a small quantity of nearly pure $^{18}O_2$ in the atmosphere (about 1% $^{18}O_2$) and Ne as inert reference gas in the plant chamber (Gerbaud and André 1979; André et al. 1985). During the time course of the experiment the concentration of $^{18}O_2$ decreases due to (1) uptake of $^{18}O_2$ (together with $^{16}O_2$) by the plant(s) and (2) due to dilution of the gas in the chamber by the injections of (CO_2+N_2), which nearly equal the gas lost from the chamber by analysis and small leaks (Gerbaud and André 1979). The magnitude of the abiotic gas dilution due to (2) is quantitatively measured by the decrease in the concentration of Ne in the plant chamber. The rate of O_2 taken up by the plant(s) (U_0) is then derived by the ratio between the slower decrease in the Ne and the faster decrease in the $^{18}O_2$ concentration (Gerbaud and André 1979):

$$U_0=\frac{[O_2]\times V}{t}\ln\left[\frac{[^{18}O_2]_{t_0}}{[^{18}O_2]_t}\times\frac{[Ne]_t}{[Ne]_{t_0}}\right]. \tag{19}$$

$[O_2]$ is the average total O_2 concentration $([^{18}O_2]+[^{16}O_2])$ which remains almost constant. V is the volume of the chamber, t_0 the time at the beginning (zero time) and t the time later in the time course of the experiment.

The average rate of net photosynthetic O_2 evolution (NET, over hours or a day) is calculated from net CO_2 uptake P_c and the small increase in the $^{16}O_2$ concentration during the course of the experiment (Gerbaud and André 1979):

$$NET=\frac{1}{1-[^{16}O_2]}\times\left[\frac{V\dot{\times}[^{16}O_2]}{t}+k\times P_c\times[^{16}O_2]\right], \tag{20}$$

where $[^{16}O_2]$ is the average O_2 concentration in the chamber and k is the volume of N_2 injected together with one volume of CO_2 into the chamber.

Finally, the average rate of gross O_2 evolution by photosystem II (E_0) is calculated as the sum of U_0 and NET:

$$E_0=NET+U_0\,. \tag{21}$$

For further details see applications by Gerbaud and André (1979, 1980), Ishii and Schmid (1982, 1983), Aro et al. (1984), and André et al. (1985).

4.2 Determination of U_0 and E_0 over Short Time Intervals

For the determination of fast changes in the rates of O_2 evolution and uptake by an intact leaf over a period of a few to several minutes a small gas-exchange system attached to the MS by means of a thermostated membrane inlet is required. The prototype of such a system has been developed by Berry et al. (1978) and was improved by Canvin et al. (1980; Fig. 4). This closed system consists of a thermostated leaf cuvette, a CO_2 IRGA, a gas-tight pump, a capillary from a pressurized CO_2 cylinder (10% CO_2, 90% N_2) connected to a calibrated manometer for CO_2 supply and a four-way valve. The total gas volume is 74.2 ml.

A leaf is placed in the cuvette, illuminated and aerated. When the stomates are open, the air is replaced by flushing the system with argon. Thereafter, a defined amount of $^{18}O_2$ is injected through the four-way valve into the system which is almost free of $^{16}O_2$ after Ar flushing. Then the system is closed again, the gas is pumped over the leaf and through the system, and the gas exchange of the leaf is measured. O_2 exchange is measured by means of a magnetic sector MS (Varian MAT GD 150/4) which has four collectors allowing each mass to be collected sep-

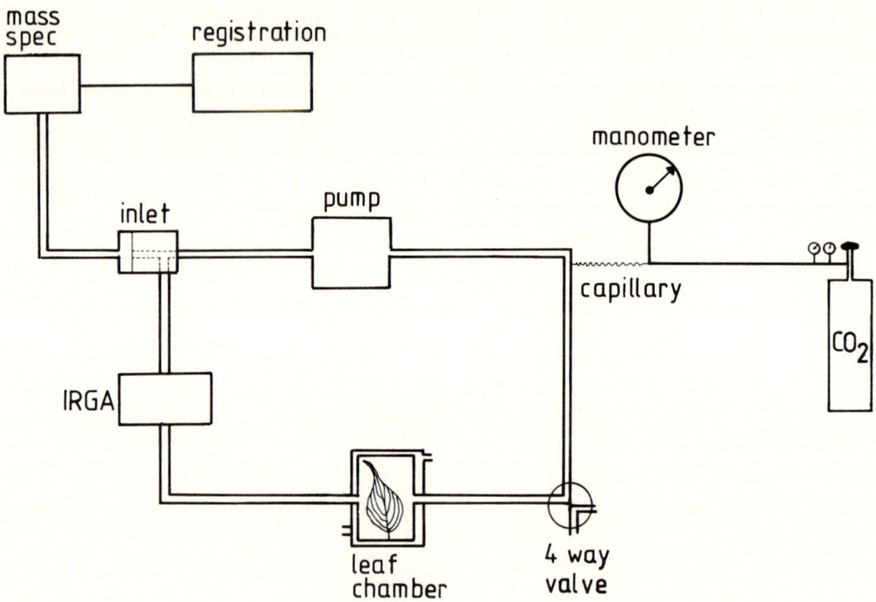

Fig. 4. Closed system for measuring O_2 and CO_2 gas exchange by a single leaf. (After Berry et al. 1978)

arately and simultaneously. Ar is used as the reference gas to correct for the rates of gas lost from the system and to calculate rates of O_2 uptake and evolution according to Eqs. (16) and (17b).

The CO_2 concentration in the closed system is measured by CO_2 IRGA and kept constant during photosynthesis by introducing 10% CO_2 in nitrogen into the system through the capillary at the desired pressure (Fig. 4). At constant CO_2 concentration in the system, net CO_2 uptake is calculated from the rate of CO_2 supply obtained from the reading of the manometer (after proper calibration).

The interested reader is referred to several applications of this gas-exchange system (Berry et al. 1978; Canvin et al. 1980; Furbank and Badger 1982, 1983; Furbank et al. 1982, 1983).

5 O_2 Exchange of Aquatic Suspensions (Algae, Chloroplasts)

The gas exchange of algae or chloroplasts in suspensions can either be determined from the gas dissolved in the liquid suspension (Hoch and Kok 1963; Hoch et al. 1963; Radmer and Ollinger 1980) or from the gas phase in equilibrium with the suspension (Bréchignac et al. 1983). In long-term experiments a gas phase above an aqueous system is required (Bréchignac et al. 1983; Bréchignac and André 1984; Peltier and Thibault 1985b).

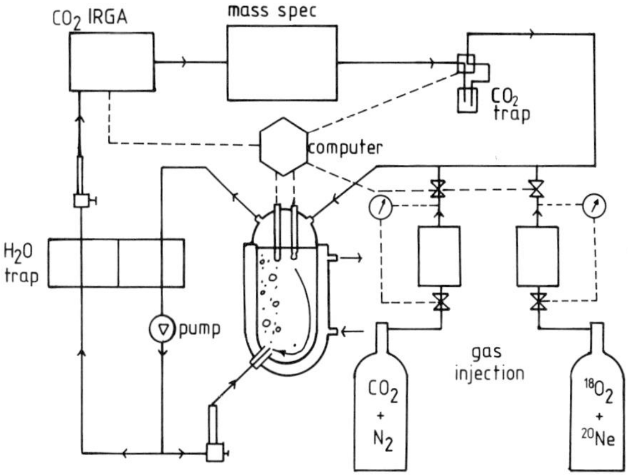

Fig. 5. General diagram of the experimental setup for measuring O_2 and CO_2 gas exchange by submersed organisms over long intervals. (After Bréchignac et al. 1983)

5.1 Determination of U_0 and E_0 over Long Periods of Time

Figure 5 shows a modification of the solenoid valve-controlled gas-exchange system described in Sect. 4.1 (André et al. 1985) which is suitable for gas-exchange measurements of algae over several days and weeks (Bréchignac et al. 1983; Bréchignac and André 1984). The test plant material was the red alga *Chondrus crispus* but similar investigations with *Chlamydomonas* have also been reported by Peltier and Thibault (1985 a).

The thermostated algal cuvette contains 3 litres sea water and 1 litre of a CO_2 and O_2 regulated gas phase which is attached to two gas cycles. The first cycle includes a pump and tubing to recirculate the air through the liquid to the gas phase. Thus, the liquid phase is strongly aerated and sufficient equilibration with the gas phase is ensured. The second cycle contains CO_2 IRGA, MS, gas injection ports for CO_2, $^{18}O_2$, ^{20}Ne, and N_2 supply, and a CO_2 trap and thus functions as a gas regulating and analyzing loop. Long-term experiments with a liquid suspension also require the control of physical parameters such as pH, temperature, light intensity and cell density. All regulating, analyzing and calculating steps are performed by the computer. The $^{18}O_2$ concentration in the gas phase is adjusted daily to around 1% of total O_2 ($^{16}O_2 + ^{18}O_2$) by injecting an $^{18}O_2$/Ne mixture (Fig. 5). Rates of gross O_2 uptake, net O_2 evolution and gross O_2 evolution are determined by Eqs. (19)–(21) (Gerbaud and André 1979).

5.2 Determination of U_0 and E_0 over Short Time Intervals

The common feature of these gas-exchange systems is that they analyze the gas dissolved in a liquid phase and, therefore, they are connected to the MS via a membrane inlet system. If the gases in the cuvette are evenly distributed by proper stirring and if the MS signals are calibrated, then rates of O_2 gas exchange may be determined (Fig. 6). In contrast, if cells have been allowed to settle down on

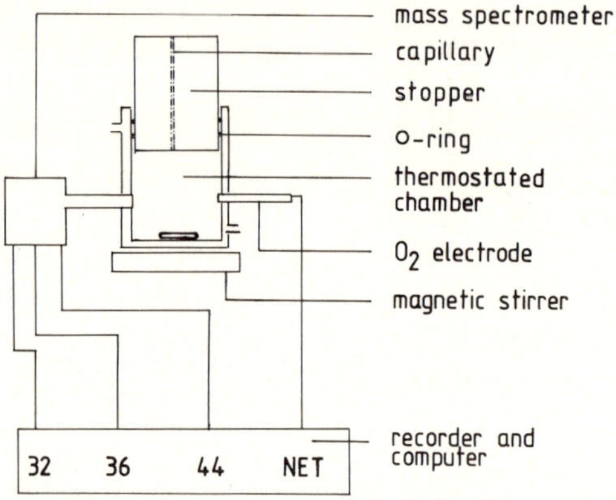

Fig. 6. Diagram of the closed gas-exchange system used in the authors' experiments for measuring O_2 gas exchange by cells or chloroplast suspensions over short time intervals (Sültemeyer at al. 1986)

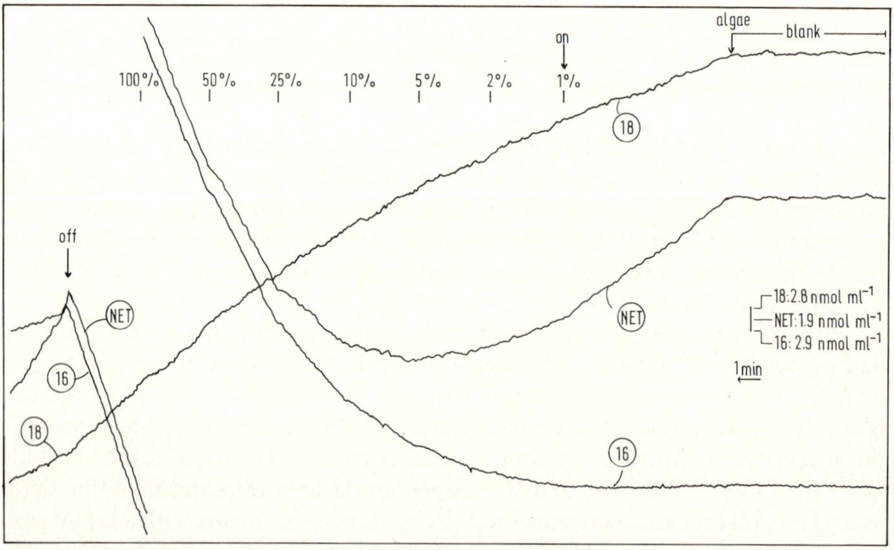

Fig. 7. O_2 exchange in the dark and in the light with a suspension of *Chlamydomonas reinhardtii* (chlorophyll content: 2.1 μg ml^{-1}). The experiment progressed from *right to left*. During illumination light was adjusted between 1 and 100% as indicated by *vertical bars* (100% light = 750 μE $m^{-2}s^{-1}$). Light was switched on and off as indicated by *arrows*. *18* $^{18}O_2$ uptake; *NET* net O_2 exchange; *16* $^{16}O_2$ evolution; *blank* O_2 consumption by MS, leaks and O_2 electrode in the absence of cells

the membrane in an unstirred suspension, the mechanisms and the kinetics of the photosynthetic O_2-generating and -consuming reactions may be studied (Fig. 7).

Figure 6 shows the standard gas-exchange apparatus that is routinely used in our studies to determine rates of gross O_2 evolution and uptake by blue-green algae and green algae (Sültemeyer and Fock 1986; Sültemeyer et al. 1986, 1987a, b; Bate et al. 1988). Similar systems for measuring rates of photosynthetic O_2 exchange by aquatic organisms have been used (Hoch et al. 1963; Egneus et al. 1975;

Radmer and Kok 1976; Radmer and Ollinger 1980; Fock et al. 1981; Furbank et al. 1982; Peltier and Thibault 1985b).

The membrane inlet described in Fig. 2 is placed on the side of the thermostated reaction chamber. On the opposite side an O_2 electrode (model 5331 Yellow Springs, Ohio) measures the total O_2 concentration ($^{18}O_2 + ^{16}O_2$) in the cuvette (Fig. 7). It is further used for the calibration of the $^{18}O_2$ signal (see below). Additionally, two gas-tight ports are mounted at the side of the cuvette (not shown in Fig. 6) which enable the injection and the withdrawal of samples during an experiment. The isotope composition of gas is analyzed by a magnetic sector field MS (GD 150/4, Varian MAT, Bremen, FRG).

An experimental protocol is listed below. The medium in the cuvette is replaced by 40 ml fresh nutrient solution with low $^{16}O_2$ concentration and the cuvette is sealed by the stopper. One ml of $^{18}O_2$ gas (99.8% purity) is injected into the cuvette and allowed to equilibrate with the medium until the relative total O_2 content (low $^{16}O_2$, high $^{18}O_2$) reaches about 21% (measured by O_2 electrode). After removing the bubble, changes in $^{16}O_2$, $^{18}O_2$ and total O_2 concentrations of the medium are continuously recorded for at least 10 min (blank; Fig. 7). Then an aliquot of a concentrated algal suspension is introduced into the chamber to yield a final chlorophyll concentration of 1–3 μg ml^{-1} and after a period of dark respiration the algae are illuminated with a projector lamp (Fig. 7). With this low Chl content, O_2 gas exchange may be measured for about 1 h, with an increase in the relative total O_2 concentration in the suspension from about 21% to about 31% O_2. During that time the relative $^{16}O_2$ content increases from about 4 to 18%, whereas the relative $^{18}O_2$ concentration decreases from about 17 to 13%. All these measurements are performed with an insignificant rate of gas lost by the MS and the O_2 electrode ($\leqq 4$ μm O_2 h^{-1} = blank; Fig. 7) and therefore, U_0 and E_0 are calculated from the decrease and increase of the 32 and 36 signals using Eqs. (4) and (14). Rates for net O_2 evolution (NET) are calculated by two independent methods, firstly, by the O_2 electrode and secondly by MS measurements. Both methods should lead to similar results and, in fact, differ by less than 5% thus enabling a control of the MS measurements by the O_2 electrode (Sültemeyer and Fock 1986; Sültemeyer et al. 1986).

The $^{16}O_2$ signal and the O_2 electrode are calibrated with 40 ml nutrient solution in equilibrium with air at the beginning of an experiment. The $^{18}O_2$ signal is calibrated after $^{18}O_2$ equilibration from the total O_2 and the $^{16}O_2$ concentrations of the medium:

$$[\text{total } O_2] - [^{16}O_2] = [^{18}O_2] \, . \qquad (22)$$

A system suitable for experiments on fast O_2 kinetics is illustrated in Fig. 8 (Bader et al. 1987), but similar systems have been reported (Radmer 1979; Radmer et al. 1986). The reaction chamber contains a gaseous (21 ml) and an unstirred liquid phase (2–3 ml), the gas composition of which is analyzed (Fig. 7). The membrane inlet is mounted at the bottom of the chamber so that the cells or organelles may sediment directly onto the membrane.

Two to three ml of photosynthetically active material (about 30 μg Chl ml^{-1}) are carefully placed over the active membrane area and after sedimentation a thin film of the particles covers the membrane. The chamber is closed gas tight with

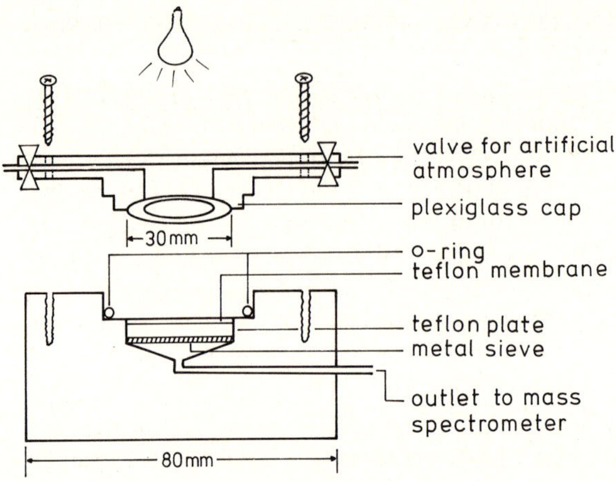

Fig. 8. Schematic diagram of an uncalibrated gas-exchange system for measuring fast O_2 kinetics (Bader et al. 1987)

a plexiglass cap. With its two valves open the gaseous phase can be easily replaced against defined gas compositions containing $^{18}O_2$, $^{16}O_2$ or Ne, or solutions (e.g. $H_2{}^{18}O$) may be added to the suspension. Light flashes (e.g. of 8 μs duration) are provided by a stroboscope (model 1539A, General Radio) mounted at the top of the cuvette.

For measuring O_2 gas exchange induced by single light flashes an MS with a high sensitivity is necessary. This is achieved by using a modified magnetic sector field MS (model Delta, Finnigan MAT, Bremen, FRG) which is a stable isotope ratio MS for monitoring changes in $^{16}O_2$, $^{16}O^{18}O$, and $^{18}O_2$ concentrations. Since the commercial inlet system of this MS is not suitable for dynamic gas-exchange measurements, it is used for pre-evacuation of the assay system after starting a new experiment. After establishing a stable forevacuum, a specifically adapted valve arrangement (Fig. 1 b in Bader et al. 1987) allows the direct connection of the measuring cell to the ion source. In addition, a large active area (1257 mm^2) of a thin membrane (5–10 μm) and a minimal tube volume (20 cm long, 0.5 cm thick) between reaction chamber and the MS are required to measure fast O_2 kinetics (Bader et al. 1987).

Acknowledgements. We wish to thank Drs. Klaus Bader and G. Schmid, University of Bielefeld for providing the original of Fig. 8 and for many helpful discussions.

References

André M, Daguenet A, Massimino D, Vivoli JP, Richaud C (1979) Le laboratoire C 3A. Un outil au service de la physiologie de la plante entière. I. – Les chambres de culture et les systèmes de mesures associés. Ann Agron 30:139–151

André M, Daguenet A, Massimino D, Gerbaud A (1985) The $C_2$3A system, an example of quantitative control of plant growth associated with a data base. SAE Tech Pap Ser 851395:1–10

Aro EV, Gerbaud A, André M (1984) CO_2 and O_2 exchange in two mosses, *Hypnum cupressiforme* and *Dicranum scoparium*. Plant Physiol 76:431–435

Bader KP, Thibault P, Schmid GH (1983) A study on oxygen evolution and on the S-state distribution in thylakoid preparation of the filamentous blue-green alga *Oscillatoria chalybea*. Z Naturforsch 38c:778–792

Bader KP, Thibault P, Schmid GH (1987) Study on the properties of the S_3-state by mass spectrometry in the filamentous cyanobacterium *Oscillatoria chalybea*. Biochim Biophys Acta 893:564–570

Bate GC, Sültemeyer DF, Fock HP (1988) $^{18}O_2/^{16}O_2$ analysis of oxygen exchange in *Dunaliella tertiolecta*. Evidence for the inhibition of mitochondrial respiration in the light. Photosynth Res 16:219–231

Berry JA, Osmond CB, Lorimer GH (1978) Fixation of $^{18}O_2$ during photorespiration. Kinetic and steady-state studies of the photorespiratory carbon oxidation cycle with intact leaves and isolated chloroplasts of C_3 plants. Plant Physiol 62:952–967

Bréchignac F, André M (1984) Oxygen uptake and photosynthesis in the red macroalga, *Chondrus crispus*, in seawater. Plant Physiol 75:919–923

Bréchignac F, André M, Daguenet A, Massimino D (1983) Mesure en continu des échanges de O_2 et de CO_2 d'un végétal aquatique. Physiol Veg 21:665–676

Canvin DT, Berry JA, Badger MR, Fock H, Osmond CB (1980) Oxygen exchange in leaves in the light. Plant Physiol 66:302–307

Egneus H, Heber U, Matthiesen U, Kirk M (1975) Reduction of oxygen by the electron transport chain of chloroplasts during assimilation of carbon dioxide. Biochim Biophys Acta 408:252–268

Fock HP, Canvin DT, Osmond CB (1981) Oxygen uptake in air-grown *Chlamydomonas*. In: Akoyunoglou G (ed) Regulation of carbon metabolism. Photosynthesis, vol 4. Balaban, Philadelphia, pp 677–682

Furbank RT, Badger MR (1982) Photosynthetic oxygen exchange in attached leaves of C_4 monocotyledons. Aust J Plant Physiol 9:553–558

Furbank RT, Badger MR (1983) Oxygen exchange associated with electron transport and photophosphorylation in spinach thylakoids. Biochim Biophys Acta 723:400–409

Furbank RT, Badger MR, Osmond BC (1982) Photosynthetic oxygen exchange in isolated cells and chloroplasts of C_3 plants. Plant Physiol 70:927–931

Furbank RT, Badger MR, Osmond CB (1983) Photoreduction of oxygen in mesophyll chloroplasts of C_4 plants. A model system for studying an in vitro Mehler reaction. Plant Physiol 73:1038–1041

Gerbaud A, André M (1979) Photosynthesis and photorespiration in whole plants of wheat. Plant Physiol 64:735–738

Gerbaud A, André M (1980) Effect of CO_2, O_2, and light on photosynthesis and photorespiration in wheat. Plant Physiol 66:1032–1036

Glidewell SM, Raven JA (1975) Measurement of simultaneous oxygen evolution and uptake in *Hydrodictyon africanum*. J Exp Bot 26:479–488

Hoch G, Kok B (1963) A mass spectrometer inlet system for sampling gases dissolved in liquid phases. Arch Biochem Biophys 101:160–170

Hoch G, Owens OH, Kok B (1963) Photosynthesis and respiration. Arch Biochem Biophys 101:171–180

Ishii R, Schmid GH (1982) Studies on $^{18}O_2$-uptake in the light by entire plants of different tobacco mutants. Z Naturforsch 37c:93–101

Ishii R, Schmid GH (1983) Consequences of Warburg effect conditions on growth parameters and CO_2-exchange rates in tobacco mutants. Plant Cell Physiol 24:1525–1533

Miller AG, Espie GS, Canvin DT (1988) Active transport of CO_2 by the cyanobacterium *Synechococcus* UTEX 625: measurement by mass spectrometry. Plant Physiol 86:677–683

Peltier G, Thibault P (1985a) Light-dependent oxygen uptake, glycolate, and ammonia release in L-methionine sulfoximine-treated *Chlamydomonas*. Plant Physiol 77:281–284

Peltier G, Thibault P (1985b) O_2 uptake in the light in *Chlamydomonas*. Plant Physiol 79:225–230

Radmer R (1979) Mass spectrometric determination of hydroxylamine photooxidation by illuminated chloroplasts. Biochim Biophys Acta 546:418–425
Radmer R, Kok B (1976) Photoreduction of O_2 primes and replaces CO_2 assimilation. Plant Physiol 58:336–340
Radmer R, Ollinger O (1980) Measurements of the oxygen cycle: the mass spectrometric analysis of gases dissolved in a liquid phase. Meth Enzymol 69:547–560
Radmer R, Cammarata K, Tamura N, Ollinger O, Cheniae O (1986) Depletion of photosystem II H-extrinsic proteins. I. Effects on O_2- and N_2-flash yields and steady-state O_2 evolution. Biochim Biophys Acta 850:21–32
Sültemeyer DF, Fock HP (1986) Mass spectrometric analysis of photosynthetic oxygen evolution and uptake by *Chlamydomonas reinhardtii*. In: Marcelle R, Clijsters H, Van Poucke M (eds) Biological control of photosynthesis. Nijhoff, Dordrecht Lancaster, pp 135–142
Sültemeyer DF, Klug K, Fock HP (1986) Effect of photon fluence rate on oxygen evolution and uptake by *Chlamydomonas reinhardtii* suspensions. Plant Physiol 81:372–375
Sültemeyer DF, Klug K, Fock HP (1987a) Effect of dissolved inorganic carbon on oxygen evolution and uptake by *Chlamydomonas reinhardtii* suspensions adapted to ambient CO_2-enriched air. Photosynth Res 12:25–33
Sültemeyer DF, Stuhlfauth T, Fock HP (1987b) Is pseudocyclic ATP formation involved in providing energy for the HCO_3^--concentrating mechanism in blue green algae? Plant Physiol (Suppl) 83:161

Microassay of O_2 Evolution from Single Plant Cells

R. HAMPP and W. MEHRLE

1 Introduction

The measurement of O_2 evolution in a closed system is one of the easiest means of demonstrating, or following the process of photosynthesis in a leaf, a suspension of leaf cells or of isolated chloroplasts. Conventional and widely applied techniques are Warburg manometry or Clark-type oxygen electrodes (e.g. Delieu and Walker 1972). For the assay of particle suspensions (cells, chloroplasts) volumes of typically 1 ml are employed, corresponding to, e.g. 10^5 to 10^6 leaf mesophyll cells. With an ordinary Clark-type O_2 electrode, as used for leaf discs, the lower limit of detection corresponds to a change in O_2 of about 1 nmol (Delieu and Walker 1981). This is equivalent to the amount of O_2 evolved by about 10^3 to 10^4 mesophyll cells per minute.

Leaf mesophyll cells, free of cell wall material ("protoplasts") constitute an important tool for physiological, biochemical or genetic research. However, the isolation of protoplasts may result in physiological perturbations that introduce artefacts. Thus, assessing the integrity of protoplasts should be a routine procedure for many types of investigations. The most commonly used indicators available are vital stains and vital fluorochromes (see Bornman and Bornman 1983). These are rapid procedures, but are less accurate then a test of the ability of protoplasts to regenerate a cell wall and divide. Unfortunately, the latter tests are not suitable for routine use, particularly when time is of importance. In experiments on protoplast fusion, we used biochemical parameters such as the determination of the cellular energy state in addition to staining procedures (Verhoek-Köhler et al. 1983). A system of higher complexity is photosynthesis. High rates of photosynthetic oxygen evolution are possible only if there is a high degree of cellular integrity. In experiments with oat mesophyll protoplasts we showed that damage not detected with staining (FDA = fluorescein diacetate) is manifested by decreased rates of photosynthesis (Hampp et al. 1986).

Our need to assess the viability of hybrids obtained by electrofusion of mesophyll cell protoplasts (Zimmermann et al. 1985) led to the development of a miniaturized assay for changes in oxygen concentration. Here, we describe a bacteria-based semiquantitative technique for the assay of photosynthetic oxygen evolution at the single cell level. Sensitivity, short response time and general applicability are demonstrated with green protoplasts isolated from several species and with hybrids obtained by an electrofusion procedure.

2 Historical Background

In 1881 Engelmann published a paper entitled „Neue Methode zur Untersuchung der Sauerstoffausscheidung pflanzlicher und thierischer Organismen". In this communication Engelmann demonstrated light-dependent O_2 evolution of algal cells and leaf tissue by the response of aerotactic bacteria. When droplets of a suspension of *Bacterium termo* Cohn were added to cells of *Euglena*, the bacteria accumulated at the surface of the alga upon illumination. In contrast, bacteria evenly distributed when the illumination was ended. With the same assay system Engelmann (1882) demonstrated the efficiency of blue and red light in causing light-dependent oxygen evolution. Engelmann (1881) stated that the sensitivity of his assay would be as low as 10^{-14} mg of O_2 (attomol range).

In the following we describe an extension of the "Engelmann experiment" which employs microphotometry for a semiquantitative determination of rates of alteration of O_2 concentration at the fmol level.

3 Culture, Preparation and Incubation of Bacteria and Protoplasts

3.1 Bacteria

As an indicator of gradients of O_2 concentration *Pseudomonas aeruginosa* (ATCC 10145; German Collection of Microorganisms, Göttingen) was used. *Ps. aeruginosa* is a Gram-negative bacterium which is facultatively aerobic. In the absence of O_2 nitrate is used as proton acceptor and molecular nitrogen is released. Aerobic conditions suppress the synthesis of enzymes involved in denitrification. As the bacterium is potentially pathogen (Cross 1985) precautions are suggested for handling: all experimental equipment which had contact with bacterial suspensions should be stored in lysoformine (2% v/v) and residues of bacterial suspensions are best autoclaved at 135° C. The bacteria were cultured in nutrient agar [medium 1: peptone, 5.0; meat extract, 3; agar, 15; ($g\,l^{-1}$); pH 7.0 (Claus et al. 1983), fortified with 2 $g\,l^{-1}$ NaCl and 0.1 $g\,l^{-1}$ KCl and sterilized for 15 min at 121° C]. About 12 h before starting an experiment, bacteria were transferred from culture tubes to 10 ml medium 1 (devoid of agar) and kept at 37° C on a rotatory shaker (60 oscillations min^{-1}). Aliquots (1 ml) from the bacterial suspension were taken during the logarithmic growth phase (optical density at 578 nm: 1.5 to 1.6), and centrifuged for 1 min at 10000 g. The pellet was resuspended in 1 ml of a medium that was also used for the resuspension of leaf cell protoplasts [7.5 m*M* $CaCl_2$, 25 m*M* Tricine (pH 7.6), 5 m*M* $NaHCO_3$ and sorbitol as required; medium 2].

If the bacteria are kept on agar for weeks, their vitality is decreased. In order to select for the most viable (i.e. most responsive towards O_2) bacterial cells, culture aliquots were transferred to the centre of a petri dish containing medium 1 with 0.35% (w/v) agar. After 2 to 4 days at 37° C only those bacteria were collected and used for further culture which had moved the largest distance from the point of inoculation.

3.2 Isolation of Protoplasts

Leaf cell protoplasts from *Avena sativa* L. (cv. Arnold) were isolated from 7-day-old, light-grown seedlings as reported (Hampp and Ziegler 1980), except, instead of cutting leaf segments, the lower epidermis was peeled off. *Nicotiana tabacum* L. (cv. Samsun) was grown at 20° to 22° C, 70% rel. himidity and an 18-h light period (about 8 W m^{-2}) for 4 weeks. Plants were kept in darkness before removing leaves. The abaxial epidermis was abraded (carborundum GC 120; Schleifmittelwerk Düsseldorf) using a water colour paintbrush (Beier and Bruening 1975). Then the leaves were rinsed with water and incubated for 1 h in 0.5 *M* mannitol (to plasmolyze the cells). Mesophyll protoplasts were isolated in 0.5 *M* mannitol, 1 m*M* $CaCl_2$, 5 m*M* MES-KOH (pH 5.6), 10 m*M* ascorbic acid, 0.5% (w/v) BSA, 2% cellulase "Onozuka R-10" (Serva) and 0.5% Macerozym R-10 (Serva) (2 h, 30° C, occasional shaking). Purification of protoplasts by floatation on a step gradient (100 g, 90 s, swing-out rotor) was carried out as described for oat (Hampp and Ziegler 1980). *Vicia faba* L. (cv. Hangdown) mesophyll protoplasts were isolated (Schnabl et al. 1978) from 2- to 3-week-old plants that were cultured like tobacco. Three-week-old *Phaseolus coccineus* plants (cv. Preisgewinner), grown in a 9-h light/15-h dark cycle at 23° C, were used for the isolation of pulvinus protoplasts. The primary pulvini of about 30 plants previously trimmed to two leaves each were excised. The extensor regions (abaxial part of the pulvinus; see Erath et al. 1988) were dissected out, chopped into about 0.5-mm pieces and rinsed in 0.6 *M* sorbitol, containing 0.1 m*M* $CaCl_2$ and 5 m*M* MES (pH 5.6). The tissue slices were then transferred to 10 ml of digestion medium [0.5 *M* sorbitol, 0.1 m*M* $CaCl_2$, 5 m*M* MES (pH 5.6), 0.5% (w/v) BSA, 0.5% (w/v) polyvinylpyrrolidone (insoluble) 1 µg ml^{-1} Pepstatin A (Sigma), and enzymes (w/v): 2% cellulase (Sigma), 0.05% pectolyase Y23 (Pacscl)] and incubated for 3 h at 30° C without shaking. The digested material was filtered through a 100-µm nylon mesh, and washed with 10 ml of 0.55 *M* raffinose. The resulting suspension was transferred to a centrifuge tube, overlayered with 400 µl 0.55 *M* sorbitol and centrifuged (2 min, 200 g, swing-out rotor). Protoplasts that banded at the interphase were removed, resuspended in 10 ml 0.55 *M* raffinose and the purification step repeated as above, but using medium 2 (see below) as the upper layer instead of sorbitol only.

Protoplast numbers were counted on a Fuchs-Rosenthal haemocytometer. Chlorophyll was determined according to Arnon (1949).

3.3 Evacuolation and Electrofusion of Protoplasts

Evacuolation was performed on a self-generating Percoll (Pharmacia) gradient according to Griesbach and Sink (1983) in a modification as described by Naton et al. (1986). Electrofusion of individual protoplasts (Zimmermann 1982; Zimmermann et al. 1985) was essentially as reported earlier (Naton et al. 1986), using a commercial fusion generator (GCA, Chicago, Ill., USA).

3.4 Assay of Photosynthetic Oxygen Evolution

For the microscopic assay of photosynthesis, 5 µl of protoplast and *Pseudomonas* suspension (in medium 2; see above; about 10^4 protoplasts ml^{-1}) were mixed on a microscope slide and covered with a cover slip, the edges of which were coated with Vaseline in order to reduce the rate of oxygen exchange between assay medium and ambient air. Before starting an experiment, the sample was kept in darkness for at least 15 min. This dark incubation increased sensitivity (we speculate that respiration lowered the oxygen content of the system). Photosynthesis was induced by illumination (halogen lamp, 320 W m^{-2}; Leitz Diavert). Semi-quantitative determinations of oxygen evolution were obtained with a Diaplan microscope (dark field illumination; Leitz), equipped with a photomultiplier (MPV compact, Leitz) and connected to a Hewlett-Packard 87 microcomputer (Outlaw et al. 1985). The rectangular aperture at the photomultiplier was set to about twice the diameter of the protoplast under investigation. Readings were taken continuously or in 15- to 30-s intervals. An increase in bacterial numbers was thus measured by the amount of light adding to that scattered by the protoplast and a background of dead or slowly moving bacteria.

In parallel to the *Pseudomonas*-based assay light-dependent oxygen evolution of protoplast suspensions was monitored in a Hansa-Tech oxygen electrode (Bachofer, Reutlingen; see Goller et al. 1982).

Photomicrographs of bacteria were taken with a Leitz microflash (100 W s^{-1}).

4 Evaluation of the Microtechnique

Under illumination leaf mesophyll protoplasts evolve oxygen at rates of between 5 and 30 µmol/10^6·h. This calculates as about 0.1 to 0.5 pmol min^{-1} for a single protoplast and is thus well above the lower limit of detection suggested by Engelmann (1881).

4.1 Microphotographic Studies

After a 15-min dark pre-incubation of protoplasts and bacteria, the latter were randomly distributed (Fig. 1 a). Illumination for as few as 30 s was sufficient to cause an increase in the number of bacteria surrounding a photosynthesizing protoplast (Fig. 1 b). As the bacteria are most visible under phase contrast or dark

→

Fig. 1 a–c. Flashlight photomicrographs of a *Phaseolus* protoplast isolated from primary pulvinus tissue and suspended together with *Pseudomonas aeruginosa* bateria. The bacteria respond positively by chemotactis towards oxygen. **a** Control (15 min dark incubation); **b** same protoplast after 30 s of illumination (microscope lamp, 320 W m^{-2}); **c** as **b**, but after an illumination period of 3 min. Note the considerably increased density of the bacterial population around the photosynthesizing protoplast

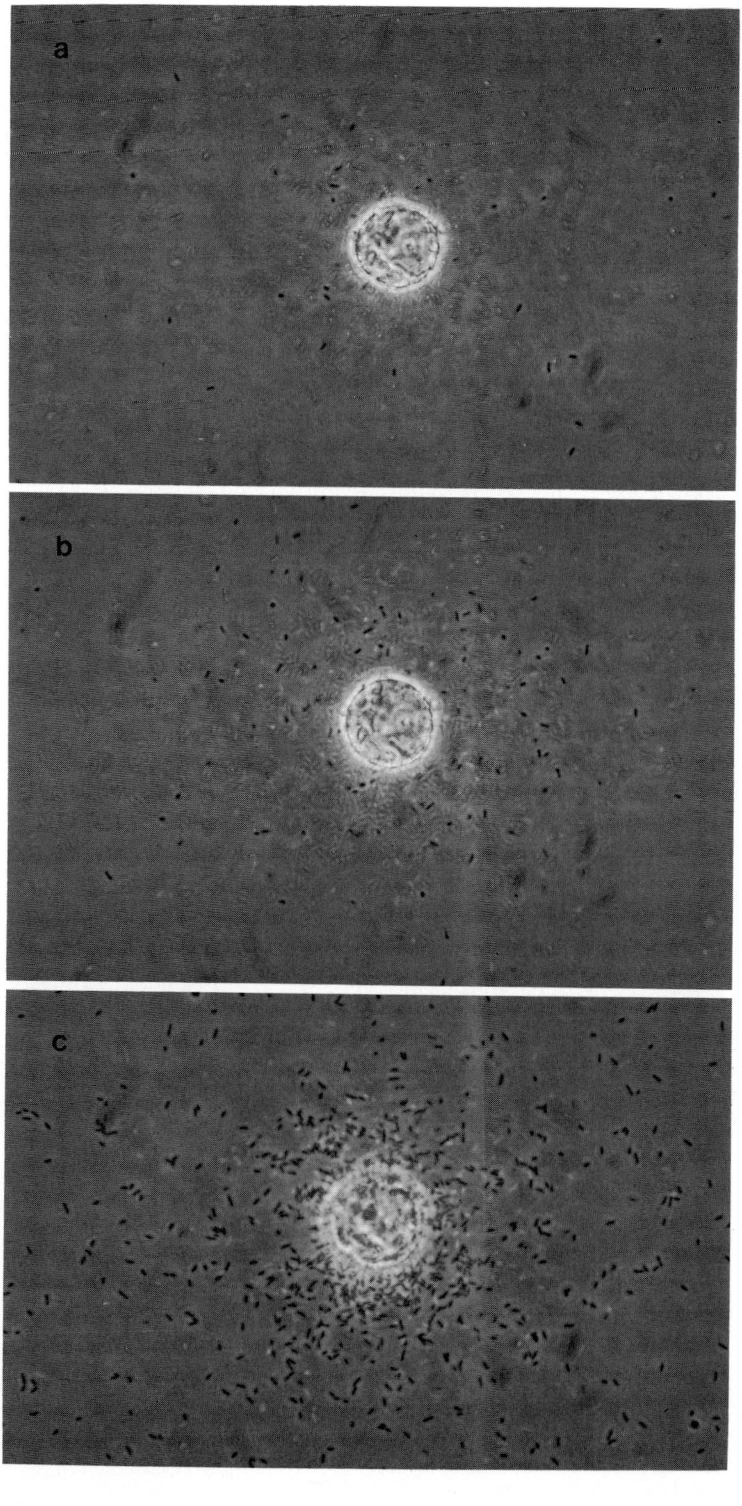
a
b
c

field microscopy, conditions which result in a considerable loss of light intensity, high light fluence rates are necessary. These were obtained by a maximum output of the microscope illumination, and, if larger areas were to be scanned, by additional glass fibre illumination (Schott, cold light, Mainz, FRG). The use of filters (red, blue) did not improve the bacterial response but deteriorated visibility. The maximum effect was observed after about 3 to 5 min of illumination (Fig. 1c). Due to the motion of the bacteria, protoplasts sometimes started to rotate at this stage. These observations show that the bacteria respond to an oxygen gradient (cf. Engelmann 1881). Thus, the bacteria accumulate where the gradient is steepest (i.e. near the surface of a photosynthesizing protoplast). After prolonged illumination (no significant increase in temperature was detected), bacteria are not preferentially localized near protoplasts. We interpret this observation to mean that diffusion of oxygen had occured in the incubation medium. The initial attraction is reversible. Returning the mixture to darkness resulted in a completely random distribution of bacteria within minutes (sample viewing was under green light). At this stage the experimental procedure could be started from the beginning. Even after keeping the sealed mixture (cover slip with Vaseline) for about 24 h in the dark (20° C) the system was still functional in some experiments.

4.2 Discrimination Between Aerotactic and Chemotactic Responses

The aerotactic bacteria also tend to be attracted by broken protoplasts, especially during or shortly after lysis. This effect is of dual nature, consisting of light-dependent (O_2) and a light-independent component.

As far as light is concerned lysing protoplasts tend to evolve O_2 for about 10 to 20 min after signs of plasma membrane rupture have become visible. Thereafter, possibly owing to the dilution of solutes within the cytosol, these protoplasts stop evolving O_2 at rates perceptible by the bacteria. In order to be able to distinguish between lysing and intact protoplasts without a time lag we significantly decreased photosynthesis from broken protoplasts by the addition of 7.5 m*M* $CaCl_2$. Such a treatment has been reported to prevent chloroplasts, which are exposed due to the rupture of protoplasts, from evolving oxygen (Wirtz et al. 1980; Leegood and Walker 1983).

The light-independent component of bacterial attraction is possibly caused by leaking solutes. Due to diffusion, effective gradients of chemical attractants obviously disappear within 10 to 20 min of protoplast lysis. After this period the enhanced aggregation of bacteria around the respective protoplast ends. There is still the possibility that ions, e.g. K^+, leaking from intact protoplasts could act as an attractant in the light rather than oxygen. However, even after addition of 5 m*M* KCl the bacteria responded to illumination as described above.

Other attempts to diminish the chemotactic response included a decrease in assay pH to 4.5 and the substitution of the incubation medium (medium 2, see Sect. 3.1) by a complex nutrient solution (Seitz and Richter 1970). These alterations, however, did not reduce bacterial attraction in the dark.

In contrast, the sensitivity of the bacteria (in the presence of leaking solutes) towards O_2 could largely be increased when the O_2 concentration in the assay medium was brought to a minimum before starting illumination. This could be caused by either respiratory consumption or enzymatic conversion of assay O_2. For consumption by bacterial and protoplast respiration the sealed (cover slip) suspension was kept in darkness for up to 1 h. This treatment not only reduced the concentration of free O_2 but also, owing to diffusion, decreased solute gradients originating from leaky protoplasts.

A second approach was the addition of glycolate (75 m*M*) to the assay medium. Leaf mesophyll protoplasts contain glycolate oxidase which, under consumption of molecular O_2, converts glycolate to glyoxylate. As the plasma membrane of intact protoplasts is impermeable towards glycolate, the reaction will only take place with broken protoplasts and is used as a measure of protoplast integrity (Nishimura et al. 1985). Under these conditions leaky protoplasts constitute an O_2 sink even under illumination and thus are completely unattractive for *Pseudomonas* bacteria. This considerably improves the quality of the assay when used for the identification of intact protoplasts.

Addition of dibromothymoquinone (DBMIB, 15 μ*M*), a plastoquinone antagonist (Trebst et al. 1970; Crowther and Hind 1980), which was shown to inhibit light-driven electron flow in intact mesophyll protoplasts (Goller et al. 1982), rendered previously bacteria-attracting protoplasts unattractive. The motility of the bacterial suspension was not affected.

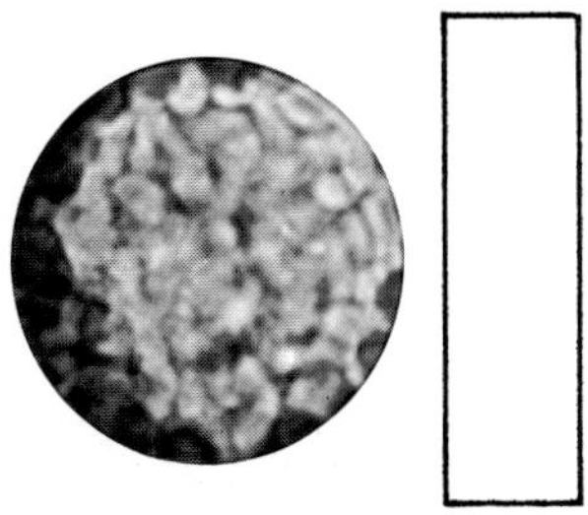

a

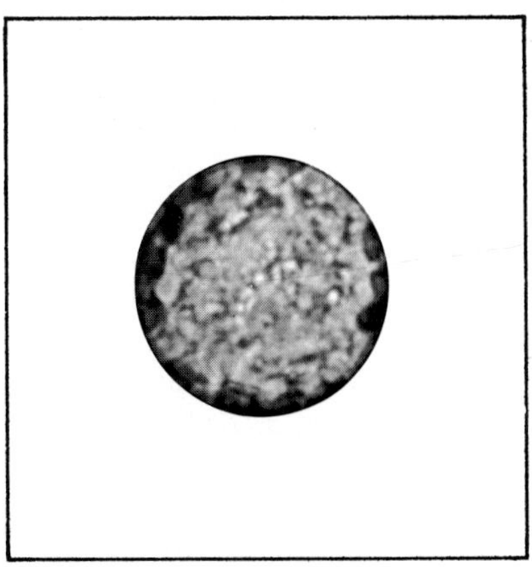

b

Fig. 2 a, b. Aperture settings for the microphotometric determination of changes of light scattering under dark field illumination. *Sphere* protoplast (about 30 μm diameter); *rectangle* measuring frame; **a** and **b** are examples for different positioning of the measuring frame

4.3 Semiquantitative Assay of Changes in O_2 Concentration

In order to improve the "contrast" between dark and light under dark field illumination it is important to keep the proportion of inactive bacteria at a minimum as these contribute to background light-scattering. Thus, largely diluted suspensions of protoplasts (see Sect. 3.4) and bacteria were employed and the most suitable ratio bacteria/protoplast determined empirically before starting an experiment.

As the protoplast is the largest particle, it contributes most to the background of scattered light under dark field illumination. In order to obtain the best signal (light scattered by attracted bacteria) to noise (protoplast) ratios, different settings of the aperture at the photomultiplier were tested. Placing the measuring frame in an area close to the protoplast surface (Fig. 2a) resulted in the best responses but gave a very inconsistent reading due to protoplast movement at higher bacterial population densities. A somewhat decreased sensitivity, but readings not affected by slight protoplast movements, resulted when the protoplast was centred in the measuring frame (Fig. 2b). Best results were obtained when the aperture size was about twice the protoplast diameter.

As the degree of scattering depends on the wavelength (blue light is scattered more than red light) and as both blue and red light are photosynthetically active, we used blue light illumination when highest sensitivities were requested.

4.4 Kinetic Studies

A semiquantitative assay of light-dependent O_2 evolution by a single tobacco mesophyll protoplast is shown in Fig. 3a (trace I). The determination is based on dark field illumination. As discussed above, with this technique only light scattered by particles is recorded, whereas the background is dark. Thus, with a protoplast surrounded by few bacteria (darkness), light scattering is at a low level (Fig. 3a, I, A). From the onset of illumination (and O_2 evolution), bacteria respond aerotactically and accumulate around the cell (cf. Figs. 1, 4). This accumulation is measured as an increase in light scattering. Interestingly, the time course of changes in light scattering is biphasic (Fig. 3a, I); there are two periods exhibiting a fast increase in the population density (0 to 1 and 1.5 to 2.5 min of illumination) which are separated by a short period without major changes (about 30 s). Thus, these kinetic studies, obtained by single cell techniques, are in substantial agreement with studies on the phenomenon of photosynthetic induction. "Induction" is used to describe the delayed onset of photosynthesis when illumination follows a period of darkness (Walker 1976). This phenomenon is related to the coupling between carbon assimilation and the activity of the photochemical apparatus. Thus, NADPH and ATP accumulate during the initial 60 s of illumination (for mesophyll protoplasts see Hampp et al. 1985, where enzymes involved in CO_2 fixation are still inactive, Buchanan 1980). High stromal ratios of ATP/ADP and NADPH/NADP, however, will decrease photosynthetic electron transport and thus lower the rate of oxygen evolution. Rates of light-dependent O_2 evolution (=electron transport) are inversely related to chlorophyll fluorescence.

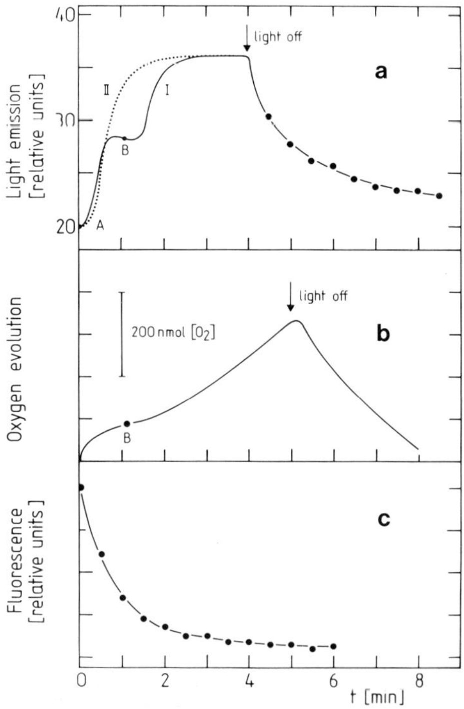

Fig. 3a–c. Microphotometric recordings of light scattered by a mesophyll protoplast (tobacco) and *Pseudomonas aeruginosa* under dark field illumination (cf. Fig. 4). Following a 15-min dark pre-incubation protoplasts were illuminated. The increase in light scattering during illumination is due to an accumulation of bacteria around the protoplast. **a**, *Trace I*: light scattering during photosynthetic induction; background reading: *level A*. Light scattered by the protoplast itself is measured (dark treatment, cf. Fig. 4a). Intermediate halt in light-dependent oxygen evolution of the protoplast during photosynthetic induction: *level B*. *Trace II*: Incubation after addition of dichlorophenol indophenol (100 μ*M*), an electron acceptor. **b** Oxygen electrode tracing of the protoplast suspension. *B* Same state as in *trace I*. The assay volume (1 ml) contained protoplasts equivalent to about 50 μg chlorophyll. **c** Microfluorometric determination of chlorophyll fluorescence. Protoplast and conditions of incubation as in **a**

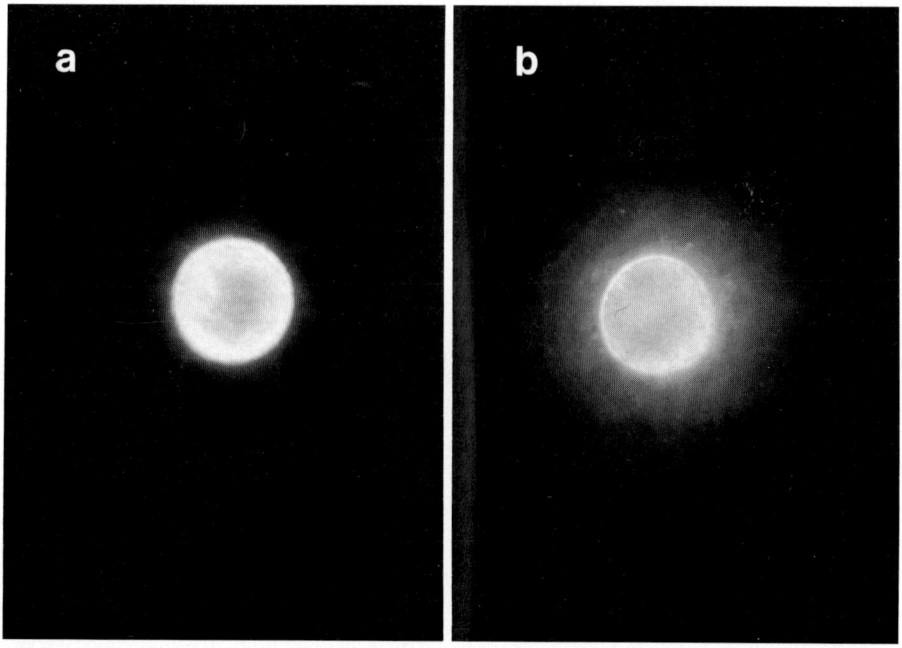

Fig. 4a, b. Photomicrographs of a tobacco mesophyll protoplast under dark field illumination and in the presence of *Pseudomonas aeruginosa*. **a** Dark-treated protoplast; **b** same protoplast after 5 min of illumination (320 W m^{-2}). The halo results from light scattered by the aerotactic bacteria

Assayed with a single tobacco mesophyll protoplast (epifluorescence, filter combination H2, Leitz) this inverse relationship is shown in Fig. 3 (a, trace II; c).

We would like to emphasize that our method results in a different measurement than that of the O_2 electrode. While the latter measures overall O_2 concentrations, our method is sensitive to a gradient (cf. above). Thus, traces from the two methods should not be identical: when O_2 evolution ceases, the electrode trace should remain virtually horizontal. Under the same condition, the trace obtained with the bacterial method would decline because of diffusion and O_2 depletion in the vicinity of a protoplast (respiration; Fig. 3a, I, B).

With the start of CO_2 fixation NADPH and ATP are consumed and electron flow is no longer restricted. This leads to a second steep increase in bacterial numbers around the protoplast. After about 3 min of illumination a new steady state is reached between O_2 evolution and diffusion that results in a constant O_2 gradient and therefore in a constant number of bacteria. When larger numbers of individual traces are accumulated and averaged, approximately the same curve develops as is obtained with a conventional O_2 electrode assay during the first minutes of illumination (Fig. 3b). When the light is switched off, bacteria respond immediately with a decrease in population density (Fig. 3a; determinations in 30-s intervals with 2.5 s of illumination each time). With tobacco protoplasts, bacteria were statistically scattered after 5 min, while after an additional 10 min of darkness protoplasts were avoided by bacteria up to a distance of about a quarter of the protoplast diameter. We interpret this as a negative O_2 gradient towards the protoplast surface owing to dark respiration. The whole experimental sequence could be repeated several times without any signs of decay.

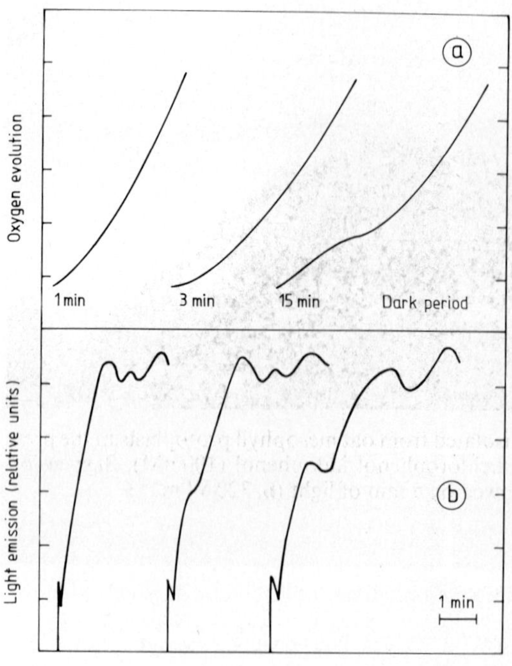

Fig. 5a, b. Time course of photosynthetic induction of a suspension of tobacco mesophyll protoplasts (**a** Clark-type oxygen electrode) and an individual protoplast (**b** *Pseudomonas* assay). With increasing length of the dark interval in between illuminations (1 to 15 min) an intermediate break in the rates of oxygen evolution appears. Initial increase in **b**: photomultiplier response to "light on"

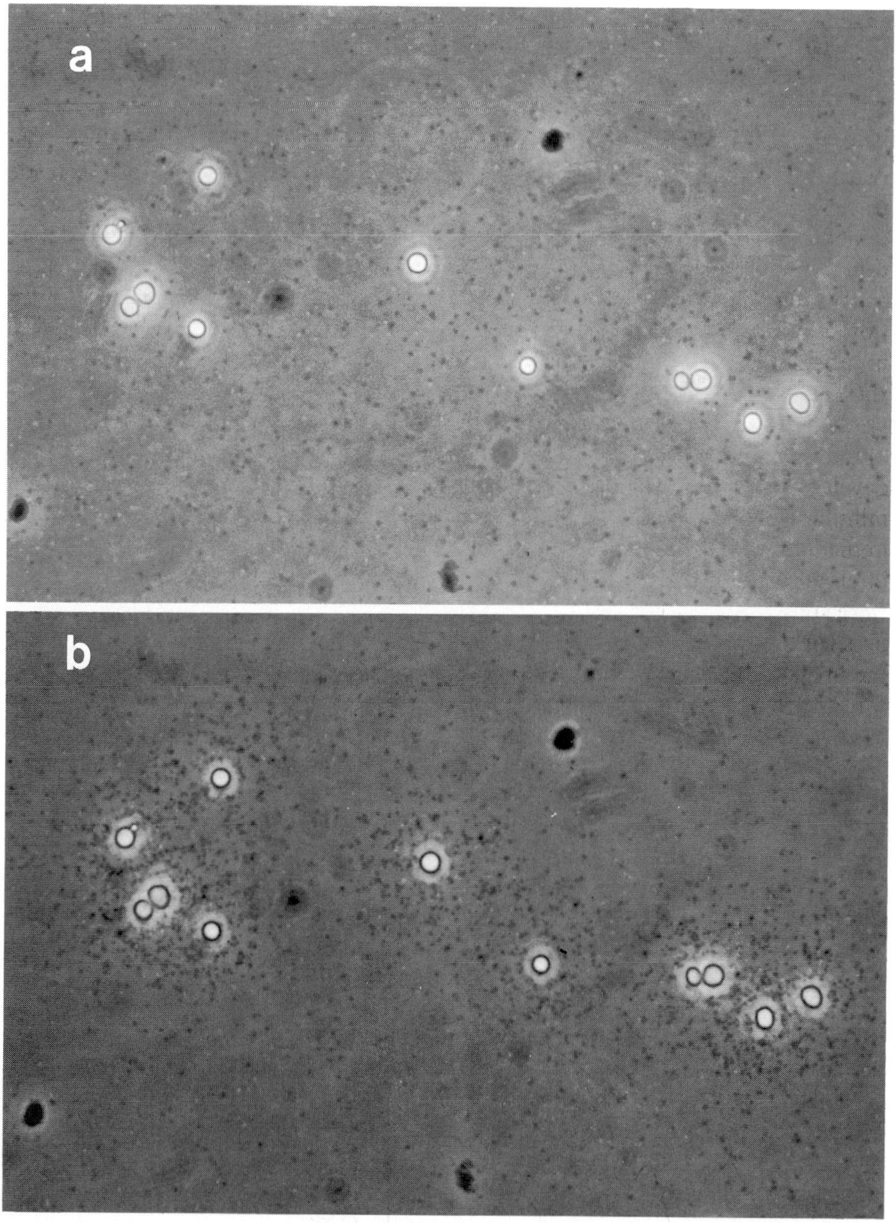

Fig. 6 a, b. Illumination of chloroplasts isolated from oat mesophyll protoplasts in the presence of *Pseudomonas aeruginosa* and dichlorophenol indophenol (100 μM). Suspension after 15 min of dark treatment (**a**), followed by 5 min of light (**b**, 320 W m^{-2})

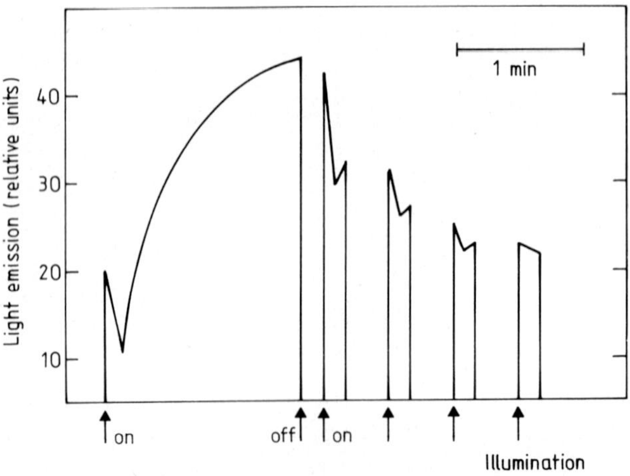

Fig. 7. Bacterial response during the initial phase of illumination of tobacco mesophyll protoplasts. Note the decrease of light scattering shortly after the onset of illumination. The framing lines, marked by *arrows*, result from the response of the photomultiplier to switching "on" and "off" and are not caused by bacteria

Increasing the dark interval in between two illumination periods decreased the rate of bacterial accumulation i.e. the initial rate of light-dependent O_2 evolution was retarded (Fig. 5). A dark interval of more then 5 to 10 min resulted in a lag of bacterial accumulation as shown and discussed above (Fig. 3a, B). This behaviour of an individual protoplast (Fig. 5) is essentially identical to that when about 0.2×10^6 protoplasts are averaged in a conventional O_2 electrode assay (Fig. 5). These observations are consistent with recent knowledge about kinetics of activation and inactivation of enzymes involved in light-dependent CO_2 fixation (Buchanan 1980) and are thus easily verified for individual protoplasts.

The induction-dependent intermediate break in O_2 evolution (Fig. 3a, I, B) disappears when a membrane-permeable electron acceptor such as dichlorophenol indophenol (DCPIP; 100 μ*M*) is added to the assay (Fig. 3a; trace II). In this case electrons, originating from the water-splitting site are directly transferred to the oxidized dye and thus no limitation of O_2 evolution is observed. Owing to the considerably higher rates of O_2 evolution, addition of DCPIP to isolated chloroplasts (*Avena sativa*) rendered these attractive to bacteria too (Fig. 6). An interference of DCPIP with bacterial motility was not detected.

A higher resolution in time for the initial stages of illumination is given in Fig. 7. Illumination of light-treated protoplasts after a dark interval of a few seconds only caused bateria to avoid the protoplast for about 10 s before they were again attracted by O_2. At the moment we are not able to explain this behaviour. As it should not be due to a delay in O_2 evolution, we suggest that possibly light-induced changes in the energy state of the chloroplast could be accompanied by an altered electrical potential of the cell which is perceived by the bacteria.

5 Applications

5.1 Protoplast Viability as Assayed with *Pseudomonas* Versus Conventional Techniques

Commonly used substances for assessing viability of intact protoplasts are fluorescence reagents like FDA (Larkin 1976), and for damage and death, exclusion dyes such as Evan's blue, bromphenol blue or phenosafranine (Bornman et al. 1982). Other techniques like protoplasmic streaming and plasmolysis have also been employed to estimate the relative viability of plant cells. However, the most convenient and reliable method appeared to be that of vital staining.

In order to compare the degree of viability as assessed with *Pseudomonas* with that obtained by other commonly used techniques, 4-day-old *Vicia* mesophyll protoplasts (kept in darkness at 4° C) were either studied by phase contrast microscopy or incubated in the presence of Evan's blue, phenosafranine or FDA. Representative results are shown in Fig. 8. Of three protoplasts appearing intact by FDA staining (Fig. 8 f) only one was able to evolve O_2 in the light (Fig. 8 d, e). This example is typical of the different results on vitality obtained with staining methods compared to the physiological test. All protoplasts that appeared intact under phase contrast (100%) also excluded Evan's blue and phenosafranine, which are deflected by an intact plasma membrane. By contrast, only 60 to 70% of the protoplasts were judged to be intact by the FDA method. This method is based on FDA permeability and its subsequent hydrolysis by cytosolic esterases to the fluorescent compound, fluorescein. Thus, fluorescein, which is impermeable, accumulates in intact cells only. The *Pseudomonas* assay yielded an even lower figure: only about 50% of the protoplasts judged to be intact by phase contrast microscopy evolved O_2 at detectable rates.

The reliability of staining procedures has been questioned previously. Bornman et al. (1982) pointed out that even though conditions for vital staining may be rigorously standardized, caution should be exercised in the interpretation of the fluorescent image. These authors showed that not only were concentrations and freshness of both dye and protoplasts, and time of staining critical, but also the photographic exposure itself could result in progressive fading and damage of the protoplast due to UV irradiation. In addition, it was frequently observed that fluorescence was limited to certain areas of "intact protoplasts" which was interpreted as indicating leakage. Similarly, Smith et al. (1982) reported that staining properties of cell cultures did not correlate well with their ability to be subcultured. This obvious inaccuracy of viability tests that rely on vital staining is further corroborated by the experiment on protoplast senescence shown in Fig. 9. In this example oat mesophyll protoplasts were kept at 4° C for up to 7 days. In parallel to the *Pseudomonas*-based assay, light-dependent O_2 evolution was measured in an O_2 electrode. As shown in Fig. 9, the bacterial assay yielded by far the lowest number of intact protoplasts (based on the evaluation of about 200 phase contrast-positive protoplasts for each datum). Interestingly, integrity as measured with FDA is nearly unchanged with incubation time, while the capacity for O_2 evolution (*Pseudomonas* assay) indicates a considerable decrease.

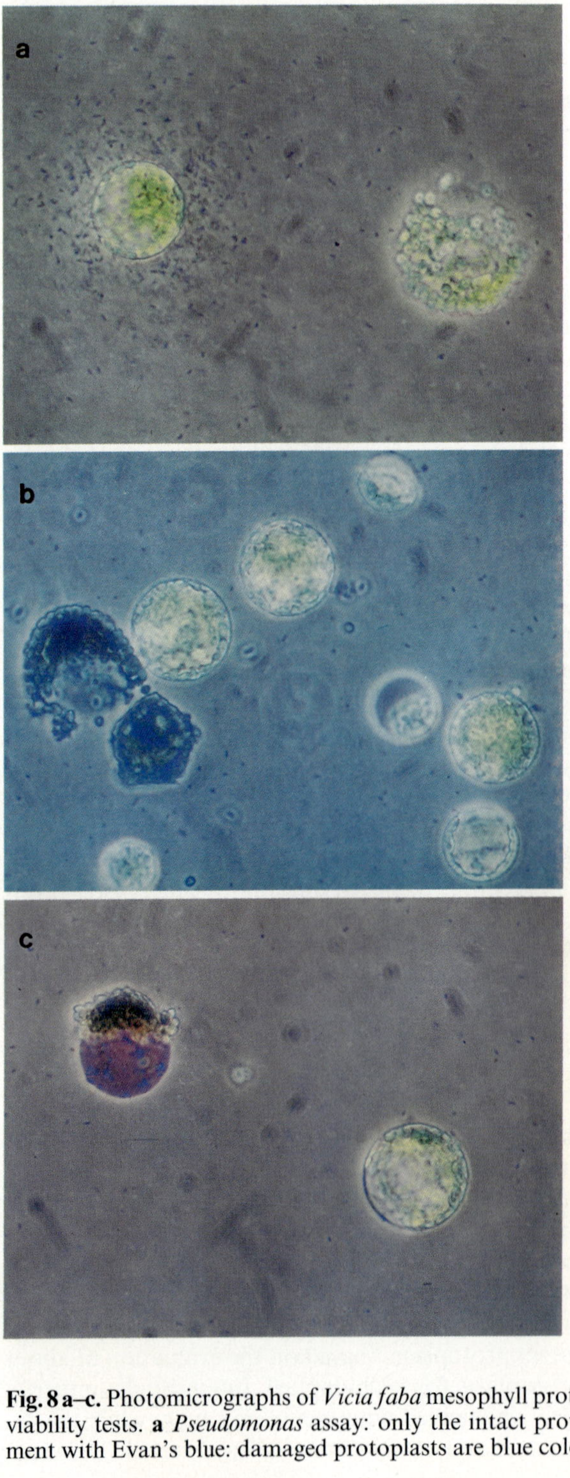

Fig. 8 a–c. Photomicrographs of *Vicia faba* mesophyll protoplasts. Comparison of different viability tests. **a** *Pseudomonas* assay: only the intact protoplast attracts bacteria; **b** treatment with Evan's blue: damaged protoplasts are blue coloured; **c** phenosafranine, as **b**

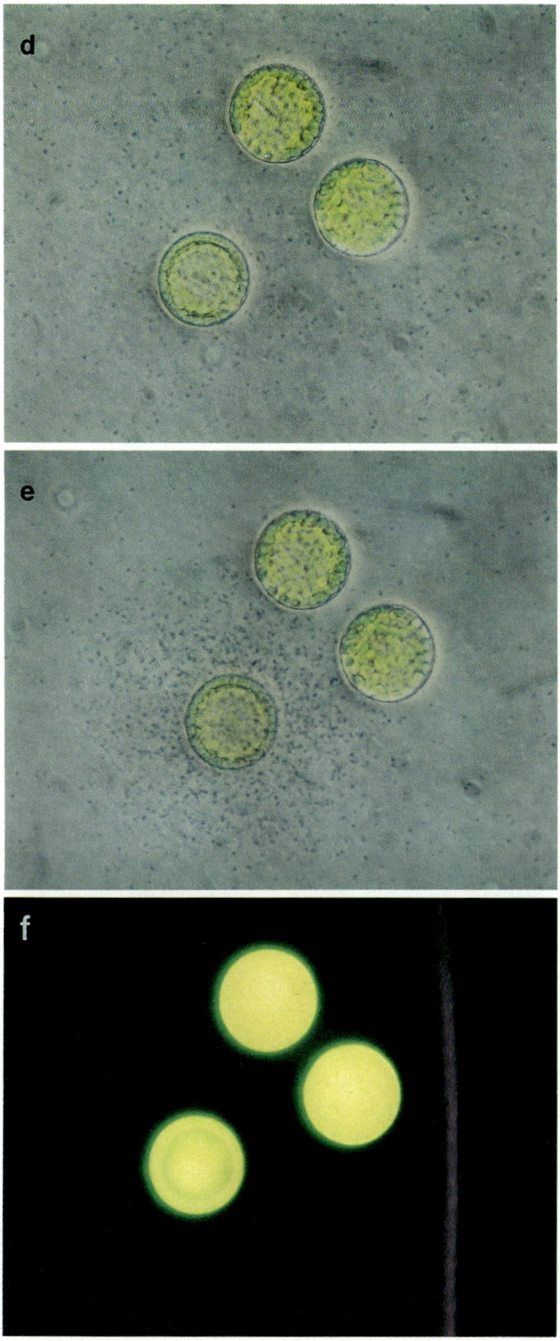

Abb. 8 d–f Same group of protoplasts, but incubated either with bacteria in the blue (**d**) or light (**e**), or with fluorescein diacetate (FDA; **f**); note, while all protoplasts are FDA-positive (i.e. "intact") only one of them is able to evolve oxygen

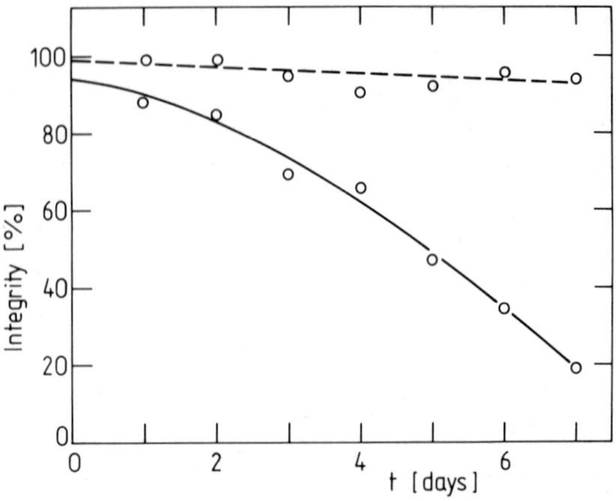

Fig. 9. Viability of a population of oat mesophyll protoplasts over 7 days at 4° C. Integrity is expressed as the percentage of those protoplasts that still appeared intact under phase contrast microscopy. *Dashed line*: fluorescein diacetate staining; *solid line*: *Pseudomonas* assay

This difference shows that deterioration of physiological and plasma membrane integrity proceeds at a different speed.

5.2 Integrity of Manipulated Protoplasts and Hybrids of Mesophyll Cells After Electrofusion

Manipulation of plant cell protoplasts is hampered by their vacuolar compartment. Poration or rupture of the vacuolar membrane (tonoplast) can result in severe poisoning of the cytosol and thus reduce cell viability. In order to improve protoplast quality for hybridization and regeneration experiments evacuolation of ordinary protoplasts is requested (Griesbach and Sink 1983; Naton et al. 1986). As the process of evacuolation by itself imposes severe stress on protoplast preparations, a reliable test for viability of evacuolated protoplasts is imperative. Evacuolated protoplasts surrounded by bacteria are shown in Fig. 10a under bright, in Fig. 10b under dark field illumination. Despite about the same number of chloroplasts per cell, evacuolated protoplasts attracted *Pseudomonas* at lower rates while qualitatively the kinetics were comparable to control (vacuolated) protoplasts (Fig. 11). This should be due to lower rates of O_2 evolution by evacuolated protoplasts and can be explained by a lower light efficiency (more chloroplasts per volume).

Photosynthesis of single protoplasts is also a valuable measure in order to assay the viability of hybrids obtained from mesophyll protoplasts. Our aim in this context is to monitor the impact of electrofusion (Zimmermann 1982; Verhoek-Köhler et al. 1983; Zimmermann et al. 1985) on protoplast viability. Twenty-four hours after electrofusion 83 of 95 homospecific hybrids of oat mesophyll protoplasts attracted bacteria under illumination (Fig. 12). This was about the same percentage of viability as assayed with unfused controls. In heterospecific hybrids (control × evacuolated protoplast) bacteria preferentially gathered at that part of the hybrid surface with the highest chloroplast number (evacuolated part of the hybrid, Fig. 13). In contrast to controls hybrid protoplasts typically showed a

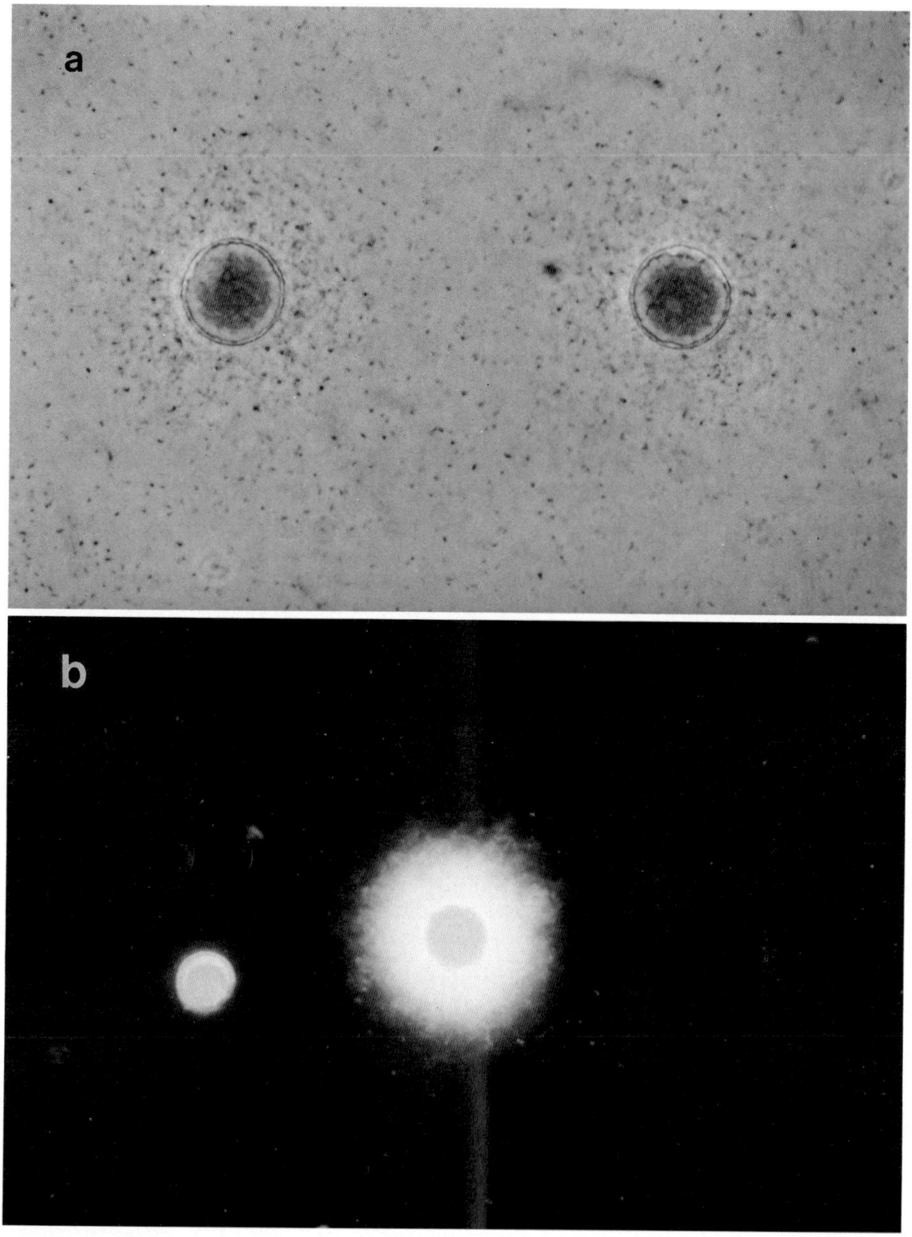

Fig. 10a, b. Assay of integrity of tobacco mesophyll protoplasts after evacuolation. Bacterial response as shown by bright light (**a**) and dark field illumination (**b**). In **b**, discrimination by bacteria between a broken (*left*) and an intact (*right*) protoplast is shown. Note the high density of the chloroplast population (**a**)

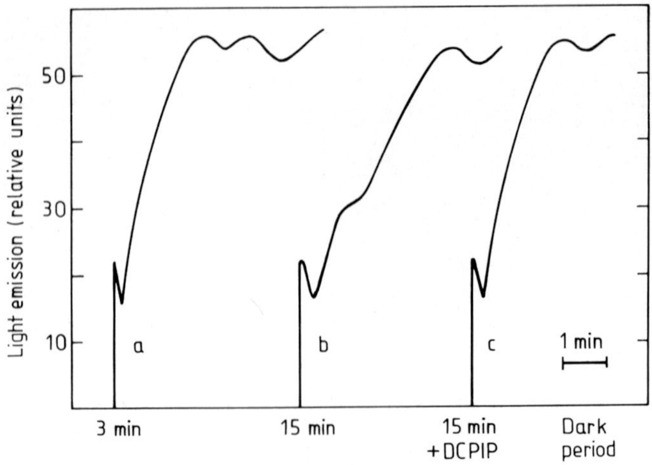

Fig. 11. Photosynthetic induction of a tobacco mesophyll protoplast 24 h after evacuolation after different times of pre-incubation in darkness, and in the absence or presence of an electron acceptor. Initial increase: photomultiplier response to "light on"

much more pronounced lag of photosynthetic O_2 evolution as indicated by the kinetics of bacterial light scattering (Fig. 14).

6 Summary

A semiquantitative assay for light-dependent oxygen evolution from single mesophyll protoplasts is described. The assay indicator is the density of aerotactic bacteria (*Pseudomonas aeruginosa*, ATCC 10145; "Engelmann experiment") attracted to the protoplast. Quantification is by dark field microphotometry. The sensitivity is about 50 fmol oxygen (protoplast min^{-1}). The results demonstrate (1) the biphasic nature of oxygen evolution of a single protoplast during photosynthetic induction, and (2) the superiority of this bacterial assay over conventional staining techniques when protoplast viability (e.g. after cell fusion or protoplast evacuolation) is to be assayed. Computerized data acquisition yields traces which, until a steady state of photosynthetic oxygen evolution is reached, are comparable to ordinary oxygen electrode traces.

Fig. 12a–d. Comparison of fluorescence labelling and light-dependent bacterial response for hybrids 24 h after electrofusion. Oat mesophyll protoplasts were labelled with either fluorescein isothiocyanate (FITC, yellow) or rhodamine isothiocyanate (RITC, red). Fusion products were identified by showing both RITC (dark) and FITC-dependent (bright) fluorescence: large protoplast in **a** and **b**. **c, d** Same protoplasts as in **a** and **b** but in the presence of bacteria after dark incubation (15 min; **c**) or illumination for 5 min (**d**). Both control (*small*) and hybrid protoplasts attract bacteria

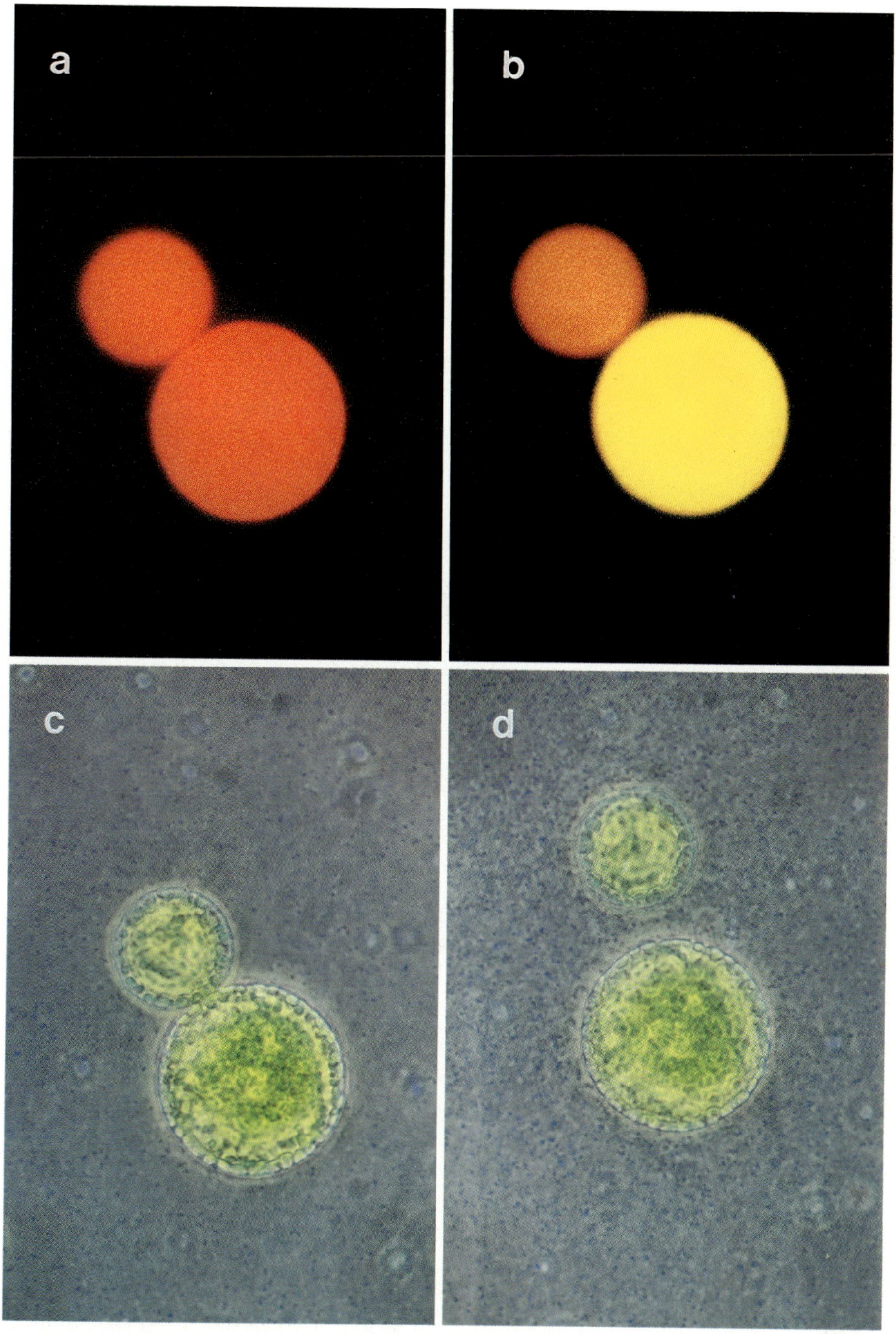
a
b
c
d

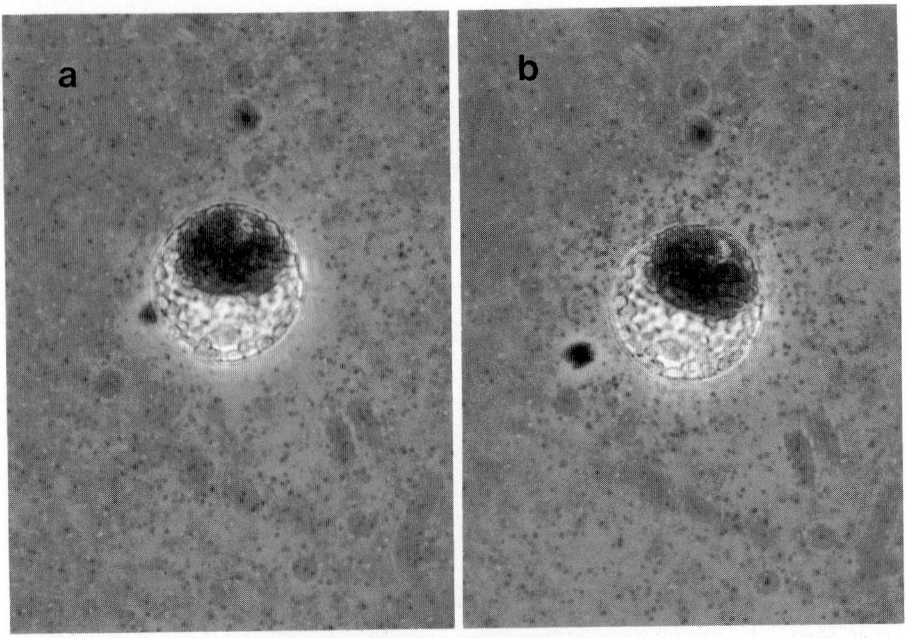

Fig. 13 a, b. Integrity of hybrids obtained by electrofusion of vacuolated and evacuolated oat mesophyll protoplasts. The *dark area* of the hybrid indicates the evacuolated fusion partner (higher chloroplast number per volume). Note that under illumination (**b**) *Pseudomonas* bacteria are preferentially attracted by this part of the hybrid. **a** Dark control

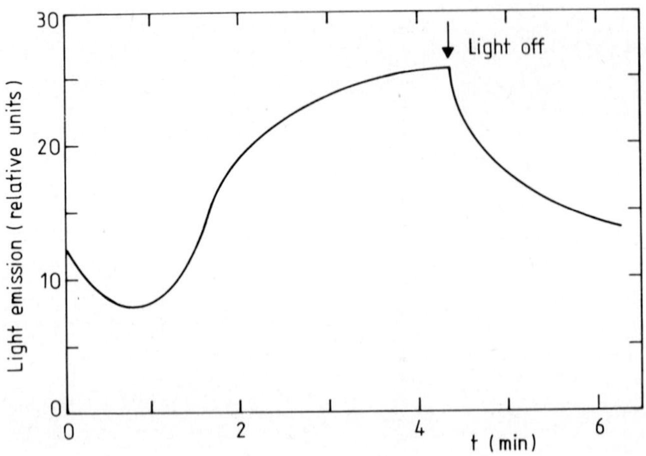

Fig. 14. Bacterial assay of the kinetics of photosynthetic oxygen evolution of an individual hybrid (vacuolated × evacuolated tobacco mesophyll protoplast) 4 h after electrofusion. Start of trace indicates start of illumination

Acknowledgments. The authors are indebted to Prof. W. H. Outlaw, Jr., Florida State University, Tallahassee, USA, for help in establishing a system of computerized data acquisition (microphotometry). This work was financed by grants from the Deutsche Forschungsgemeinschaft and the Bundesministerium für Forschung und Technologie (01QV8520). Prof. Outlaw's work was supported by the Humboldt Foundation (FRG) and the US Department of Energy.

References

Arnon DI (1979) Copper enzymes in isolated chloroplasts. Phenoloxidase in *Beta vulgaris*. Plant Physiol 24:1–15

Beier H, Bruening G (1975) The use of an abrasive in the isolation of cowpea leaf protoplasts which support the multiplication of cowpea mosaic virus. Virology 64:272–276

Bornman JF, Bornman CH (1983) Protoplast viability – a relative concept. In: Potrykus I, Harms CT, Hinnen A, Hütter R, King PJ, Shillito RD (eds) Protoplasts. Birkhäuser, Basel Boston Stuttgart, pp 208–209

Bornman JF, Bornman CH, Björn LO (1982) Effects of ultraviolet radiation on viability of isolated *Beta vulgaris* and *Hordeum vulgare* protoplasts. Z Pflanzenphysiol 105:297–306

Buchanan BB (1980) Role of light in the regulation of chloroplast enzymes. Annu Rev Plant Physiol 31:341–374

Claus D, Lack P, Neu B (1983) German collection of microorganisms. Catalogue of strains. Gesellschaft für Biotechnologische Forschung mbH, Braunschweig, p 265

Cross AS (1985) Evolving epidemiology of *Pseudomonas aeruginosa* infections. Eur J Clin Microbiol 4:156–159

Crowther D, Hind G (1980) Partial characterisation of cyclic electron transport in intact chloroplasts. Arch Biochem Biophys 204:568–577

Delieu T, Walker DA (1972) An improved cathode for the measurement of photosynthetic oxygen evolution by isolated chloroplasts. New Phytol 71:201–225

Delieu T, Walker DA (1981) Polarographic measurement of photosynthetic oxygen evolution by leaf discs. New Phytol 89:165–178

Engelmann TW (1881) Neue Methode zur Untersuchung der Sauerstoffausscheidung pflanzlicher und thierischer Organismen. Bot Z 39:441–448

Engelmannn TW (1882) Über Sauerstoffausscheidung von Pflanzenzellen im Mikrospectrum. Bot Z 40:419–426

Erath F, Ruge WA, Mayer WE, Hampp R (1988) Isolation of functional extensor and flexor protoplasts from *Phaseolus* pulvini: potassium induced swelling. Planta 173:447–452)

Goller M, Hampp R, Ziegler H (1982) Regulation of the cytosolic adenylate ratio as determined by rapid fractionation of mesophyll protoplasts of oat. Planta 156:255–263

Griesbach RJ, Sink KC (1983) Evacuolation of mesophyll protoplasts. Plant Sci Lett 30:297–301

Hampp R, Ziegler H (1980) On the use of *Avena* protoplasts to study chloroplast development. Planta 147:485–494

Hampp R, Goller M, Füllgraf H, Eberle I (1985) Pyridine and adenine nucleotide status, and pool sizes of a range of metabolites in chloroplasts, mitochondria and the cytosol/vacuole of *Avena* mesophyll protoplasts during dark/light transition: effect of pyridoxal phosphate. Plant Cell Physiol 26:99–108

Hampp R, Mehrle W, Zimmermann U (1986) Assay of photosynthetic oxygen evolution from single protoplasts. Plant Physiol 81:854–858

Larkin PJ (1976) Purification and viability determinations of plant protoplasts. Planta 128:213–216

Leegood RC, Walker DA (1983) Chloroplasts. In: Hall JL, Moore AL (eds) Isolation of membranes and organelles from plant cells. Academic Press, New York London, pp 185–210
Naton B, Mehrle W, Hampp R, Zimmermann U (1986) Mass electrofusion and mass selection of functional hybrids from vacuolate × evacuolate protoplasts. Plant Cell Rep 5:419–422
Nishimura M, Douce R, Akazawa T (1985) A simple method for estimating intactness of spinach leaf protoplasts by glycolate oxidase assay. Plant Physiol 78:343–346
Outlaw WH Jr., Springer SA, Tarczynski MC (1985) Histochemical technique. A general method for quantitative enzyme assays of single cell 'extracts' with a time resolution of seconds and a reading precision of femtomoles. Plant Physiol 77:659–666
Schnabl H, Bornman CH, Ziegler H (1978) Studies on isolated starch-containing (*Vicia faba*) and starch-deficient (*Allium cepa*) guard cell protoplasts. Planta 143:33–39
Seitz HU, Richter G (1970) Isolierung und Charakterisierung schnell markierter, hochmolekularer RNS aus frei suspendierten Kalluszellen der Petersilie (*Petrosilium sativum*). Planta 92:309–326
Smith BA, Reider ML, Fletcher JS (1982) Relationship between vital staining and subculture growth during senescence of plant tissue cultures. Plant Physiol 70:1228–1230
Trebst A, Harth E, Draber W (1970) On a new inhibitor of photosynthetic electron transport in isolated chloroplasts. Z Naturforsch 25b:1157–1159
Verhoek-Köhler B, Hampp R, Ziegler H, Zimmermann U (1983) Electro-fusion of mesophyll protoplasts of *Avena sativa*. Determination of the cellular adenylate levels of hybrids and its influence on the fusion process. Planta 158:199–204
Walker DA (1976) Photosynthetic induction. In: Akoyunoglou G (ed) Photosynthesis. IV. Regulation of carbon metabolism. Balaban, Philadelphia, pp 189–202
Wirtz W, Stitt M, Heldt HW (1980) Enzymic determination of metabolites in the subcellular compartments of spinach protoplasts. Plant Physiol 66:187–193
Zimmermann U (1982) Electric field-mediated fusion and related electrical phenomena. Biochim Biophys Acta 694:227–277
Zimmermann U, Vienken J, Halfmann J, Emeis CC (1985) Electrofusion: a novel hybridization technique. In: Mizrahi A, Wezel AL van (eds) Advances in biotechnological processes. Liss, New York, pp 79–150

O_2 Exchange Measurement Using a Platinum Polarographic Electrode

W. VIDAVER and S. SWENSON

1 Introduction

The platinum polarographic electrode has been used extensively to study O_2 exchange in photosynthetic organisms for several decades (Haxo and Blinks 1950; Myers and Graham 1963; Blinks 1964; Joliot and Joliot 1968; Joliot et al. 1970; Kok et al. 1970; Chandler and Vidaver 1971; Forbush et al. 1971; Delieu and Walker 1981; Swenson et al. 1986). One of the earliest applications of the platinum electrode resulted in photosynthetic action spectra for various aquatic and marine algae that remain as definitive examples of qualitative light-use efficiency by plants (Haxo and Blinks 1950). Subsequent studies have utilized polarographic techniques to investigate every conceivable aspect of O_2 evolution or uptake in intact macroorganisms (Chandler and Vidaver 1970; Weiss and Sauer 1970; Swenson et al. 1986), cell suspensions or single cells (Joliot 1968; Ried 1968; Delrieu 1972; Greenbaum and Mauzerall 1976; Diner 1977; Jursinic 1981; Delrieu 1983a), isolated chloroplasts (Fork 1963b; Joliot and Joliot 1968; Kok et al. 1970; Schmid and Thibault 1979; Wydrzynski and Sauer 1980; Delrieu 1984; Sinclair 1984; see Inoue, this Vol.), thylakoid preparations (Yamaoka et al. 1978; Bader et al. 1983; Vermaas et al. 1984; Tang and Satoh 1985) and submembrane fractions of the photosynthetic apparatus, such as Photosystem II (PS II) particles (Lavorel and Seibert 1982; Clement-Metral and Gantt 1983; Cohen and Barton 1983; Wensink et al. 1984; Ikeuchi et al. 1985; Cole et al. 1986).

Although polarography has been applied to various kinds of biological measurements (Clark et al. 1953; Carritt and Kanwisher 1959; Davies 1962; Hoare 1968; Schwan 1968; Kreuzer and Kimmich 1976; Hitchman 1978; Koryta and Brezina 1979), only its application to photosynthetic systems will be considered here. This chapter is not intended to be a comprehensive review but rather as an overview of the methodology and its applications. We also hope that it is a starting point of access to the many published works of both the authors cited here and the many important contributors who are not. Text citations marked with an asterix (*) include electrode descriptions.

1.1 Basic Components of a Polarographic System

The basic components of a platinum polarographic electrode system are (1) the working or indicator electrode, the counter or auxiliary electrode and a reference electrode; (2) a current source to polarize the electrodes; (3) an electrolyte medium; (4) a means of controlling temperature; (5) a device to record the signal;

and (6) a light source for illumination of the photosynthetic sample. The working electrode is the platinum cathode, and in most applications to photosynthetic systems, the counter electrode is silver, with the redox couple Ag/AgCl (+0.222 V vs NHE at 25° C) or Ag/Ag_2O (+0.342 V vs NHE at 25° C) serving as the reference electrode.

1.2 O_2 Exchange Measurements

Polarographic O_2 measurements fall into two main categories: those which provide (1) an estimation of the instantaneous rate of O_2 exchange by a photosynthetically active sample or (2) a determination of the concentration (or change in concentration) of dissolved O_2 in an aqueous suspension of photosynthetic cells, chloroplasts or PS II particles. The objectives of the experiment and the properties of the sample materials generally dictate the methodology of the polarographic application. Consequently, the platinum electrode has been incorporated into many different systems (for reviews see Hoare 1968; Mancy 1971; Fork 1972*; Fatt 1976). With some instruments it is possible to measure O_2 exchange and other manifestations of photosynthetic activity such as chlorophyll fluorescence or CO_2 exchange simultaneously. In this chapter, various approaches to photosynthetic O_2 polarography and some of the results obtained from their use are examined.

2 Polarographic Principles

2.1 Basic Principles

An electrochemical cell basically consists of two electrodes, the anode and cathode, and a solution which provides an electrical contact between them. A voltage applied across the cell results in a current which causes electrochemical reactions to occur at both anode and cathode. The current generated as a result of these reactions is usually a function of the applied voltage; the study of the current-voltage characteristics is referred to as voltammetry. In common usage, the term polarography is often used interchangeably with the term voltammetry.

The electrochemical parameters of the system are the working electrode material, the reference electrode, the electrode potential and the electrolyte medium. The sensitivity and specificity of the system can be altered by varying these parameters (Lucero 1969).

The electrochemistry of polarographic measurements has been thouroughly reviewed (Davies 1962; Hoare 1968; Albery 1975; Degn et al. 1976; Fatt 1976; Bard and Faulkner 1980) and will be considered here only when required to clarify specific applications of the platinum electrode to the measurement of photosynthetic O_2 exchange.

2.2 O_2 Reduction

Polarographic O_2 measurement depends on the reduction of diatomic oxygen at the surface of a polarized electrode. Oxygen reduction at this surface provides a current which alters both the electrode potential and the polarizing current. Thus, either changes in voltage (potentiometric measurement) or current (amperometric measurement) can reflect the oxygen reduction rate. Commonly, the current due to O_2 reduction at the cathode is measured across a resistor in series with a voltage divider (Delieu and Walker 1972 *). The current generated by O_2 reduction can also be measured with a potentiostat which maintains the electrode polarization at a constant potential (Meunier et al. 1987) which also improves the response time of the system (Meunier and Popovic 1988 b).

When a Pt electrode is negative with respect to a reference electrode in a solution containing dissolved O_2, the O_2 at the cathode surface undergoes electrolytic reduction. At a Pt potential of -0.6 to -0.9 V vs a calomel electrode, the limiting factor is the rate of O_2 diffusion from the solution to the cathode surface (Davies 1962). In this potential range, the cathodic current is proportional to O_2 concentration in the solution (Davies 1962).

2.2.1 Platinum Electrode Reactions

Various materials have been utilized as electrodes for O_2 measurements and the reaction chemistry is dependent on a number of variables such as electrode and membrane material, polarization potential and electrolyte media. In practice, for photosynthetic measurements, the Pt cathode paired with an Ag/AgCl anode has been the most widely used.

Several models for O_2 reduction at a Pt cathode have been proposed (Hoare 1968, 1985; Hitchman 1978; Appleby and Savy 1978). The chemical reactions at the surface of the Pt electrode vary according to the pH of the electrolyte medium in the vicinity of the cathode. At a potential of -0.7 V with respect to Ag/AgCl, two electrons are required for the reduction of each O_2 molecule to H_2O_2:

$$O_2 + 2H_2O + 2e^- \rightarrow H_2O_2 + 2OH^- . \tag{1}$$

At the Pt surface, H_2O_2 is decomposed spontaneously with the fastest reaction rate at an alkaline pH ($\geqq 11$). Hydrogen peroxide exists in two forms, H_2O_2 and the peroxide anion, $HO_2{}^-$. Hydrogen peroxide dissociates to the peroxide anion by:

$$H_2O_2 \rightarrow HO_2{}^- + H^+ , \tag{2}$$

where:

$$\log \frac{[HO_2-]}{[H_2O_2]} = pH - 11.63 , \tag{3}$$

and the peroxide ion may be catalytically decomposed at the Pt (Hitchman 1978):

$$2HO_2^- \xrightarrow{Pt} 2OH^- + O_2 . \tag{4}$$

The proposed reaction scheme for the reduction of O_2 at the Pt electrode in alkaline media may occur via the following steps (Hoare 1968):

$$O_2 + e^- \longrightarrow O_2^- ; \qquad (5)$$

$$O_2- + H_2O \longrightarrow HO_2 + OH^- ; \qquad (6)$$

$$HO_2 + e^- \longrightarrow HO_2^- . \qquad (7)$$

The decomposition of HO_2^- leads to the formation of an O_2 molecule [Eq. (4)] which may also undergo the electron transfer steps of Eqs. (5)–(7). Thus, the overall reaction may be written as.

$$O_2 + 2H_2O + 4e^- \rightarrow 4OH^- . \qquad (8)$$

In non-alkaline media, the overall reaction for the reduction of O_2 is (Hoare 1968):

$$O_2 + 4H^+ + 4e^- \leftrightarrow 2H_2O . \qquad (9)$$

Oxygen reduction at the Pt electrode follows the relation (Hoare 1968; Hitchman 1978):

$$-\frac{dN_{O_2}}{dt} = \frac{j}{nF} = K_1 [O_2]_{el} - K_2 [OH^-]_{el} , \qquad (10)$$

where $N_{O_2}O_2$ represents the number of moles of O_2 reduced at the cathode per unit area per unit time, n is the number of electrons transferred from one O_2 molecule, j is the current density (amp m^{-2}), F is Faraday's constant, $[O_2]_{el}$ and $[OH^-]_{el}$ are the concentrations of the two species at the surface of the electrode and K_1 and K_2 are rate constants for the forward and backward reactions of Eq. (8), i.e. O_2 reduction and OH^- oxidation respectively.

2.2.2 Electrode Sensitivity

The sensitivity of an electrode system is defined as the ability to accurately determine the total amount of dissolved O_2 over a range of temperatures, to respond rapidly to changes in dissolved O_2 concentration and to accurately follow rates of O_2 evolution or uptake by photosynthetic systems (Wise and Naylor 1985). Electrode sensitivity is affected by parameters which can alter the cathodic reaction. The O_2 reduction process is both pH- and temperature-dependent and also affected by the presence of electroactive solutes (both organic and inorganic) in the medium. The diffusion current is sensitive to temperature changes; for O_2 with a Teflon membrane, the temperature coefficient is 3–4%/°C at room temperature (Sawyer et al. 1959). Quantitative measurements of O_2 in aqueous systems therefore require both precise temperature regulation and control of media constituents which may undergo chemical reactions at the electrode surface. Temperature control is usually achieved by use of a water jacket. A buffer may be added to the electrolyte solution to stabilize the pH. Chemical reactions which compete with the desired electrode reactions may be prevented by isolating the Pt surface from the medium by means of a membrane permeable to O_2 but impermeable to other electroactive solutes (Sawyer et al. 1959; Hitchman 1978).

2.3 The Silver Anode and Electrolyte Medium

The silver electrode serves two functions by acting as both the counter and the reference electrode. The most commonly used reference electrode with a Pt cathode for photosynthetic studies is the redox couple Ag/AgCl which can be prepared simply by oxidizing the Ag in the presence of Cl^- ions:

$$Ag + Cl^- \rightarrow AgCl + e^- . \tag{11}$$

The electrolyte solution provides the electrochemical contact between the cathode and anode and must contain the anion(s) necessary to provide the reference couple for the anode. Satisfactory operation of a Pt and Ag/AgCl electrode system is obtained using 0.1 *M* NaCl as the medium; millipore-filtered seawater can be used with marine algae.

3 Electrode Systems

The two oxygen polarographs which have proven most suitable for photosynthetic studies are the Clark electrode (Clark et al. 1953; Clark 1956) and the bare Pt electrode (Haxo and Blinks 1950). The design of the Clark-type electrode has been the basis of almost all subsequent membrane-covered detectors, while the bare Pt electrode system has been modified by a number of researchers for use with flash illumination as well as with continuous light.

3.1 The Membrane-Covered (Clark-Type) Electrode

This electrode has the platinum cathode and the Ag/AgCl reference electrode immersed in an electrolyte solution confined by a thin membrane permeable to gases but much less so to other solutes in the medium (Fig. 1). Presence of the membrane permits the addition of reductants or oxidants and electroactive substances to the medium. Its best use is as a concentration electrode but it is frequently used for rate determinations (see Fork 1972*). Use of a membrane with selective permeability restricts O_2 diffusion towards the Pt electrode surface and membranes are usually chosen for their high O_2 permeability. For much photosynthesis work a Teflon membrane 10–25 μm thick is commonly used (see Sect. 3.1.1 for membrane characteristics).

In its simplest form the Clark-type electrode consists of a small plastic probe with platinum and silver electrodes imbedded in its tip. A drop of KCl solution is applied to the tip and a thin Teflon membrane is stretched over it and usually held in place by an O-ring located by a groove in the probe body (see Fig. 1). Measurements of O_2 exchange can then be made by immersing the probe tip in a stirred cuvette containing the medium and suspended sample particles, cells or tissue sections. Commercial versions of the electrode system are available which are provided with circuitry for electrode polarization, system calibration and a recorder output. In this form its main application is to measure changes in the concentra-

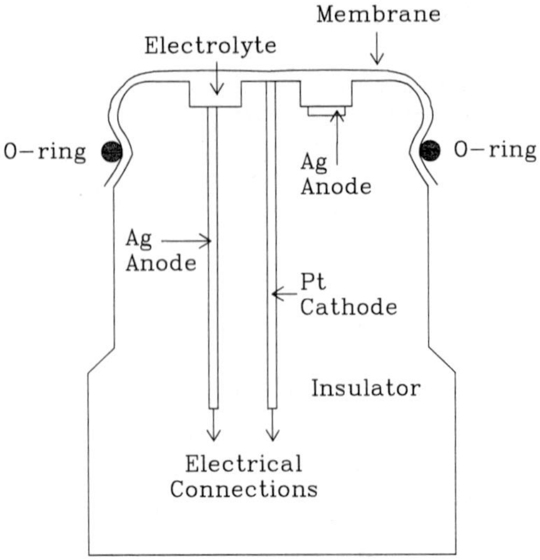

Fig. 1. Cross-section of a membrane-covered polarographic electrode showing the relationship of the Pt cathode, Ag anode, membrane and electrolyte medium

tion of dissolved O_2 in the medium. Results obtained can easily be quantitated, and with proper care, are highly reproducible.

For use as a rate electrode signal amplitudes may be increased by using large electrode surfaces (Fork 1972*). In this mode a Teflon membrane confines a thin film of KCl to the electrodes and the sample is placed on the membrane directly over the platinum surface. The sample, which may consist of particles, liposomes, chloroplasts, tissue or organ sections can be fixed in place by stretching a cellophane membrane over the entire assembly. (For some variations in these systems, see Delieu and Walker 1981*, 1983* and the review of Fork 1972*.) For further information on O_2 evolution by chloroplast preparations, see Inoue (this Vol.).

In either application the membrane is the greatest barrier to diffusion of O_2 to the Pt cathode. Diffusion across it can be rate-limiting and therefore can restrict the time resolution of transient changes in O_2 concentration in the system (Hitchman 1978). Delieu and Walker (1972*) described an electrode system which addressed membrane diffusion resistance and other operational problems arising from the use of the Clark-type electrode for photosynthesis studies.

3.1.1 Membranes and Membrane Materials

The role of the membrane in a membrane-covered electrode system is to act as a selective barrier. Thus for the oxygen polarograph, O_2 may diffuse through the membrane, but the membrane is impermeable to other inorganic or organic solutes which may affect the reduction of O_2 at the Pt electrode. Membrane-covered electrodes permit analysis of a wide range of concentrations of dissolved O_2 by appropriate selection of membrane material since the diffusion current is inversely proportional to the membrane thickness, and proportional to the permeability of the gas through the membrane (Sawyer et al. 1959). Thus, the sensitivity of the membrane-covered Pt electrode depends not only on the electrode area and surface of the electrode against the inside of the membrane, but on the membrane material and thickness as well (Sawyer et al. 1959; Lucero 1969). The thickness of the membrane is generally on the order of 10–25 μm (Hitchman 1978) since thinner membranes result in a shorter electrode response time (Sawyer et al. 1959). However, the physical strength of the membrane is the limiting factor in how thin it can be. Thus, the criteria for a suitable membrane for polarographic O_2 detectors are adequate physical strength, high permeability to O_2, permeability characteristics, which do not vary with time, and availability in thin sheets (Hitchman 1978).

Many different types of membrane materials have been used for polarographic O_2 detectors. They include cellophane (Clark et al. 1953), polyethylene (Clark 1956; Watanabe and Leonard unpublished 1957; Sawyer et al. 1959), Saran, Mylar, polyvinyl chloride, natural and silicone rubber and Teflon (Sawyer et al. 1959), polydimethylsiloxane (Dow Corning "Medical Silastic"), Lexan, cellulose and polypropylene (Hitchman 1978).

A discussion of membrane selection and diffusion may be found in Hwang and Kammermeyer (1975) and Hitchman (1978).

3.2 The Bare Electrode

The bare electrode differs mainly from the Clark-type electrode in that the selectively permeable membrane is eliminated (Fig. 1). As arrival of O_2 at the Pt surface is diffusion-limited, the advantage of this arrangement is removal of the diffusion barrier imposed by a selective membrane isolating the electrode surface from the medium. Typical usage is to place a section of leaf, algal thallus or a filter (paper or membrane disc) impregnated with cells, chloroplasts, etc. directly on to the electrode surface. A thin cellophane or other highly permeable membrane is then stretched tightly over the electrode sample and secured (see Fig. 2 for an example). Results are best if the sample and the electrode surfaces are of the same dimensions since this restricts the diffusion pathway to the contact area between them. Time resolution can be enhanced by limiting the aqueous phase of the system to only the moisture held by the covering membrane, again decreasing the

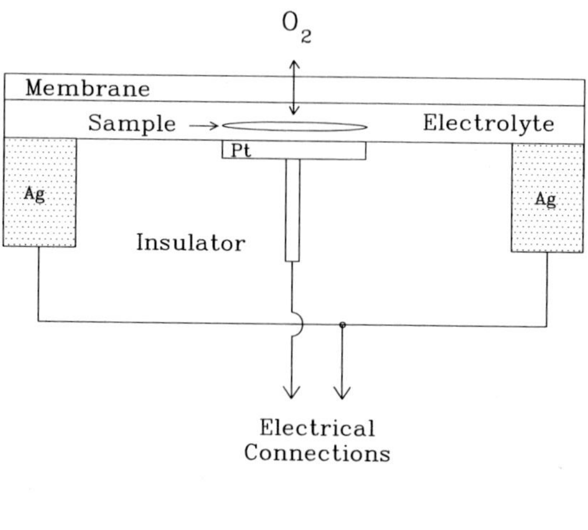

Fig. 2. Schematic diagram of a bare platinum electrode showing the relationship of the Pt and Ag electrodes to the photosynthetic sample, the covering membrane and electrolyte solution

length of the diffusion path and eliminating the need for stirring (Chandler and Vidaver 1971 *; Swenson et al. 1986). The O_2 detected is that reaching the electrode surface by diffusion from the aqueous medium plus or minus release or uptake by the sample (Vidaver and French 1965; Chandler and Vidaver 1970; Swenson et al. 1986). When used properly the bare electrode provides the fastest possible time resolution for the detection of O_2 release or uptake by the sample. Unless compensated for, system response or excitation light rise times, such as shutter opening, can mask the earliest detectable O_2 exchange.

Even though the bare electrode has the disadvantage of permitting electroactive solutes to access the electrode surface it has been utilized by many investigators. The marked increase in time resolution permits measurement of the fast kinetics of O_2 exchange and has provided information about the participation of photosynthetic partial reactions in the overall process unobtainable by other means (Joliot 1965a *; de Kouchkovsky and Joliot 1967; Joliot and Joliot 1968 *; Clement-Metral and Lavorel 1969; Delrieu and de Kouchkovsky 1971 *; Forbush et al. 1971; Diner and Mauzerall 1973a *, 1973b; Swenson et al. 1986).

Despite its superior time resolution there are serious problems with the bare electrode. Among these are the difficulty in obtaining quantitative data and that without special precautions (see Joliot and Joliot 1968 *), electroactive substances, i.e. donors or acceptors capable of reacting at the electrode surface, cannot normally by used. Recently, some progress has been made in obtaining quantitative data with the bare electrode (Meunier et al. 1987; Swenson et al. 1987b).

3.3 Choice of Electrode Type

The bare Pt electrode differs from the membrane-covered electrode in that the electrolyte medium is not separated from the Pt cathode by a membrane (Fig. 2). In general, the Clark-type electrode is the most practical concentration electrode. Because of simplicity of interpretation of the data it is the best choice for quantitative O_2 exchange measurements. As long as rapid time resolution is not required it serves equally well as a rate electrode.

For the study of rapid O_2 exchange kinetics the bare electrode is the more applicable because of its superior time resolution. The bare Pt electrode permits the photosynthetic sample to be tightly appressed to the electrode surface. Satisfactory operation is obtained using 0.1 *M* NaCl as the medium which is also the electrolyte and millipore-filtered seawater can be used with marine algal samples.

Two types of bare Pt electrode systems are commonly used for O_2 exchange measurements in photosynthetic systems using a series of brief, saturating flashes. The modulated polarographic electrode of Joliot (Joliot and Joliot 1968) attempts to discriminate between a fast, light-induced response (e.g. O_2 evolution) and any slower light-induced responses (e.g. O_2 uptake) by determining the first derivative of the O_2 signal. The O_2 reduction at the bare Pt electrode (Haxo and Blinks 1950; Chandler and Vidaver 1971; Swenson et al. 1986; Meunier and Popovic 1988a) provides the current to the recorder as a function of time which can be used to study both O_2 uptake and evolution.

Where it is not essential to resolve rapid transient changes in O_2 exchange rates either the bare or covered membrane electrode is satisfactory. Much of the photosynthetic O_2 exchange data referred to here and reported in the literature could have been obtained with either type.

3.4 The Modulated Polarographic Electrode

Joliot (1965a) devised a bare electrode system which could be used with both flashing and continuous saturating light and which had a time resolution of approximately 0.15 s. Using this system he estimated the concentration of photosynthetic intermediates formed by the two photosystems. Improvements and modifications (Joliot 1966; Joliot et al. 1966) culminated in a bare electrode system consisting of three chambers isolated by membranes (Joliot and Joliot 1968). The top chamber held buffer solution, the second contained buffer and a Hill reagent if required and the lower chamber held the chloroplast preparation or algal sample in contact with the platinum surface. All the fluids could be renewed or adjusted to a continuous flow rate during an experiment. The platinum electrode could be polarized negatively for O_2 detection or positively for the measurement of Hill oxidants. Two light sources were available, one providing continuous monochromatic background illumination or a modulated detecting beam, the other, higher intensity broad band illumination. Either beam could be modulated using a chopper. In addition, 20 μs saturating flashes could be provided with a flash lamp. The polarizing current could be modulated with a lock-in amplifier and synchronized with the light beam chopper. By applying a positive voltage to the Pt electrode and adjustment of the phase angle between the modulated light and the modulated electrode polarization, it was also possible to measure the reduction of Hill oxidants.

Joliot's initial results with this electrode showed that there are two limiting processes occurring between the photochemical act in the chloroplast and O_2 reduction at the Pt cathode (Joliot et al. 1966). The two processes are diffusion of O_2 towards the Pt electrode and a first-order thermal reaction which occurs between the reaction center of Photosystem II and the water-splitting act (Joliot et al. 1966).

3.5 Improvements in Bare Platinum Electrode Systems

The bare Pt electrode system of Haxo and Blinks (1950) has been modified many times (Fork 1963a; Myers and Graham 1963; Chandler and Vidaver 1970, 1971; Swenson et al. 1987b; Meunier and Popovic 1988a, b) with increasing ability to accurately determine O_2 exchange in photosynthetic systems. The latest improvement in the bare Pt electrode system uses a polyacrylamide gel containing the electrolyte NaCl to provide the electrical contact between the Pt and Ag/AgCl electrodes (Meunier and Popovic 1988a, b). This minimizes the electrical resistance in the system and eliminates the pile-up of current pulses obtained with a dialysis membrane (Swenson et al. 1986, 1987a, b). The redesigned electrode system improves the response time of the electrode to a rise time of 4 ms and a decay time constant of 21 ms for the algae *Dunaliella tertiolecta* (Meunier and Popovic 1988 a).

Some results obtained with these electrode systems will be discussed in Section 4.

4 Photosynthesis Studies

4.1 Photosynthetic Action Spectra

Haxo and Blinks (1950) obtained action spectra (photosynthetic activity as a function of wavelength) for several algal species using a bare Pt electrode connected by a seawater-agar salt bridge to a calomel reference electrode. The Pt was biased to -0.5 V vs the calomel electrode and a 100-W incandescent lamp through a monochromator provided a monochromatic light source. The algal thalli were held tightly against the electrode surface by a water-permeable cellophane membrane. The light flux was adjusted to equal incident energy (but recalculated in terms of equal incident quanta before plotting) for each wavelength and the relative steady state rates of O_2 evolution were recorded at 10-nm intervals. A striking result of this investigation was that in red algae (e.g. *Porphyra, Delesseria*), only the phycobilin pigments appeared to be photosynthetically active and chlorophyll a contributed little to the action spectrum. Photosynthetic activity, as measured by O_2 evolution, was almost minimal at 435 and 675 nm, where chlorophyll shows maximal absorption. Green algae (*Ulva* and *Monostroma*) and a brown alga (*Coilodesme*) showed action spectra which corresponded closely to their absorption spectra. This is now explained by the fact that in red algae, PS II excitation is mainly by energy transfer to the PS II reaction center chlorophyll a via phycoerythrin → phycocyanin → allophycocyanin in ordered phycobilisome structures (Gantt et al. 1976; Gantt 1981). Since wavelengths greater than 680 nm contribute little to PS II excitation, activity in this range was also low because in vivo both PS I and PS II must function for water-splitting to occur. Action spectra for PS II and PS I obtained polarographically with intact green algae have been reported by Vidaver and French (1965), Vidaver (1966), and Wang and Myers (1976).

4.2 Chromatic Transients

The Blinks apparatus (Blinks 1957, 1960) was used to investigate transient changes in the O_2 evolution rate which occurred when excitation light was switched from short to long wavelengths and vice versa. These transients appeared to result from differential activation of PS II and PS I on switching between excitation wavebands (Joliot et al. 1968).

4.3 O_2 Evolution and the S-State Hypothesis

Until the last few years, the molecular mechanisms of O_2 evolution remained obscure. By 1960, the participation of two photochemical systems, PS I and PS II, in photosynthesis was generally accepted, however, their contribution to water-splitting was poorly understood. It soon began to be recognized that quantitative kinetic studies of photosynthetic O_2 production might provide information about the actual process. The platinum polarograph appeared to provide the best approach to kinetic studies. Although membrane-covered electrodes could provide quantitative data, their slow response time limited their usefulness. On the other hand, the difficulty of obtaining quantitative data with the bare electrode was a serious obstacle.

Application of the Joliot electrode (Sect. 3.4) led to the now widely accepted Kok hypothesis of the four-step (S-state) system by which electrons are removed singly from water with the release of an O_2 molecule after four charges are accumulated (Kok et al. 1970; Forbush et al. 1971). Support for the hypothesis arose from observations that when a dark-adapted sample is illuminated with brief, saturating, light flashes given at approximately 300-ms intervals, no O_2 is released in response to the first flash, little or none with the second, and the maximum yield occurs on the third flash followed by decreasing yields with flashes four, five and six (see Fig. 3). Starting with flash seven, the oscillations are repeated but are somewhat damped. After several cycles, the O_2 yield becomes virtually equal for each flash. In part, this damping out is interpreted as indicating that double hits and misses occur with each saturating flash (Kok et al. 1970; Lavorel 1978; Delrieu 1978, 1983b). Taking into account double hits, misses and dark S-state rever-

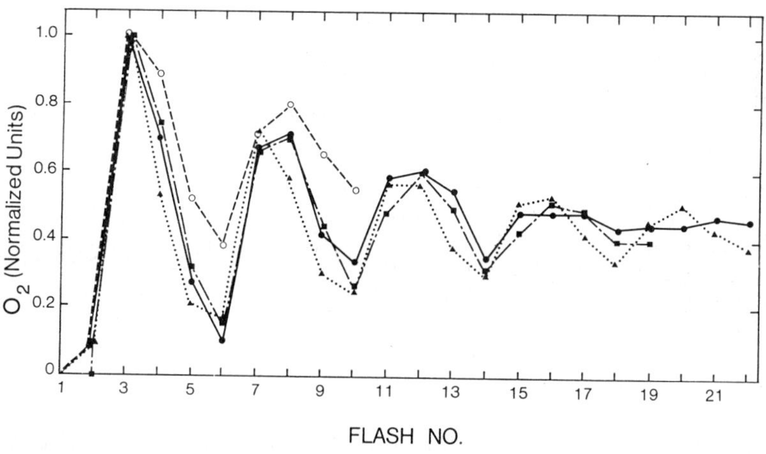

Fig. 3. Comparison of O_2 flash yield sequence for dark-adapted samples under atmospheric conditions during saturating light flashes (Swenson et al. 1986). Data for *Ulva* sp. using 4-μs flashes at 3.3 Hz (●—●) (Swenson et al. 1986); data of Joliot et al. (1971) for chloroplasts using 2-μs pulses 320 ms apart (■·—·■); data of Forbush et al. (1971) for isolated spinach chloroplasts with 1 s between flashes (▲....▲); data of Diner (1975) for *Chlorella* cells using 4-μs pulses 320 ms apart (○---○)

sions, attempts have been made to construct models which duplicate the observed oscillations in O_2 yield (Joliot 1968; Joliot et al. 1969; Kok et al. 1970; Forbush et al. 1971; Mar and Govindjee 1972; Delrieu 1974; Lavorel 1976; Greenbaum 1977; Thibault 1978; Delrieu 1983 b; Swenson et al. 1986). None of these models appear to completely account for the observed damping, which suggests the intervention of some, as yet undetected, rate process. Some of these studies have been made with a membrane-covered electrode (Delrieu 1974). This four-step cycle has been shown to occur in all types of O_2-evolving systems. A comparison of the four-step sequence of O_2 exchange is shown in Fig. 3 for the green algae, *Ulva* and *Chlorella*, and chloroplasts (Swenson et al. 1986).

4.4 Measurement of the Activity of O_2-Evolving Particles

In recent years, interest has focused on the molecular organization of the PS II reaction center and its associated oxygen-evolving complex (Briantais 1966; Govindjee et al. 1980, 1985; Beck et al. 1985; Dismukes 1986). Two main questions arise from such studies: to determine the minimum organization required for the retention of light-dependent O_2-evolving capacity, and the minimum required to maintain the integrity of the charge accumulation (S-state) system. For the first of these questions, the application of the simple, unmodified membrane-covered Clark-type electrode (see Sect. 3.1) usually suffices, since only the O_2 evolution rate needs to be determined (Kukidome et al. 1986; Lavorel and Seibert 1982; Seibert and Lavorel 1983). Akerlund et al. (1984) used a flash polarographic system incorporating a Clark-type electrode to study the role of a 23 kD protein in O_2 evolution in inside-out chloroplasts. For the latter, it is essential to detect the O_2 produced from single, saturating, light flashes, often in the presence of electron donors, acceptors or other substances that may affect the electrode response. Such measurements require a rapid response and can be accomodated by a modulated system such as the Joliot-type electrode system described in Sect. 3.4 or the bare Pt electrode system discussed in Sect. 3.2.

4.5 Hydrostatic Pressure Effects

Hydrostatic pressure can act as a reversible inhibitor on O_2 exchange reactions and preferentially affect some photosynthetic reactions, but have little effect on others (Vidaver 1969).

4.5.1 Pressure Effects on O_2 Evolution

Vidaver (1969) investigated the effects of hydrostatic pressure up to 132 MPa on the photosynthetic O_2 evolution of several species of marine algae using a bare Pt cathode and Ag/AgCl anode enclosed in a stainless steel vessel. Hydrostatic pressure inhibited steady state O_2 evolution more than it inhibited the initial O_2 evolution spike occurring with the onset of illumination. For example, in *Ulva*, at 15° C, steady state evolution was 50% inhibited at about 65 MPa, but twice this pressure was required to inhibit the initial spike by 50%. This indicates that the limiting reactions of photosynthesis are much more sensitive to pressure than photochemical water-splitting. This can be explained by the activation volume change or final product volume, or both (Johnson et al. 1954) of the limiting reaction being larger than the volume changes associated with photochemical water-splitting reactions.

4.5.2 Pressure Effects on O_2 Uptake

In further investigations of hydrostatic pressure effects on photosynthesis, Vidaver and Chandler (1969; Chandler and Vidaver 1971) utilzed a redesigned electrode system which had the advantages of convenience and stability over previous configurations. They demonstrated in *Ulva* that 54 MPa hydrostatic pressure completely inhibited a PS I-driven O_2 uptake induction transient but this pressure had virtually no effect on the initial PS II-driven O_2 gush. Since the O_2 uptake transient probably reflects the Mehler reaction (Mehler 1951), this result suggests that O_2 reduction in chloroplasts involves a relatively large activation volume change but for S-state charge accumulation (Kok et al. 1970), the volume changes are small.

4.6 Electron Transfer Reactions

The O_2 polarograph has also been widely used as a means of monitoring electron flow between PS II and PS I (Joliot and Joliot 1968; Joliot et al. 1968; Jursinic 1978). In isolated chloroplasts, electron acceptors such as methyl viologen have been used to study the chloroplast electron transport involving PS I (Jursinic 1978). The reduction of electron acceptors and their consequent autooxidation (Good and Hill 1955) can most easily be followed by monitoring the uptake of O_2.

4.7 Simultaneous Measurement of O_2 Exchange and Variable Chlorophyll a Fluorescence

One of the earliest detectable manifestations of photosynthetic photochemistry after illumination is the variable fluorescence emission of chlorophyll a (Fv). The fluorescence yield is believed to reflect the redox state of the primary PS II quinone electron acceptor Q_A (for a review, see Papageorgiou 1975). Electron transfer from the PS II reaction center to Q_A results in an increase in Fv, while oxidation of Q_A causes a decline in Fv. Therefore, comparison of the kinetics of both variable fluorescence emission and O_2 evolution yields information about interactions between the water-splitting enzyme complex (OEC), the charge accumulating system, intersystem electron transport and even CO_2 assimilation. Methods for simultaneous measurements of these two phenomena have been devised in several laboratories (Wiltens et al. 1978; Cerovic et al. 1984; Delieu and Walker 1983; Horton 1983b; Walker et al. 1983a, b). A commercially available Hansatech electrode system incorporating the design of Delieu and Walker (1982,

1983 b), has the capacity to measure O_2 evolution and variable chlorophyll fluorescence simultaneously, while maintaining CO_2 at saturating levels. The instrument can be easily adapted to use a modulated excitation light and detector system. Using a system based on the Hansatech apparatus, Horton (1983 b) investigated relations between electron transport and carbon assimilation by simultaneously measuring O_2 exchange, Fv and 9-aminoacridine fluorescence.

4.8 Light-Dependent O_2 Uptake

Green plants and algae show a light-dependent O_2 uptake which may be either PS I (Vidaver and French 1965) or PS II mediated (Beck et al. 1985). Oxygen uptake in the light may occur by direct photoreduction of O_2 (Mehler 1951), the oxygenase reaction of RuBP carboxylase-oxygenase and the subsequent photorespiratory metabolism of glycolate (Andrews et al. 1971) and mitochondrial respiration (Jackson and Volk 1970). Light-induced transients of O_2 uptake are frequently observed during polarographic O_2 exchange measurements. French and Fork (1963) considered O_2 uptake transients a result of light-induced respiratory stimulation. This concept was supported by studies which showed O_2 uptake in the presence of DCMU and in darkness following illumination (Ried 1969). Vidaver and French (1965) described a DCMU-insensitive uptake transient displaying a PSI action spectrum. Subsequent studies indicated a competing O_2 evolution and uptake during the first seconds of illumination (Chandler and Vidaver 1970; Vidaver and Chandler 1969) which was followed by a subsequent dark release of O_2. From an investigation of tobacco chloroplasts using pulsed light Schmid and Thibault (1979) concluded that a transient O_2 uptake results from the reoxidation of an endogenous PSI electron acceptor in a Mehler-type reaction. These authors suggest that the uptake serves to dissipate excess reducing power. Pulsed light experiments with *Chlorella* (Peltier and Ravenal 1987) showed that uptake began only after three brief light flashes, suggesting that an activation step is necessary. In a kinetic study with *Chlorella*, Greenbaum et al. (1987) utilized O_2 uptake to estimate the optical cross-section of PSI. A suggested model to account for the uptake and subsequent dark O_2 release is as follows: electrons are transferred in light to an endogenous acceptor by PSI reaction centers, this acceptor is subsequently oxidized by O_2, causing the uptake and resulting in the production of superoxide, superoxide dismutase then produces H_2O_2 which is then enzymatically broken down to H_2O and O_2. The O_2 released accounts for the O_2 release transient following the uptake (Chandler and Vidaver 1971). Since no net photochemical energy storage results, this could represent the dissipation of excess reducing power (Schmid and Thibault 1979). This endogenous uptake would not be detected by a modulated pulsed light system such as the Joliot electrode apparatus (see also Delrieu and de Kouchkovsky 1971). If, as reported (Swenson et al. 1986; Peltier and Ravenal 1987), the uptake begins with the third flash, then unless a donor and an electron transport inhibitor is present this will effectively diminish the amplitude of yields measured for flash 4 of the oscillatory O_2 release pattern (Kok et al. 1970) and subsequent flash yields until the uptake transient is completed after about 5 s (Swenson et al. 1986).

4.9 Measurement of Oxygen Evolution by Leaf Discs (The Hansatech Electrode)

Direct measurements of O_2 exchange in higher plant leaves are difficult to obtain because of the complex anatomy of most angiosperm or gymnosperm leaves: diffusion pathways tend to be long and are complicated by such factors as a relatively impermeable leaf surface cuticle, leaf hairs and stomatal regulation of gas exchange. These complexities have led to the use of simpler photosynthetic structures such as unicell or chloroplast preparations, very thin algal thalli or the thin leaves of some aquatic plants for polarographic O_2 exchange measurements. Delieu and Walker (1981) described a leaf disc system incorporating a membrane-covered electrode which is intended to minimize or compensate for some of the barriers to obtaining interpretable data. A version of their system is commercially available (see Sect. 6.2) and perhaps its greatest value is as a teaching aid or in productivity assessments. Adams et al. (1986) have used this system to determine photosynthetic quantum yields of CAM plants.

5 The Future of Polarographic O_2 Exchange Measurement

The remarkable development of polarographic electrode systems over the last 4 decades seems to have provided for almost every conceivable requirement for the measurement of any aspect of photosynthetic O_2 exchange in plants. Interest is currently developing in both regulatory aspects of photosynthesis (Heber et al. 1978; Quick and Horton 1984; Adams et al. 1986; Falkowski et al. 1986; Peltier and Ravenal 1987) and the relationship between the physical environment and photosynthetic activity of plants (Boyer and Bowen 1970; Sibbald and Vidaver 1987; Gui-Ying Ben et al. 1987; Toivonen and Vidaver 1988). Polarography combined with scientific ingenuity is certain to make a significant contribution to these investigations.

6 Commercial Suppliers of Polarographic Systems

6.1 Clark-Type Systems

Beckman Instrument Inc. 2500 Fullerton Blvd., Fullerton, CA 92634 (USA).
Bionic Instruments, Rank Brothers, Cambridge, England.
Yellow Springs Instrument Co. Yellow Springs, OH 45387 (USA).

6.2 The Hansatech Electrode

It is manufactured by Hansatech Ltd., Kings Lynn, Norfolk, England and available in North America from Decagon Devices Inc., PO Box 835, Pullman, WA 99163 (USA).

6.3 Bare Electrode Systems

None of these appear to be commercially available and the reader is referred to the publications of the authors reporting their use for details.

References

Adams WW, Nishida K, Osmund CB (1986) Quantum yields of CAM plants measured by photosynthetic O_2 exchange. Plant Physiol 81:297–300

Akerlund H-E, Renger G, Weiss W, Hagemann R (1984) Effect of partial removal and readdition of a 23 kilodalton protein on oxygen yield and flash-induced absorbance changes at 320 nm of inside-out thylakoids. Biochim Biophys Acta 765:1–6

Albery J (1975) Electrode kinetics. Clarendon, Oxford

Andrews TJ, Lorimar GH, Tolbert NE (1971) Incorporation of molecular oxygen into glycine and serine during photorespiration in spinach leaves. Biochemistry 10:4777–4782

Appleby AJ, Savy M (1978) Kinetics of oxygen reduction reactions including catalytic decomposition of hydrogen peroxide. J Electr Chem 92:15–30

Bader KP, Thibault P, Schmid GH (1983) A study on oxygen evolution and on the S-state distribution in thylakoid preparations of the filamentous blue-green alga *Oscillatoria chalybea*. Z Naturforsch 38c:778–792

Bard AJ, Faulkner LR (1980) Electrochemical methods. Fundamentals and applications. Wiley, New York Chichester Brisbane Toronto

Beck WF, dePaula JC, Brudvig G (1985) Active and resting states of the O_2-evolving complex of photosystem II. Biochemistry 24:3035–3043

Blinks LR (1957) Chromatic transients in photosynthesis of red algae. In: Gaffron (ed) Research in photosynthesis. Wiley, New York, pp 444–447

Blinks LR (1960) Action spectra of chromatic transients and the Emerson effect in algae. Proc Natl Acad Sci USA 46:327–333

Blinks LR (1964) Photophysiology. Academic Press, New York London, pp 199–221

Blinks LR, Givan CV (1961) The absence of daily photosynthetic rhythm in some littoral marine algae. Biol Bull 121:230–233

Boyer JS, Bowen BL (1970) Inhibition of oxygen evolution in chloroplasts isolated from leaves with low water potentials. Plant Physiol 45:612–615

Briantais J-M (1966) Echanges d'oxygène induits par la lumière dans des fragments de chloroplastes. C R Acad Sci Paris 263:1899–1902

Carritt DE, Kanwisher JW (1959) An electrode system for measuring dissolved oxygen. Anal Chem 31(1):5–9

Cerovic ZG, Sivak MN, Walker DA (1984) Slow secondary fluorescence kinetics associated with the onset of photosynthetic carbon assimilation in intact isolated chloroplasts. Proc R Soc London Ser B 220:327–338

Chandler MT, Vidaver WE (1970) Photosynthetic oxygen induction transients in the alga *Ulva lactuca* L. Phycologia 9:133–142

Chandler MT, Vidaver WE (1971) Stationary platinum electrode for measurement of O_2 exchange by biological systems under hydrostatic pressure. Rev Sci Instr 42:143–146

Clark LC (1956) Monitor and control of blood and tissue oxygen tensions. Trans Am Soc Art Intern Organ 2:41–48

Clark LC, Wold R, Granger D, Taylor F (1953) Continuous recording of blood oxygen tensions by polarography. J Appl Physiol 6:189–193

Clement-Metral J, Gantt E (1983) Isolation of oxygen-evolving phycobilisome-photosystem II particles from *Porphyridium cruentum*. FEBS Lett 156:185–188

Clement-Metral J, Lavorel J (1969) Etude dun modèle cinétique applicable aux transitoires de fluorescence de la chlorophylle et au „Jet" d'oxygène des chloroplastes isolés. Photosynthesis 3:233–243

Cohen WS, Barton JR (1983) The use of O_2-evolving subchloroplast particles to study acceptor and inhibitor sites on the reducing side of photosystem II. Z Naturforsch 38c:793–798
Cole J, Boska M, Blugh NV, Sauer K (1986) Reversible and irreversible effects of alkaline pH on photosystem II electron-transfer reactions. Biochim Biophys Acta 848:41–47
Davies PW (1962) The oxygen cathode. In: Nastuk WL (ed) Physical techniques in biological research vol 4: Special methods. Academic Press, New York London, pp 173–179
de Kouchkovsky Y, Joliot P (1967) Cinétique des échanges d'oxygène et de la fluorescence des chloroplastes isolés. Photochem Photobiol 6:567–587
Degn H, Balslev I, Brooks R (1976) Measurement of oxygen. Elsevier, Amsterdam
Delieu TJ, Walker DA (1972) An improved cathode for the measurement of photosynthetic oxygen evolution by isolated chloroplasts. New Phytol 71:201–225
Delieu TJ, Walker DA (1981) Polarographic measurement of photosynthetic O_2 evolution by leaf discs. New Phytol 89:165–178
Delieu TJ, Walker DA (1983) Simultaneous measurement of oxygen evolution and chlorophyll fluorescence from leaf pieces. Plant Physiol 73:534–541
Delrieu M-J (1972) Changes in oxygen evolution induced by a long preillumination at 650 nm with *Chlorella pyrenoidosa*. Biochim Biophys Acta 256:293–299
Delrieu M-J (1974) Simple explanation of the misses in the cooperation of charges in photosynthetic O_2 evolution. Photochem Photobiol 20:441–454
Delrieu M-J (1978) Oscillatory kinetics of the number of photosynthetic system II centers in S_2 and S_3 states after flashes under various conditions. Plant Cell Physiol 19:1447–1456
Delrieu M-J (1983a) Relations between the auxiliary donor D, state S_2 and unequal misses obtained from oxygen and fluorescence measurements. In: Sybesma C (ed) Advances in photosynthesis research. Nijhoff/Junk, The Hague, pp 291–294
Delrieu M-J (1983b) Evidence for unequal misses in oxygen flash yield sequence in photosynthesis. Z Naturforsch 38c:247–258
Delrieu M-J (1984) Studies on the water-oxidizing system by the effects of different treatments in chloroplasts. Biochim Biophys Acta 767:304–313
Delrieu M-J, de Kouchkovsky Y (1971) Relationships between the photon distributions between the two photosystems, the concentration of system II reaction centers and the intersystem equilibrium constant in *Chlorella pyrenoidosa*. Biochim Biophys Acta 226:409–421
Diner B (1975) Dependence of the turnover and deactivation reactions of photosystem II on the redox state of the pool A varied under anaerobic conditions. In: Avron M (ed) Proceedings IIrd International Congress on Photosynthesis, Elsevier, Amsterdam, pp 589–601
Diner B (1977) Dependence of the deactivation reactions of photosystem II on the redox state of plastoquinone pool A varied under anaerobic conditions. Equilibrium of the acceptor side of photosystem II. Biochim Biophys Acta 460:247–258
Diner B, Mauzerall D (1973a) Feedback controlling oxygen production in a cross reaction between two photosystems in photosynthesis. Biochim Biophys Acta 305:329–352
Diner B, Mauzerall D (1973b) The turnover times of photosynthesis and redox properties of the pool of electron carriers between the photosystems. Biochim Biophys Acta 305:353–363
Dismukes GC (1986) The metal centers of the photosynthetic oxygen evolving complex. Photochem Photobiol 43:99–115
Falkowski PG, Fujita Y, Ley A, Mauzerall D (1986) Evidence for cyclic electron flow around photosystem II in *Chlorella pyrenoidosa*. Plant Physiol 81:310–312
Fatt I (1976) Polarographic oxygen sensors. CRC, Cleveland
Forbush B, Kok B, McGloin MP (1971) Cooperation of charges in photosynthetic O_2 evolution – II. Damping of flash yield oscillation, deactivation. Photochem Photobiol 14:307–321
Fork DC (1963a) Action spectra for O_2 evolution by chloroplasts with and without added substrate, for regeneration of O_2 evoling ability by far-red, and for O_2 uptake. Plant Physiol 38:323–332

Fork DC (1963 b) The influence for a Hill-oxidant on the action spectrum for oxygen production in Swiss chard chloroplasts. Photosynthese 119, Coll Int Centre Nat Rech Sci, 23–27 July 1962, Gif-Sur-Yvette et Saclay, pp 244–259

Fork DC (1972) Oxygen electrode. Methods Enzymol 24:113–122

French CS, Fork DC (1963) Two primary photochemical reactions driven by different pigments. Proc 5th Annu Congr Biochemistry. Pergamon, Oxford, pp 122–137

Gantt E (1981) Phycobilisomes. Annu Rev Plant Physiol 32:327–347

Gantt E, Lipschultz CA, Zilinskas B (1976) Further evidence for a phycolbilisome model from selective dissociation, fluorescence emission, immunoprecipitation, and electron microscopy. Biochim Biophys Acta 430:375–388

Good N, Hill R (1955) Photochemical reduction of oxygen in chloroplast preparation – II. Mechanisms of the reaction with oxygen. Arch Biochem Biophys 57:355–366

Govindjee, Fork D, Wydrzynski T, Spector M, Winget GD (1980) Photosystem II reactions in liposomes reconstituted with cholate-extracted thylakoids and a manganese containing protein. Photochem Photobiophys 1:347–351

Govindjee, Kambara T, Coleman W (1985) The electron donor side of photosystem II: the oxygen evolving complex. Photochem Photobiol 42:187–210

Greenbaum E (1977) Photosynthetic oxygen evolution under varying redox conditions: new experimental and theoretical results. Photochem Photobiol 25:293–298

Greenbaum E, Mauzerall DC (1976) Oxygen yield per flash of *Chlorella* coupled to chemical oxidants under anaerobic conditions. Photochem Photobiol 23:369–372

Greenbaum NI, Ley AC, Mauzerall DC (1987) Use of a light-induced respiratory transient to measure the optical cross section of photosystem I in *Chlorella*. Plant Physiol 84:879–882

Gui-Ying Ben, Osmund CB, Sharkey TD (1987) Comparisons of photosynthetic responses of *Xanthium strumarium* and *Helianthus annuus* to chronic and acute water stress in sun and shade. Plant Physiol 84:476–482

Haxo FT, Blinks LR (1950) Photosynthetic action spectra of marine algae. J Gen Physiol 33:389–422

Heber U, Egneus H, Hanck U, Jensen M, Koster S (1978) Regulation of photosynthetic electron transport and photophosphorylation in intact chloroplasts and leaves of *Spinacia oleracea* L. Planta 143:41–49

Hitchman ML (1978) Measurement of dissoived oxygen. Wiley, New York London Sydney Toronto

Hoare JP (1968) The electrochemistry of oxygen. Interscience, New York

Hoare JP (1985) The kinetics of platinum-oxygen local cells. J Electrochem Soc 132:301–305

Horton P (1983 a) Effects of changes in the capacity for photosynthetic electron transfer and photophosphorylation on the kinetics of fluorescence induction in isolated chloroplasts. Biochim Biophys Acta 724:404–410

Horton P (1983 b) Relations between electron transport and carbon assimilation; simultaneous measurement of chlorophyll fluorescence, transthylakoid pH gradient and O_2 evolution in isolated chloroplasts. Proc R Soc London Ser B 217:415–416

Hwang S-T, Kammermeyer K (1975) Membranes in separations. Techniques of chemistry, vol 3. Wiley, New York

Ikeuchi M, Yuasa M, Inoue Y (1985) Simple and discrete isolation of an O_2-evolving PS II reaction center complex retaining Mn and the extrinsic 33 kDa protein. FEBS Lett 185:316–322

Jackson WA, Volk RJ (1970) Photorespiration. Annu Rev Plant Physiol 21:385–432

Johnson FH, Eyring H, Polissar M (1954) The kinetic basis of molecular biology. Wiley, New York London Sydney Toronto

Joliot P (1965 a) Cinétiques des réactions linés a l'émission d'oxygène photosynthétique. Biochim Biophys Acta 102:116–134

Joliot P (1965 b) Etudes des cinétiques de fluorescence et d'émission d'oxygène photosynthétique. Biochim Biophys Acta 102:135–148

Joliot P (1966) Oxygen evolution in algae illuminated by modulated light. Brookhaven Symp 19, Upton, New York, pp 418–433

Joliot P (1968) Kinetic studies of photosystem II in photosynthesis. Photochem Photobiol 8:451–463

Joliot P, Joliot A (1968) A polarographic method for the detection of oxygen production and reduction of Hill reagent by isolated chloroplasts. Biochim Biophys Acta 153:625–634

Joliot P, Hofnung M, Chabaud R (1966) Etude de l'émission d'oxygène par des algues soumises à un éclairment module sinusoidalement. J Chim Phys 63:1423–1441

Joliot P, Joliot A, Kok P (1968) Analysis of the interactions between the two photosystems in isolated chloroplasts. Biochim Biophys Acta 153:635–652

Joliot P, Barbieri G, Chabaud R (1969) Un nouveau modèle des centres photochimiques du système II. Photochem Photobiol 10:309–329

Joliot P, Joliot A, Bouges B, Barbieri G (1971) Studies of system II photocenters by comparitive measurements of luminescence, fluorescence, and oxygen emission. Photochem Photobiol 14:287–305

Jursinic P (1978) Flash polarographic detection of superoxide production as a means of monitoring electron flow between photosystem I and II. FEBS Lett 90:15–20

Jursinic P (1981) Investigation of double turnovers in photosystem II charge separation and oxygen evolution with excitation flashes of different duration. Biochim Biophys Acta 635:38–52

Kok B, Forbush B, McGloin M (1970) Cooperation of charges in photosynthetic O_2 evolution – I. A linear four step mechanism. Photochem Photobiol 11:457–475

Koryta J, Brezina M (1979) Methods for electroanalysis in vivo. In: Bard AJ (ed) A series of advances, vol 11. Electroanalytical chemistry. Dekker, New York Basel, pp 85–140

Kreuzer F, Kimmich HP (1976) Recent developments in oxygen polarography as applied to physiology. In: Degn H, Balslev I, Brook R (eds) Measurement of oxygen. Elsevier, Amsterdam Oxford New York, pp 123–158

Kukidome H, Kobayashi Y, Oku T (1986) Properties of photosystem II particles prepared from chloroplasts of spruce seedlings. J Fac Agric Kyushu Univ 30:267–274

Lavorel J (1976) Matrix analysis of the oxygen evolving system of photosynthesis. J Theor Biol 57:171–185

Lavorel J (1978) On the origin of damping of the oxygen yield in sequences of flashes. In: Metzner H (ed) Photosynthetic oxygen evolution. Academic Press, New York London, pp 249–268

Lavorel J, Seibert M (1982) Patterns of oxygen emission from active oxygen-evolving photosystem II particles subjected to sequences of flashes. FEBS Lett 144:101–103

Lucero DP (1969) Design of membrane-covered polarographic gas detectors. Anal Chem 41(4):613–622

Mancy KH (1971) Instrumental analysis for water pollution control. Ann Arbor Sci Publ, Ann Arbor, Michigan

Mar T, Govindjee (1972) Kinetic models of oxygen evolution in photosynthesis. J Theor Biol 36:427–446

Mehler AG (1951) Studies on the reactions of illuminated chloroplasts II. Stimulation and inhibition of the reaction with molecular oxygen. Arch Biochem Biophys 34:339–351

Meunier CP, Popovic R (1988a) High accuracy oxygen polarograph for photosynthetic systems. Rev Sci Instr (in press)

Meunier CP, Popovic R (1988b) Optimization of the bare platinum electrode as an oxygen measurement system in photosynthesis. Photosynth Res (in press)

Meunier CP, Swenson SI, Colbow K (1987) A dynamic model for the bare platinum electrode. In: Biggens (ed) Progress in photosynthesis research, vol 1. Nijhoff, Dordrecht, pp 737–740

Myers J, Graham J (1963) Further improvements in the stationary platinum electrode of Haxo and Blinks. Plant Physiol 38:1–5

Papageorgiou G (1975) Chlorophyll fluorescence: an intrinsic probe of photosynthesis. In: Govindjee (ed) Bioenergetics of photosynthesis. Academic Press, New York London, pp 319–371

Peltier G, Ravenal J (1987) Oxygen photoreduction and variable fluorescence during a dark-to-light transition in *Chlorella pyrenoidosa*. Biochim Biophys Acta 894:543–551

Quick WP, Horton P (1984) Studies on the induction of chlorophyll fluorescence in barley protoplasts. I. Factors affecting the observation of oscillations in the yield of chlorophyll fluorescence and the rate of oxygen evolution. Proc RSoc London, Ser B 220:361–370

Ried A (1968) Interactions between photosynthesis and respiration in *Chlorella*. I. Types of transients of oxygen exchange after short light exposures. Biochim Biophys Acta 153:653–663

Ried A (1969) Studies on light-dark transients in *Chlorella*. Progr Photosynth Res 1:512–530

Sawyer DT, George RS, Rhodes RC (1959) Polarography of gases. Quantitative studies of oxygen and sulfur dioxide. Anal Chem 31:2–5

Schmid GH, Thibault P (1979) Evidence for a rapid oxygen uptake in tobacco chloroplasts. Z Naturforsch 34c:414–418

Schwan HP (1968) Electrode polarization impedance and measurements in biological materials. Ann New York Acad Sci 148:191–209

Seibert M, Lavorel J (1983) Oxygen evolution patterns from spinach photosystem II preparations. Biochim Biophys Acta 723:160–168

Sibbald PR, Vidaver W (1987) Photosystem I-mediated regulation of water splitting in the red alga, *Porphyra sanjuanenesis*. Plant Physiol 84:1373–1377

Sinclair J (1984) The influence of anions on oxygen evolution by isolated spinach chloroplasts. Biochim Biophys Acta 764:247–252

Stewart AC, Bendall DS (1979) Preparation of an active photosystem II particle from a blue-green alga. FEBS Lett 107(2):308–312

Swenson SI, Colbow K, Vidaver WE (1986) Oxygen exchange in *Ulva* using a bare platinum electrode with 4 microsecond light flashes. Plant Physiol 80:346–349

Swenson SI, Meunier CP, Colbow K (1987a) Dynamic linearity of the bare platinum electrode for oxygen exchange measurements in marine algae. In: Biggens (ed) Progress in photosynthesis research, vol 1. Nijhoff, Dordrecht, pp 733–736

Swenson SI, Meunier CP, Whelan JH, Colbow K (1987b) Dynamic linearity of the bare platinum electrode system. J Plant Physiol 130:147–156

Tang X-S, Satoh K (1985) The oxygen-evolving photosystem II core complex. FEBS Lett 179:60–64

Thibault P (1978) A new attempt to study the oxygen evolving system of photosynthesis: determination of transition probabilities of a state i. J Theor Biol 73:271–284

Toivonen P, Vidaver W (1988) Variable chlorophyll a fluorescence and CO_2 uptake in water stressed White spruce seedlings. Plant Physiol 86:744–748

Vermaas WFJ, Renger G, Dohnt G (1984) The reduction of the oxygen-evolving system in chloroplasts by thylakoid components. Biochim Biophys Acta 764:194–202

Vidaver WE (1966) Separate action spectra for the two photochemical systems of photosynthesis. Plant Physiol 41:87–89

Vidaver WE (1969) Hydrostatic pressure effects on photosynthesis. Int Res Ges Hydrobiol 54:697–747

Vidaver WE, Chandler T (1969) Metabolic inhibitors and photosynthetic induction transients. Progr Photosynth Res 1:514–520

Vidaver WE, French CS (1965) Oxygen uptake and evolution following monochromatic flashes in *Ulva* and an action spectra for system I. Plant Physiol 40:7–12

Walker DA, Horton P, Sivak MN, Quick WP (1983a) Antiparallel relationship between O_2 evolution and slow fluorescence kinetics. Photobiochem Photobiophys 5:35–39

Walker DA, Sivak MN, Prinsley RT, Cheesbrough JK (1983b) Simultaneous measurement of oscillations in oxygen evolution and chlorophyll a fluorescence in leaf pieces. Plant Physiol 73:542–549

Wang RT, Myers J (1976) Simultaneous measurement of action spectra for photoreactions I and II of photosynthesis. Photochem Photobiol 23:411–414

Weiss C, Sauer K (1970) Activation kinetics of photosynthetic oxygen evolution under 20–40 nanosecond laser flashes. Photochem Photobiol 11:495–501

Wensink J, Dekker JP, Gorkom HJ van (1984) Reconstitution of photosynthetic water splitting after salt-washing of oxygen-evolving photosystem-II particles. Biochim Biophys Acta 765:147–155

Wiltens J, Schreiber U, Vidaver W (1978) Chlorophyll fluorescence induction: an indicator of photosynthetic activity in marine algae undergoing desiccation. Can J Bot 56:2787–2794

Wise RR, Naylor AW (1985) Calibration and use of a Clark-type oxygen electrode from 5 to 45° C. Anal Biochem 146:260–264

Wydrzynski T, Sauer K (1980) Periodic changes in the oxidation state of manganese in photosynthetic oxygen evolution upon illumination with flashes. Biochim Biophys Acta 589:56–70

Yamaoka T, Satoh K, Katoh S (1978) Preparation of thylakoid membranes active in oxygen evolution at high temperature from a thermophilic blue-green alga. In: Metzner H (ed) Photosynthetic oxygen evolution. Academic Press, New York London San Francisco, pp 105–115

Measurement of O_2 Evolution in Chloroplasts

Y. INOUE

1 Introduction

Oxygen evolution is one of the most unique reactions among the variety of reactions involved in photosynthesis. A light quantum absorbed by light harvesting chlorophyll migrates as an exiton to the reaction center of PSII, where a pair of chlorophyll a molecules suspended between a pair of homologous proteins (D1 and D2) undergo charge separation. The created negative charge (electron) is transferred to Q_B plastoquinone via pheophytin and Q_A plastoquinone, whereas the positive charge is transferred to the O_2-evolving enzyme complex, which is presumably located in a corner of the PSII complex on lumenal side of thylakoids, being associated with four Mn atoms as catalyst for oxidizing water to evolve molecular oxygen (O_2).

As is often documented, O_2 evolution by plant photosynthesis involves a linear four-step oxidation of water, which has made this reaction of particular interest. However, in addition to this intrinsic interest regarding its mechanism, O_2 evolution by chloroplasts has been often used to assure the involvement of the PSII photoreaction in the phenomenon in question, and is also employed for practical use as a means to examine the herbicidal activity of various chemicals.

Various methods have been employed for the measurement of O_2 evolution by plants; the paramagnetic method, mass spectrometric method (Radmer and Ollinger 1980), galvanic method, and the polarographic method. Of these, the polarographic method is most widely used for photosynthesis studies. There are several variations among the reported polarographic methods so far, but only the Clark-type electrode (Fork 1972) and Joliot-type electrode (Joliot 1972) are widely used for measurement of O_2 evolution by chloroplasts. Of these two methods, the latter is not always popular, but is mostly used by specialists in the mechanism of four-step oxidation of water. This chapter, which focuses on very practical methods, will be useful for students and technicians with no experience in handling polarographic O_2 electrodes.

2 The Principle of Polarographic O_2 Electrode

The principle electrochemical reactions of both Clark-type and Joliot-type O_2 electrodes are the same and are described as follows:

$$\text{Cathode (Pt)} \quad O_2 + 4\,e^- + 4\,H^+ \rightarrow 2\,H_2O$$

$$\text{Anode (Ag/AgCl)} \quad 4\,Ag + 4\,Cl^- \rightarrow 4\,AgCl + 4\,e^- .$$

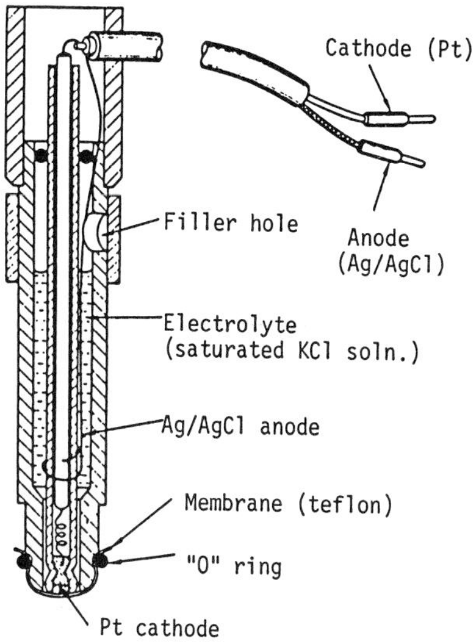

Fig. 1. Construction of a typical membrane coated Clar-type O_2 electrode (YSI model 4004)

The electric current resulting from these electrochemical reactions is proportional to the concentration of O_2 dissolved in liquid phase, so that the O_2 concentration or its changes in the sample solution can be monitored by measuring the electrochemical current between the two electrodes.

In Joliot-type electrodes, sample solutions (suspension of thylakoids or algal cells) are placed directly onto the Pt electrode, which is electrically connected with a salt bridge (usually by electrolyte solution compartimented by a semi-permeable membrane) to the Ag/AgCl electrode placed away from the Pt electrode. The Joliot-type electrode has a high sensitivity and high response (a few ms), but is less stable due to staining of the surface of the Pt electrode by heavy metals and proteins, so that this electrode is mostly employed for special purposes, e.g., measurement of flash O_2 yield. In this section we omit this electrode and focus on the more general Clark-type electrode in greater detail.

Figure 1 shows the construction of the most traditional Clark-type O_2 electrode, distributed by Yellow Springs Instrument Co. (USA). The Pt and Ag/AgCl electrodes are installed in a pencil-shaped rod, on top of which the polished surface of the Pt electrode and a part of the electrolyte (saturated KCl solution) are exposed to the sample solution through a thin membrane made of Teflon or polyethylene. The O_2 gas dissolved in the sample solution permeates through the membrane, and is reduced at the surface of the Pt electrode to yield electrochemical current proportional to O_2 concentration in the sample solution.

3 Reaction Vessels and Electronic Circuits

Reaction vessels equipped with a Clark-type O_2 electrode and the electronic circuits for measurement of electrochemical current are nowadays commercially

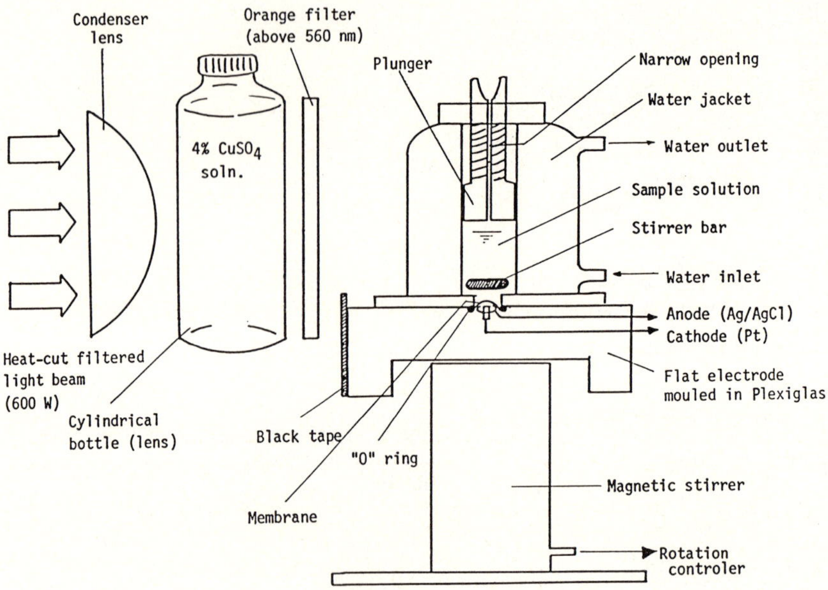

Fig. 2. A typical vessel for O_2-electrode with a water jacket, magnetic stirrer and light source. (A kit distributed by Rank Brothers)

available: Biological Oxygen Monitor YSI model 53 (Yellow Springs Instrument Co. USA), Rank Oxygen Monitoring Kit (Rank Brothers U.K.). Figure 2 shows an example of such vessel distributed by Rank Brothers. A tiny flat Pt and Ag/AgCl electrodes half molded in a Plexiglas plate and covered with a thin membrane and a piece of lens tissue soaked with electrolyte is placed on the bottom of the sample suspension in a cell jacketed with thermostated water, and the suspension is agitated with a magnetic stirrer placed below the electrode. Illumination is given from the side through the water jacket. The narrow opening on top of the cell prevents diffusion of atmospheric O_2 into the suspension, and facilitates administration of samples, cofactors, or inhibitors by use of a microsyringe. The cell volume can be varied by moving the plunger with a screwed stopper.

The electrochemical current through the electrode is seriously influenced by temperature, so that a well-stabilized (ca. $\pm 0.05°$ C) temperature controller is indispensable. For the same reasons, the light beam must pass through at least a layer of heat-cut filter and a 5- to 10-cm water layer to eliminate infra-red light, especially when an incandescent lamp or other heat-generating lamps is used as a light source. To eliminate infra-red light, inclusion of $CuSO_4$ (ca. 4%) in the water filter is more effective. Direct exposure of the electrode to the illumination beam must be carefully avoided by use of a piece of black tape, since the exposure often generates abnormal current and the electrode rapidly deteriorates.

When such O_2 monitoring kits are not available, an ad hoc cell can be easily constructed, if a Clark-type electrode is provided. An example of such hand-made Plexiglas cells is shown in Fig. 3. The electrochemical current can be measured with a simple circuit, as indicated in Fig. 4B. A variable resistor (R_1) regulates

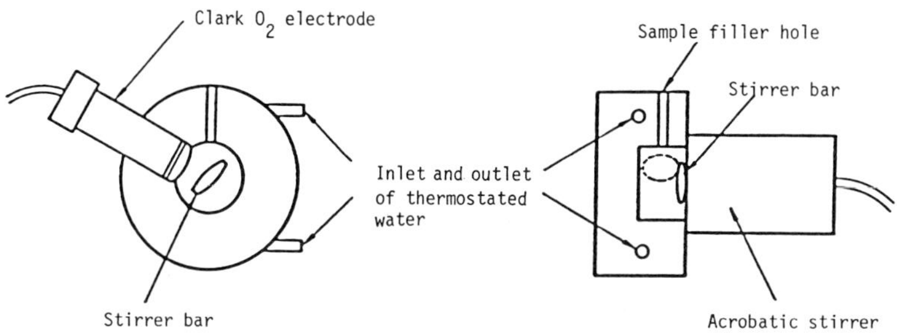

Fig. 3. An ad hoc vessel made of Plexiglas equipped with an YSI 4004 O_2-electrode

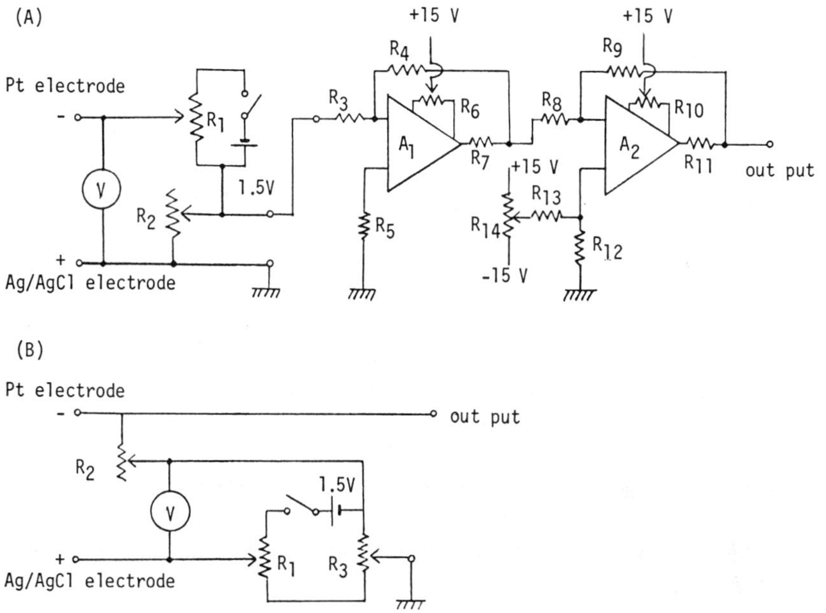

Fig. 4 A, B. Typical electric circuit for current measurement from an O_2 electrode. **A** V voltmeter (0.6 V); R_1 (electrode voltage controller), 10 kΩ; R_2 (amperometric gain controller), 25 kΩ; R_3 5 kΩ; $R_4 = R_5$, 1 MΩ; $R_6 = R_{10}$ 20 kΩ: $R_7 = R_{11}$ 330 Ω; $R_8 = R_{12}$ 10 kΩ; $R_9 = R_{13}$ 200 kΩ; R_{14} 50 kΩ; $A_1 = A_2$ CF 357 (operational amplifier). **B** V voltmeter (0.6 V); R_1 (electrode voltage controller), 10 kΩ; R_2 (amperometric gain controller), 15 kΩ; R_3 (pen position controller) 500 Ω

the electrode voltage (usually set at 0.6 V, see later), and R_2 controls the gain in converting the amperometric current to voltage. Too high a value of R_2 should be avoided, since it may result in a slight difference in the electrode voltage, particularly when a large change in O_2 concentration occurs (equivalent to a large change in current through the electrode).

In most cases, measurement of O_2 evolution must be done under saturating light intensity, so that a high concentration of chlorophyll in sample solution must be avoided. Due to these requirements, we are usually forced to measure small changes in O_2 concentration, which are far smaller than the concentration of O_2 equilibrated with air level O_2. For this reason, a backing circuit to off-set a large part of the signal due to the background O_2 concentration is needed. If a recorder with a high impedance ($\geqq 1$ MΩ) at a high sensitivity of 2 to 5 mV full scale is available, backing can be simply done by controlling R_3 in Fig. 4 B. In general, however, use of a simple operational amplifier with an off-set function as shown in Fig. 4 A is recommended, since the amplifier simultaneously solves the two problems of impedance matching and off-set.

4 General Directions for Measurement of O_2 Evolution

When the electrochemical current from the O_2 electrode immersed in an air-equilibrated solution is measured by varying the electrode voltage, the profile shown in Fig. 5 is obtained. The electrochemical current (expressed as voltage read out) steeply increases as the electrode voltage is increased from 0 to 0.4 V, keeps at a constant level between 0.4 and 0.9 V, and then again increases steeply above 1.0 V. For determination of O_2 concentration, it is desirable to use the electrode voltage giving the plateau read-out. The electrode voltage for this condition is usually between 0.6 and 0.8 V.

When the electrode voltage is fixed, the current reading must be correlated with O_2 concentration. At an electrode voltage of ca. 0.6 V, the current usually contains a few % of O_2-insensitive signal. This O_2-insensitive current must be carefully removed by the following procedures: A portion of distilled water well equilibrated with air level O_2 at room temperature (ca. 23° C) is applied to the electrode, and the gain controller (R_2 in Fig. 4 A, B) is adjusted to give about 80% read-out of the recorder full scale, and recorded. Then a small amount of sodium dithionite or an aliquot of its solution is added to eliminate O_2, and the read-out

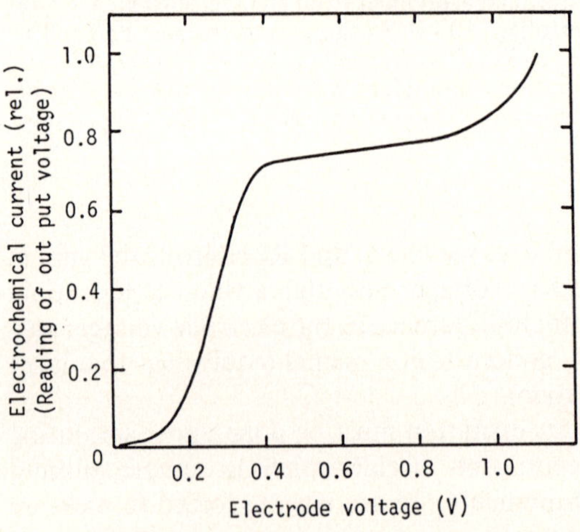

Fig. 5. Dependence of O_2-dependent amperometric current on electrode voltage

Table 1. Concentration of O_2 in distilled water equilibrated with air level O_2 at various temperatures

°C	μmol/l	°C	μmol/l	°C	μmol/l
5	398	15	314	25	258
6	388	16	307	26	253
7	378	17	301	27	248
8	369	18	295	28	244
9	360	19	289	29	240
10	352	20	283	30	236
11	343	21	278	31	232
12	336	22	272	32	228
13	328	23	267	33	224
14	321	24	262	34	221

for zero O_2 is recorded. Usually a few % of the signal remains even after complete elimination of O_2. The amount of dithionite must be enough to consume all O_2 in the cell. The difference in the two read out values between the absence and presence of dithionite corresponds to the concentration of O_2 equilibrated with air level O_2 at a given temperature, as indicated in Table 1 (267 μmol/l at 23° C).

After cleaning the cell by several washes with distilled water, a buffer solution equilibrated at the same temperature is applied to the cell, and then sample thylakoids and an electron acceptor (see later) are added in darkness. Then the large part of the read-out due to O_2 contained in the buffer solution is cancelled by adjusting the off-set level (R_3 in Fig. 4 B or R_{14} in Fig. 4 A), and the sensitivity of recorder is increased by a factor of 4 to 5. After a few minutes of further temperature equilibration in darkness, light is turned on and the O_2 evolution is recorded for 30 to 60 s. Usually a few seconds lag time precedes O_2 evolution. If a 6 mV/min increase is observed by a sample containing 10 mg Chl/l with a gain-calibrated instrument settings which gives 30 mV as corresponding to 250 μmol/l O_2, the O_2 evolving activity can be calculated as follows:

$$250\ (\mu\text{mol/l}) \times 6\ (\text{mV/min})/30\ (\text{mV}) \times (\text{min/h})\ 10\ (\text{mg/l})$$
$$= 300\ (\mu\text{mol O}_2\ \text{evolved/mg Chl} \cdot \text{h})\,.$$

5 Additional Remarks

Temperature Control. The O_2-dependent electrochemical current is highly sensitive to temperature. When the thermostat system has a fluctuation of $\pm 0.5°$ C, the O_2 electrode often records the temperature changes. It is desirable to control the temperature within $\pm 0.05°$ C. Even if a thermostat device has a high capability and accuracy, it is recommended to put a heat-insulated mixing tank (e.g., 1-l Dewar bottle) between the thermostat device and O_2 electrode vessel, especially when the thermoelement of the device is placed close to its outlet.

Stirring. Agitation of sample solution is important to facilitate smooth permeation of O_2 through the electrode membrane to yield electrochemical reactions proportional to O_2 concentration with high response. However, too vigorous agitation results in uneven whirling and increases the noise level. A suitable stirring condition can be found by gradually increasing the rotation speed of the stirrer and fixing the knob at a position where the current reading is least dependent on the rotation rate. Selection of a stirrer bar to give smooth rotation is also important. The rotation rate must not be changed throughout the set of experiments.

Illumination. In order to attain light saturation, a bright light source is required. A handy light source to suffice this requirement is a 500- to 600-W fan-cooled incandescent slide projector equipped with a reflector mirror, condenser lens system and a heat-absorbing filter. The light beam from such a projector should pass through a layer (a few cm) of water containing $CuSO_4$ (1 to 4%) to further eliminate infra-red component, then be focused on the vessel by use of a lens system including a cylindrical one. It is also recommended to apply a yellow filter ($\geqq$ 430 nm) before the vessel to eliminate ultra-violet component, which affects the functioning of Ag/AgCl electrode. Use of an orange ($\geqq$560 nm) or red ($\geqq$600 nm) filter is also recommended particularly when ferricyanide is the electron acceptor. The typical light intensities obtained from this type of light source are approx. 1700 W/m^2 with red filter, 2300 W/m^2 with orange filter, 3600 W/m^2 with yellow filter and 4500 W/m^2 with no filter, all of them are strong enough to saturate O_2 evolution by a sample containing 5 to 10 μg Chl/ml. Light saturation can be easily checked by use of a neutral density filter having 80 to 90% transmittance. Xenon lamps are not the ideal light source for O_2 measurement with an electrode, since its beam contains strong ultra-violet component. Ultra-violet light not only affects the electrode but inactivates photosynthesis in intact algal cells.

Sample Manipulation. Sample injection to the cell should be done with an injection syringe through the narrow opening. Sometimes a tiny stopper is applied in the opening during measurement. Use of an aspirator is helpful in discarding the sample and washing the cell. When a hydrophobic electron acceptor or inhibitor is used, repeated washes with ethanol are recommended.

Maintenance of Electrode. After use, the cell and electrode should be well washed with distilled water, and then immersed in half-saturated KCl solution. If the membrane is left stained with protein or lipid, response becomes slower. When carefully treated, the electrode maintains good sensitivity and good response for a few to several months without renewal of the membrane. Ag/AgCl electrode deteriorates faster among the other parts of the O_2 electrode. The deteriorated electrode can be revived by immersing the electrode in 2% KCN, and then electrolyzing in 0.1 NHCl at 5 V (with Pt as cathode) for several minutes after washing with distilled water.

Linearity Check. The electrochemical current usually shows good linearity with the O_2 concentration. A simple way to check the linearity is to use O_2 consumption by yeast (*Saccharomyces cervisiae*) cells, which proceeds linearly to a very low O_2 concentration. The minimal significant read-out change on the recorder of an O_2-electrode set can be roughly estimated by this way.

6 Typical Experimental Conditions

Intact chloroplasts

Reaction mixture: 0.33 *M* sorbitol, 40 m*M* HEPES-KOH (pH 7.6), 1 m*M* $MgCl_2$, 1 m*M* $MnCl_2$, 2 mM EDTA, 10 m*M* NaCl, spinach intact chloroplasts (50 to 100 μg Chl/ml), 2 m*M* HCO_3^- as electron acceptor, 20° C.
Electron acceptors: $HCO_3^- >$ 3-phosphoglycerate $> NO_2^- \geqq$ oxalate.
Typical activity: 100 to 150 μmol O_2/mg Chl · h.

Note: HEPES-KOH is better than HEPES-NaOH. The activity is usually limited by various processes involved in carbon metabolism and phosphorylation as well.

Thylakoids (broken chloroplasts)

Reaction mixture: 0.4 *M* sucrose, 50 m*M* HEPES-NaOH (ph 7.0), 10 m*M* NaCl, 5 m*M* $MgCl_2$, 20 m*M* Methylamine, 2 m*M* KCN, spinach thylakoids (5 to 10 μg Chl/ml), 1 m*M* DMQ (2,5-dimethyl-1,4-benzoquinone) as electron acceptor, 20 to 25° C.
Electron acceptors: DMQ > DCBQ (dichlorobenzoquinone) ≧ PBQ (phenyl-p-benzoquinone) > ferricyanide.
Typical activity: 350–500 μmol O_2/mg Chl · h.

PSII submembranes (BBY particles)

Reaction mixture: 0.4 *M* sucrose, 40 m*M* MES-NaOH (pH 6.5), 20 m*M* NaCl, PSII submembranes (5 to 10 μg Chl/ml), 2 m*M* DMQ as electron acceptor, 20 to 25° C.
Electron acceptors: PBQ (0.6 m*M*) > DMQ (2 m*M*) ≧ DCBQ (0.6 m*M*) > Ferricyanide.
Typical activity: 300 to 900 μmol O_2/mg Chl · h.

Note: Optimum pH is not at pH 7 but at around 6.0 to 6.5. The hierarchy in efficiency among the electron acceptors varies depending on the properties of preparations.

PSII core complex (see note)

Reaction mixture: 0.4 *M* sucrose, 40 m*M* MES-NaOH (pH 6.0 to 6.5), 10 m*M* NaCl, 10 m*M* $CaCl_2$, 0.1% digitonin, PSII core complex (1 to 2 μg Chl/ml), 1 m*M* Ferricyanide as electron acceptor, 25° C.
Electron acceptor: Ferricyanide > DCBQ > PBQ = DMQ.
Typical activity: 1100 to 1700 μmol O_2/mg Chl · h.

Note: The O_2 evolving PSII core complex is composed of CP47, CP43, D1, D2, cyt b_{559} and 33 kDa extrinsic proteins and retains 4 Mn/reaction center. Inclusion of Ca^{2+} and Cl^- at a few mM is strictly required for O_2 evolution. Digitonin (0.1%) or dodecylmaltoside (0.2%) enhances the activity by two fold. The activity is DCMU-insensitive.

Algal cells

Reaction mixture: BG-11 culture medium (pH 8.0), *Anacystis nidulans* cells (10 μg Chl/ml), 2 m*M* HCO_3^- as electron acceptor.

Electron acceptor: Several benzoquinone derivatives (DMQ, PBQ) can also be used as electron acceptor.

Typical activity: 130 to 180 μmol O_2/mg Chl · h.

Note: O_2 consumption due to respiration is recorded in darkness.

References

Fork DC (1972) Oxygen electrode. In: San Pietro A (ed) Methods in enzymology, vol 24. Photosynthesis and nitrogen fixation, part B. Academic Press, New York London, pp 113

Joliot P (1972) Modulated light source use with the oxygen electrode. In: San Pietro A (ed) Methods in enzymology, vol 24. Photosynthesis and nitrogen fixation, part B. Academic Press, New York London, pp 123

Radmer R, Ollinger O (1980) Measurement of the oxygen cycle: the mass spectrometric analysis of gasses dissolved in a liquid phase. In: San Pietro A (ed) Methods in enzymology, vol 69. Photosynthesis and nitrogen fixation, part C. Academic Press, New York London, pp 547

Carbon Dioxide

Analytical Gas Exchange Measurements of Photosynthetic CO_2 Assimilation

T. D. SHARKEY

1 Introduction

Carbon dioxide is assimilated by plants in the process of photosynthesis. Virtually all life depends on this process. The measurement of carbon dioxide assimilation is one method for studying photosynthesis which is adaptable both to reductionist questions such as what specific biochemical process limits the overall rate of photosynthesis and to ecophysiological questions such as how does water stress affect photosynthesis. The techniques required by reductionists and ecophysiologists are similar and are the subject of this chapter. Other descriptions of these methods will also be useful (Bloom et al. 1980; Field et al. 1982 and in press; Ball 1987; Field and Mooney in press).

1.1 Historical Perspective

The beginning of modern analytical gas exchange is often traced to Gaastra's thesis which was published in 1959. In it he describes an infrared gas analyzer which he constructed and other equipment necessary to make the measurements of photosynthesis which will be described below. More importantly, he measured photosynthesis under a range of conditions and interpreted the responses of photosynthesis to environmental variables such as light. His work was a landmark because he focused on the responses of photosynthetic rates to various parameters rather than on the particular rate of photosynthesis under a particular set of conditions. I will emphasize the techniques required for measuring responses of photosynthesis to the environment rather than individual measures of rate.

The second most important measurement to make, after the CO_2 assimilation rate measurement, is the measure of CO_2 inside the leaf. This is usually expressed in terms of partial pressure (as described below) and is called the intercellular CO_2 partial pressure, C_i. Some researchers call this P_i to indicate that it is a partial pressure inside the leaf but since P_i also means inorganic phosphate, I have resisted this abbreviation. When the measure is expressed in terms of mole fraction, I recommend c_i for consistency with earlier work.

This measure is almost always estimated from measurements of conductance to gas exchange and CO_2 assimilation rate. The first description of such an estimate is that by Penman and Schofield (1951). They concluded that the CO_2 level inside leaves of the crop they studied was about two-thirds the CO_2 level in the atmosphere. This is completely consistent with current measurements. Gaastra alluded to this measure but did not estimate the CO_2 level inside his leaves. Moss and Rawlins (1963) were the first to calculate an intercellular CO_2 concentration. They found that in corn there was 110 ppm or $\mu l\,l^{-1}$ CO_2 inside the leaves.

The equations for calculating the intercellular CO_2 level were modified by Jarman (1973) von Caemmerer and Farquhar (1981) and Leunig (1984). The equations given in von Caemmerer and Farquhar (1981) and Ball (1987) are easily adapted to particular systems, the other two papers are more theoretical. These modified equations were tested by Sharkey et al. (1982) by clamping an amphistomatous leaf between two chambers. One chamber was made part of a standard gas exchange measuring system; intercellular CO_2

partial pressure was estimated as described below. The other chamber was made part of a closed loop containing a peristaltic pump to move the air slowly around the loop without introducing large pressure gradients and an infrared gas analyzer to measure CO_2. The CO_2 level in the closed loop came to equilibrium and this level was taken as the CO_2 level inside the leaf, since there was no net flux of CO_2 across the stomates on the closed loop side of the leaf. The intercellular CO_2 partial pressure measured in this way was almost the same as the estimates made from CO_2 assimilation measurements and conductance measurements made on the other side of the leaf.

Most recently, there has emerged evidence that this bulk measure of intercellular CO_2 concentration may not always be completely correct under water stress conditions or after feeding abscisic acid. As always, caution is warranted when interpreting data.

1.2 Current Interest

The current interest in analytical gas exchange analysis results from advances in technology and advances in theory relating the biochemistry of photosynthesis to specific behaviors which can be observed by gas exchange analysis. The technological advances, especially the availability of high quality gas flow controllers, has made it possible to build much smaller systems which can, in many cases, be taken out of the laboratory and to the plants in the field. This has made analytical gas exchange analysis a valuable tool for the plant ecophysiologist.

The theoretical advances can be traced to the model published by Farquhar et al. (1980). They combined as much biochemical detail as possible with gas exchange expertise to make predictions about how photosynthesis should respond to environmental parameters and what the state of the biochemical components should be. They tested their predictions (Seemann et al. 1981; von Caemmerer and Farquhar 1981, 1984; Brooks and Farquhar 1985) and found many of the unusual predicted behaviors. This work also spawned a great interest in measurements of photosynthetic metabolite pool sizes and enzyme amounts and activities (Badger et al. 1984; Mott et al. 1984; Seemann and Sharkey 1986, 1987; Sharkey et al. 1986a, b; von Caemmerer and Edmondson 1986). Two significant modifications of the original theory have been proposed as a result of the testing that has occurred recently (Mott et al. 1984; Sharkey 1985).

2 The Basic Measurements

The measurements required by ecophysiologists and reductionists are the following: photosynthetic CO_2 assimilation, rate of water loss, and the water vapor pressure difference between the leaf and the air. Other measurements are usually made such as irradiance and air temperature; these other measurements will be dictated by the specific research questions.

2.1 Units

Traditional units of gas exchange analysis have been abandoned in favor of units constructed according to SI guidelines. The familiar unit of mg CO_2 dm^{-2} h^{-1}

has given way to μmol m^{-2} s^{-1}. Rules used to construct this unit are (paraphrasing): (1) use moles of a substance whenever the molecular weight is known (so mg is out); (2) only modify the first unit (in this case moles becomes μmoles and dm^2 is not allowed); (3) only use mks units or allowed derivatives. K. Raschke (personal communication) points out that according to this rule the weight of 1 ml water is about 1 millikilogram. Nevertheless, SI units should be followed unless there is some justification for another unit.

2.1.1 Leaf Area

Photosynthetic CO_2 assimilation rates have most often been reported relative to leaf area. This is particularly appropriate when measurements are made on large, flat leaves which approximate a plane. Many leaves move through the day tracking the movement of the sun. Area-based rates are then easily compared with the photon flux densities which are also measured per unit area. However, area is not the only basis on which CO_2 assimilation rates can be based and sometimes area can be an inappropriate basis for expressing rates.

2.1.2 Other Units for Expressing Photosynthetic Rate

Chlorophyll is often the basis used by biochemists for expressing photosynthesis rates on the assumption that since chlorophyll is required for photosynthesis, CO_2 assimilation rates should be related to chlorophyll. I suspect that the simplicity of chlorophyll assays is also a significant factor. It has been found that chlorophyll and CO_2 assimilation are often not well correlated and that RuBP carboxylase and CO_2 assimilation rates are better correlated. It is very rare that anyone has expressed CO_2 assimilation rates on a RuBP carboxylase basis (but see Seemann and Sharkey 1986). Fresh weight and dry weight have also been used. The basis which is best for any given study depends upon the question studied and an arbitrary basis of measurement should not be forced upon unwilling data.

2.1.3 Mole Fraction for Gas Concentration

There is a great diversity of opinion on how to express the levels of the various gases. Least understandable to me are the units of g m^{-3}. This unit is often adopted by researchers serious about converting to SI. But SI recommendations state clearly that moles should always be used whenever possible. I also do not like mol m^{-3} but prefer mole fraction for expressing gas concentrations.

The mole fraction of a gas is moles of gas per mole of air (for example). An extremely important relationship among expressions of mole fraction can be derived from the ideal gas law:

$$\frac{\text{mol}}{\text{mol}} = \frac{\text{bar}}{\text{bar}} = \frac{\text{liter}}{\text{liter}} = \frac{\text{m}^3}{\text{m}^3}. \tag{1}$$

This relationship simplifies gas exchange calculations tremendously and should be well understood by anyone wishing to study gas exchange equations. Mole fraction is what people have been using to express the CO_2 concentration in the atmosphere. The units of ppm (parts per million by volume) can also be written $\mu l\,l^{-1}$. From Eq. (1) it is evident that ppm is also $\mu bar\,bar^{-1}$.

2.1.4 Partial Pressure of Gases

Concentration is not, however, the best way to express the amount of gas to which a leaf is exposed. The chemical activity of a gas is proportional to its partial pressure, not its concentration. This is why it is harder to breath at high altitude even though the concentration of O_2 is the same at the bottom and the top of the mountain. The total pressure is lower at the top of the mountain and so the partial pressure of O_2 is also lower. At 1500 m altitude the atmospheric pressure is about 15% less than at sea level so the partial pressure of O_2 is about 15% less, making it hard to breath. The same thing occurs for plants. The ambient CO_2 partial pressure at sea level is above 350 μbar but at 1500 m it is less than 300 μbar. The level of a gas should always be expressed as partial pressure. Converting between mole fraction and partial pressure only requires knowing the total pressure (which varies throughout a gas exchange system). Multiplying mole fraction by total pressure yields partial pressure [recall Eq. (1)].

Partial pressure measurement of the CO_2 level has an additional benefit. CO_2 gas analyzers respond to partial pressure of CO_2, not concentration. Calibrations of CO_2 analyzers in terms of concentrations must be corrected for changes in total pressure but calibrations in terms of partial pressure do not require compensation for pressure changes.

Despite the exhortation to use SI units given above, I cling tenaciously to the unit of bar for pressure rather than the Pascal. The reason is that 1 atm is very nearly 1 bar and bar is a multiple of ten of a proper SI unit. This has the nice effect of making partial pressure of CO_2 expressed in μbar nearly the same number as the corresponding mole fraction.

2.2 Combined Gas Exchange and Biochemical Measurements

The usefulness of gas exchange measurements for physiological investigations is greatly enhanced by making biochemical measurements. Rapidly stopping metabolism under defined conditions allows measurements of metabolite levels and enzyme activities that are related to measurable gas exchange characteristics of leaves. Plant metabolism is very rapid, so Badger et al. (1984) built a freeze clamp mounted in a way that it clamped the leaf inside a gas exchange chamber. It is reasonably easy to lower the leaf temperature to less than 0° C within 0.1 s using such a device.

3 Measuring CO_2 Uptake

Measuring the rate of CO_2 uptake is the central measurement in analytical gas exchange mesurements of photosynthesis. It also is one of the easier measurements to make. There are several methods used to measure CO_2 uptake involving compensating, differential, or kinetic systems. In each case the net rate of carbon uptake (assimilation) is measured. I see no reason to call this net carbon exchange (NCE) as many investigators do. Exchange does not have to involve assimilation as when a leaf is held at the compensation point. Then there is a great deal of carbon exchange but no CO_2 assimilation.

3.1 Compensating Systems

A compensating system is one where CO_2 flows into a leaf chamber at a rate sufficient to balance the rate of removal of CO_2 by the leaf. In such a system the CO_2 analyzer is used as a null detector, and calibration is unnecessary. The rate of flow of CO_2 into the chamber can be controlled electronically using a feedback loop between the CO_2 analyzer and the CO_2 flow controller. This is unnecessary, however, since the flow is easily controlled manually. Compensating systems have become more popular because of advances in flow controller technology. The accuracy of the CO_2 assimilation rate measurement depends on the accuracy of the flow measurement, and very accurate flow meters are now available (see below). To make the measurement easier, a mixture of CO_2 in air is usually used so that the compensating flow rate is at least 1 μmol s^{-1}.

Compensating systems are excellent for studies in a wide variety of gas compositions since it is not necessary to calibrate the CO_2 analyzer at all the different gas compositions nor is it necessary to rely on the calibrations to separate the analyzer response from the plant response to, for example, changes in ambient partial pressure of O_2. However, this system configuration is more difficult than others, especially at low photosynthetic rates. Moreover, oscillations in the rate of CO_2 assimilation can unbalance the operator of such systems. Compensating systems can be either open or closed.

3.2 Differential Systems

A second configuration for measuring CO_2 assimilation rate is to simply measure the difference in CO_2 content of a gas stream before and after it passes over a leaf. This is done with a differential CO_2 analyzer and extremely small changes in CO_2 level (<0.1 μbar in 300 μbar) are easily detected. In this system configuration, oscillations in CO_2 assimilation are easily followed. In my experience it is easier for new users to understand this type of measurement.

In practice three air streams are used. One is the reference air stream which always flows through the analyzer. The second air stream is identical to the first but it flows through the measuring cell of the analyzer to obtain the analyzer zero. This air stream is then diverted and a third air stream, which has passed over the leaf, is switched to flow through the measuring cell. The difference in CO_2 level is detected and can be determined from the instrument calibration. The analyzer must be calibrated for the different conditions that will be used since the responsiveness of the analyzer to the small differentials depends on background CO_2 level to some degree.

3.3 Combined Systems

The most versatile systems are combined systems which can work either in the compensating mode or the differential mode or both. This greatly eases the task of compensating the rate of CO_2 assimilation since any mistake in compensation flow rate will be accurately measured as a differential. When oscillations occur a certain rate of compensation can be set and the oscillations can be watched as changes in the differential. Most compensating systems also allow for some differential measurement. These systems are the most versatile systems for measuring CO_2 assimilation rate.

3.4 Kinetic Systems

It is also possible to measure the rate at which CO_2 is depleted from a closed system. This method has the drawback that the conditions around the leaf are changing during the measurement. However, there are now such good analyzers available that only a small depletion is required to obtain a measure of the rate of photosynthesis. The measurement depends on the accuracy of the CO_2 analyzer calibration and also on the determination of the volume of the system. Leaks are also a problem with a closed system, especially when making measurements at other than ambient CO_2 partial pressures. In a closed system a leak out at one place is balanced by a leak in somewhere else. Leaks are much less a problem with the other systems since any leak is a leak out. The air in a closed system must be pumped from the leaf chamber to the CO_2 analyzer and back, and so there will be regions of high and low pressure, which can be difficult to contain. Despite their problems, reasonably good, portable closed systems are now commercially available.

3.5 CO_2 Analyzers

The CO_2 analyzers most often used today have been developed within the past 10 years. All of the analyzers operate on the same basic principles but they use slightly different detectors to overcome the inherent problems in measuring CO_2.

3.5.1 Differential CO_2 Analyzers

CO_2 analyzers use infrared absorption characteristics to measure CO_2. The induced dipole moment of CO_2 which results from the thermal motion of the atoms within the molecule give rise to the CO_2 infrared absorption bands.

Infrared gas analyzers (IRGAs) have an infrared source (like an incandescent light but at lower temperature), two gold-lined tubes, and a detector. The analyzers most often used by plant physiologists all have a chopper just before the detector, but the speed and configuration of the chopper varies from one model to the next. By far the most variability between analyzers is in the method of detection of the infrared energy which has passed through the gas being measured. Because these instruments do not select a particular wave band, the selectivity for the gas being measured must be provided by the detector. Since all of the infrared energy passes through the sample, these analyzers are called nondispersive infrared gas analyzers.

3.5.1.1 Luft Detector

Named after the inventor K. F. Luft, this was the most common detector until about 10 years ago. The infrared energy which passes through the gas being measured enters a chamber filled with the gas of interest, in this case CO_2. The gas in this detector cell then heats up and the pressure increases. If more energy was absorbed in one of the long, gold-lined cells than the other, then there is a pressure differential between the two detector cells. This pressure differential causes a thin metal membrane to move. The metal film will relax when the infrared beam is interrupted by the chopper. The metal film is made to be part of a capacitor and the alternations in the capacitance are converted into a voltage proportional to the concentration in the gas stream. The most popular analyzer still using the Luft detector is the Beckman 865. This type of detector is damaged by long periods of large difference in CO_2 level between the two cells as can often happen when a gas exchange system is turned off and left overnight. S. C. Wong found that it was extremely important to leave the analyzer with air levels of CO_2 in both cells when the analyzer was not in use to avoid stretching the metal film.

3.5.1.2 Mass Flow Detector

Leybold-Heraeus developed a different detector for their Binos analyzers. Instead of the thin metal film, this detector has a small orifice that allows the gas to flow from one detector cell to the other. This flow is sensed and the measure of the flow is converted to a voltage proportional to the CO_2 concentration. The chopper turns very fast in this instrument and has an unusual configuration which allows an internal calibration of the machine each time a measurement is made. This detector is much more stable than the thin metal film detectors and is substantially less sensitive to vibration. This plus the availability of a 12-V power supply option has made the Binos a favorite for field gas exchange.

3.5.1.3 Solid State Detector

The newest method of detection used on commercially available units is the solid state detector. Solid state detectors are very temperature sensitive and early analyzers had sensors and correction systems to account for the changes in detector temperature. LiCor applied a different solution. They mount a solid state detector on a Peltier block and cool the detector to a constant temperature. Not only does this do away with the temperature corrections of earlier solid state detector analyzers, it also allows the detector to operate cooler where the signal to noise ratio is more favorable. The small size and 12-V power requirement may make the LiCor the new analyzer of choice for field work.

3.5.2 Absolute CO_2 Analyzers

There are no absolute CO_2 analyzers in routine use today. What are sold as absolute analyzers are differential analyzers with one of the gas paths sealed. This reduces the versatility of the instrument and there is little reason for ordering gas analyzers in this restricted configuration.

3.5.3 Effects of Water on the CO_2 Measurement

The presence of water, as either liquid or vapor, affects the measure of CO_2. Water vapor has three separate effects on the CO_2 measurement by IRGAs.

3.5.3.1 Liquid Water

The presence of liquid water anywhere in the system will cause changes in CO_2 level to be slow because the CO_2 in the gas phase must come into equilibrium with the CO_2 dissolved in the liquid water. It is annoying when a change in CO_2 level can take over 5 min. This is easily avoided by adding CO_2 only after the humidity of the air has been set. If ice traps are used to remove water vapor before the air enters the CO_2 analyzer, the liquid water in the ice traps can also slow the system response. This is usually not as much a problem as putting the CO_2 in before the humidifier but it can cause problems when the kinetics of photosynthesis are to be followed after a large jump in CO_2 level.

3.5.3.2 Infrared Absorption Band Overlap

Water absorbs infrared energy and in some regions of the spectrum, some of the absorption bands of CO_2 and water vapor overlap. For many years air was routinely dried either by passing through a desiccant or by passing through an ice trap. This problem was overcome by using interference filters to select only the strongest absorption band of CO_2 which did not overlap with water vapor. These optical filters allowed people to do away with the water traps in their systems but this gave rise to two additional problems, one solvable, the other not.

3.5.3.3 Dilution of CO_2 by Water Vapor

As air passes over a leaf, the air picks up water vapor, as much as 4% of its original volume. This dilutes the CO_2 in the air. When the water was removed in the older systems, this dilution was reversed but once interference filters were used and the water no longer removed, this dilution effect had to be accounted for. This is easily done by using the equations of von Caemmerer and Farquhar (1981) and Ball (1987).

3.5.3.4 Band Broadening Effect of Water Vapor

The presence of water vapor causes a slight change in the infrared absorption band of CO_2. This effect is known as collision broadening of the absorption bands (Hill and Powell 1968) and was found to affect some studies of humidity effects on photosynthesis, though the effect is generally small (Sharkey 1984). This effect is difficult to detect because the cross sensitivity of a CO_2 analyzer is usually checked with CO_2 absent. Since this effect depends on the interaction between water vapor and CO_2, it can only be seen when CO_2 is present. There is no easy way to correct for this effect, though it is a relatively small effect. It can be ignored in all but the most demanding analyses and it can be overcome by simply removing the water before the air enters the CO_2 analyzer.

3.6 Considerations for Handling CO_2

It is relatively easy to handle air in such a way that the CO_2 concentration remains constant. Tygon tubing and other polyvinyl chloride (PVC) tubing works very well (but see water-handling properties of this material). The only problem that comes up is when long runs of wide bore tubing are used. In particular, low density polyethylene is fairly permeable to CO_2. Most plastics are permeable to CO_2 to some degree but PVC has one of the lowest permeabilities. Whenever the gas is dry, I use PVC tubing. To reduce the surface area use the smallest bore tubing that can be used without excessive pressure buildup. One of the plasticizers used in PVC, dibutylphthalate, can dramatically reduce plant growth (Hardwick et al. 1984) and photosynthesis (Sharkey unpublished). Use of PVC inside growth chambers should be avoided.

3.7 CO_2 Source Gas

While it is possible to use pure CO_2 in gas exchange systems, it generally is not practical. Most people use 3–5% CO_2 mixed in air or N_2. Although it is somewhat expensive to buy air mixtures, a tank lasts a long time so the cost is not prohibitive.

3.8 CO_2 Absorbers

Two materials are generally used to absorb CO_2 from air. Soda lime works best when the air contains water vapor. Soda lime can be exhausted ten times faster in dry air than in humid air (S. C. Wong unpublished data), presumably because the CO_2 cannot diffuse to the interior of the soda lime granule when the granule is dry. Soda asbestos is sold as Ascarite. If Ascarite is used with humid air a mess is often created (Sharkey unpublished data). Ascarite works very well with dry air. When used properly, both soda lime and Ascarite remove CO_2 very effectively.

4 Measuring Water Loss

There is less diversity in the configuration of systems for measuring water but more diversity in the method used for detecting water vapor.

4.1 Differential Systems

Almost all gas exchange systems use the difference in water vapor content before and after passing over a leaf to measure water loss from the leaf. There is some diversity concerning the water content of the air which enters the leaf chamber.

4.1.1 Wet Incoming Air

The water vapor content of air is often controlled by passing the air stream through warm water, then through a condenser in a temperature-controlled water bath. The total pressure in the condenser is measured and the temperature is also measured. The vapor pressure of water at various temperatures is determined from tables and the vapor pressure of water in the condenser divided by the total pressure is the mole fraction of water vapor in the air. If CO_2 is added after the condenser, this will change the mole fraction of water vapor in the air but this effect is easily calculated. The partial pressure of water (and also the dew point) will fall as the pressure in the system drops, but the mole fraction will remain constant. Some people have a variable amount of the gas flow through the humidifier so that humidity levels can be changed rapidly by diverting more or less flow through the humidifier. This configuration is most often used when CO_2 is measured by the differential configuration.

4.1.2 Dry Incoming Air

It generally is not practical to have a water bath in the field, so many field systems use dry air and allow the leaf to humidify the air to the desired level. The humidity in the leaf chamber can be varied by changing the rate of flow of dry gas into the chamber. This system works well when the leaf loses a lot of water, but relatively inactive leaves present some difficulty. One trick that is often overlooked is that an ice temperature condenser can be put in the line supplying the dry gas to the leaf to put a known amount of water vapor in the air before the air enters the chamber. This addition of water can easily be accounted for in the calculations of evaporation rate.

Systems using dry incoming air for water vapor usually are configured as compensating systems for CO_2 (or combined compensating-differential). These systems are very easy to take out of the laboratory. Changes in water loss rate are compensated by a change in total flow rate of air through the system and photosynthesis is compensated by changes in the flow rate of CO_2 into the chamber. This is, however, a very difficult configuration to work with, especially for beginners.

4.2 Closed Systems

There are two types of closed configurations which can be used to measure water loss from leaves, kinetic systems, and constant humidity closed systems.

4.2.1 Kinetic Systems

For this measurement a leaf is enclosed in a chamber and the rate at which the chamber air gains water vapor is determined. Like the CO_2 closed system measurements, this measure causes the environment of the leaf to change and during water measurements this effect is more pronounced than during CO_2 measurements. This is the method used by the old transit time porometers which are now rarely used.

4.2.2 Constant Humidity Closed Systems

The transit time porometers were rendered obsolete by the introduction of the steady state porometer. In this configuration air is passed through a drying agent at a rate that keeps the humidity in the chamber constant. (The LiCor steady state porometer is actually a differential system using dry entering air.) This system is approximated when people use a drying loop in a chamber. This is sometimes necessary when studying stable carbon isotope fractionation since it is important to have a lot of the entering CO_2 used and this leads to excessively high humidity if a drying loop is not used.

4.3 Water Vapor Detectors

Water vapor is measured in one of three ways in most gas exchange systems: by measuring the dew point, by infrared gas analysis (as for CO_2), and by a humidity-sensitive capacitor.

4.3.1 Dew Point Hygrometers

Dew point hygrometers have a mirror mounted on a Peltier block which is thermoelectrically cooled. The mirror is in the flowing gas stream and is positioned to reflect light from a light source to a detector. When the temperature of the mirror falls below the dew point of the air, water condenses on the mirror and the amount of reflected light falls. By controlling the mirror temperature at just the point of dew formation, as sensed by the drop in light received at the detector, it is possible to measure the dew point temperature of the air. This dew point temperature can be converted to a partial pressure using standard tables. In practice these conversions from temperature to saturation partial pressure of water are performed by computer and there are several equations which can approximate the relationship between temperature and saturation vapor pressure. In addition to the ones listed by Ball (1987) is the following:

$$e_0 = 6.108 \times 10^{(7.5 \times T/237.3 + T)}, \qquad (2)$$

where e_0 is the saturated vapor pressure in mbar of water at temperature T in °C.

This measure of water vapor, in theory, is an absolute measure once the temperature detection of the mirror is calibrated. Most people do not use dew point hygrometers this way, but instead calibrate the machines using a condenser and a temperature-controlled water bath. The Dew 10 (General Eastern) combined with the linearizing board designed by Bingham is a very easy system to install and provides a voltage that varies linearly with dew point temperature and is easily scaled to read directly in °C. This is generally helpful to people not familiar with gas exchange analysis.

Dew point hygrometers should be calibrated in terms of temperature. I have seen instances where people have plotted hygrometer output as a function of water vapor pressure and then fitted an equation to the relationship. This person was, in fact, reinventing the wheel by including in his calibration regression the relationship between temperature and water vapor pressure.

Because these machines are measuring temperature, the resolution falls off at higher water vapor pressures because of the relationship between saturation water vapor pressure and temperature. This does not present much of a problem since the signals can be stable enough to resolve hundredths of a degree. This extremely quiet signal was obtained by installing a 20-cm (uncoild length) coil of 5-mm copper tubing in the air path just before the dew point mirror. This coil was ventilated with air from a fan. This coil may reduce temperature gradients within the air that are introduced by the solenoid valves used to switch air streams going to the dew point mirror; in any case, the coil reduces noise in the signal.

4.3.2 Water Vapor IRGAs

Water vapor absorbs infrared energy and so it is possible to measure water vapor with the same type of IRGA as is used for CO_2. Instead of a CO_2-filled detector, these machines have a water vapor-filled or an ammonia-filled detector. Ammonia is used because of the large overlap between water vapor and ammonia infrared absorption bands. The cell length for water vapor can be one-tenth the length for CO_2 and still there is more signal than required. This way of measuring water vapor has the highest initial cost in that the analyzers are more expensive than dew point hygrometers, but the reliability and accuracy of these analyzers often justify the cost.

4.3.3 Capacitance-Based Water Vapor Sensors

The best known of the capacitance-based water vapor sensors is the Vaisala chip and these sensors are generically referred to as vaisala sensors. These sensors are capacitors whose capacitance depends upon the relative humidity of the air. These capacitors are made part of an oscillating electrical circuit and as the capacitance of the sensor changes, the speed of the oscillations changes and this is converted to a voltage proportional to relative humidity. These sensors respond to relative humidity, but not well enough to make a simple detector. The sensors are also hysteretic at very high and very low humidity. Most of these problems can be overcome by putting the sensors and the oscillating circuit inside a heated block. This works well but the system is no longer less expensive than a dew point hygrometer. Only people with good electronic support should attempt to save money by using capacitance-based water vapor sensors.

4.4 Considerations for Handling Water Vapor

Handling air in a way that does not affect the water vapor content is difficult because water is easily condensed in cool sections of the system and because it is absorbed by many materials commonly found in laboratories (Bloom et al. 1980).

4.4.1 Condensation

If the leaf is exposed to bright light, it will be above the air temperature and it will be necessary to cool the chamber substantially. It is not unusual to have the chamber temperature within half of a degree of the dew point temperature. If there are any cold spots in the chamber the potential for condensing water in the chamber is great. This problem is avoided to some degree by having a very high boundary layer conductance. A boundary layer conductance three times the stomatal conductance may be sufficient from the viewpoint of measuring stomatal conductance, but it may be inadequate to keep leaf temperature near air temperature under high radiation loads. In many systems a high boundary layer conductance may be more important for sensible heat loss, so that the chamber temperature need not be too low, than for considerations of stomatal conductance measurements.

4.4.2 Water Absorption

The absorption of water vapor is the most important criterion for selecting material for gas exchange systems. Polyvinyl chloride tubing is perhaps the best-known example of a material which cannot be used because of water vapor absorption. Plexiglas also absorbs water fast enough to cause problems.

Many people use tubing which is available from Cole-Parmer called "Bev-a-line IV". This tubing is polyethylene on the inside and vinyl chloride on the outside. The vinyl chloride makes it much easier to handle than plain polyethylene tubing and probably helps reduce the permeability to CO_2. The polyethylene inside keeps water absorption to acceptable levels.

4.5 Water Vapor Absorbers

There are a number of ways to change the water vapor content of air. Chemical drying agents, ice traps, and chemical humidifying agents are used in gas exchange analysis.

4.5.1 Drying Agents

Phosphorus pentoxide (P_2O_5) and Dehydrite ($MgClO_4$) are excellent drying agents for gas analysis. Dririte ($CaSO_4$) can also be used but it can affect the CO_2 content of the air (Sestak et al. 1971). Sulfuric acid is no longer in general use for safety reasons.

Often it is acceptable to have some water vapor in the gas, provided it is constant and of known amount. A coil of copper packed in ice and water is a practical method for drying air to a constant, low dew point. This method is very convenient in the laboratory, though less so in the field.

4.5.2 Humidifying Gas Streams

The most versatile way to add water vapor to dry gas is bubbling the gas through warm water, then condensing the excess water vapor out of the air at the desired dew point (see also Sect. 4.1.1). This usually requires a refrigerated water bath but an ice and water bath can be used to provide air with a 0° C dew point. Such an air supply can be useful for calibrating water vapor sensing machines and in certain configurations of gas exchange systems described in Sect. 4.1.2.

It is also possible to establish a known humidity using the change in hydration of $FeSO_4 \cdot 7H_2O$. The heptahydrate will lose water to become the pentahydrate when the humidity of air in contact with the crystals is below a certain point (Parkinson and Day 1981). Provided the air flow rate is not extreme, the dew point temperature of the air after passing over the crystals, T_D, is $1.134\,T_C - 11.6$ where T_C is the temperature of the crystals in °C (data of Parkinson and Day 1981, my measurements were substantially in agreement). This provides an extremely convenient way of checking the calibration of water vapor sensors in the field.

5 Vapor Pressure Difference

To understand the effects that stomates have on photosynthesis, stomatal conductance must be calculated. This is calculated from the rate of water loss and the potentials for water loss. The potential for water loss is often called the leaf to air vapor pressure difference and abbreviated VPD. The modern units for expressing stomatal conductance (mol m^{-2} s^{-1}) require the potential for water loss to be expressed in the water vapor mole fraction difference between the leaf and air.

5.1 Humidity in the Air

Determining the humidity in the air around the leaf is easy when the air inside the chamber is recirculated. If a dew point hygrometer is used to measure the water content of air coming from the chamber, the mole fraction is simply the partial pressure determined from the dew point divided by the total pressure at the dew point hygrometer. The mole fraction of water measured this way is the mole fraction of water to which the leaf is exposed. The partial pressure of water to which the leaf is exposed can be determined by multiplying the mole fraction by the total pressure in the leaf chamber. The pressure inside the chamber is different from the atmospheric pressure and should be measured.

This applies if the air inside the chamber is well mixed. In some chambers, the air passes over the leaf once and changes in humidity from one end of the chamber to the other. If the flow is laminar, then the average humidity to which the leaf is exposed is the incoming humidity plus half of the humidity added by the leaf. If the flow is turbulent, as it is in most gas analysis chambers, then the effective humidity is the incoming humidity plus two-thirds of the added humidity (Raschke unpublished).

5.2 Humidity Inside the Leaf

To determine the humidity inside the leaf, it is assumed that the leaf intercellular spaces are at 100% relative humidity. Corrections for leaf water poential can be made using the equation:

$$RH = e^{(\psi \cdot v/R \cdot T)}, \tag{3}$$

where RH means relative humidity, e is the base of natural logarithm (2.72), ψ is the water potential, V is the molar volume of water, R is the gas constant, and T is the temperature. The units for ψ and the other parameters must all cancel. This equation is derived from Raoult's Law. These corrections are only significant when the water potential is low. From time to time there are reports that this assumption (of 100% relative humidity) is not correct, but these are largely unsubstantiated and a number of investigators have demonstrated the validity of this assumption (Laisk 1977; Sharkey et al. 1982; Mott and O'Leary 1984).

The humidity inside the leaf is determined from leaf temperature. The measure of leaf temperature is perhaps the most difficult measurement to make properly, and most commercially available systems are very inadequate. Most of the time, leaf temperature is measured using a thin wire thermocouple, with copper-constantan (type T) the most popular. A junction of two dissimilar metals can develop a potential. If a second junction is made, a potential difference or voltage will be proportional to the difference in temperature between the two junctions. The reference junction can be any temperature as long as that temperature is known precisely. Many instruments measure the temperature of the terminal block to which thermocouples are attached. Thermal gradients along the terminal blocks introduce errors.

A more accurate way to establish the reference junction temperature is to pack the reference junction in ice and water. Since the bottom of an ice bath can warm up to 4° C, I keep the reference ice bath inside a second ice bath. This arrangement keeps the temperature of the reference junction within 0.01° C of zero.

A common mistake is to have straight leads of the thermocouple measuring junction at a right angle to the leaf with the junction pushing against the leaf. The common occurrence of punctured leaves is one of the lesser problems with this method. The biggest problem is that the measuring junction of the thermocouple is in better thermal contact with the wire of the thermocouple than the leaf. The wire nearest the junction is in the boundary layer surrounding the leaf, and the temperature of the thermocouple tip will be more influenced by the boundary layer temperature than the leaf temperature.

To overcome this thermal conductivity error, the thermocouple must be laid along the leaf for 1–2 cm. This can be difficult with very thin wires. Stainless steel-sheathed thermocopules available from Omega Engineering are very thin and hold their shape so that they can be bent into a spring that gently pushes against the leaf inside the leaf chamber.

One company uses heat balance equations to estimate the leaf temperature. I am skeptical that this would be reliable under a range of conditions but have no firsthand knowledge that it is unreliable.

Once all technical problems are solved, there is still the uncertainty of temperature variations across the leaf. Under extreme conditions I have measured temperature gradients $>3°$ C over a 2.5-cm-long chamber. Since this temperature is used to determine the humidity inside the leaf and the VPD is the difference between this number and the humidity of the air, a small error in temperature measurement can have a large effect on the measure of stomatal conductance. Errors of $0.1°$ C can be translated into errors of 5% in the estimate of stomatal conductance.

Keeping the boundary layer conductance very high will cause the leaf temperature to be near the air temperature. This reduces or eliminates many of the problems associated with temperature measurements. As discussed in Sect. 4.4.1, a high boundary layer conductance may be more important for heat balance considerations than for water loss considerations.

6 Chambers

The single most important part of any gas analysis system used for measuring photosynthesis is the chamber containing the photosynthesizing material. There is an extreme variety of chamber designs in current use reflecting the variations in questions asked and in operator style. Many of the chambers fall into one of two general types, the defined area chamber or clamp-on chamber, and the undefined area or whole leaf chamber. In general, the defined area chamber is used when stomatal conductance is an important part of the question studied or when the system is designed more for laboratory use. For field use, the whole leaf chambers are generally preferred.

While some chambers have no provision for temperature control, chambers generally are built so that the leaf temperature can be manipulated. The simplest method is by water channels for the flow of water from a thermostated water bath. It is now common to have Peltier blocks from Melcor mounted on chambers so that the temperature can be electronically controlled.

7 Putting the System Together

There are a number of products that are used by a large number of people doing gas exchange analysis. Knowing the sources of these products is often half the battle for setting up a gas exchange system.

7.1 Mass Flow Meters

The second most expensive part of a gas exchange system, after the CO_2 analyzer, is the flow control apparatus. Mass flow controllers from Datametrics are the current favorites. These devices require a 10–15 psi pressure drop for control which can limit some configurations such as controlling the flow of humid air. Flow meters from Datametrics require a minimal pressure drop and so are useful as well. These thermal conductivity-based measuring devices are extremely accurate and reproducible. Anyone contemplating measuring over a range of CO_2 levels or, even more so, over a range of O_2 levels, should consider mixing all of their gases from N_2, O_2, and 3–5% CO_2 in air using mass flow meters. Most compressed air available from medical or scientific suppliers in the USA is a mixture of N_2 and O_2 with the O_2 content variable between 18 and 21%. Why pay someone to do a poor job of mixing gases when, for a modest capital investment, it can be done very accurately and with more flexibility?

7.2 Barometer

It is important to know the atmospheric pressure and to know the pressure at several places within the gas flow system such as the condenser, the leaf chamber, and the dew point hygrometer. All of these measurements can be made with a single electronic barometer. I have used the Weathertronics model 705. This device requires a 15-V supply and produces a voltage proportional to temperature. It is relatively easy to scale a panel meter to read directly in mbar pressure.

7.3 Tubing Fittings

Most of the fittings in general use for gas exchange systems are made by the Clippard Co. When high pressures or vacuum is needed then Swagelock and other fittings from the Crawford Fitting Company are used.

8 Three Different System Designs

To illustrate how the various possibilities can be used to construct a system for measuring gas exchange, three systems will be presented. These are not meant to represent particular systems but to serve as starting points for designing new systems.

8.1 Laboratory-Based System

The laboratory-based system is shown in Fig. 1. This system measures water and CO_2 by the differential configuration. This system is often used with defined area

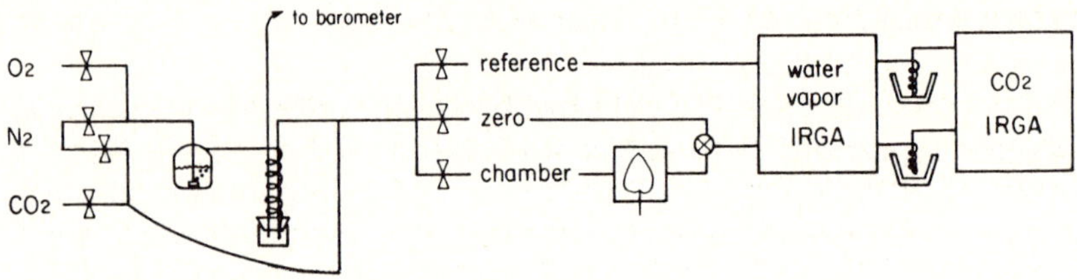

Fig. 1. Typical laboratory-based gas analysis system (see Sect. 8.1)

chambers and the amount of leaf material inside the chamber can be quite small. This is advantageous because the changes in the air as it passes over the leaf will be small and because it is less likely that inhomogeneities over the leaf will affect the results. The small changes in gas composition make this configuration the most taxing on the gas measuring devices but the required sensitivity is easily obtained from IRGAs. Water vapor is condensed in ice traps between the two IRGAs to improve the precision of the CO_2 measurement. Control of the conditions to which the leaf is exposed is easiest with this configuration since the leaf has little effect on the gas composition. Setting the humidity is most often accomplished with a condenser in a refrigerated water bath. These systems are not generally commercially available.

8.2 Expedition Size Field System

The system shown in Fig. 2 is easily transported to the field. A system very similar to this was described in detail by Field et al. (1982). Similar systems are available commercially from Bingham Interspace Co. Gases are mixed in the field or premixed gases from tanks are supplied to a manifold. One gas stream serves as the reference stream in the CO_2 IRGA, one stream is switched to the IRGA to determine the zero point, and the third stream passes over the leaf. The leaf provides all of the water vapor unless an ice trap is used to humidify the air upt to 0° C dew point. Water vapor is measured with a dew point hygrometer. The water configuration is differential with dry air coming in. The depletion of CO_2 is matched by the flow of CO_2 to the chamber. In practice these systems almost always are calibrated so that the compensation of photosynthesis does not have to be perfect. The CO_2 part of the system is a combined compensating-differential.

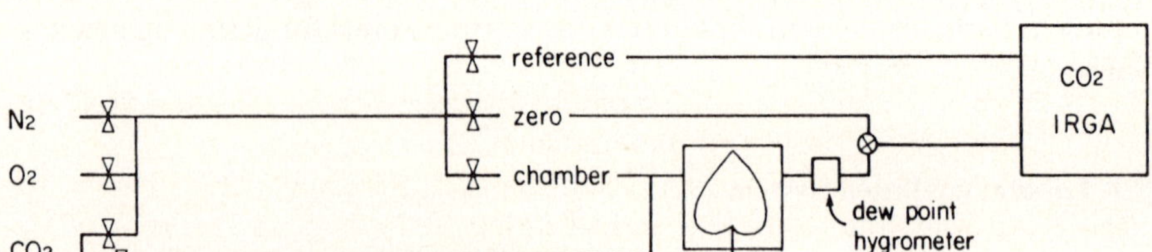

Fig. 2. Portable gas analysis system (see Sect. 8.2)

There is no provision for controlling water vapor before the gas passes into the CO_2 analyzer to economize on weight and complexity.

These systems do not require a refrigerated water bath or other heavy equipment. Such systems can be run with only a 12-V power supply and one lead acid battery can run such a system for over a day.

These systems are more difficult for beginners to operate and even experienced users have difficulty when the leaf does not lose water very fast. Oscillations in stomatal conductance or photosynthesis are very difficult to measure with this type of system.

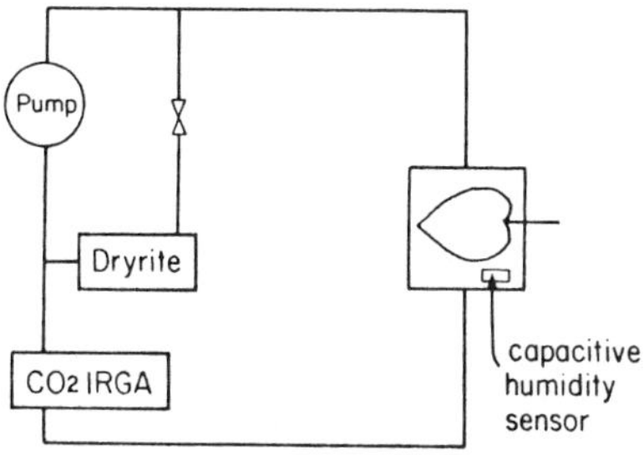

Fig. 3. Small-sized gas analysis system (see Sect. 8.3)

8.3 Personal Size Portable System

The system shown in Fig. 3 is similar (but not identical) to systems available from ADC and LiCor. The configuration is kinetic-closed for CO_2 and constant humidity-closed for water vapor. CO_2 depletion from the system is measured with an IRGA and water loss by the leaf is measured by determining the amount of air that must go through a drying loop to keep the humidity in the leaf chamber at some predetermined point. This design does not require a supply of compressed gas, thus making it very easy to transport.

Appendix

The following is a partial list of some of the suppliers often useful in building gas exchange systems. All suppliers are in the USA unless noted otherwise.

Gas Exchange Systems

The Analytical Development Company Ltd., Pindar Road, Hoddesdon, Herts, EN11 OAQ, ENGLAND, Tel. Hoddesdon 69638

Bingham Interspace, PO Box 340, Hyde Park, UT 84318 (801) 563–6316

Heiz Walz Meß- und Regeltechnik, Eichenring 10–14, D-8521 Effeltrich, FRG, Tel. (09133) 29 72

LiCor, Inc., PO Box 4425, Lincoln, NE 68504, (402) 467–3576

Fittings for Tubing

Clippard Instrument Laboratory, Inc. 7390 Colerain Road, Cincinatti, OH 45239, (513) 521–4261

Crawford Fitting Co. (Swagelock and others) 29500 Solon Road, Solon, OH 44139, (216) 248–4600

Flow Meters and Controllers, Electronic

Datametrics, 340 Fordham Rd., Wilmington, MA 01887, (617) 658–5410

IRGAs

The Analytical Development Company Ltd., Pindar Road, Hoddesdon, Herts, EN11 OAQ, ENGLAND, Tel. Hoddesdon 69638

Anarad, Inc., 534 Ortega St., Santa Barbara, CA 93103, (805) 963–6583

Beckman Instruments, Inc. 2500 Harbor Blvd., Fullerton, CA 92634, (714) 871–4848

Inficon Leybold-Heraeus, Inc., (US agent, Binos analyzers), 6500 Fly Road, East Syracuse, NY 13507, (315) 437–0377

LiCor, Inc., PO Box 4425, Lincoln, NE 68504, (402) 467–3576

Thermocouples

Omega Engineering Inc., PO Box 2669, Stamford, CT 06906, (203) 359–1660

References

Badger MR, Sharkey TD, Caemmerer S von (1984) The relationship between steady-state gas exchange of bean leaves and the levels of carbon-reduction-cycle intermediates. Planta 160:305–313

Ball JT (1987) Calculations related to gas exchange. In: Zeiger E, Farquhar GD, Cowan IR (eds) Stomatal function. Stanford Univ Press, Stanford, pp 445–476

Bloom AJ, Mooney HA, Björkman O, Berry J (1980) Materials and methods for carbon dioxide and water exchange analysis. Plant Cell Environ 3:371–376

Brooks A, Farquhar GD (1985) Effects of temperature on the O_2/CO_2 specificity of ribulose-1,5-bisphosphate carboxylase/oxygenase and the rate of respiration in the light. Estimates from gas exchange measurement on spinach. Planta 165:397–406

Caemmerer S von, Edmondson DL (1986) The relationship between steady-state gas exchange, in vivo RuP2 carboxylase activity and some carbon reduction cycle intermediates in *Raphanus sativus*. Aust J Plant Physiol 13:669–688

Caemmerer S von, Farquhar GD (1981) Some relationships between the biochemistry of photosynthesis and the gas exchange of leaves. Planta 153:376–387

Caemmerer S von, Farquhar GD (1984) Effects of partial defoliation, changes of irradiance during growth, short-term water stress and growth at enhanced $p(CO_2)$ on the photosynthetic capacity of leaves of *Phaseolus vulgaris* L. Planta 160:320–329

Farquhar GD, Caemmerer S von, Berry JA (1980) A biochemical model of photosynthetic CO_2 assimilation in leaves of C3 species. Planta 149:78–90

Field CB, Mooney HA (in press) Measuring photosynthesis under field conditions – past and present approaches. In: Kramer PJ, Strain BR, Funada S, Hashimoto Y (eds) Scientific instruments in physiological plant ecology. Academic Press, New York London

Field C, Berry JA, Mooney HA (1982) A portable system for measuring carbon dioxide and water vapour exchange of leaves. Plant Cell Environ 5:179–186

Field CB, Ball JT, Berry JA (in press) Photosynthesis: principles and field techniques. In: Pearcy RW, Ehlringer J, Mooney HA, Rundel P (eds) Physiological plant ecology. Field methods and instrumentation

Gaastra P (1959) Photosynthesis of crop plants as influenced by light, carbon dioxide, temperature, and stomatal diffusion resistance. Meded Landbouwhogesch Wageningen 59(13):1–68

Hardwick RC, Cole RA, Fyfield TP (1984) Injury to and death of cabbage (*Brassica oleracea*) seedlings caused by vapours of dibutylphthalate emitted from certain plastics. Ann Appl Biol 105:97–105

Hill DW, Powell T (1968) Non-dispersive infrared gas analysis in science, medicine and industry. Plenum, New York

Jarman PD (1974) The diffusion of carbon dioxide and water vapour through stomata. J Exp Bot 25:927–936

Laisk A (1977) Kinetics of photosynthesis and photorespiration of C3 plants. Nauka, Moscow (in Russian)

Leunig R (1983) Transport of gases into leaves. Plant Cell Environ 6:181–194

Moss DN, Rawlins SL (1963) Concentration of carbon dioxide inside leaves. Nature 197:1320–1321

Mott KA, O'Leary JW 81984) Stomatal behavior and CO_2 exchange characteristics in amphistomatous leaves. Plant Physiol 74:47–51

Mott KA, Jensen RG, O'Leary JW, Berry JA (1984) Photosynthesis and ribulose 1,5-bisphosphate concentrations in intact leaves of *Xanthium strumarium* L. Plant Physiol 76:968–971

Parkinson KJ, Day W (1981) Water vapour calibration using salt hydrate transitions. J Exp Bot 32:411–418

Penman Hl, Schofield RK (1951) Some physical aspects of assimilation and transpiration. Symp Soc Exp Biol 5:115–129

Seemann JR, Sharkey TD (1986) Salinity and nitrogen effects on photosynthesis, ribulose-1,5-bisphosphate carboxylase and metabolite pool sizes in *Phaseolus vulgaris* L. Plant Physiol 82:555–560

Seemann JR, Sharkey TD (1987) The effect of abscisic acid and other inhibitors on photosynthetic capacity and the biochemistry of CO_2 assimilation. Plant Physiol 84:696–700

Seemann JR, Tepperman JM, Berry JA (1981) The relationship between photosynthetic performance and the levels and kinetic properties of RuBP carboxylase-oxygenase from desert winter annuals. Carnegie Inst Washington Yearb 80:67–72

Sestak Z, Catsky J, Jarvis PG (1971) Plant photosynthetic production manual of methods. Junk, The Hague

Sharkey TD (1984) Transpiration-induced changes in the photosynthetic capacity of leaves. Plant Physiol 160:143–150

Sharkey TD (1985) Photosynthesis in intact leaves of C3 plants: physics, physiology and rate limitations. Bot Rev 51:53–105

Sharkey TD, Imai K, Farquhar GD, Cowan IR (1982) A direct conformation of the standard method of estimating intercellular partial pressure of CO_2. Plant Physiol 69:657–659

Sharkey TD, Seemann JR, Berry JA (1986a) Regulation of ribulose-1,5-bisphosphate carboxlase activity in response to changing partial pressure of O_2 and light in *Phaseolus vulgaris*. Plant Physiol 81:788–791

Sharkey TD, Stitt M, Heineke D, Gerhardt R, Raschke K, Heldt HW (1986b) Limitation of photosynthesis by carbon metabolism II. O_2-insensitive CO_2 uptake results from limitation of triose phosphate utilization. Plant Physiol 81:1123–1129

Respiration Measurements in Plant Roots Throughout Development

A. M. Johnson-Flanagan

1 Introduction

Respiration can be defined in the simplest of terms as the consumption of oxygen. In reality, it is a complex process involving chemical reactions in glycolysis and the Krebs cycle and electron transfer in the electron transport chains. The process of respiration is controlled by interactions at many levels, including organ, tissue, cell, organelle and pathway. In addition, there are many other causes of oxygen consumption. Despite these complexities, respiration is usually measured simply as oxygen consumption. The purpose of this chapter is to demonstrate how measurements of oxygen consumption can be used to study differences in respiration in plant roots throughout development. Techniques will be outlined for apportioning respiratory activity, determining the impact of tissue organization and accounting for the confounding effects of extramitochondrial oxygen consumption.

2 Defining the Problem

Root respiration is a good indicator of metabolic status, providing the system is adequately defined and the appropriate methods are implemented. Throughout development, root structure and function change. For example, morphological change such as the development of protective layers may influence respiration rates by impeding gas exchange. Conversely, the metabolic pathway functioning to produce the protective layer may consume oxygen. Different morphological segments of a root will differ functionally. For example, an absorbing (root is hair-covered) root segment will not be comparable to the apical root segment. Other considerations include the ambient state of the plant and the developmental status of the shoot. Therefore, it is important to define the system under investigation as accurately as possible.

Consideration must be given to the parameters being assessed before methods are implemented. Root respiration can be measured in mitochondria isolated from roots, in root segments, in excised intact roots or in intact plants. In each case different parameters and interactions are being assessed. Respiratory measurements of isolated mitochondria can be used to study differences in respiratory capacity and variations in utilization and potential of the electron transport chains throughout development. Mitochondrial biogenesis will be the only constraint. Measurement of respiration in root segments provides data on tissue respiration at different developmental stages. The impact of cell function and organogenesis on mitochondrial activity are assessed simultaneously. A further level of complexity is added in studies of intact root systems because there are many developmental stages present, both within a given root and between different roots. The problem is further cxacerbated in intact plants because the physiology of the whole plant must be considered. The researcher must define the parameters and interactions of interest in order to study the appropriate level of complexity.

3 Mitochondria

3.1 Factors Affecting Respiratory Measurements

3.1.1 Extramitochondrial Oxygen Consumption

There are numerous causes of oxygen consumption other than the respiratory pathways. Those that are not inhibited by cyanide or inhibitors of the alternative pathway are referred to as residual respiration (the mathematical calculation of residual respiration is dealt with in Sect. 9.1). Residual respiration contributes significantly to total respiration (Huq and Palmer 1978; Janes and Chin 1981; Cole et al. 1982). Therefore, the discovery of residual respiration has resulted in a reassessment of many experiments and a search for more specific inhibitors (Day et al. 1980).

Lipoxygenase is a major contributor to extramitochondrial oxygen consumption. It catalyzes oxidation of polyunsaturated fatty acids. Lipoxygenase activity is cyanide-insensitive and hydroxamic acid (i.e. SHAM, salicylhydroxamic acid) sensitive, and therefore, elevates the cyanide-insensitive respiration component (Parrish and Leopold 1978). In fact, Goldstein et al. (1981) reported a complete loss of cyanide-insensitive respiration when lipoxygenase was removed.

Lipoxygenase activity can be minimized by gradient purification of the preparation (Goldstein et al. 1980, 1981; Siedow and Girvin 1980; Shingles et al. 1982; see Table 1). Currently, there does not appear to be an inhibitor that can discriminate between lipoxygenase activity and the alternative pathway.

Disulfiram (tetraethylthiuram disulphide), was expected to be a specific inhibitor of the alternative respiratory path (Grover and Laties 1978; Miller and Obendorf 1981). However, lipoxygenase is also inhibited by disulfiram (Hausknecht and Funk 1984).

Propyl gallate is an inhibitor of lipoxygenase activity (Tappel 1961). Therefore, it has been used in studies of alternative respiration (Parrish and Leopold 1978). However, propyl gallate does not discriminate between lipoxygenase and the alternative pathway (Siedow and Girvin 1980).

3.1.2 Phenolics

Standard methods for the preparation of intact plant mitochondria frequently must be modified for successful preparation of root mitochondria because of a

Table 1. Respiratory parameters of mitochondria prepared by differential centrifugation, by sucrose density gradient centrifugation and by Percoll density gradient centrifugation

	Differential[a, b]	Sucrose gradient[a]	Percoll gradient[b]
State III rate[c]	98	150	–
(natoms min^{-1} mg^{-1} protein)	145	–	205
ADP:O[c]	1.3	1.9	–
	1.45	–	1.5
Respiratory control[c]	3.8	3.5	–
	2.74	–	2.74
Antimycin A-resistant NADPH cytochrome C reductase (nmol cyt.c. reduced min^{-1} mg^{-1} protein)	5.0	2.9	–
Lipoxygenase (µmol O_2 min^{-1})	187	–	19

[a] Johnson-Flanagan (1980). [b] Neuburger et al. (1982). [c] Succinate oxidation.

preponderance of phenolics. Phenolics interfere with the isolation of mitochondria as a result of protein-phenolic interactions. These include hydrophobic interactions, ionic interactions, hydrogen bonding and salt linkages (Loomis 1974). Phenolics are readily oxidized to quinones. In this form, they bind covalently to proteins or oxidize functional groups.

Numerous methods for overcoming phenolic interactions are outlined in the literature (see Loomis 1974; Laties 1974). The most common method is the addition of PVP (polyvinylpyrrolidone) to bind the phenolics. Similarly, synthetic resins such as Amberlite can be used to bind phenolics. For our purposes, high pH (7.9) in the presence of a reducing agent such as cysteine was adequate (Johnson-Flanagan and Owens 1986).

3.2 Isolation of Mitochondria

3.2.1 Washed Mitochondria

The methods for the preparation of intact mitochondria from roots are modifications of Johnson-Flanagan and Spencer (1981) (Johnson-Flanagan and Owens 1986): Roots are washed, excised and washed again in cold distilled water. Approximately 200 ml of roots are ground in a mortar and pestle for 3 min in 300 ml of ice-cold extraction medium: 0.5 *M* mannitol; 5 m*M* EDTA; 0.5% fatty acid poor BSA; 0.05% cysteine and 0.05 *M* Tes. The pH is adjusted to 7.9 at 25° C with KOH (Møller 1978). The brei is filtered through two layers of cheesecloth and the filtrate is then centrifuged at 700 *g* for 7 min in a fixed angle rotor. The pellet is discarded and the supernatant layer is centrifuged at 21 000 *g* for 5 min in a fixed angle rotor. The pellet is resuspended in 50 ml of ice-cold, wash medium (0.3 *M* mannitol, 25 m*M* Tes and 0.3% fatty acid poor BSA, adjusted to pH 7.9

at 25° C with KOH). Centrifugation is at 21 000 *g* for 5 min in a fixed angle rotor. The pellet is resuspended in 3 ml suspend medium (0.3 *M* mannitol, 4 m*M* $MgCl_2$ and 25 m*M* Tes) and either loaded onto a density gradient or used as such for mitochondria prepared by differential centrifugation. All steps of the isolation are carried out at 0 to 4° C.

3.2.2 Density Gradient Purified Mitochondria

Density gradient purification of mitochondria improves the respiratory parameters of the preparation (Table 1). Microsomal contamination is reduced significantly, as indicated by the decreased antimycin A-resistant cytochrome c reductase activity.

3.2.2.1 Sucrose Step Gradient

Purification of mitochondria on a sucrose step gradient is according to the methods of Johnson-Flanagan and Spencer (1981). The sample is loaded onto a sucrose density gradient (26 ml 0.6 *M* sucrose and 10 ml 1.6 *M* sucrose, both with 50 mM Tes and 0.1% BSA) and centrifuged for 1 h at 30000 *g* in a swinging bucket rotor. The fraction at the interface is removed and diluted slowly with a buffered solution (25 m*M* Tes and 0.1% BSA). The fraction is then centrifuged for 5 min at 21 000 *g*, and the pellet is resuspended in the suspension medium used above. All solutions are adjusted to pH 7.9 at 25° C with KOH. All steps of the isolation are carried out at 0 to 4° C.

3.2.2.2 Percoll Gradient

Purification of mitochondria on a Percoll (Pharmacia) gradient is essentially according to Shingles et al. (1982). The sample is loaded onto a continuous Percoll gradient (10–60% v/v; 50 m*M* Tes, 0.1% BSA and 0.3 *M* mannitol) and centrifuged at 10000 *g* for 20 min in a fixed angle rotor. The mitochondrial sample is removed, diluted and pelletted as above. The pH is adjusted to 7.9 at 25° C with KOH and all steps of the isolation are at 0 to 4° C. The respiratory parameters of mitochondria enriched on a Percoll gradient are not significantly different from those attained from sucrose step gradients. However, the conformation is orthodox and more closely resembles the ultrastructure of mitochondria in tissue (Dizengremel 1985).

4 Root Segments

4.1 Factors Affecting Respiratory Measurements

4.1.1 Developmental Stage

The developmental stage of roots has a profound influence on respiration rates (Table 2). Root anatomy, root age and phase of the growth cycle must be consid-

Table 2. Respiratory consequences of developmental stage and root zone

Root zone	Actively growing root	
	Characteristic	Respiratory consequence
Root apex	Polysaccharide layer Rapid cell division Secretion of mucopeptides Immature mitochondria	Impedes O_2 movement High respiratory requirement High respiratory requirement Low respiration rate Low alternative pathway activity
Zone of elongation and differentiation	Primary endodermis Mature mitochondria Root hairs (nutrient transport)	Impedes O_2 movement High respiration rates High alternative pathway activity High respiratory requirement
Zone of suberization	Secondary endodermis Cell necrosis (phenol oxidases) Senescent mitochondria Suberization (peroxidase)	Impedes O_2 movement Increased extramitochondrial O_2 consumption Decreased respiration rates Increased extramitochondrial O_2 consumption
Root zone	Dormant root	
	Characteristic	Respiratory consequence
Root apex	Dormancy layer Starch accumulation	Impedes O_2 movement Decreased alternative pathway activity
Differentiated tissue	Dormancy layer	Impedes O_2 movement
	Quiescent root	
	Characteristic	Respiratory consequence
Root apex	Dormancy layer Increased cell division Mobilization of starch	Impedes O_2 movement Increased respiration rates Increased alternative pathway activity
Differentiated tissue	Dormancy layer	Impedes O_2 movement
	Developing storage root	
	Characteristic	Respiratory consequence
	Starch accumulation	Decreased alternative pathway activity

ered before comparisons between respiration rates can be made. Frequently, these factors can be controlled by standardization of the growth regime coupled with limited morphological classification.

4.1.1.1 Root Anatomy

Actively growing lateral roots are composed of three morphologically distinct segments; the root apex, including the root cap; the zones of elongation and differentiation; and the zone of suberization (Johnson-Flanagan and Owens 1985a). Many functional differences are associated with different morphological segments of roots. Factors to consider include secretion of mucopeptides, rapid cell division and cell expansion in the root apex, cell elongation and ion uptake in the zones of elongation and differentiation and cell senescence and secondary layer development in the zone of suberization. These functional differences may (Johnson-Flanagan and Owens 1986) or may not be associated with differences in respiratory activities (Lahde 1967; Boyer et al. 1971; Janes and Chin 1981).

The cessation of growth in lateral roots with episodic growth causes a loss of demarcation between the zones as differentiation proceeds acropetally. This eventually produces a brown root. Although a brown root is a distinct morphological class, there is a great variation in metabolic activity depending on whether the root is dormant or quiescent. Therefore, the root must be defined as dormant (lacking the potential to elongate) or quiescent (having the ability to elongate) by placing the plant under favorable growth conditions. Dormant roots have low respiration rates while the respiration rate in quiescent roots is ever increasing (Johnson-Flanagan and Owens 1986).

4.1.1.2 Root Age and Phase of Growth Cycle

Total respiration rates decrease with age in cultured tomato roots (Janes and Chin 1981) and carrot taproots (Steingröver 1981). The decreased rate in tomato roots probably reflects decreased growth as a result of root age. However, in carrot taproots, there is a shift in the metabolic activity as the root enters the storage phase of the growth cycle. Lambers and van de Dijk (1979) found the decrease in total respiration rates were caused by decreased alternative pathway activity. Therefore, the efficiency of respiration actually increased. These findings point to the importance of defining root age and the phase of the growth cycles before comparisons are made, and the value of inhibitor studies for the elucidation of metabolic status.

4.1.2 Osmotic Potential

The use of a Clark-type oxygen electrode for respiration measurements of root segments necessitates the inclusion of an osmoticum in the medium providing the roots are not grown in liquid medium. The osmoticum should maintain the cells in a turgid or slightly plasmolyzed state. Use of incorrect osmotic potentials rapidly alters the apportioning of respiratory activity. Lambers et al. (1981) demonstrated a reduction in alternative respiration following inclusion of 50 m*M* NaCl to the assay medium. The correct osomotic potential can be determined by microscopic examination of thin tissue slices at varying osmolarities. This will vary with the physiological status of the tissue (Johnson-Flanagan and Singh 1986). In studies of spruce root respiration, 0.3 *M* mannitol was utilized (Johnson-Flanagan and Owens 1986).

4.1.3 Bacterial Contamination

Respiratory measurements of intact tissue are subject to error resulting from bacterial contamination. This can be assessed by measuring respiration rates in the presence and absence of chloramphenicol to a final concentration of 0.5 $\mu g\ ml^{-1}$ (Lambers and Steingröver 1978; Johnson-Flanagan and Owens 1986).

4.1.4 Wound Response

Wound respiration is a consequence of tissue excision. It is composed of oxidative reactions such as the formation of quinones from phenolics (Rich et al. 1978), the breakdown of lipids, mediated by lipoxygenase (Parrish and Leopold 1978), and increased activity of the alternative respiratory pathway (Theologis and Laties 1978 a) and cytochrome-mediated pathway (Theologis and Laties 1980).

Wound respiration causes an increase in respiratory activity ranging in duration from a few minutes in ground soybeans (Parrish and Leopold 1978) to approximately 1 h in white spruce roots (Johnson-Flanagan and Owens 1986). Thereafter, a more constant rate of oxygen consumption is maintained. A constant rate does not preclude the involvement of a wound respiration component. Further examination of the contribution of wound respiration to total respiration involves the use of respiratory inhibitors.

4.1.5 Lipoxygenase

Lipoxygenase activity is not dealt with easily in tissues. In many plants lipoxygenase is constitutive. Furthermore, wounding during tissue preparation may elevate lipoxygenase activity (Parrish and Leopold 1977). Erroneous readings caused by wounding may be circumvented by allowing the tissue to sit until the burst of activity has passed. This does not remove the basal activity. Therefore, specific inhibitors are imperative in studies of root respiration.

4.1.6 Other Oxygen-Consuming Reactions

There are a number of extramitochondrial oxygen-consuming reactions that interfere specifically with measurements of tissue respiration. These are mediated by enzymes such as peroxidase, tyrosinase and polyphenol oxidase. In general, oxygen is utilized as the electron acceptor, resulting in free radical polymerization of the substrate.

Peroxidase activity is associated with suberization and lignification of the root (Johnson-Flanagan and Owens 1985 b). Peroxidase activity and residual respiration increased basipetally. However, peroxidase did not contribute to residual respiration, but rather, it resulted in an overestimation of the alternative pathway.

Both tyrosinase and polyphenol oxidase catalyze the production of quinones. These are not only characteristic of the wounding response, but are also produced during senscence of root cortical cells following formation of the secondary state of the endodermis (unpublished observation). Results from Rich et al. (1978) indicated that the oxygen-consuming capacity of tyrosinase in potato slices was at least 100-fold greater than the oxygen-consuming capacity of the respiratory pathways. These enzymes are inhibited by SHAM and, therefore, their activity results in an overestimation of the alternative pathway.

4.1.7 Assessment of Physiological Respiration Rates

There are a number of boundary layers in roots. Depending upon the developmental stage, these layers may or may not impede the movement of gases in the root. The suberized layers of the hypodermis, primary endodermis (Clarkson and Robards 1975; Peterson et al. 1981), secondary endodermis (Clarkson and Robards 1975) and the metacutization layer (Johnson-Flanagan 1985) all act as apoplastic barriers.

Apoplastic movement is also restricted in the root apex of actively growing roots (Peterson and Edgington 1975; Peterson et al. 1981; Johnson-Flanagan 1985). This may be attributed to polysaccharide secretions (Peterson and Edgington 1975) or a thin suberin layer (Johnson-Flanagan and Owens 1985a).

Measurements of physiological respiration rates must reflect the correct functioning of these layers. To this end, root segments must be sealed at the excised end. A small amount of Kerr's sticky wax effectively seals the root. Problems with air bubbles can be alleviated by treating the root segment briefly with a surfactant such as Tween-20 at 0.01%.

Studies to determine the implications of boundary layers on root respiration must measure maximal respiration rates in addition to physiological respiration rates. Elevation of the external oxygen concentration during respiratory measurements will determine whether diffusion is a limiting factor. Similar studies have been conducted on potato tubers. Although the periderm is considered to be relatively impermeable, there was no increase in respiration rates in either intact tubers (Burton 1950) or slices (Loughman 1960) when external oxygen levels were increased. Similar results would be expected in roots because the periderm of potato is both chemically and functionally similar to the suberized layers in roots (Johnson-Flanagan and Kolattukudy, unpublished).

5 Intact Excised Roots

The factors affecting respiratory measurements in root segments apply to measurements of intact excised roots. In addition, the anatomy of the entire root system must be considered. In complex systems, the relative proportion of each roots class and the rate of root elongation will bear upon the respiration rates.

6 Intact Plants

Measurement of respiration rates in roots of intact plants cannot be accurately assessed by measuring changes in the oxygen concentration of the bathing medium. Root respiration in this case utilizes oxygen supplied from the shoot and from the bathing medium. Webb and Armstrong (1983) have devised a Clark-type electrode that is inserted in the root and measures change in the internal oxygen concentration.

The ambient state of the shoot is critical in studies of root respiration of intact plants. Root respiration rates are high during periods of active photosynthesis (Hansen 1976; Szaniawski 1981) because of the availability of photosynthate (Lambers 1980). A decrease in the supply of photosynthate causes decreased respiration. This is almost exclusively a result of decreased alternative pathway activity (Lambers 1980). Changing photosynthate levels may result in diurnal variation in addition to variation throughout the life cycle of the plant. Therefore, the importance of standardization and accurately defining the developmental stage of shoot development cannot be overemphasized in studies of root respiration in intact plants.

7 Roots Grown in Liquid Culture

Root respiration can be measured polarographically directly in unmodified nutrient medium providing inhibitors are not added. The excised end of the root should be sealed with Kerr's sticky wax. If inhibitors are used, all ions that could interfere with the action of the inhibitor must be removed (see Sect. 8.2 for details).

8 Problems Associated with Inhibitors

8.1 Disulfiram

Although disulfiram was considered to be a specific inhibitor of the alternative pathway, it may lack specificity. Evidence to support this include inhibition of cytochrome-mediated electron transport in white potato mitochondria (Grover and Laties 1978) and soybean mitochondria (Miller and Obendorf 1981), inhibition of peroxidase activity in white spruce roots (Johnson-Flanagan and Owens 1985b), inhibition of lipoxygenase type 2 isozyme in soybean (Hausknecht and Funk 1984) and a decrease in *Vres* not attributable to decreased peroxidase activity in white spruce roots (Johnson-Flanagan and Owens 1985b). On the basis of the results from peroxidase and lipoxygenase studies it seems clear that disulfiram inhibits reactions involving free radical production. This, therefore, makes it an unsuitable inhibitor in many studies of root respiration (see Sect. 4.1.6 for details).

A consequence of disulfiram inhibition of the cytochrome-mediated pathway may be an overestimation of *p* in calculations of the relative activities of the respiratory pathways (Miller and Obendorf 1981). However, the increase in *p* could also result from the reduction of *Vres* (Johnson-Flanagan and Owens 1985b). The effectiveness of disulfiram in tissue is not unequivocal. While we found it effective in white spruce roots (*Ki* 10 μ*M*; Johnson-Flanagan and Owens 1985b), Grover and Laties (1978) did not find it effective in either Russet potato discs or red sweet potato discs. Problems may arise in penetration, non-specific binding or metabolic breakdown of disulfiram.

8.2 SHAM

The lack of specificity of SHAM as a respiratory inhibitor has been discussed in other sections. Briefly, SHAM inhibits lipoxygenase (Parrish and Leopold 1977), peroxidase (Rich et al. 1978; Johnson-Flanagan and Owens 1985b), tyrosinase and numerous other enzymes (see Rich et al. 1978).

SHAM and all other substituted hydroxamic acids are chelators of metal ions (Rich et al. 1978). Therefore, care must be taken to remove these ions from nutrient media prior to respiratory measurements. Ferric Fe, in particular, is effectively chelated by SHAM.

Different concentrations of SHAM may be required at different developmental stages. For example, in spruce roots, brown and suberizing segments were titrated with SHAM concentrations up to 8 m*M*, while all other root segments were titrated up to 2 m*M* (Johnson-Flanagan and Owens 1986).

In general, the concentration of SHAM required in in vivo experiments is frequently higher in comparison to concentrations used in experiments with isolated mitochondria (Lambers 1980). Concentrations up to 25 m*M* have been required to inhibit root respiration (Lambers and van de Dijk 1979). It is expected that this reflects non-specific binding, presence of endogenous SHAM chelators (Lambers 1980) and enzymes that bind SHAM (Rich et al. 1978). On the other hand, Webb and Armstrong (1983) caution against the indiscriminate use of high SHAM concentrations because it becomes lethal. They noted death of pea roots at concentrations above 10 m*M*.

8.3 Antimycin A

Studies of the alternative pathway should utilize cyanide in preference to antimycin A for inhibition of the cytochrome pathway. Antimycin A may inhibit respiration at one (Ikuma and Bonner 1967) or two sites (Theologis and Laties 1978b). Apparently, the two sites not only differ in affinity, but the affinities vary with the developmental state of the tissue (Theologis and Laties 1978b). In addition to these confounding effects, inhibition by antimycin A is incomplete (Bonner and Slater 1970).

8.4 Uncouplers

Measurements of uncoupler-stimulated respiration may overestimate the capacity of the cytochrome pathway in tissues possessing an alternative respiratory pathway. Theologis and Laties (1978a) reported stimulation of the alternative pathway from $p=0$ to $p=1.0$ by carbonyl-cyanide *m* chlorophenyl hydrazone (CCCP). This was attributed to stimulation of glycolysis resulting in an oversaturation of the cytochrome pathway.

9 Measuring Respiration Rates

Once the preceding considerations have been taken into account, accurate respiratory measurements should be attainable. There are a number of techniques available for the measurement of respiration, including the Warburg respirometer, Gilson respirometer, oxygen gas analyzer and Clark-type oxygen electrode. The latter is the system of choice because of the small tissue requirements, ease of adding inhibitors, rapid temperature regulation and accuracy of measurements.

Standard methods for polarographic measurement of oxygen consumption in mitochondria (Laties 1974) are implemented in studies of mitochondria isolated from roots. Polarographic measurements of tissue respiration are as follows: The reaction medium consists of 0.3 *M* mannitol and 25 m*M* Tes adjusted to pH 7.1 at 25° C with KOH. Approximately 100 mg samples of 1-cm-long root segments can be accommodated in a 3-ml reaction volume. Inhibitors are added after a steady oxygen uptake rate is attained (Table 3; Johnson-Flanagan and Owens 1986).

9.1 Apportioning Respiratory Activity

Information about the metabolic status of tissues can be greatly expanded by studying the apportioning of respiratory activity. Residual respiration and respiration mediated by the alternative pathway result in an overestimation of oxygen

Table 3. Working concentrations of inhibitors

Inhibitor	Final concentration	
	Mitochondria	Tissue
Antimycin A	0.4 µg ml^{-1}	0.2 µ*M* – 20 µ*M*
SHAM, mCLAM, etc.	5 m*M*	10 m*M*
KCN	0.1 m*M*	1–5 m*M*
Rotenone	20 µ*M*	?
Disulfiram	50 µ*M*	100 µ*M*

consumption coupled to phosphorylation (Theologis and Laties 1978a). Therefore, the relative activities of these respiratory components indicate the phosphorylative efficiency of tissue respiration.

Equations to express these parameters quantitatively have been developed for purified mitochondria (Bahr and Bonner 1973) and for intact tissue (Theologis and Laties 1978a). The equation for purified mitochondria is as follows:

$$V = pg(i) + Vcyt\,,$$

where V represents the observed rate of oxygen uptake; g(i) represents the maximum possible rate of the alternative pathway as a function of the hydroxamic acid concentration; *p*, a constant between zero and one, indicates the fraction of the alternative pathway operating; and *Vcyt* represents the contribution of the saturated or nearly saturated cytochrome pathway and is the respiration rate in the presence of the maximum hydroxamic acid or disulfiram concentration. *Valt* is the cyanide-insensitive respiration and as such, is the maximum g(i). The equation was modified for intact tissue as follows:

$$V = pg(i) + Vcyt + Vres\,,$$

where *Vres* represents the oxygen uptake that is both cyanide-insensitive and hydroxamic acid or disulfiram-insensitive. *Vres* is subtracted from V to give V', a value which represents the oxygen uptake as a result of the activity of the alternative pathway and the cytochrome pathway. A typical experiment used to determine these values is shown in Fig. 1. Results are then expressed graphically in Fig. 2.

The maximum contribution of the alternative pathway (*Valt*) and the actual contribution of the alternative pathway (*Valt* × *p*) can be expressed as a percentage or a rate. This allows for comparisons between different tissues.

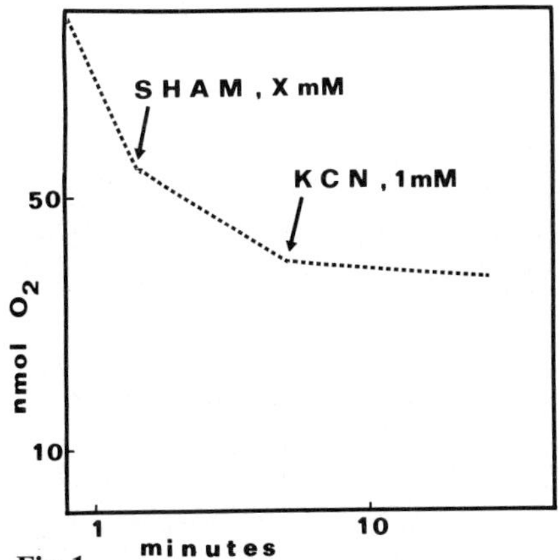

Fig. 1

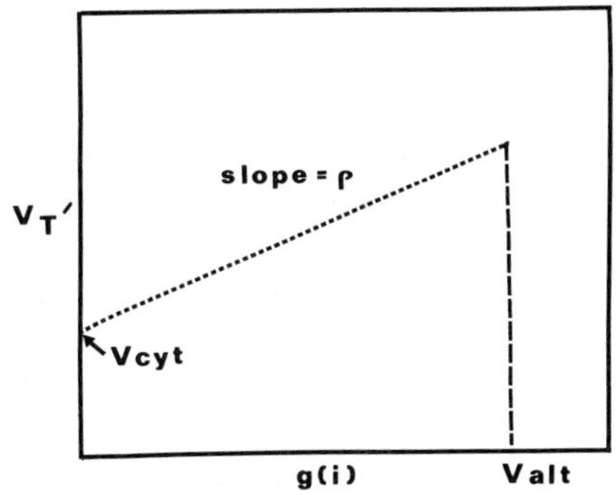

Fig. 2

Fig. 1. Experimental method for calculating contributions of each respiratory component in root tissue. *X* refers to variable concentrations of *SHAM* from 0 to 10 m*M* (After Bahr and Bonner 1973)

Fig. 2. Graphic representation of data. (After Bahr and Bonner 1973)

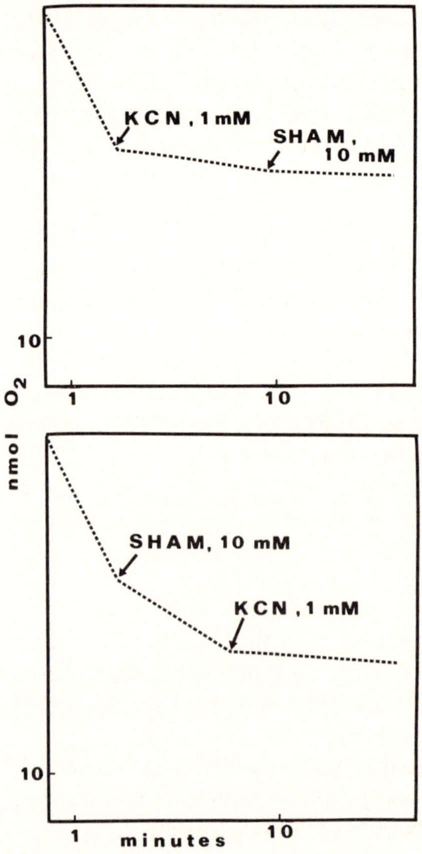

Fig. 3. Experimental method for estimating contributions of each respiratory component in root tissue

The percent of the maximal operation of the alternative pathway in the absence of cyanide can be estimated according to the method of Theologis and Laties (1980). *Valt* is the respiration rate in the presence of 1 m*M* potassium cyanide and *Vcyt* is the respiration rate in the presence of 2 m*M* SHAM or 100 *M* disulfiram. *Vres* is subtracted from each value and *p* is calculated. A typical experiment is shown in Fig. 3. For routine work, use of the method to estimate the maximal operation of the alternative pathway (Theologis and Laties 1980) can replace the more accurate, but time-consuming method.

The normal respiration rate in tissues is intermediate between State 3 and State 4 rates in intact mitochondria. It is limited by the availability of ADP (Wiskich 1980). Uncouplers function by releasing electron transport from the constraints of the ATP production. This raises tissue respiration to the level of State 3 respiration. Therefore, the role of an uncoupler is two-fold: Firstly, it verifies that tissue respiration is coupled and secondly, the maximum capacity of the cytochrome chain is determined.

The most commonly used uncouplers are 2,4- and 2,6-dinitrophenol (DNP). The concentration required for maximal stimulation is pH-dependent. For example, the concentration inducing maximal uncoupling of succinate oxidation in mitochondria ranges from 2.7 μ*M* at pH 6 to 270 μ*M* at pH 8 (Slater 1969). Uncoupled respiration in root segments was invoked by 1.65 m*M* DNP (Johnson-Flanagan 1984). CCCP at 10 m*M* is also an effective uncoupler of tissue respiration (Theologis and Laties 1978 b).

9.2 Rotenone-Resistant Respiration

A rotenone-resistant pathway has been recognized in a number of higher plants (Palmer 1976). This pathway bypasses site I and re-enters the cytochrome-mediated pathway beyond the branching point for the alternative pathway (Johnson-Flanagan and Spencer 1981). Therefore, utilization of this pathway precludes entry of electrons into the alternative pathway and results in an overestimation of respiration mediated by the cytochrome pathway. The maximum activity of the rotenone-resistant pathway can be determined by the addition of rotenone, however, there is no method to accurately assess the contribution of this pathway in the absence of inhibitors. Rotenone was found to be ineffective in studies of root respiration (unpublished observation).

10 Adjunct Methods

A number of non-quantitative, but nonetheless valuable methods exist to provide insight into quantitative measurements of oxygen consumption. These include electron microscopy and histochemistry. In addition, assays of respiratory enzymes can provide data on overall respiration rates.

Variations in quantity, spatial organization and developmental state of mitochondria can be observed with electron microscopy. Changes in respiratory parameters have been correlated with different developmental stages of mitochondria. Poorly developed inner membranes, characteristic of early stages of biogenesis (Solomos et al. 1972), are associated with low respiration rates and low alternative pathway activity (James and Spencer 1979). Fully developed mitochondria, characterized by distinct cristae and an electron-lucent matrix (Solomos et al. 1972) are associated with high rates of total respiration and alternative pathway-mediated respiration (James and Spencer 1979). Senescence is characterized by a contracted inner membrane and a highly condensed matrix (Solomos et al. 1972). At this stage, respiration rates decrease.

Histochemical analysis of roots provides information regarding the spatial distribution of respiration in the roots in addition to a non-quantitative estimation of the intensity of respiration. The method for succinate dehydrogenase histochemistry is from Jensen (1962): Fresh roots are frozen at $-12°$ C and sections are cut on a cryostat, dry mounted on slides and treated with equal volumes of sodium succinate (1%) and 2 (*p*-iodophenyl)-3-(*p*-nitrophenyl)-S-phenyl tetrazolium chloride (0.2%) and phosphate buffer (ph 7.2) (0.1 *M*) at 37° C for 1 h in the dark.

Succinate dehydrogenase activity is indicative of cytochrome-mediated respiration rates. Therefore, it can be assayed to estimate respiratory activity. Succinate dehydrogenase is measured according to the methods of Solomos et al. (1972): The mitochondria are added to 3 ml containing 30 μmol potassium phosphate, pH 7.4, 1.5 mg BSA, 6 μmol potassium cyanide, 30 μmol succinate, 60 μg 2,6-dichlorophenol indophenol and 3 μg antimycin A. The activity is expressed as nmol indophenol reduced per mg protein per min (Green et al. 1955).

References

Bahr JT, Bonner WD Jr (1973) Cyanide-insensitive respiration. I. The steady state of skunk cabbage spadix and bean hypocotyl mitochondria. J Biol Chem 248:3441–3445

Bonner WD Jr, Slater EC (1970) Effect of antimycin on the potato mitochondrial cytochrome *b* system. Biochim Biophys Acta 223:349–358

Boyer WD, Romancier RM, Ralston CW (1971) Root respiration rates of four tree species grown in the field. For Sci 17:492–493

Burton WG (1950) Studies on the dormancy and sprouting of potatoes. I. The oxygen content of the potato tuber. New Phytol 49:121–134

Clarkson DT, Robards AW (1975) The endodermis, its structural development and physiological role. In: Torrey JJ, Clarkson DT (eds) The development and function of roots. Academic Press, New York London, pp 415–436

Cole ME, Solomos T, Faust M (1982) Growth and respiration of dormant flower buds of *Pyrus communis* and *Pyrus calleryana*. J Am Soc Hort Sci 107:226–231

Day DA, Arron GP, Laties GG (1980) Nature and control of respiratory pathways in plants: the interaction of cyanide-resistant respiration with the cyanide-sensitive pathway. In: Davies DD (ed) The biochemistry of plants. Academic Press, New York London, pp 197–241

Dizengremel P (1985) Potato respiration: electron transport pathways. In: Li P (ed) Potato physiology. Academic Press, New York London, pp 59–109

Goldstein AH, Anderson JO, McDaniel RG (1980) Cyanide-insensitive and cyanide-sensitive O_2 uptake in wheat. Plant Physiol 66:488–493

Goldstein AH, Anderson JO, McDaniel RG (1981) Cyanide-insensitive and cyanide-sensitive O_2 uptake in wheat. II. Gradient-purified mitochondria lack cyanide-insensitive respiration. Plant Physiol 67:594–596

Green DE, Mii S, Kohaut PM (1955) Studies on the terminal electron transport system. I. Succinic dehydrogenase. J Biol Chem 217:551–556

Grover SD, Laties GG (1978) Characterization of the binding properties of disulfiram, an inhibitor of cyanide resistant respiration. In: Ducet G, Lance C (eds) Plant mitochondria. Elsevier New York, pp 259–266

Hansen GK (1976) Adaptation to photosynthesis and diurnal oscillations of root respiration rates for *Lolium perenne*. Physiol Plant 39:275–279

Hausknecht EC, Funk MO (1984) The differential effect of disulfiram on lipoxygenases from *Glycine max*. Phytochemistry 23:1535–1539

Huq S, Palmer JM (1978) Superoxide and hydrogen peroxide production in cyanide resistant *Arum maculatum* mitochondria. Plant Sci Lett 11:351–358

Ikuma H, Bonner WD (1967) Properties of higher plant mitochondria. III. Effects of respiratory inhibitors. Plant Physiol 42:1535–1544

James TW, Spencer MS (1979) Cyanide-insensitive respiration in pea cotyledons. Plant Physiol 64:431–434

Janes HW, Chin CK (1981) The effect of age and growing conditions on cyanide resistance in culture tomato roots. Plant Sci Lett 23:307–313

Jensen WA (1962) Botanical histochemistry. Freeman, San Francisco

Johnson-Flanagan AM (1980) Rotenone-resistant respiration in mitochondria isolated from etiolated pea cotyledons. Thesis, Univ Alberta, Edmonton
Johnson-Flanagan AM (1984) Growth and development of styroplug white spruce [*Picea glauca* (Moench) Voss] seedling roots. Thesis, Univ Victoria
Johnson-Flanagan AM, Owens JN (1985a) Development of white spruce [*Picea glauca* (Moench) Voss] seedling roots. Plant Physiol 79:103–107
Johnson-Flanagan AM, Owens JN (1985b) Peroxidase activity in relation to suberization and respiration in white spruce [*Picea glauca* (Moench) Voss] seedling roots. Plant Physiol 79:103–107
Johnson-Flanagan AM, Owens JN (1986) Root respiration in white spruce [*Picea glauca* (Moench) Voss] seedlings in relation to morphology and environment. Plant Physiol 81:21–25
Johnson-Flanagan AM, Singh J (1986) Membrane deletion during plasmolysis in hardened and non-hardened plant cells. Plant Cell Environ 9:299–305
Johnson-Flanagan AM, Spencer MS (1981) The effect of rotenone on respiration in pea cotyledon mitochondria. Plant Physiol 68:1211–1217
Lahde E (1967) Studies on the respiration rate in the different parts of the roots systems of pine and spruce seedlings and its variation during the growth season. Acta For Fenn 81:5–24
Lambers H (1980) The physiological significance of cyanide-resistant respiration in higher plants. Plant Cell Environ 3:293–302
Lambers HS, van de Dijk SJ (1979) Cyanide-resistant root respiration and tap root formation in two subspecies of *Hypochaeris radiata*. Physiol Plant 45:235–239
Lambers H, Steingröver E (1978) Efficiency of root respiration of a flood-tolerant and flood-intolerant *Senecio* species as affected by low oxygen tension. Physiol Plant 42:179–184
Lambers H, Blacquiere T, Stuiver B (CEE) (1981) Interactions between osmoregulation and the alternative respiratory pathway in *Plantago coronopus* as affected by salinity. Physiol Plant 51:63–68
Laties GG (1974) Isolation of mitochondria from plant material. In: Fleischer S, Packer L (eds) Methods of enzymology, vol 31. Biomembranes. Academic Press, New York, pp 589–606
Ledig FT, Drew AP, Clark JG (1976) Maintenance and constructive respiration, photosynthesis and net assimilation rate in seedlings of pitch pine (*Pinus rigida* Mill). Ann Bot 40:289–300
Loomis WD (1974) Overcoming problems of phenolics and quinones in the isolation of plant membranes and organelles. In: Fleischer S, Packer L (eds) Methods of enzymology, vol 31. Biomembranes. Academic Press, New York, pp 528–553
Loughman BC (1960) Uptake and utilization of phosphate associated with respiratory changes in potato tubes slices. Plant Physiol 35:418–424
Miller MG, Obendorf RL (1981) Use of tetraethylthiuram disulphide to discriminate between alternative respiration and lipoxygenase. Plant Physiol 67:962–964
Neuburger M, Journet EP, Bligny R, Carde JP, Douce R (1982) Purification of plant mitochondria by isopycnic centrifugation in density gradients of Percoll. Arch Biochem Biophys 217:312–323
Palmer JM (1976) The organization and regulation of electron transport in mitochondria. Annu Rev Plant Physiol 27:133–157
Parrish DJ, Leopold AC (1977) Transient changes during soybean inhibition. Plant Physiol 59:1111–1115
Parrish DJ, Leopold AC (1978) Confounding of alternative respiration by lipoxygenase activity. Plant Physiol 62:470–472
Peterson CA, Edgington LV (1975) Uptake of the systemic fungicide methylo-2-benzimidazolecarbamate and the fluorescent dye PTS by onion roots. Phytopathology 65:1254–1259
Peterson CA, Emanuel ME, Humphreys GB (1981) Pathway of the movement of apoplastic fluorescent dye tracers through the endodermis at the site of secondary root formation in corn (*Zea mays*) and broad bean (*Vicia faba*). Can J Bot 59:618–625

Rich PR, Weigand NK, Blum H, Moore AL, Bonner WD Jr. (1978) Studies on the mechanism of inhibition of redox enzymes by substituted hydroxamic acids. Biochim Biophys Acta 525:325–337

Shingles RM, Arron GP, Hill RD (1982) Alternative pathway respiration and lipoxygenase activity in aged potato slice mitochondria. Plant Physiol 69:1435–1438

Siedow JN, Girvin ME (1980) Alternative respiratory pathway. Its role in seed respiration and its inhibition by propyl gallate. Plant Physiol 65:669–674

Slater EC (1969) Application of inhibitors and uncouplers for a study of oxidative phosphorylation. In: Estabrook RW, Pullman ME (eds) Methods of enzymology, vol 10. Academic Press, New York, pp 48–56

Solomos T, Malhotra SS, Prasad S, Malhotra AK, Spencer M (1972) Biochemical and structural changes in mitochondria and other cellular components of pea cotyledons during germination. Can J Biochem 50:725–737

Steingröver E (1981) The relationship between cyanide-resistant root respiration and the storage of sugars in the taproot in *Daucus carota* L. J Exp Bot 32:911–919

Szaniawski RK (1981) Growth and maintenance respiration of shoots and roots in Scots pine seedlings. Z Pflanzenphysiol 101:391–398

Tappel AL (1961) Biocatalysts: lipoxidase and hematin compounds. In: Lundberg WO (ed) Autoxidation and antioxidants, vol 1. Wiley, New York, pp 325–366

Theologis A, Laties GG (1978 a) Relative contribution of cytochrome-mediated and cyanide-resistant electron transport in fresh and aged potato slices. Plant Physiol 62:232–237

Theologis A, Laties GG (1978 b) Antimycin-insensitive cytochrome-mediated respiration in fresh and aged potato slices. Plant Physiol 62:238–242

Theologis A, Laties GG (1980) Membrane lipid breakdown in relation to wound-induced and cyanide-resistant respiration in tissue slices. Plant Physiol 66:690–896

Webb T, Armstrong W (1983) Effects of KCN and salicylhydroxamic acid on the root respiration of pea seedlings. Plant Physiol 72:280–286

Wiskich JT (1980) Controls of the Krebs cycle. In: Davies DD (ed) The biochemistry of plants, vol 2. Academic Press, New York London, pp 243–278

Water Vapor

Psychrometric Water Potential Analysis in Leaf Discs

D. M. Oosterhuis and S. D. Wullschleger

1 Introduction

The importance of water potential (ψ), and its components, in studies of plant-water relations is well recognized (Kramer 1983; Turner and Burch 1983). Although numerous methods are currently available for monitoring plant-water status, the use of thermocouple psychrometers for the determination of leaf ψ under both field and laboratory conditions is increasing (Walker et al. 1983; Bennett and Cortes 1985). Compared to other methods, the psychrometric technique can handle a large number of samples and also permit the determination of the components of ψ.

In spite of the widespread acceptance of thermocouple psychrometry, results have not always been satisfactory due to substantial variability in the ψ measurements. Considerable research has addressed the variability associated with the instrument itself including calibration, thermal gradients and equilibration times (Wiebe et al. 1971; Turner 1981; Savage and Cass 1984c). However, relatively few studies have addressed the techniques required during tissue sampling and the interpretation of results for accurate psychrometric measurement of ψ. This chapter addresses the precautions for sampling of leaf discs and methods of analysis for accurate and reliable psychrometric measurement of leaf ψ.

2 Theory of Thermocouple Psychrometers

2.1 Concepts of Water Potential

In the last 2 decades, significant advances have been made in the development of thermodynamic principles used to express the water relations of soil and plant tissue (Brown 1970; Wiebe et al. 1971; van Haveren and Brown 1972). These advances have made possible the quantitative description of water in natural systems using the concepts of free energy to account for changes in the water status of plants. The free energy of water in the soil-plant-atmosphere continuum influences both the movement of water along energy gradients and water availability in the plant. Application of these concepts has proven extremely meaningful, since the chemical potential of water and dissolved solutes greatly affects cell growth (van Haveren and Brown 1972).

The chemical potential of water is related to the change in the free energy of the system and can be expressed in terms of the partial water vapour pressure (Slatyer 1967). In an isothermal system the volumetric ψ (MPa) is given by the Kelvin equation:

$$\psi = (RT/Vw)\ln(e/e_0) , \qquad (1)$$

where R is the universal gas constant (8.3143×10^{-6} m^3 MPa mol^{-1} K^{-1}), T the absolute temperature (K), Vw the partial molar volume of pure water (1.805×10^{-5} m^3 mol^{-1}), and e and e_0 are the partial and saturated vapour pressures of water (relative humidity) at temperature T respectively (Slatyer 1967). The ratio e/e_0 gives the relative humidity of the air in the psychrometer chamber expressed as a fraction. Therefore, the ψ of a system can be determined if the equilibrium water vapour pressure (e/e_0) is measured at a known temperature and pressure. The thermocouple psychrometer is based upon this concept and upon the principle that the vapour pressure above a solution or segment of plant tissue is related to its water potential according to Eq. (1).

2.2 Principles of Operation

Two fundamental designs of thermocouple psychrometers have been used to determine water potential in plant tissues (Spanner 1951; Richards and Ogata 1958), and a number of modifications and advances have been suggested for both. The Spanner-type psychrometer, however, has certain advantages over the Richards and Ogata instrument (Barrs 1965; Zollinger et al. 1966; Brown 1970) and is more widely used.

The theory, design criteria and accuracy of the Spanner psychrometer have been extensively investigated (Rawlins 1966; Peck 1968, 1969; Wiebe et al. 1971; Brown and van Haveren 1972). The thermocouple is usually constructed from chromel and constantan wire of approximately 25-μm diameter (Wiebe et al. 1971) to meet the requirements of both high temperature sensitivity (Campbell et al. 1973) and small junctions. The typical Spanner psychrometer (Fig. 1) consists of a thermocouple sensing-junction (constantan-chromel) and two reference junctions (copper-constantan and copper-chromel) (Chow and de Vries 1973; Savage et al. 1981).

Three primary methods of using thermocouple psychrometers are currently available including the (1) psychrometric (Spanner 1951), (2) dew point (Campbell et al. 1973) and (3) isopiestic methods (Boyer and Knipling 1965). For the pschrometric method, a sample is sealed into the chamber, allowed to reach both temperature and vapour pressure euqilibrium and then the wet bulb temperature of the air in the chamber is measured relative to the dry bulb temperature. This method requires that water be condensed onto the sensing-junction by applying an electric cooling current (Wiebe 1984). This Peltier cooling current continues until the sensing-junction temperature is below the dew point temperature of the chamber air and water condenses on the thermocouple junction (Spanner 1951; Wiebe et al. 1971; Savage et al. 1981). When the current is discontinued, the droplet evaporates and the voltage output is monitored (Fig. 2). In the dew point method, the depression of the dew point temperature is measured and again related to the relative humidity within the chamber, and hence, to the ψ of the sample at the prevailing temperature (Rawlins 1966; Savage et al. 1981). The isopiestic variation is a null method of measurement in which the vapour pressure of a sucrose solution is balanced against the water potential of the sample (Boyer

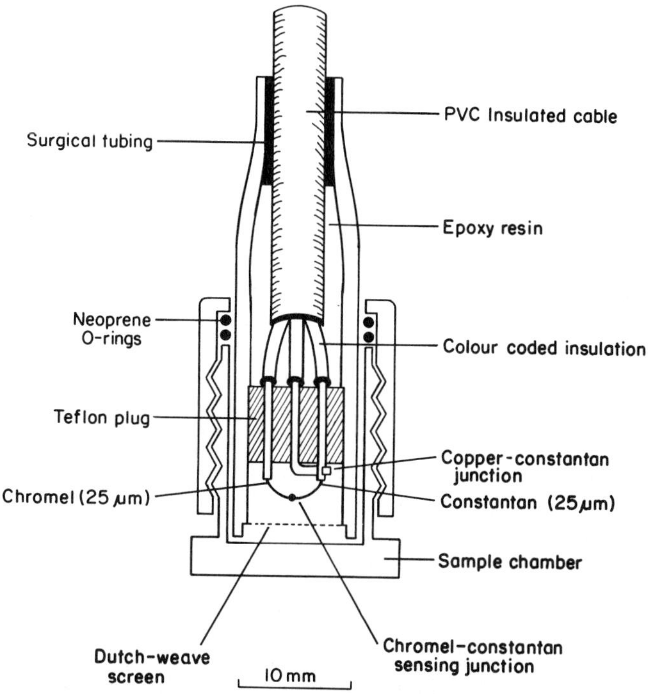

Fig. 1. Diagrammatic representation of a Spanner-type, end-window, thermocouple psychrometer used for measuring leaf-disc water potential

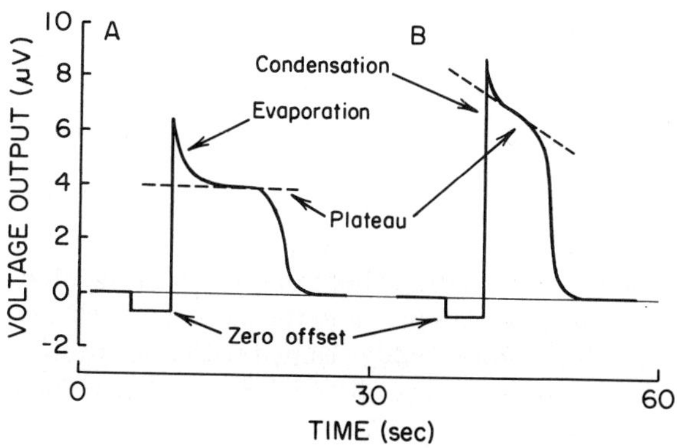

Fig. 2 A, B. A typical chart-recorder trace during the determination of a relatively high (**A**) and low (**B**) leaf-disc water potential

and Knipling 1965). The isopiestic and the dew point methods involve no net transfer of water once condensation has occurred.

Although each of these methods has its advantages, the psychrometric and dew point techniques are more widely used, with the former method being the more popular. Both techniques use identical sensors but different microvoltmeter circuitry. In this chapter, we use thermocouple psychrometer as a collective term for both thermocouple psychrometers and dew point hygrometers.

3 Types of Thermocouple Psychrometers

Many different psychrometer designs have been developed for leaf ψ measurement, and a number of these are commercially available (Oosterhuis 1987b). These include the end-window psychrometers, leaf-cutter psychrometers, and screen-caged psychrometers (all with sample chambers), the leaf in situ psychrometers, Wescor C-52 psychrometer, porous ceramic shield psychrometers, and a multi-chambered psychrometer apparatus. For a list of manufacturers see Appendix (p. 130). The majority of these instruments use either a leaf disc or a segment of leaf tissue for analysis of leaf ψ. In contrast, the leaf in situ psychrometer is attached directly to an intact leaf.

All the above psychrometers are generally used without modifications except for the leaf in situ psychrometer, which should be modified by insulating the housing assembly with a covering of foam insulation and reflective aluminium tape for temperature control (Oosterhuis et al. 1983; Savage et al. 1983). Special modifications, together with techniques and precautions to follow during construction and use of psychrometers have also been reported by a number of researchers (Manohar 1966a, b; Merrill et al. 1968; Brown 1970; Wiebe et al. 1971; Brown and van Haveren 1972; Campbell 1979; Walker et al. 1983).

Choice of the most appropriate psychrometer has often involved some uncertainty, mainly because of the range of different size psychrometers available, the cost thereof, and a lack of understanding of the sampling precautions and possible errors involved in measurement.

4 Psychrometric Method

4.1 Preparation of Psychrometers

Although the thermocouple junction is normally protected by a stainless steel housing (except in the in situ types), new psychrometers should be inspected to ensure that the thermocouple junction itself has not been damaged during shipment. Suspected defects in the circuit can be checked with the aid of a microvoltmeter. New psychrometers should also be thoroughly cleaned with a solution of boiling 10% acetone or a jet of steam to remove any oil or debris which may have accumulated during construction.

All psychrometers and sample chambers must be scrupulously cleaned before and after use by repeated flushing of the psychrometer and the sample chamber with deionized water. A directed stream of deionized water from a laboratory wash bottle will generally suffice. If possible, the psychrometer should also be periodically inspected under a dissecting microscope to check the cleanliness and the physical state of the thermocouple junction. The use of a detergent, such as Teepol, or steam may help to remove stubborn deposits. After being cleaned, the psychrometers and sample chambers should be partially dried with filterd, compressed air and then placed in an oven (35° C) for a few hours. After drying, the psychrometers should be allowed to cool to prevent possible condensation before being sealed and stored in their sample chambers or in clean plastic bags.

4.2 Calibration

Accurate calibration of thermocouple psychrometers is the fundamental step necessary for accurate, reliable and meaningful measurements of water potential and its components. Basic requirements are a constant temperature water bath (i.e. 25° or 30° C), an appropriate microvoltmeter, a graded series of standard NaCl or KCl solutions (i.e. 0.1, 0.3, 0.5, 0.7, and 1.0 mol kg^{-1}), filter paper (Whatman No. 1) cut to the appropriate disc size, and forceps. The procedure consists of placing a filter paper disc in the sample chamber of a previously cleaned psychrometer with the forceps. A small quantity of the appropriate standard solution, sufficient to saturate the filter paper, is added to the filter paper disc in the sample chamber with a syringe or eye dropper beginning with the most dilute calibration solution. The microvolt output (water potential) is then determined after a 4-h vapour pressure equilibration in a constant temperature water bath (see Sect. 4.3). Each standard is measured in turn after careful washing and drying of the psychrometers between measurements. A calibration curve is then constructed from conversion tables (Lang 1967) by which future measurements of the microvolt output can be converted to the equivalent leaf ψ. All psychrometers are thus individually calibrated within a range of ψ obtained from the standard solutions on filter paper discs. If a psychrometer is in constant use, it should be recalibrated every few months (Wiebe et al. 1971).

4.3 Measurement Procedure

After psychrometer selection, initial preparation and calibration, the actual measurement procedure involves tissue sampling, equilibration in an isothermal water bath and recording of the voltage output. The psychrometer-sample chamber assembly is placed in an isothermal water bath for an appropriate vapour pressure equilibration time (4 h is usually sufficient; see Sect. 4.4). The psychrometric mode is then used and water condensed on the measuring junction by applying a 5-mA Peltier cooling current for 15 s. These are the recommended and most widely used values; however, optimum cooling times and cooling currents may vary with the tissue and condition of measurement (Savage and Wiebe 1987). The voltage output should be monitored continuously during evaporation with an appropriate microvoltmeter (Merrill or Wescor) and a chart recorder (Bristow and de Jager 1980). Care is required in analysis of the voltage output plateau (Savage and Wiebe 1987) since it indicates the equilibrium ψ of the sample in the psychrometer chamber. The chart recorder allows an accurate and permanent record of the voltage output.

4.4 Temperature and Vapour Pressure Equilibration

Accurate ψ measurement depends on attaining thermal and vapour pressure equilibration between the sample and the air in the sample chamber surrounding the thermocouple junction (Spanner 1951; Nelsen et al. 1978). Precise equilibration to the water bath temperature is also important as the voltage output from the thermocouple is highly temperature-dependent (Wiebe et al. 1971). Working with wheat in screen-caged psychrometers, Walker et al. (1983) showed that thermal equilibration was achieved within 4 min of immersion in the water bath, and vapour equilibration within 4 h. They reported that an equilibration time of 4 h sufficed regardless of tissue water content or species. For leaf samples in metal chambers, reported equilibration times vary from 24 h to 1 h or less with the C-52 (King and Bush 1985), although the latter would seem to be inadequate (Talbot et al. 1975; Brown and Collins 1980; Phillips 1981; Walker et al. 1983). Equilibration times should be determined for each type of psychrometer under the particular environmental conditions that will be used. The C-52 (Wescor) and the multichambered SC-10A (Decagon) psychrometers were not designed for use in a water bath so use of a styrofoam box or a constant temperature room is recommended to ensure adequate temperature control. Special attention should be given to minimizing the psychrometer thermal gradients (see Sect. 7.7) as they can affect the ψ measurement.

Resistance of the cuticle-stomate system to water vapour diffusion between the substomatal cavity and the sensing-junction can affect the time for vapour pressure equilibration (Wullschleger and Oosterhuis 1987; Oosterhuis et al. 1988). Various techniques, including cuticular abrasion (removal or scarification of the epidermis), are effective in reducing the cuticular resistance to water vapour movement and, therefore, in reducing equilibration times (Savage et al. 1984; Wullschleger and Oosterhuis 1987). This abrasion can be important when working with leaves that have a particularly high cuticular resistance and when using in situ psychrometers (Savage and Cass 1984b). The main disadvantage of abrasion is an increase in sample variability.

5 Techniques for Sampling Leaf Discs

The use of leaf discs in ψ measurement provides a convenient and rapid method of sampling, particularly when small leaves or limited leaf material is available, and when uniform sample sizes are required. There are, however, certain disadvantages which will be addressed. The major considerations in sampling leaf discs for psychrometric measurement of ψ were recently reviewed by Oosterhuis and Wullschleger (1987). These include leaf selection within the plant or canopy, location on the leaf to be sampled, the size of the leaf disc and the method of excision, prevention of evaporative losses after excision and care in handling the leaf disc.

5.1 Leaf Selection for Tissue Sampling

Leaf samples are usually excised from leaves of uniform size and age, fully exposed to thc sun. Shaded leaves and leaves lower in the canopy are likely to have a less negative ψ than leaves higher up the plant and fully exposed to the sun because of the increasingly negative ψ which exists along the soil-plant-atmosphere continuum (Kramer 1983).

Any solutes, dust or exudations on the leaf surface will result in an excessively low ψ measurement with the psychrometric technique (Wiebe et al. 1971). Such surface accumulations can be removed by washing the leaf a few hours prior to sampling with deionized water and allowing it to dry. Some species, such as cotton, may continue to excrete salt while in the psychrometer chamber and thereby lower ψ values will be measured (Klepper and Barrs 1968), although this has not been a problem in our laboratory. If such complications are expected, however, the pressure chamber may be a preferable method. Any moisture on the leaf from dew or irrigation must also be carefully removed with absorbent paper prior to leaf sampling.

5.2 Location and Selection of Leaf-Disc Samples

Numerous precautions must be observed in relation to sample location on the leaf and selection of the tissue to be excised for the leaf disc. Gradients of leaf ψ have been shown to exist across leaves (Wiebe and Prosser 1977), and these gradients can be expected to increase as the evaporative demand increases and water stress develops. In cotton, for example, under a low evaporative demand the ψ of the cotton leaf varied from -1.22 MPa at the base of the leaf to -1.31 MPa near the tip (Fig. 3). Similarly, under a high evaporative demand, ψ of the cotton leaf varied from -1.62 MPa at the base of the leaf to -1.82 MPa near the tip (Oos-

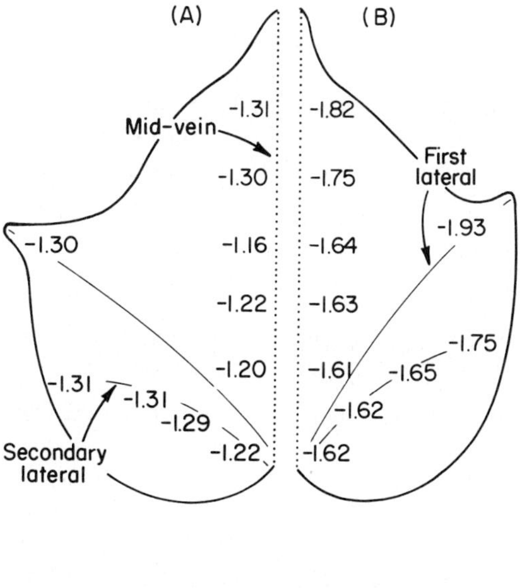

Fig. 3 A, B. Cotton leaf water potential gradients under low (**A**) and high (**B**) evaporative conditions (Oosterhuis and Wullschleger 1987)

Table 1. Effect of leaf veins on measured leaf water potential for cotton, corn and soybean (Oosterhuis and Wullschleger 1987)

Crop and sample location	Leaf water potential (MPa) and % of the control			
	Well-watered	(%)	Water-stressed	(%)
Cotton				
Interveinal	−1.04 (0.04)[a]	100	−1.66 (0.03)	100
Mid-vein	−0.80 (0.03)	77	−1.32 (0.08)	79
First lateral	−0.95 (0.04)	91	−1.41 (0.06)	85
Second lateral	−0.94 (0.05)	90	−1.55 (0.04)	93
Corn				
Interveinal	−0.74 (0.03)	100	−1.53 (0.04)	100
Mid-vein	−0.61 (0.04)	82	−1.37 (0.03)	89
Soybean				
Interveinal	−1.04 (0.03)	100	−1.57 (0.05)	100
Mid-vein	−1.00 (0.03)	96	−1.49 (0.04)	95

[a] ± Standard error of the mean.

terhuis and Wullschleger 1987). Hence, leaves should be sampled across the gradient to minimize sampling error.

The presence of leaf veins within the leaf disc can also influence the leaf ψ value. Inclusion of a mid- or lateral vein in leaf discs increases ψ compared to the interveinal disc ψ (Table 1). In addition, the error associated with inclusion of a vein in a leaf sample can increase under water-stress conditions. Ideally, in dicotyledonous plants, leaf discs should be sampled exclusively from interveinal areas, whereas in monocotyledonous plants, the mid-vein should be avoided.

5.3 Method of Leaf-Disc Excision

Leaf discs can be excised and placed in the psychrometer sample chamber with a number of devices. These include a standard laboratory cork-borer of the required diameter, a modified hole punch or a rapid disc-sampler (Wullschleger and Oosterhuis 1986). Although selection of a method for leaf-disc excision may seem a minor point, we have observed under laboratory conditions that leaf ψ can decrease at a rate of approximately 0.24 MPa min^{-1} between excision and insertion into a sample chamber. Similar observations by Brown (1976) led to the commercial development of the leaf-cutter psychrometer which enabled leaf discs to be conveniently sampled with a sharpened external housing. Whichever method is employed, the primary objective is to obtain a cleanly cut leaf-disc sample and to place it in the psychrometer sample chamber as quickly as possible.

5.4 Effects of Evaporative Losses

Since excision of plant tissue is inevitable when using leaf discs in thermocouple psychrometers, the error due to water evaporated from the disc, and the cut surfaces in particular, is of importance. Evaporative water losses during leaf excision can be the single most important factor contributing to errors in psychrometric leaf ψ determinations. The magnitude of these errors is related to the size of the leaf sample (Walker et al. 1984; Johnson et al. 1986) and the evaporative demand of the atmosphere at the time of excision. Losses after excision as large as 0.70 MPa min^{-1} have been reported by Savage and Cass (1984 a) for whole citrus leaves, and Walker et al. (1983) reported losses of 0.53 MPa min^{-1} for leaf sections of wheat. We have verified this loss by varying the time between excision and sealing into the sample chamber and also by following weight losses of leaf discs over time (Oosterhuis, unpublished data). These errors can be effectively minimized by conducting the leaf-disc sampling in a humidified box lined with saturated filter paper (Wiebe et al. 1971; Oosterhuis 1987 a), by rapid disc excision and sealing in the psychrometer sample chamber (less than 10 s) or simply by shading the leaf briefly during excision (Oosterhuis and Wullschleger 1987).

5.5 Use of Multiple Leaf Discs

More than one leaf disc per psychrometer has been used on occasion in psychrometric ψ measurement (Box 1965; Bennett and Cortes 1985; Oosterhuis and Wullschleger 1987). Brown (personal communication) used multiple leaf discs in the leaf-cutter psychrometer in order to fill the chamber volume and Bennett and Cortes (1985) showed an increased ψ with increased number of leaf discs. However, Oosterhuis and Wullschleger (1987) reported no significant advantage from one, two or five leaf discs stacked upon each other in the end-window psychrometer. More than one leaf disc is probably unnecessary provided the leaf disc is sufficiently large in relation to the size of the psychrometer chamber (see Sect. 7.4).

5.6 Handling of Leaf Discs

Damage to leaf discs during sampling can significantly influence the measured ψ (Table 2), with bruised samples having a lower ψ compared to controls, and slightly crushed or cut samples having a higher ψ. In corn for example, bruising resulted in a 26% or 0.27 MPa decrease in the measured ψ compared to the control, crushing caused a 17% or 0.17 MPa increase and slicing resulted in a 11% or 0.11 MPa increase (Oosterhuis and Wullschleger 1987). Higher ψ from sliced tissue has also been reported by Manohar (1966 a), Barrs and Kramer (1969), and Savage and Cass (1984 a). Crushed tissue could be expected to have an effect on ψ similar to that of slicing. Crushing and slicing of leaf tissue probably allows the remaining intact cells to actively accumulate solutes released from the ruptured cells. The diluted sap then diffused into the intact cells, raising their turgor poten-

Table 2. Effect of tissue damage on measured leaf water potential (Oosterhuis and Wullschleger 1987)

Condition of leaf disc	Leaf water potential (MPa) and % of the control					
	Cotton		Corn		Soybean	
	MPa	(%)	MPa	(%)	MPa	(%)
Control	−1.20 (0.04)[a]	100	−1.03 (0.06)	100	−1.22 (0.06)	100
Bruised	−1.49 (0.06)	124	−1.30 (0.07)	126	−1.24 (0.03)	102
Crushed	−0.78 (0.03)	65	−0.86 (0.05)	83	−0.88 (0.05)	72
1 cut	−0.97 (0.03)	81	−0.90 (0.06)	87	−0.82 (0.05)	67
4 cuts	−0.85 (0.01)	71	−0.92 (0.03)	89	−0.54 (0.04)	44

[a] ± Standard error of the mean.

tial and ψ (Barrs and Kramer 1969). The decrease in the ψ of bruised leaf discs is more difficult to explain but could be related to reduced turgor potential from disruption of internal cells.

Orientation of the leaf disc inside the sample chamber so that either the adaxial or abaxial surface faces the thermocouple measuring-junction apparently has no effect on the measured ψ regardless of stomatal densities, i.e. even with hypostomatous species (Oosterhuis, unpublished data). This consistency may be expected as stomates should close fairly rapidly under the dark conditions of the sample chamber and play little role in vapour transfer within sealed chambers.

6 Components of Leaf Water Potential

Measurement of leaf ψ alone does not reveal the relative importance of its constituent parts under conditions of water stress (Wiebe et al. 1971). The components of leaf ψ are subject to change, so ψ does not necessarily have a direct influence over certain plant processes, even though it may be related to them (Sinclair and Ludlow 1985; Bennett et al. 1987). A measure of the components of ψ, therefore, is necessary to fully understand and explain the nature of stress. However, the components of leaf ψ are probably the most difficult parameters to measure in studies of plant-water relations. These components, namely osmotic, turgor and matric potentials, represent the principal forces affecting the energy status of water in plant tissues (Brown 1972). Estimates of the components of leaf ψ may give some insight into the growth and development of plants and their response to stress (Oosterhuis and Walker 1982).

At equilibrium, the energy status of water in plant tissues can be described as the algebraic sum of a number of components acting on the water in the system. These occur as a result of the presence of solutes, hydrostatic pressure, matric surfaces and other variables:

$$\psi = \psi_s + \psi_p + \psi_m + \psi_g \,, \tag{2}$$

where ψ_s is the osmotic potential, ψ_p is turgor potential, ψ_m is matric potential and ψ_g is the gravitational component (van Haveren and Brown 1972). Sometimes an interaction term is included in the above equation to emphasize that the terms are interdependent (Brown 1972). The matric and gravitational components of Eq. (2) are usually regarded as negligible (Boyer 1968).

Osmotic potential is due to the presence of dissolved solutes and their attraction for cell water. The solution is retained within the cell by the plasmalemma and tonoplast, both semi-permeable membranes. Osmotic potential, which has a negative value because of the presence of solutes, decreases the free energy in the solution and can be measured by a number of methods which include use of the thermocouple psychrometer, vapour pressure osmometer and cryoscope. Measurement of ψ_s with thermocouple psychrometry is made after freezing the psychrometer assembly with the enclosed leaf sample in liquid nitrogen for 3 min and then allowing the assembly to thaw for about 30 min. This process effectively disrupts the cell membranes and eliminates the ψ_p of Eq. (2). Since ψ can be measured before and after freezing with thermocouple psychrometers, an estimate of both ψ_s and ψ_p is obtained. The magnitude of the ψ_s of cell sap is of both ecological and physiological interest, because this factor determines the degree of hydration of the cytoplasm (Warren Wilson 1967).

Turgor potential results from the difference between the internal hydrostatic pressure of the water against the cell membranes and the reference pressure (usually atmospheric pressure) (Taylor and Ashcroft 1972; Zimmermann 1977) and is estimated by subtracting ψ_s from ψ. Turgor potential is caused by the increase in volume of vacuolar sap which is opposed by an equal cell wall pressure (Zimmermann 1977). The value of ψ_p varies from zero in flaccid cells to the ψ_s in a fully turgid cell (Kramer 1983) so that, as plants begin to wilt, the value of turgor pressure approaches zero. Turgor pressure is important with respect to plant turgidity, cell enlargement, guard cell movements and other processes dependent on changes in cell volume (Kramer 1983). Thus, estimates of turgor potential are desirable and can be obtained with thermocouple psychrometers.

7 Interpretation of Psychrometric Water Potential Measurements

Accurate psychrometric measurement of leaf-disc ψ depends not only upon correct sampling and psychrometric procedures, but also upon the correct interpretation of data. Some of the more common and important sources of errors are discussed below.

7.1 Accuracy of Psychrometer Measurements

The accuracy and reliability of psychrometric measurements of leaf ψ have been demonstrated in many studies. Comparisons of psychrometers with Scholander-type pressure chambers for measurement of leaf ψ have generally exhibited close

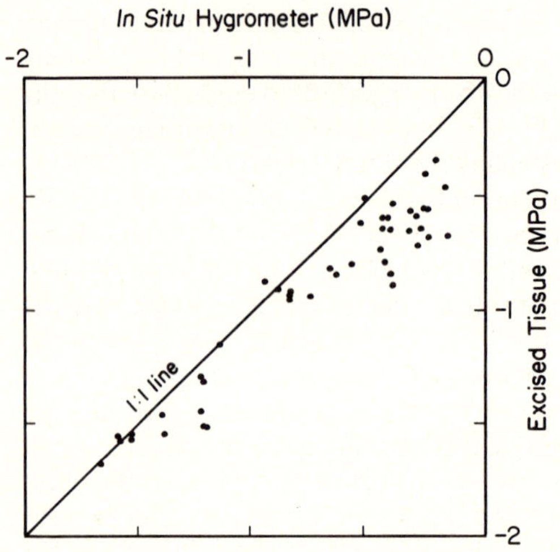

Fig. 4. Comparison of water potential measured using leaf discs in an end-window thermocouple psychrometer and in situ psychrometer. (Adapted by Campbell 1985 from Baughn and Tanner 1976)

agreement (West and Gaff 1971; Campbell and Campbell 1974; Walker et al. 1983). At high water potentials, the psychrometric ψ tends to be more negative than ψ measured with the pressure chamber, but as the ψ decreases, the pressure chamber values become more negative (Oosterhuis et al. 1983). Boyer (1967) suggested that the lower pressure chamber values may be due to resistance to water movement through the xylem towards the cut surface as a result of compression of the vascular tissue.

The accuracy of the psychrometer with excised leaf discs can also be assessed in comparison with other psychrometric measurements. Baughn and Tanner (1976) made such comparisons on intact and excised samples of soybean using leaf in situ psychrometers (Fig. 4). Their results indicated that psychrometric measurements on excised tissues were generally more negative than those of in situ values. Deviations from the 1:1 relationship were greatest at high water potentials with errors often exceeding 0.3 MPa. The most probable source of error for these consistently lower ψ values was that associated with evaporative water losses during sampling.

In a field comparison using five of the main commercially available thermocouple psychrometers to measure the leaf ψ of several crops (Oosterhuis, unpublished data), some differences were noted between the various psychrometers. These were attributed to the size of the tissue sample (Walker et al. 1984) and evaporative losses (Oosterhuis and Wullschleger 1987). The screen-caged psychrometer and the thermally insulated leaf in situ psychrometer most closely correlated with the pressure chamber measurements of ψ. Measurements of leaf ψ with the end-window and leaf-cutter types of psychrometer (both 5.5-mm-diameter discs) were similar but slightly more negative and variable than the larger screen-caged psychrometer (20×60 mm leaf section), while the C-52 sample chamber was the most variable of the psychrometers tested. In a subsequent test, a newer version of the end-window psychrometer with a larger 9.0-mm-diameter leaf disc provided a more accurate measure of leaf ψ than its smaller counterpart.

7.2 Types of Leaf Material

The nature of the leaf from which the disc is excised may require special sampling and psychrometric measurement procedures. Certain leaves with waxy cuticles may require the use of abrasion to reduce cuticular resistance and vapour pressure equilibration times. Species differences in equilibration time could also be expected. Water loss following sample excision will probably be greatest for succulent tissue and turgid leaf samples which could, therefore, exhibit a large decrease in ψ. These materials will require more care during disc sampling to reduce potentially high evaporative water losses.

7.3 Water Potential Changes Following Leaf-Disc Excision

Leaf ψ can rise within a few minutes after excision because xylem tension is released (Barrs and Kramer 1969). Thus, Wiebe et al. (1971) recommended that samples be punched directly from the attached leaves into the psychrometer chamber with only one sample being taken from each leaf. The leaf-cutter psychrometer was later developed by Brown (1976) with this concept in mind, as well as to reduce evaporative losses following excision. Savage and Cass (1984a) used leaf in situ psychrometers to confirm the immediate small, but transient, increase in leaf ψ after excision of the leaf petiole (Fig. 5). This was followed by a decrease in ψ dependent on the evaporative demand. The rapid decline in leaf ψ following excision suggests that leaf-disc ψ measurements, especially under conditions of high evaporative demand, will be in error if precautions are not taken to reduce evaporative losses after excision.

7.4 Leaf Tissue in Relation to the Size of the Sample Chamber

Tissue sample size can affect the measurement of leaf ψ (Barrs and Kramer 1969; Talbot et al. 1975; Walker et al. 1984), although results are inconclusive as to the optimal size which should be used with a particular psychrometer chamber volume (Bennett and Cortes 1985). The relative amount of the chamber volume occupied by leaf tissue and air is important as this introduces problems associated

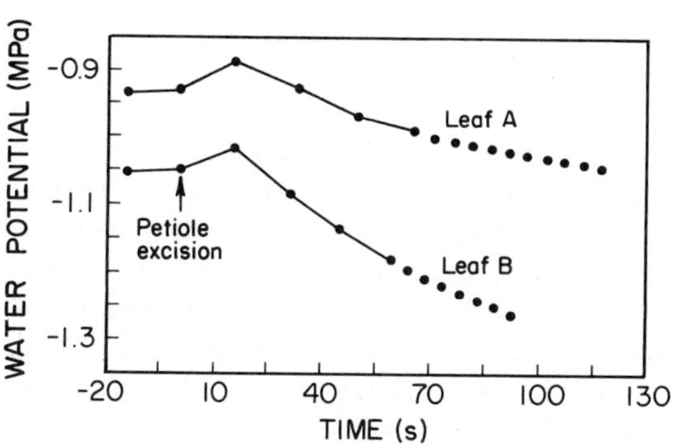

Fig. 5. Psychrometric field measurement of water potential changes following leaf excision (Savage and Cass 1984a)

with vapour pressure equilibration. Furthermore, Bennett and Cortes (1985) suggested that errors due to adsorption of water by the psychrometer assembly are negligible when sufficient tissue is used but significant with small volumes of tissue. As a general rule, the larger the volume of the psychrometer sample chamber, the larger the leaf material sample (R. W. Brown, personal communication); i.e. the chamber should be filled with as much leaf material as practically possible. This will also reduce the problems associated with sources and sinks of water vapour on the chamber walls (Wiebe et al. 1971).

Excessively small samples may require longer vapour pressure equilibration times because less tissue is available to contribute water vapour. Therefore, the size of the disc in relation to the size of the sample chamber should be as large as possible, and in some cases for large sample chambers, more than one leaf disc may be necessary. However, the configuration of the commercially available end-window and leaf-cutter psychrometers (Merrill) is such that one leaf disc fits across the width of the relatively small sample chamber in close proximity to the thermocouple junction, and therefore, a single leaf disc is usually sufficient.

7.5 Water Adsorption by Thermocouple Psychrometer Assemblies

The adsorption of water by thermocouple psychrometer assemblies is known to cause errors in the determination of water potential (Boyer 1972; Bennett and Cortes 1985). Dixon and Grace (1982) observed that many of the materials used in the construction of thermocouple psychrometers act as vapour sinks and adsorb much more water than required to saturate the volume of air within the sample chamber. Psychrometer chamber walls constructed of stainless steel adsorb small amounts of water (Boyer 1972; Campbell 1972; Dixon and Grace 1982). These authors also showed that rubber was a potentially strong vapour sink. For this reason, Bennett and Cortes (1985) suggested that the latex tubing used in some larger psychrometers may act as a strong vapour sink, as may the neoprene o-rings, used to form the water seal with the sample chamber in most psychrometers. Water adsorption problems will give erroneously low ψ values; however, these errors may be overcome by covering both the inside of the chamber and the neoprene o-rings with a thin coating of Vaseline (Boyer 1972).

7.6 The Cut Edge and Evaporative Losses During Sampling

The ratio of the cut surface area to the volume of the leaf sample (A/V ratio) has been used as a measure of the number of cells ruptured during excision relative to the number of cells remaining intact in the leaf sample (Talbot et al. 1975). This ratio has also been used to give an estimate of the effect of evaporation from the cut edge in relation to sample size on the value of ψ. Leaf samples with A/V values less than 0.2 $mm^2\ mm^{-3}$ resulted in psychrometric leaf ψ measurements that compared favourably with pressure chamber measurements (Walker et al. 1984). Leaf samples with A/V ratios of 0.15 $mm^2\ mm^{-3}$ have been used successfully (Nelsen et al. 1978), whereas samples with ratios of 0.3 $mm^2\ mm^{-3}$ (Barrs and

Kramer 1969) and 0.57 mm^2 mm^{-3} (Nelsen et al. 1978) resulted in ψ values that differed from those of larger leaf samples. Bennett and Cortes (1985) suggested that, in order to show the importance of the cut edge effect, the volume of tissue in the psychrometer must be kept constant as the cut surface to volume ratio is varied.

Most data suggest that the measured leaf ψ is higher in tissue having a high cut surface area to sample volume ratio (Macklon and Weatherley 1965; Barrs and Kramer 1969; Talbot et al. 1975; Nelsen et al. 1978), although Walker et al. (1984) reported the opposite. The latter result, however, may have been due to differences in tissue volume rather than the effects of the A/V ratio (Bennett and Cortes 1985). Nevertheless, the area of the cut surfaces represents a potential site for excessive evaporative losses, and the A/V ratio gives some indication of the possible extent of these losses. In general, using the largest possible leaf disc to fill the chamber will ensure that the A/V ratio is minimized and the effects of evaporative losses concomitantly reduced.

7.7 Thermal Gradients and Zero Offsets

Thermocouple psychrometers are typically placed in isothermal water baths to minimize temperature-related errors in ψ measurements. However, failure to understand and adequately quantify these errors can seriously affect the accuracy of experimental results. Temperature gradients within the psychrometer can arise from thermal fluctuations in the environment, heat produced by sample respiration and heating of the reference junctions during the Peltier cooling operation (Rawlins 1972). These gradients can introduce systematic error either through temperature differentials between the sensing-junction and the sample, or by causing temperature-induced zero offsets within the thermocouple measuring circuit.

Because thermocouple psychrometers measure the relative humidity of the air in equilibrium with the sample (see Sect. 2.1), any difference in temperature between the sample and chamber air will introduce significant error. This error results from the fact that the air in the chamber and the sample come to the same vapour pressure, not the same relative humidity (Rawlins 1972). The error in ψ introduced is approximately 7.77 MPa $°C^{-1}$ (Dixon and Tyree 1984). Commercial psychrometers which utilize leaf-disc samples do not currently allow for the measurement and correction of this error.

Temperature gradients between the references junction and the sensing-junction can cause additional errors in the measuring circuit which are ultimately included in the wet bulb temperature depression. These differences (zero offsets) are easily measured immediately prior to Peltier cooling (see Fig. 2). If zero offsets are stable with time, the measured voltage prior to cooling need only be compensated for to eliminate it from the measurement of water potential. Care should be taken to ensure that the zero offsets between the reference and sensing-junctions result in an output less than 0.5 μV prior to measurement (Walker et al. 1983). Equations are available for correcting these temperature gradients if so desired (Michel 1979; Brown and Bartos 1982).

Transient electrical zero offsets are another source of possible error in the use of thermocouple psychrometers. Dixon and Tyree (1984) working with dew point stem hygrometers reported that the zero offset of the Wescor HR-33T microvoltmeter was affected by the proximity to other electrical equipment and to human bodies. Poorly earthed equipment and the proximity of AC main cables to the hygrometer output leads were also found to cause significant zero offsets and errors in ψ. Shielding the wires did not eliminate the problem, but spatial isolation from other electrical equipment within at least a 2-m radius minimized these errors.

7.8 Problems Associated with Equilibration Times

Estimates of leaf ψ can be affected by the length of the vapour pressure equilibration time. Failure to achieve complete vapour equilibrium within the sample chamber due to an insufficient equilibration period can result in excessively low ψ measurements. In contrast, non-representative ψ values can also result from long equilibration times due to metabolic changes in the sample tissue (Macnicol 1976). Starch hydrolysis which occurs within the leaf tissue during the equilibration period and its contribution to the osmotic potential can be a major source of error. Recent evidence suggests that, although starch hydrolysis does occur in leaf-disc samples, the associated errors are typically less than 0.1 MPa (Bennett et al. 1986). However, care should be taken to minimize equilibration times particularly when sampling tissues are known to be high in starch.

Errors associated with equilibration times can also result from changes in cellular turgor which accompany growth when the leaf-disc tissue is separated from its water source (Campbell 1985). When an excised leaf sample of high turgor is placed in a psychrometer chamber, cell enlargement can occur during the equilibration process (Baughn and Tanner 1976). Without an adequate supply of water, this continued growth could decrease cell turgor pressure and, hence, the measured leaf ψ. This error is greatest when sampling from young, actively growing tissues, but is presumably of only minor concern with mature tissues.

Additional factors can also influence vapour pressure equilibration, not the least of which is the sample chamber material (Dixon and Grace 1982). Chambers with rubber seals or dirty or oxidized metal surfaces can display equilibration characteristics dominated by the chamber material. Another factor influencing equilibration is the cuticular resistance of the leaf sample (see Sect. 4.4).

7.9 Interpretation of the Psychrometer Output Plateau

Accurate determination of leaf ψ with thermocouple psychrometers requires reliable and accurate determination of the plateau voltage output (see Fig. 2). If the leaf sample has a relatively high ψ, then the plateau may be horizontal and easy to interpret. With drier samples, however, the plateau may become increasingly transient and interpretation more subjective (Savage and Wiebe 1987). Characteristics of the psychrometric output also depend on the circuitry of the microvoltmeter used and it is suggested that users consult the manufacturer concerning the specifics of their microvoltmeter. Although several approaches to determining the plateau can be used, the one most typically used is to extrapolate the plateau back to intersect the vertical line corresponding to the beginning of the evaporation period. The voltage corresponding to this intersection point is then used to calculate ψ. Caution should be exercised to ensure that identical methods of interpretation are used in psychrometer calibration and in the actual measurement of leaf sample ψ.

7.10 Considerations for Statistical Analysis

Variability in ψ measurements requires that relatively high sample and replication numbers be used. Some knowledge of the sources of variation is essential to determine the number of samples and replications required to achieve a given level of statistical precision for a given experiment and measurement technique. An understanding is required, therefore, of the sampling error due to instrument variation, leaf to leaf variation and plant variation to devise a sampling scheme (discs per leaf, leaves per plant and number of replications) that minimizes the variability, achieves maximum efficiency and gives the required precision. For example, total error (experimental + sampling) is significantly larger ($P<0.05$) for stressed than for well-watered wheat leaves (Johnson et al. 1986). Based on the mean total error for stress treatments only, a combination of replications or samples of about 12 per treatment was required to obtain a 95% confidence interval on a treatment of ± 0.50 MPa in wheat (Johnson et al. 1986). However, this may be expected to vary with species and should be considered for each experiment.

7.11 Consistency in Methodology

An underlying requirement often overlooked in psychrometric measurement of leaf disc ψ is the need for consistency in all sampling procedures from one sample to the next. This is of particular importance in the time delay between excision and sealing in the chamber, as well as in leaf selection, measurement and interpretation of results. Strict adherence to experimental protocol will greatly enhance the reproducibility of the data and will ensure more meaningful and reliable results with less variability.

8 Conclusion

Use of thermocouple psychrometers in plant-water relation studies demands that proper sampling techniques and precautions be adopted and results carefully analyzed to ensure accurate and reliable determinations of leaf ψ. In the past, results with psychrometers have not always been satisfactory or reliable due to poor sampling techniques and improper measurement procedures. The accuracy of results can be improved by prevention of excessive evaporative losses during tissue sampling and minimizing the time between excision and sealing in the psychrometer chamber. Attention should also be addressed to adjusting the leaf sample size to the characteristics of the psychrometer being used, to minimizing damage to the leaf tissue and to consistency in sample selection and handling during the sampling procedure. With good techniques and adequate precautions during sampling of leaf discs and careful interpretation of the recorded data, thermocouple psychrometers offer a convenient, accurate and reliable method of measuring leaf ψ.

Appendix

List of manufacturers of thermocouple psychrometers

Decagon Devices, Inc.
NW 115 State Street, Rm 211
Pullman, WA 99163, USA
(509) 332-2756

JRD Merrill Specialty Equipment
1105 West 2200 South
Logan, UT 84321, USA
(801) 752-8403

Wescor, Inc.
459 South Main Street
Logan, UT 84321, USA
(801) 752-6011

References

Barrs HD (1965) Comparison of water potential in leaves as measured by two types of thermocouple psychrometers. Aust J Biol Sci 18:36–52

Barrs HD, Kramer PJ (1969) Water potential increase in sliced leaf tissue as a cause of error in vapor phase determinations of water potential. Plant Physiol 44:959–964

Baughn JW, Tanner CB (1976) Excision effects on leaf water potential of five herbaceous species. Crop Sci 16:184–190

Bennett JM, Cortes PM (1985) Errors in measuring water potentials of small samples resulting from water adsorption by thermocouple psychrometer chambers. Plant Physiol 79:184–188

Bennett JM, Cortes PM, Lorens GF (1986) Comparison of water potential components measured with a thermocouple psychrometer and a pressure chamber and the effects of starch hydrolysis. Agron J 78:239–244

Bennett JM, Sinclair TR, Muchow RC, Costello SR (1987) Dependence of stomatal conductance on leaf water potential, turgor potential, and relative water content in field-grown soybean and maize. Crop Sci 27:984–990

Box JE (1965) Measurement of water stress in cotton plant leaf discs with a thermocouple psychrometer. Agron J 57:367–370

Boyer JS (1967) Leaf water potential measured with a pressure chamber. Plant Physiol 42:133–137

Boyer JS (1968) Relationship of water potential to growth of leaves. Plant Physiol 43:1056–1062

Boyer JS (1972) Use of the isopiestic technique in thermocouple psychrometry III. Application to plants. In: Brown RW, Haveren BP van (eds) Psychrometry in water relations research. Agric Exp Stn, Utah State Univ, Logan, Utah, p 220

Boyer JS, Knipling EB (1965) Isopiestic technique for measuring leaf water potentials with a thermocouple psychrometer. Proc Natl Acad Sci USA 54:1044–1051

Bristow KL, de Jager JM (1980) Leaf water potential measurements using a strip chart recorder with the leaf psychrometer. Agric Metereol 22:149–152

Brown RW (1970) Measurement of water potential with thermocouple psychrometers: construction and application. USDA For Ser Res Pap INT-80:27 pp

Brown RW (1972) Determination of leaf osmotic potential using thermocouple psychrometers. In: Brown RW, Haveren BP van (eds) Psychrometry in water relations research. Agric Exp Stn, Utah State Univ, Logan, Utah, p 198

Brown RW (1976) New technique for measuring the water potential of detached leaf samples. Agron J 68:432–434

Brown RW, Bartos DL (1982) A calibration model for screen-caged Peltier thermocouple psychrometers. USDA For Ser Res Pap INT-293:24 pp

Brown RW, Collins JM (1980) A screen-caged thermocouple psychrometer and calibration chamber for measurement of plant and soil water potential. Agron J 72:851–854

Brown RW, Haveren BP van (eds) (1972) Psychrometry in water relations research. Agric Exp Stn, Utah State Univ, Logan, Utah, pp 342

Campbell EC (1972) Vapor sink and thermal gradient effects on psychrometer calibration. In: Brown RW, Haveren BP van (eds) Psychrometry in water relations research. Agric Exp Stn, Utah State Univ, Logan, Utah, p 94

Campbell EC, Campbell GS, Barlow WK (1973) A dew point hygrometer for water potential measurement. Agric Meteorol 12:113–121

Campbell GS (1979) Improved thermocouple psychrometers for measurement of soil water potential in a temperature gradient. J Phys E Sci Instrum 12:739–743

Campbell GS (1985) Instruments for measuring plant water potential and its components. In: Marshall B, Woodward FI (eds) Instrumentation for environmental physiology. Soc Exp Biol Ser 22. Cambridge Univ Press, p 193

Campbell GS, Campbell MD (1974) Evaluation of a thermocouple hygrometer for measuring leaf water potential in situ. Agron J 66:24–27

Chow TL, de Vries J (1973) Dynamic measurement of soil and leaf water potential with a double loop Peltier type thermocouple psychrometer. Soil Sci Soc Am Proc 37:181–188

Dixon MA, Grace J (1982) Water uptake by some chamber materials. Plant Cell Environ 5:323–327

Dixon MA, Tyree MT (1984) A new stem hygrometer, corrected for temperature gradients and calibrated against the pressure bomb. Plant Cell Environ 7:693–697

Haveren BP van, Brown RW (1972) The properties and behavior of water in the soil-plant-atmosphere continuum. In Brown RW, Haveren BP van (eds) Psychrometry in water relations research. Agric Exp Stn, Utah State Univ, Logan, Utah, p 1

Johnson RC, Ntuyen HT, McNew RW, Ferris DM (1986) Sampling error for leaf water potential measurements in wheat. Crop Sci 26:380–383

King MJ, Bush LP (1985) Growth and water use of tall fescue as influenced by several soil drying cycles. Agron J 77:1–4

Klepper B, Barrs HD (1968) Effects of salt secretion on psychrometric determination of water potential of cotton leaves. Plant Physiol 43:1138–1140

Kramer PJ (1983) Water relations of plants. Academic Press, New York London, pp 489

Lang ARG (1967) Osmotic coefficients and water potentials of sodium chloride solutions from O° to 40° C. Aust J Chem 20:2017–2023

Macklon AES, Weatherley PE (1965) A vapour-pressure instrument for the measurement of leaf and soil water potential. J Exp Bot 16:261–270
Macnicol PK (1976) Rapid metabolic changes in the wounding response of leaf discs following excision. Plant Physiol 57:80–84
Manohar MS (1966a) Effect of the excision of leaf tissue on the measurement of their water potential with thermocouple psychrometer. Experientia 27:386–387
Manohar MS (1966b) Measurement of the water potential of intact plant tissue. 1. Design of a microthermocouple psychrometer. J Exp Bot 17:44–50
Merrill SD, Dalton FN, Herkelrath WN, Hoffman GJ, Igvalson RD, Oster JD, Rawlins SL (1968) Details of construction of a multipurpose thermocouple psychrometer. USDA Salinity Lab Res Rep 115, pp 9
Michel BE (1979) Correction of thermal gradient errors in stem thermocouple hygrometers. Plant Physiol 63:221–224
Nelsen CE, Safir GR, Hanson AD (1978) Water potential in excised leaf tissue: comparison of a commercial dew point hygrometer and thermocouple psychrometer for in situ measurement of soybean, wheat and barley. Plant Physiol 61:131–133
Oosterhuis DM (1987a) A technique to measure the components of root water potential using screen-caged thermocouple psychrometers. Plant Soil 103:285–288
Oosterhuis DM (1987b) Types of thermocouple psychrometers used for leaf water potential measurement. SA Waterbull 13(3):20–23
Oosterhuis DM, Walker S (1982) Field measurement of leaf water potential components using thermocouple psychrometers. 2. Application in plant water relation studies in wheat. Proc Crop Prod Soc S Afr 11:5–8
Oosterhuis DM, Wullschleger SD (1987) The use of leaf discs in thermocouple psychrometers for measurement of water potential. In: Proc Int Conf Measurement of soil and plant water status, vol 2. Utah State Univ, Logan, Utah, p 77
Oosterhuis DM, Savage MJ, Walker S (1983) Field use of in situ leaf psychrometers for monitoring water potential of a soybean crop. Field Crops Res 7:237–248
Oosterhuis DM, Parker ML, Wullschleger SD, Kim KS (1988) The citrus leaf cuticle in relation to measurement of leaf water potential using thermocouple psychrometers. Plant Cell Environ 11:129–135
Peck AJ (1968) Theory of the Spanner psychrometer. 1. The thermocouple. Agric Meteorol 5:433–447
Peck AJ (1969) Theory of the Spanner psychrometer. 2. Sample effects and equilibration. Agric Meteorol 6:111–124
Phillips DL (1981) End-point recognition in pressure chamber measurements of water potential of *Vigniera porteri* (Asteraceae). Ann Bot 48:905–907
Rawlins SL (1966) Theory for thermocouple psychrometers used to measure water potential in soil and plant samples. Agric Meteorol 3:293–310
Rawlins SL (1972) Theory of thermocouple psychrometers for measuring plant and soil water potential. In: Brown RW, Haveren BP van (eds) Psychrometry in water relations research. Agric Exp Stn, Utah State Univ, Logan, Utah, p 25
Richards LA, Ogata G (1958) Thermocouple for vapour pressure measurements in biological and soil systems at high humidity. Science 128:1089–1090
Savage MJ, Cass A (1984a) Psychrometric field measurement of water potential changes following leaf excision. Plant Physiol 74:94–98
Savage MJ, Cass A (1984b) Measurement of water potential using in situ thermocouple hygrometers. Adv Agron 37:73–126
Savage MJ, Cass A (1984c) Measurement errors in field calibration of in situ leaf psychrometers. Crop Sci 24:371–372
Savage MJ, Wiebe HH (1987) Voltage endpoint determination for thermocouple psychrometers and the effect of cooling time. Agric For Meteorol 39:309–317
Savage MJ, Cass A, de Jager JM (1981) Calibration of thermocouple hygrometers. Irrig Sci 2:113–125
Savage MJ, Wiebe HH, Cass A (1983) In situ field measurement of water potential using thermocouple psychrometers. Plant Physiol 73:609–613

Savage MJ, Wiebe HH, Cass A (1984) Effect of cuticular abrasion on thermocouple psychrometric in situ measurement of leaf water potential. J Exp Bot 35:36–42
Sinclair TR, Ludlow MM (1985) Who taught plants thermodynamics? The unfulfilled potential of plant water potential. Aust J Plant Physiol 12:213–217
Slatyer RO (1967) Plant-water relationships. Academic Press, New York London, pp 366
Spanner DC (1951) The Peltier effect and its use in the measurement of suction pressure. J Exp Bot 11:145–168
Talbot AJB, Tyree MT, Dainty J (1975) Some notes concerning the measurement of water potentials of leaf tissue with specific reference to *Tsuga canadensis* and *Picea abies*. Can J Bot 53:784–788
Taylor SA, Ashcroft GL (1972) Physical edaphology: the physics of irrigation and nonirrigation soils. Freeman, San Francisco, pp 533
Turner NC (1981) Techniques and experimental approaches for the measurement of plant water status. Plant Soil 58:339–366
Turner NC, Burch GJ (1983) The role of water in plants. In: Teare ID, Peet MM (eds) Crop-water relations. Wiley, New York, p 73
Walker S, Oosterhuis DM, Savage MJ (1983) Field use of screen-caged thermocouple psychrometers in sample chambers. Crop Sci 23:627–632
Walker S, Oosterhuis DM, Wiebe HH (1984) Ratio of cut surface area to leaf sample volume for water potential measurements by thermocouple psychrometers. Plant Physiol 75:228–230
Warren Wilson J (1967) The components of leaf water potential. 1. Osmotic and matric potential. Aust J Biol Sci 20:329–347
West DW, Gaff DF (1971) An error in the calibration of xylem water potential against leaf water potential. J Exp Bot 22:342–346
Wiebe HH (1984) Water condensation on Peltier-cooled thermocouple psychrometers. Agron J 76:166–168
Wiebe HH, Prosser RJ (1977) Influence of temperature gradients on leaf water potential. Plant Physiol 59:256–258
Wiebe HH, Campbell GS, Gardner WH, Rawlins SL, Cary JW, Brown RW (1971) Measurement of plant and soil water status. Utah State Univ Bull 484, pp 71
Wullschleger SD, Oosterhuis DM (1986) A rapid leaf-disc sampler for psychrometric water potential measurements. Plant Physiol 81:684–685
Wullschleger SD, Oosterhuis DM (1987) Electron microscope study of cuticular abrasion on cotton leaves in relation to water potential measurements. J Exp Bot 38:660–667
Zimmermann U (1977) Cell turgor pressure regulation and turgor pressure-mediated transport processes. In: Jennings DH (ed) Integration of activity in the higher plant. Cambridge Univ Press, London, p 117
Zollinger WD, Campbell GS, Taylor SA (1966) A comparison of water-potential measurements made using two types of thermocouple psychrometers. Soil Sci 102:231–239

In Situ Measurement of Plant Water Potential

N. L. Schaefer

1 Introduction

1.1 Background

The majority of studies on plant water relations use excised material for the estimation of water potential (ψ). However in situ techniques which make measurements directly on the plant have much to recommend them, particularly if other associated observations are also considered. In situ methods are basically non-destructive and this allows single plants to be used. Individual variation is thereby eliminated for a given run of measurements and correlations with other parameters on the same plant are improved, with the result that smaller changes in ψ become more significant. In situ techniques have the capability of continuous monitoring which means that rapidly fluctuating behaviour can be observed that might otherwise have remained undetected, or have been attributed to errors in technique where spot measurements are taken. Continuous recording of ψ in conjunction with other electronically gathered information allows parameters that are physiologically important to be calculated and displayed by computer. Results standardized for extraneous environmental data can be delivered in a "real-time" framework to the researcher permitting him to make decisions during the running of the experiment. Manpower requirements are also reduced and measurements at inconvenient times and locations are not jeopardized.

1.2 Measurement Theory

The concept of ψ and its measurement have origins in both soil physics and botany (Slatyer 1967) as similar principles apply to the behaviour of water in either soil or plants. Water potential is akin to potential energy and in thermodynamic terms is considered a state function. It is similar to the chemical potential of water except that it is expressed on a per unit volume basis. It is defined as:

$$\psi = (u_1 - u_0)/V_w \,, \tag{1}$$

where u is the chemical potential of the water under study (1) or some reference condition (0). Its units are in energy per unit volume (Jm^{-3}) or pressure (MPa).

The chemical potential of water can be written as the sum of a number of components to express the effects of hydrostatic pressure, dissolved solutes and gravity:

$$u_1 - u_0 = V_w(p_1 - p_0) - V_w RT \ln a_1/a_0 + M_w g(h_1 - h_0) \,, \tag{2}$$

where p is pressure, T is absolute temperature, a is chemical activity and h is height. These then contribute to the overall water potential such that:

$$\psi = p - \pi + \varrho g h \ , \tag{3}$$

where π is the osmotic pressure and ϱ is the density of the liquid water.

Knowledge of ψ is often the first step in determining π or p indirectly so that non-equilibrium processes such as growth or transport can be investigated. For example, volumetric flow (J_v) can be described in terms of hydraulic conductivity (L_p) and reflection coefficients (σ):

$$J_v = L_p(p - \sigma\pi) \ , \tag{4}$$

where p and π rather than ψ itself are the immediate driving forces (Katchalsky and Curran 1975).

1.3 Measurement Methods

Ideally, an observer wishes to make as little disturbance to the plant as possible. However, there are as yet no direct means by which ψ can be measured remotely. Techniques such as infrared thermometry rely on a correlation between ψ and some other parameter such as stomatal resistance which can change in an unpredictable fashion.

Current methods all involve some form of close contact between plant and instrument and can be seen in terms of two steps: (1) exchange of water between the plant and an enclosed chamber with defined conditions and (2) measurement of the water activity within the chamber. The two phases of water under ambient conditions (vapour or liquid) give rise to two general categories of techniques based on the form of water transfer in step 1. In this chapter, vapour transfer methods only will be treated.

2 Vapour Transfer Methods

2.1 Introduction

Whilst there have been many different early methods, the range of techniques in use today is much reduced, as is evidenced by the advent of commercially available hygrometers in only a limited variety of styles. This has meant with few exceptions that psychrometric and dew point methods now dominate the field. For this reason greater emphasis will be given to these techniques. Savage and Cass (1984) have reviewed some of the Peltier cooled versions of in situ hygrometers, whilst Oosterhuis describes excised tissue techniques in this volume. Earlier work has been summarized in Slavik (1974). Brown and van Haveren (1972) are considered a standard reference in the area of psychrometric ψ determination.

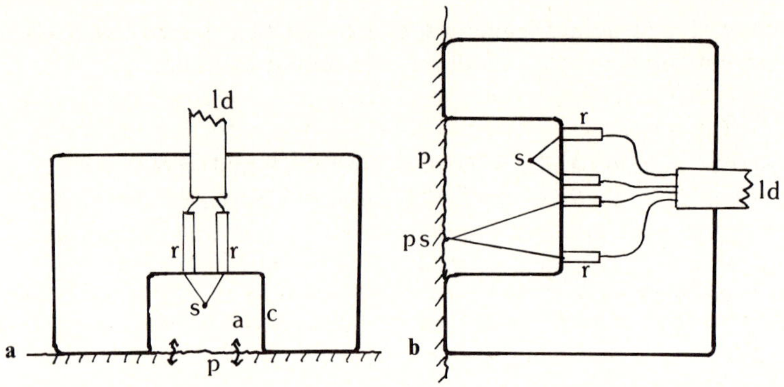

Fig. 1. a A hygrometer attached to plant (*p*) that confines an atmosphere (*a*) within the chamber cavity (*c*). Water vapour exchange between plant and chamber is indicated by *arrows*. A sensor (*s*), wetted at the apical junction, projects into the chamber. Here, the sensor consists of a thermocouple with two reference junctions (*r*) joined to a lead (*ld*) that takes the signal back to a meter. **b** As in **a**, but with an additional plant sensor (*ps*) to measure plant temperature. This can be read as a difference signal between (*ps*) and (*s*) to indicate the presence of temperature gradients from plant to sensor

2.2 General Principles

All vapour transfer techniques essentially measure the humidity of an enclosed space by observing some characteristic of a droplet of water that is free to exchange moisture with the confined atmosphere (Fig. 1 a). Once equilibrium has been achieved the water potential of the liquid phase can be expressed in terms of the partial pressure c according to Raoult's law (e = k a) and Eq. (2), neglecting pressure and gravitational effects in the vapour phase of the chamber:

$$\psi = \frac{RT}{V_w} \ln e_1/e_0 = \frac{RT}{V_w} \ln \frac{\% RH}{100} \quad . \tag{5}$$

For the range of water potentials found in most plant tissue (0 to −3.0 MPa) this corresponds to relative humidities of 100 to 97.1% at 25° C. This very compressed range necessitates techniques of extreme precision and points to the high degree of control needed in making ψ measurements, particularly in the usually more variable environment in which in situ techniques are employed.

2.3 Practical Aspects

Water Vapour Pressure. Ideally within the hygrometer, water vapour only moves between plant interior, chamber and sensing droplet. Other parts such as the interior lining of the cavity must not absorb or release significant amounts of water. It has been found that glass, epoxy or latex rubber are not suitable construction materials, whereas Teflon, brass, silver, stainless steel or resolidified paraffin wax are acceptible. Cleanliness is very important as small quantities of salts or solutes can absorb and release water. Corrosion spots also act as vapour sinks. In addition, the inside should be polished to reduce the effective surface area for absorption. The exterior cuticle of the plant can act as a sink for water vapour once it moves from the drier outside atmosphere to that of the enclosed, more humid chamber (Rawlins 1972). Some plants secrete salts and other solutes onto the surface of the leaf, etc. and this can spuriously depress measured ψ values (Klepper and Barrs 1968).

Temperature. Adequate control of temperature is perhaps the most difficult aspect of in situ ψ measurement. In many cases it operates via its effect on e_0. A 1° temperature difference between liquid and vapour phases is equivalent to approximately 8.0 MPa (Spanner 1951; see below). If an accuracy of 0.01 MPa is required then temperature control needs to be within approximately 0.001° C. Because of the high relative humidities found within the hygrometer, care must be taken to ensure that even slightly cold areas do not develop and form dew from the chamber atmosphere, thereby lowering the vapour pressure. Ideally, all parts of the hygrometer and enclosed plant part should operate isothermally ($T_a = T_p = T_c = T_r$, Fig. 1 a), the only exception being the sensor droplet.

Whilst temperature itself does influence ψ measurement, errors introduced by the choice of an incorrect value are usually far less severe than those due to thermal gradients within the hygrometer. Similarly, slow changes in temperature, even if large in amplitude, are less disruptive than rapid transients which do not allow heat to distribute itself evenly throughout the hygrometer. Internal thermal gradients can arise from external sources such as uneven heat radiation (e.g. sunshine) or advection (e.g. cool breezes). Approaches to the problem usually include one of the following aims:

1. To exclude thermal transients with insulation and materials of high thermal density (copper, aluminium, brass);
2. To dissipate internal gradients with good thermal conductors (silver, copper, brass);
3. To improve heat redistribution by reducing hygrometer size;
4. To exclude heat radiation with reflective foil.

Circulating water from a thermostatted reservoir can be used to maintain temperature in the laboratory (Boyer 1968). In the field temperature fluctuations may be damped by passing water through the hygrometer from a large underground tank (McBurney and Costigan 1987).

Within the hygrometer Barrs (1964) has shown that the heat of plant respiration can elevate the air temperature so that ψ estimates are invalidated. The problem is most acute in hygrometers where a large proportion of the inside chamber wall is covered with the plant sample such as a leaf ($T_p = T_a > T_r = T_c$, Fig. 1 a). Heat sinking the leaf with wire gauze to the chamber, using a smaller percentage area of sample or monitoring the actual air temperature, overcomes this problem.

Where isothermality cannot be guaranteed, a precise and sensitive temperature sensor should monitor the surface of the plant within the hygrometer (T_p), so that temperature gradients can be detected (Calissendorf 1970; Dixon and Tyree 1984; Fig. 1 b). If present, a correction can be made by adding the quantity $L_v \Delta T/T$ to the measured value of ψ, where L_v is the latent heat of vapourization of water and ΔT is the temperature difference between chamber atmosphere and plant surface ($T_a - T_p$). At 25° C the correction factor is 8.16 MPa $°C^{-1}$.

Attachment Precautions. It is not possible to attach the hygrometer to the plant without upsetting its water relations to some extent. This disturbance can be seen in terms of global and local effects. Global effects come from changes to the plant environment such as shading, heat from equipment and interference with air movement. Under closed conditions the investigator himself can alter humidity and CO_2 concentration and thereby perturb plant water relations via effects on stomata.

Local changes are created under or within the hygrometer and usually operate through an effect on osmotic pressure of the extracellular fluid. The hygrometer is likely to upset metabolism because the light regime is changed, respiration is impaired through lack of oxygen or the tissue has been wounded by abrasion or solvent action. Any of these can provoke leakage of solutes out of cells and hence influence the osmotic component of ψ under the sensor.

The largest potential interference by the hygrometer comes from its blocking of transpiration or water flow under the probe. The magnitude of the effect will depend on the local resistance through which the water was flowing prior to attachment ($\Delta\psi = J_v R$). If R is large, then the change in ψ will also be large. At any point in the plant away from the hygrometer, the disturbance in ψ will be moderated by the size of other water flows through that point.

Sealants. A seal needs to be made between plant and hygrometer to confine the movement of water vapour within the chamber (Fig. 1 a). This can take the form of a neoprene O-ring, a compound such as petrolatum, Vaseline, Apiezon grease or a 1:1 mixture of paraffin wax and lanolin. After prolonged use (>5 h) some sealants (e.g. Vaseline) can spread into the section of the plant under the sensor and this can impair diffusion of water vapour between the plant and chamber.

Plant to Sensor Communication. Vapour transfer techniques usually measure ψ of the extracellular fluid directly under the hygrometer. In most cases, however, there is a resistance to water movement between the two phases at the plant surface because stomates are likely to be closed and the remainder of the surface is usually covered with a waxy, hydrophobic cuticle. In early work (Barrs 1965 a), where the epidermis was left intact, several hours were needed for equilibration. Concern was then raised about local biochemical changes in the imprisoned plant part. Neumann and Thurtell (1972) removed the cuticle with organic solvents such as xylene, although in some plant species the underlying tissue can be damaged. Abrasion with fine (50 μm) carborundum (Turner et al. 1984) or emery powder (#800–#600) in a slurry (Baughn and Tanner 1976 b) or impregnated in paper has also been used (Schaefer et al. 1986). Whilst it is probably possible to selectively scratch the cuticle of plants such as *Citrus* (Savage et al. 1984), with more mesophytic plants some damage to the epidermal and even mesophyll cells is inevitable. In this case it is essential to remove cell debris and solutes by rinsing thoroughly with distilled water followed by blotting with absorbent paper tissue. In some species such as soybeans, too vigorous a treatment can lead to necrosis (Pallas and Michel 1978). For others (e.g. *Tradescantia, Carthamus*) it is possible to lower the surface resistance by peeling off the epidermis. Maintaining the stomates open with the fungal toxin fusicoccin has been tried with partial success in wheat, but possible problems with redistribution of the compound call for caution (Schaefer et al. 1986).

For in situ work it is important to know the speed with which vapour equilibration occurs when attempting to measure ψ, especially when these might be changing with time. Peck (1969) considered factors such as the resistance of the plant (r, s cm^{-1}), surface area exchanging water vapour (A, cm^2) and volume of the chamber (V, cm^3) to calculate the time (t, s) to reach within a given increment of the equilibrium ψ (d, MPa) if the initial humidities of the plant and chamber atmosphere were h_p and h_c (%) respectively:

$$t = rV/A \ln [(100\ RT/V_w d)(h_c - h_p)] \ . \tag{6}$$

For large chambers and non-scarified plant material used in earlier work, V/A might be 3.0 cm so that "t" would be greater than 60 min, as observed by Barrs (1965a). Smaller chambers of the kind used today (e.g. the Wescor L-51 leaf hygrometer) with V/A = 0.1 cm have calculated approach times of less than 10 s if the surface resistance is kept low (e.g. 10 s cm^{-1}; Savage and Cass 1984). Lambert and van Schilfgaarde (1965) theorize that the delay due to diffusion across the chamber itself is likely to be small (about 100 s) even for large chambers (V/A = 2.0 cm).

3 Psychrometry

3.1 Principles

The measurement of humidity, through its effect on evaporative cooling, is known as *psychrometry* (Greek psychros, cold). The term usually applies to wet bulb depression methods, whilst dew point methods are treated separately. As the extent of such cooling is related to the humidity (or vapour pressure and temperature) of the air, it is possible to determine the water potential directly from Eq. (5). Wet bulb depression implies the measurement of two temperatures, one of the wetted thermometer and the other of the bulk air. Although the sensor is usually considered to be the wet thermometer, it is important to remember that the dry reference plays an equal role.

Theory. When water evaporates, latent heat is lost from the liquid phase and its temperature falls. A limit is reached when the heat loss is balanced by heat influx from the outside environment. Under these conditions, a steady state rather than an equilibrium exists. In a well designed psychrometer with little heating from either the thermometer stem or radiation, the major heat gain is in the form of sensible heat coming from the warmer air. Thus, the temperature of the air falls, whilst the wet bulb thermometer also cools to a minimum known as the "thermodynamic wet bulb temperature" (Monteith 1973). The difference between ambient temperature and this is called the wet bulb depression (ΔT_{wb}). In contrast to large thermometers, small thermocouple sensors of the kind used for ψ measurement are not affected by the rate of ventilation, as diffusion is the dominant mechanism for heat transfer (Wylie 1962; Barrs 1965 a). It is possible to show that for the range of physiological water potentials, a simple linear equation can be written for the ideal psychrometer:

$$\psi = -\left[\frac{L_v}{T} + \frac{RT\gamma}{V_w e_0}\right] \Delta T_{wb}, \tag{7}$$

where γ is the psychrometric constant, $\gamma = 0.066$ kPa° C^{-1} and the psychrometer response becomes 0.0906° C MPa^{-1}.

In real psychrometers, heat is carried to the wet bulb by conduction and other transfer mechanisms, and this can degrade the output. Other factors which influence the wet bulb temperature are (1) the chemical activity of the water on the wet thermometer and (2) the boundary resistance between liquid and vapour. Both of these factors indicate the need to avoid contamination of the wet bulb with either solutes (1) or surface films (2). Controlled modification of (1) is the basis for isopiestic techniques using either osmotica (Boyer and Knipling 1965) or temperature (dew point methods, see Sect. 4).

3.2 Psychrometric Methods

There are two basic forms of psychrometry and both have been used for in situ plant ψ measurements. They are distinguished by the manner in which the sensing thermometer is wetted:

1. Peltier cooled (Spanner 1951);
2. Wet loop (droplet) (Richards and Ogata 1958).

The dominant temperature sensor in nearly all psychrometry is the thermocouple. A theoretical treatment of each type has been given by Peck (1968) and Rawlins (1966, 1972) respectively. Thermistors have been tried (Kitchen and Thames 1972) using the droplet method but there has been no substantial development since.

3.3 Peltier Cooled (Spanner) Psychrometers

3.3.1 Introduction

In these devices, moisture is condensed from the atmosphere by Peltier cooling a thermocouple junction below the dew point. This junction acts as the wet bulb, whilst a second thermocouple detects the temperature of the atmosphere (Fig. 1 a). Upon discontinuing the cooling current, the temperature of the wet

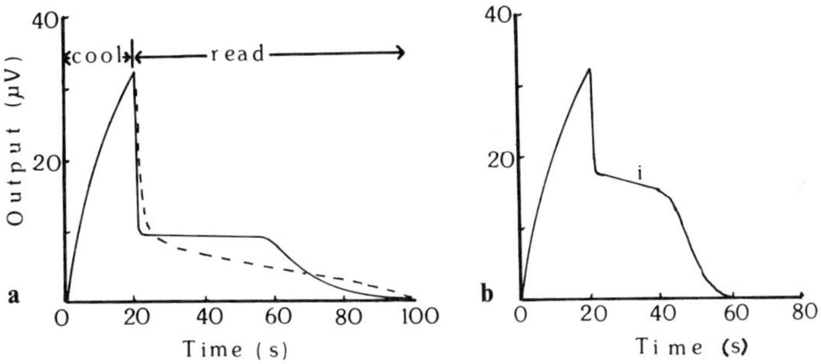

Fig. 2. a Output from a Spanner-type psychrometer with a sample at high ψ (-2.0 MPa) exhibiting a distinct plateau. Output may not always be present during the cooling phase unless specifically designed for, e.g. Wescor psychrometer, four-wire hygrometer (see Sects. 4.2 and 4.3). *Dashed line* illustrates the case where the sensor is contaminated. **b** As in **a**, but with a sample of lower ψ (-4.0 MPa). Note true plateau is replaced by sloping curve with inflection (*i*)

junction immediately begins to rise (Fig. 2a). But water evaporates back into the chamber from the junction and the cooling effect delays the further increase in its temperature. This is the wet bulb temperature. For samples where ψ is high a plateau in output is obtained, whereas those with lower values often do not achieve a true steady state because the water film on the wet bulb evaporates too quickly (Fig. 2b). It is also essential that the junction does not become contaminated as this will interfere with its water exchange characteristics and so degrade output (Fig. 2a).

Neither the wet nor dry bulb temperature of the chamber atmosphere is usually measured as such. Instead, the wet bulb depression is sensed as a difference signal between the wet sensor junction and that of a reference(s) embedded in the chamber block. This is assumed in most cases to have the same temperature as the chamber atmosphere ($T_r = T_a$, Fig. 1a). Good designs ensure that $T_r = T_c$. As mentioned above, correct operation of the psychrometer also requires $T_a = T_p$, a condition that can be checked with a second sensor on the plant surface (Fig. 1b).

3.3.2 Design Considerations

Thermocouple Choice. In the original instrument Spanner (1951) used Bi/Bi-Sn as the thermocouple sensor because of its high thermoelectric power (120 μV °C^{-1}). Although it has a lower output (60–63 μV °C^{-1}), chromel P/constantan has been adopted more widely due to its easier availability and durability. The size of the thermocouple is dictated mainly by heat transfer, vapour movement and mechanical strength considerations. Up to a certain length, long, thin wires tend to reduce heat conduction from the supports to the wet junction. Beyond this, heat transfer from the atmosphere assumes greater importance. Mathematical descriptions have been given by Spanner (1951) and Dalton and Rawlins (1968) for the cooling phase. For wires 25 μm in diameter, theory dictates an optimal length of about 5 mm. In practice this size is too fragile and much shorter lengths are used (a few mm) in modern in situ psychrometers. This should not compromise the wet bulb depression during the subsequent evaporation phase (Rawlins 1966, 1972).

Reference Junction Size. During the condensation phase, the passage of current through the reference junction tends to give rise to heating because of reverse Peltier and Joule effects. If this results in an excessive temperature elevation (e.g. $>1°$ C, Scotter 1972), then the difference signal can be accentuated at first, followed by an unwanted warming of the wet junction. Spurious positive μV outputs can be obtained at 0 MPa. Dalton and Rawlins (1968) and Peck (1968) derived an expression to calculate the required mass of the heat sinks to prevent an unacceptable temperature rise. They suggested values of about 100 or 20 g respectively, however, in practice smaller values are possible provided a standard procedure is followed for calibration solutions and plant samples.

Chamber Size. Ideally, the volume of the chamber should be small to hasten vapour equilibration and reduce heat gradients. However, it should also be large enough so that the act of condensing water from the atmosphere creates minimal change in vapour pressure. In practice the amount of water removed during Peltier cooling can cause a significant disturbance in relative humidity and hence water potential (Monteith and Owen 1958; Turner et al. 1984). Wiebe (1984) has measured condensation rates averaging 15 ng s^{-1}, not much less than that calculated by Peck (23 ng s^{-1}, 1968). If these were to apply over the whole of the condensation phase (e.g. 15 s), and water movement from the sample was restricted, then the removal of the 225 ng water would dry the atmosphere in a small chamber, e.g. 0.1 cm^{-3} by approximately 14 MPa. The problem is most acute for plants with high surface resistance to vapour movement. However, when vapour transfer is unimpeded, such as with filter paper wetted with calibration solutions, chamber volume is not critical (Hoffman and Herkelrath 1968).

With untreated plant material large volumes will be disturbed less during Peltier condensation. This probably explains the difference in opinion between Barrs (1965 b), who found no problem with large chambers, and others more recently (Shackel 1984) who used much smaller ones. Up until now the elimination of thermal gradients and rapid equilibration has dominated design considerations and so in situ chamber size tends to be kept small. Vapour pressure disturbance during condensation is generally minimized during operation by adhering to strict cooling times or ensuring that water can interchange freely between plant and chamber. When the plant does not completely surround the sensor, the use of a spherical chamber to simplify diffusion within the chamber (Baughn and Tanner 1976 b) may not be warranted if a significant quantity of water has to move from the plant during the cooling and evaporation phases of the measurement.

For hygrometers with chambers that decrease in volume when the plant is sealed in place, a small hole should allow pressure equilibration to take place. It is closed immediately after the plant part is installed (Monteith and Owen 1958; Hoffman and Herkelrath 1968).

3.3.3 Psychrometer Operation

Cooling Current. An optimum current can be found where Peltier cooling just balances Joule heating plus heat flow from the local environment. Its value is influ-

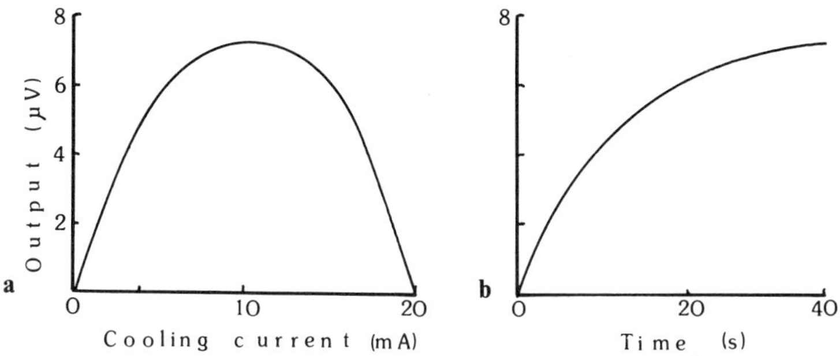

Fig. 3. a Idealized plot of psychrometer plateau values obtained for a single sample (e.g. $\psi = -1.5$ MPa) using different cooling currents for a standard time (e.g. 20 s). **b** As in **a**, but cooling current kept constant (e.g. 9 mA) and duration of cooling varied

enced by properties such as wire composition and dimensions, and is usually determined empirically for each hygrometer (Fig. 3a).

If only a small amount of water is condensed onto the sensor junction, then the wet bulb temperature will be attained only transiently during the evaporation phase. Thus, it is important to allow sufficient time for Peltier cooling to wet the junction and so achieve maximum output (Fig. 3b). Some workers have suggested that for low ψ, additional time should be allowed to condense more water so that a more definite wet bulb plateau can be obtained (Turner et al. 1984).

Calibration. Equation (7) gives the maximum sensitivity for a wet bulb psychrometer. For a chromel P/constantan sensor with a thermoelectric power of 63 $\mu V\ °C^{-1}$ the expected output is $0.0906 \times 63 = 5.71\ \mu V\ MPa^{-1}$. In practice real Spanner psychrometers do not achieve this sensitivity and so must be calibrated. Typical values at 25° C are 3.6 $\mu V\ MPa^{-1}$ (Millar et al. 1970); 4.5 $\mu V\ MPa^{-1}$ (Nnyamah and Black 1977).

The usual calibration procedure involves using solutions of known osmotic pressure (and hence ψ). A series of salt solutions of increasing concentration is commonly used, e.g. NaCl (Lang 1967) so that the range of ψ of interest is fully covered. These are often absorbed onto discs of filter paper. Care must be taken to ensure that evaporation is minimized during handling. A standard curve, usually linear. is obtained that can then be used to convert microvolt values found with plants to ψ.

As a number of factors in the conversion are temperature-sensitive, the calibration must be done at the same temperature as the plant. However, in in situ work temperature is often varying and this can mean that calibrations at several temperatures must be made. Plant ψ so obtained are often standardized back to a single temperature, e.g. 25° C (Wiebe et al. 1970; Savage and Cass 1984), however, there is no good reason for doing this, especially when the major component of ψ is "p" (Wiebe and Prosser 1977).

Taking a Reading. Before applying a cooling current, a check should be made to ensure that no spurious ZERO OFFSET voltage is present. This is usually done by comparing the emf output in READ mode with that when the meter is internally shorted. An output of $<0.3\ \mu V$ is usually acceptible. However, because three junctions are present (one sensor, two references), the signal is not entirely unambiguous in elucidating temperature gradients. Although a $0\ \mu V$ ZERO OFFSET is often the basis for relying on psychrometic ψ (Shackel 1984), this is not necessarily correct as temperature gradients can still be present between the plant and sensor (Sect. 2.3).

When the experimenter is convinced that no large thermal gradients exist, the cooling current is applied for a specified time (e.g. 10–15 s), abruptly discontinued and the μV output tracked to determine the wet bulb depression plateau or inflection point. This can now be converted to ψ from a predetermined calibration graph.

Discussion. Whilst psychrometric measurement of ψ can be thought of in two separate steps (Sect. 1.3), for small chambers the act of Peltier condensation will necessarily desiccate the atmosphere, and this will lead to water vapour movement from the plant tissue. However, calibration solutions are expected to have boundary resistances lower than plant material and this difference can create uncertainties in the determination of ψ. It is recommended therefore that psychrometric values of ψ should be checked with those obtained using another method such as dew point hygrometry or the Scholander pressure bomb (Scholander et al. 1965), especially for plants with high epidermal resistances. For example, Turner et al. (1984) obtained psychrometric ψ values for *Nerium* that were less negative than those obtained with either the dew point technique or pressure bomb. They presumed that the high surface resistance of the leaf prevented water vapour re-entering the leaf after the cooling phase, thereby resulting in spuriously high chamber humidities. But they were unable to observe genuine wet bulb plateau's so that it was difficult to determine a reliable ψ. An alternative explanation sees the high resistance preventing sufficient water from condensing on the junction and subsequent evaporative cooling unable to balance heat influx to the sensor tip. This is more consistent with the authors' observation that longer condensation times increased output (i.e. more negative ψ) than is the first explanation. Despite the anomalous behaviour the authors still believed that the psychrometric technique was useable, provided it was itself calibrated against another method, such as the Scholander bomb.

Discrepancies should not automatically be attributed to errors in the psychrometer as the potential obtained from the bomb will also need some correction. This will include addition of the osmotic component of the extracellular fluid, usually small (0.15 MPa or less for non-halophytes) and approximated by measuring the osmotic pressure of the xylem sap (Boyer 1972; Baughn and Tanner 1976b). Other problems arise due to water loss from the plant part following excision, transport and loading into the bomb (Wenhert et al. 1978; Turner and Long 1980), difficulties in end point determination due to frothing of the xylem sap and uneven refilling of the xylem during pressurization (Ritchie and Hinckley 1975).

In addition, there is the real possibility that significant gradients in ψ exist in the transpiring plant because of internal resistances to flow (Black 1979; Turner

1981). Apart from the effect of the hygrometer mentioned earlier (Sect. 2.3), these may also be completely or partially collapsed during measurement with the pressure bomb, and in this case corroboration would not be expected.

3.3.4 Campbell Leaf Hygrometer

Description. This device was developed some years ago (Campbell and Campbell 1974) but is today part of perhaps the most widely used apparatus for psychrometric ψ determination (the L-51 leaf hygrometer; Wescor, Logan, Utah, USA). A slightly different version (L-51A) with a narrow, rectangular aperture is available for grass leaves. The hygrometer consists of two parts: (1) a barrel with a cylindrical cavity that forms the chamber (Fig. 4a) and (2) a metallic block for holding the barrel up against the leaf inside a slot (Fig. 4b).

The holding block is made of material with a high thermal capacity and conductivity (e.g. aluminium, copper or brass), so that thermal gradients and transients are damped out. The circular hole should fit the barrel snugly so that heat can move between the two symmetrically with no gradients likely to be created across the two reference junctions. To help ensure that the leaf and chamber are isothermal the slot should not extend much behind the hole for the barrel nor be too open.

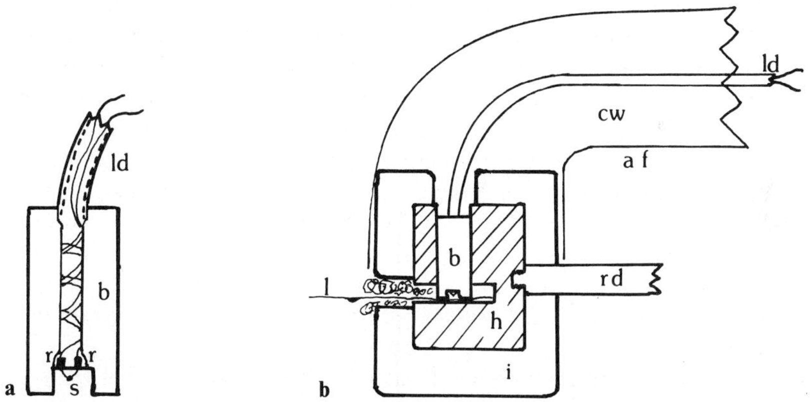

Fig. 4. a Campbell leaf hygrometer (Wescor L-51), consisting of chrome-plated brass barrel (*b*), 10-mm diameter, 31-mm-high, with chamber 3-mm diameter, 2-mm-deep. The sensor (*s*) is made from 25-µm diameter chromel/constantan thermocouple wire and reference junctions (*r*) formed with copper posts. The fine lead wires are wound around a metallic core to minimize external heat conduction to the sensor and reference junctions. The wires in the lead are shielded with metal braid (*dashed line*). **b** Campbell hygrometer attached to leaf (*l*) with aluminium or brass holder (*h*) 19 × 25 × 46 mm. The face of the barrel (*b*) is smeared with Vaseline as a sealant and the barrel held in place with a set screw (not shown). The whole unit is covered with 20-mm-thick plastic (polystyrene) foam insulation (*i*) and supported via a perspex rod (*rd*) to reduce heat transfer. Additional cotton wool insulation (*cw*), with aluminium foil casing is wrapped around the lead for at least 300 mm back from the hygrometer. Cotton wool is lightly packed around the leaf in the holder slit

Cleaning. Grease can be removed with a cotton swab and organic solvents such as petroleum spirit followed by analytical grade acetone. Distilled water will dissolve salts and other solutes. Brown and Tanner (1981) found a fine steam jet to be useful, followed by a 1 in 5 NH_4OH solution for 1 min and then finally rinsed with distilled water. Contaminated hygrometers usually exhibit drift in output prior to operation.

Attachment. A small area of a leaf is prepared to effect good water vapour communication with the chamber (Sect. 2.3). This section of the leaf, still attached to the plant is then carefully positioned in the slot of the holding block. The barrel whose annular face has been smeared lightly with sealant is lowered inside the holding block onto the prepared area of the leaf, pressed firmly down and clamped. Cotton wool is gently poked into the remaining open slit around the leaf to exclude drafts and radiation. Insulation and shielding on the sensor lead to the meter is carefully arranged for complete coverage. The leaf is now ready for ψ determinations after a suitable time has elapsed for thermal (a few minutes) and water vapour (minutes to hours) equilibration within the chamber.

3.3.5 Silver Foil Psychrometer

Hoffman and Rawlins (1972) built a small Peltier cooled psychrometer using silver foil (high thermal conductivity and low thermal mass) to ensure that the air temperature within the chamber was close to that of the leaf (Fig. 5). Tests showed that the chamber was within 0.025° C of a simulated copper leaf, producing a thermally-induced error of +0.1 MPa. The hygrometer is insulated at the back with 2.5-cm-thick plastic foam. Its operation is similar to that of other Peltier-

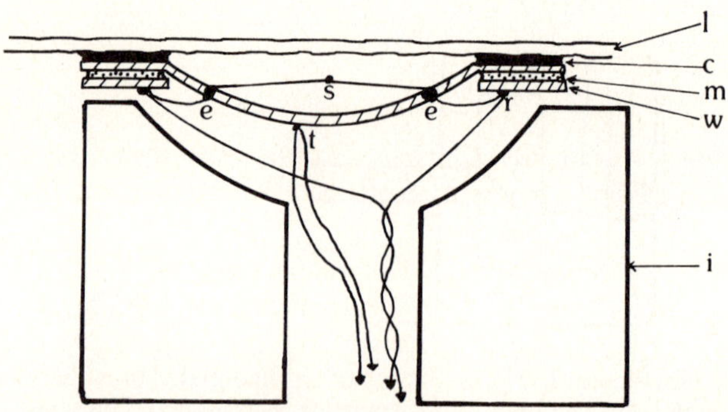

Fig. 5. Silver foil psychrometer attached to the underside of a leaf (*l*). The chamber is formed from a 13-mm diameter disc of silver foil (50 μm thick), dished to form a cavity 5 mm across and 1 mm deep. The sensor (*s*) is made from a chromel/constantan thermocouple whose wires (25-μm diameter) pass through holes in the foil and are held in place with epoxy cement (*e*). Reference junctions (*r*) are formed when the thermocouple wires are soldered with the copper lead wires to two silver half-washers (*w*) held just off the flange of the silver disc with laminating material (*m*). A copper/constantan thermocouple monitors the temperature of the psychrometer, which is entirely covered with 2–3-cm-thick plastic foam insulation (*i*, hole in insulation not to scale). The whole unit is fastened to the leaf (*l*) with silver-impregnated, water-based cement (*c*) (After Hoffman and Rawlins 1972)

cooled devices. Wiebe and Prosser (1977) found, however, that results were more variable than the Wescor L-51, probably because of thermal gradients generated by radiant heat. The silver foil psychrometer is not available commercially.

3.3.6 Other Hygrometer Designs

There have been several alternative psychrometer versions, each usually aiming to improve or account for some aspect of the thermal environment of the chamber such as (1) Peltier heating of the reference junction (Millar et al. 1970) or (2) variable chamber temperature (Calissendorff 1970; Hsieh and Hungate 1970). They have not persisted, however, because of their larger size and consequent difficulty in achieving isothermality or because the simpler designs have achieved their aims through other means (Sect. 2.3).

3.3.7 Equipment Requirements

Leads from hygrometer to voltmeter usually consist of enamelled copper wires with a further layer of plastic insulation. Braided metallic mesh within the conduit is desirable to screen the inside wires from radio frequency interference (RF pick-up). Connections and joins in leads should be avoided as these can act as thermocouples themselves. Strains in conductors resulting from bending and stretching can also be thermally active and should be avoided. Leads should be thermally insulated with material such as cotton wool and covered with reflective foil, particularly near the hygrometer.

Switches and contacts can also be a problem in a non-isothermal environment. The same principles apply here as with psychrometer design, i.e. avoidance of thermal gradients with good insulation and large thermal mass (Lang and Trickett 1965). Switch boxes and scanners that allow automatic Peltier cooling and wet bulb emf read-out are available commercially.

The Peltier cooling current is usually provided by a simple circuit with a variable resistor that allows the magnitude of the current to be varied. In some instruments the direction of current flow can be reversed to heat rather than cool the thermocouple junction.

Solid state micro- and nano-voltmeters with field effect transistors (FETs) allow precise microvoltages to be determined directly. Typically, their internal impedances are above 10 Mohm and readings are not influenced by other resistances such as might occur in long leads for in situ work. Modern meters, however, are more sensitive to RF pick-up, either through the sensor leads or the power supply. If this is AC, it should be filtered to remove RF and other interference which might originate from switches and contactors on other appliances using the same power circuit. Alternatively, the equipment can be run off a large electrical battery. If the equipment is to be run in the field, shielding from solar radiation is essential to prevent thermally-induced drift in output (Brown and Tanner 1981). Enclosure of the whole meter in a well-sealed, plastic foam box is recommended, with the output being recorded elsewhere. A remote switch for the cooling current would be advantageous under extreme climatic conditions.

Analogue display in the form of a meter is usually preferable to digital and provision for some additional output such as a chart recorder is almost essential when the wet bulb inflection point needs to be determined. A more recent trend is to convert the amplified output signal into digital so that it can be stored, displayed and processed on a computer (McBurney and Costigan 1984).

3.4 Wet Loop or Droplet Psychrometer

Instead of wetting the junction by Peltier cooling, Richards and Ogata (1958) employed a manual method to place a droplet of water on the thermocouple sensor. Once thus loaded with water the general principle of these psychrometers is much the same as those based on the Spanner design. Barrs (1965a) showed that they could achieve wet bulb depressions very close to the maximum expected for a fully ventilated, ideal psychrometer, unlike most Peltier cooled devices whose efficiency is about 70%. Because of the relatively large size of the drop (0.8 mg) the sensor remains wet for several hours and in principle this fact should allow for continuous monitoring of ψ.

Whilst they were once popular for excised tissue measurements in the 1960s, their use today, especially in in situ work, has virtually ceased. This is due to a number of reasons:

1. Difficulty in checking the offset voltage due to temperature gradients;
2. Difficulty in using small chambers because the large droplet tends to saturate the internal atmosphere and dominate the steady state humidity, especially for plants with high surface resistance;
3. The steady state water vapour concentration is a function of plant surface resistance and changes in this are often unpredictable.

Boyer (1968) enclosed an attached leaf in a water-jacketed chamber in the laboratory and used an isopiestic method to determine plant ψ. This approach overcomes objection (3), however, the method has not since found much application for in situ measurements. The wet loop method might still prove useful if a separate probe for dry bulb temperature were to be installed, as well as ensuring low cuticular resistance. The usual precautions to eliminate thermal gradients would still apply.

4 Dew Point Methods

4.1 Introduction

Dew point can also be used to measure plant water potential as the dew point is lowered with decreasing relative humidity and hence ψ. The dew point depression (ΔT_{dp}) can be defined as the amount by which the temperature of water must be lowered for its equilibrium vapour pressure (e_0^*) to be equal to that of the surrounding atmosphere (e_1). Whilst the Clausius Clapeyron equation can be used to determine e_0^* as a function of T(°C) an empirical relation has been given by Tetens (1930):

$$e_0^* = 610.8 \exp [17.273\, T/(T+237.3)] . \quad (8)$$

When combined with Eq. (5) and putting $e_1 = e_0^*$, Neumann and Thurtell (1972) showed that:

$$\Delta T_{dp} = [T+237.3][1-(18930T)/(T+237.3)\psi] . \quad (9)$$

In the physiological range of ψ of 0 to -3.0 MPa this relation becomes linear, passing through the origin with a slope of $(T+273.3)/L_v$ (i.e., 0.119° C MPa^{-1} at 25° C). For a given water potential dew point depression varies only 5% for a 10° C change around 20° C and is therefore less sensitive to changes in the general temperature than is the wet bulb method. Dew point techniques also have advantages because they are essentially equilibrium methods. In this respect dew point methods are similar to the isopiestic determination of Boyer and Knipling (1965) who used osmotica rather than cooling to depress ψ of the sensing moisture droplet. For water at the dew point there is neither net condensation nor evaporation so that properties such as shape and surface area, which affect wet bulb methods, are less important. There is a further benefit because the dew point depression is approximately twice the magnitude of the practical Spanner wet bulb, thus allowing greater precision and sensitivity in ψ determinations.

4.2 Four-Wire Hygrometer

Principle. Neumann and Thurtell (1972) devised a method that employed two thermocouples (four wires) in a way similar to that used by Millar et al. (1970). Their junctions are welded together and one is used to condense a droplet of moisture from the atmosphere by Peltier cooling. This thermocouple also controls the temperature of the droplet by varying the cooling current. The second thermocouple acts as a sensor for the droplet temperature.

The temperature characteristics of the four-wire junction are first determined by passing a Peltier cooling current through the first thermocouple in a dry atmosphere. This results in an inverted parabola where initially Peltier cooling predominates (positive slope) but is overridden by Joule heating at higher currents (negative slope, Fig. 6a; cf. Sect. 3.3.3). The sample is now introduced into the chamber and allowed to come to vapour and thermal equilibrium. Water is condensed on the combined junction and the current reduced gradually during which time temperature measurements are made with the second thermocouple. A second curve is now obtained that intersects the dry graph. At low currents the output from the sensing thermocouple is greater (i.e. colder) when wet because of evaporative cooling, whereas at higher currents warming occurs in the moist atmosphere due to the latent heat released by condensation. At the point of intersection of the two curves there is no difference between the wet and dry junction and no heat is exchanged due to the presence of the droplet. This is the dew point for the enclosed atmosphere.

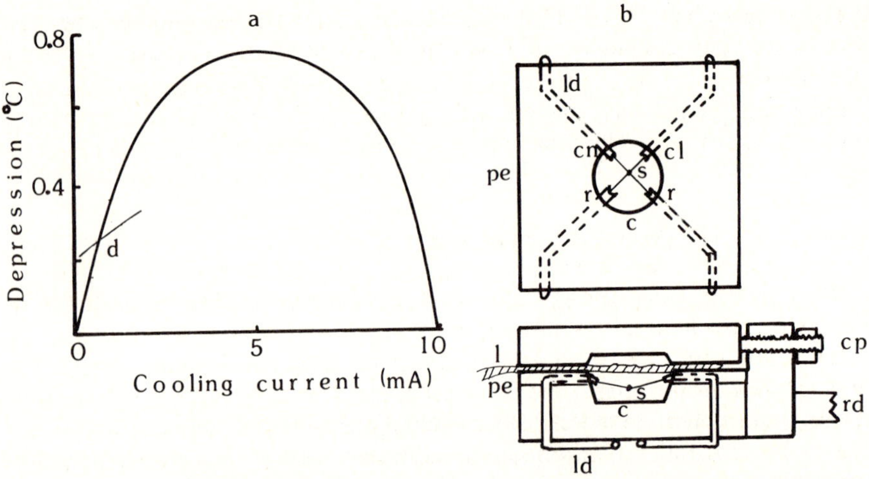

Fig. 6. a Temperature characteristics of the four-wire hygrometer as a function of cooling current. *Parabolic curve* obtained with dry junction; *small curve* obtained with sample (e.g. $\psi = -2.0$ MPa) intersecting dry curve at the dew point temperature (*d*) (After Neumann and Thurtell 1972). **b** Plan and section views of the four-wire hygrometer. The sensor (*s*) is formed at the welded junction of 25-μm-diameter chromel and constantan wires. The current carrying thermocouple wires are crimped to chromel (*cl*) and constantan (*cn*) posts, whilst the other ends are crimped into copper posts to make the reference junctions (*r*). The whole sensor assembly is suspended in a hole in a thin copper plate (*pe*) that forms the upper part of the chamber (*c*). The copper lead wires (*ld*) are wound in a serpentine manner across the base of the copper hygrometer body to reduce heat conduction to the reference posts. The leaf (*l*) is held in place between the upper and lower hygrometer blocks by means of a clamp (*cp*) that moves vertically in slots (not shown). The hygrometer can also be inverted prior to attaching the leaf. Apiezon M grease is used to effect a vapour seal between leaf and hygrometer. The hygrometer can be supported via a plastic rod (*rd*) and should be clad with plastic foam insulation (not shown)

In principle, the microvolt output can now be converted to a temperature depression by dividing by the thermoelectric power for the particular thermocouple (e.g. 63 $\mu V\,K^{-1}$ for chromel/constantan) and solving for ψ in Eq. (9). For most cases a conversion factor of $0.119 \times 63 = 7.5\ \mu V\ MPa^{-1}$ can be used.

Calibration. Unfortunately, spurious emf's can be generated in some single weld junctions during the passage of the Peltier cooling current. These are accounted for by calibrating the hygrometer against solutions of known ψ. The microvolt output thus obtained is compared with that expected theoretically and any difference is divided by the cooling current to provide a correction factor. The units for this factor are μV/mA (i.e. milliohms) and correspond to the resistance across the sensing part of the junction. During operation the expected spurious emf can be calculated by multiplying the correction factor by the cooling current and subtracting from that observed.

Construction. The best four-wire junction is formed by a single weld of two crossed thermocouple wires (25 μm diameter) such as chromel and constantan using a spot welder (Fig. 6b). This is preferable to two close but separate junctions although the applied Peltier cooling current can still induce spurious IR voltages in the sensing couple which need to be accounted for. Temperature damping is obtained by lagging the hygrometer with polystyrene foam, held in place with aluminized adhesive tape. The four-wire dew point hygrometer is not commercially available.

Application. This style of hygrometer has been used for in situ determination of ψ in both plant (leaves, Baughn and Tanner 1976a; Ike and Thurtell 1981) and soil (Brunini and Thurtell 1982). The usual considerations of thermal and vapour equilibration apply as much here as to other hygrometers. This is essentially a manual method because of the need to construct the current-microvolt curve for each dew point determination. If ψ was changing this would need to be done as quickly as possible to avoid an incorrect estimation of the intersection point of wet and dry graphs. Such rapid determinations appear to be possible, allowing near continuous monitoring of ψ in a number of plant species (Nulsen et al. 1977; Nulsen and Thurtell 1978).

4.3 Pulsed Dew Point Hygrometer

Introduction. An alternative dew point hygrometer, using a single thermocouple to both cool the junction and measure its temperature, was devised by Campbell et al. (1973). This equipment is now manufactured by Wescor Inc., Utah, USA. In this system cooling current is pulsed through the junction whilst the temperature (microvolt output) is measured during the inactive periods.

Principle. The Wescor dew point hygrometer depends on the fact that if there are no outside heat transfers besides latent heat exchange then the temperature of a droplet of moisture will tend towards the dew point until $e_0^* = e_1$. For a droplet of water that has been condensed onto the junction of a thermocouple, however, there are indeed extraneous heat flows. These are principally by conduction through the thermocouple wires and contact heat transfer from the atmosphere to the droplet and wires, with a much smaller component from radiation. The Wescor hygrometer nullifies these by adjusting the duration of cooling current pulses to exactly balance the heat inflow to the cool junction. The signal from the thermocouple is read between current pulses and processed through a "holding" circuit so that a continuous microvolt output is obtained (Fig. 7a). This can then be converted to ψ by calibrating the apparatus with solutions of known osmotic strength. Agreement with theory is usually very good for ψ down to about -4.0 MPa.

In the dew point mode the thermocouple signal drives a feedback loop that controls the duration of each cooling pulse (Fig. 7c). The correct operation of the instrument rests on the assumption that the flow of heat from the outside is proportional to the differential between the junction and chamber (reference) temperatures. The proportionality constant of this linear relation is expressed in the slope of a series of ramp functions (i.e. a sawtooth), the height of which is gov-

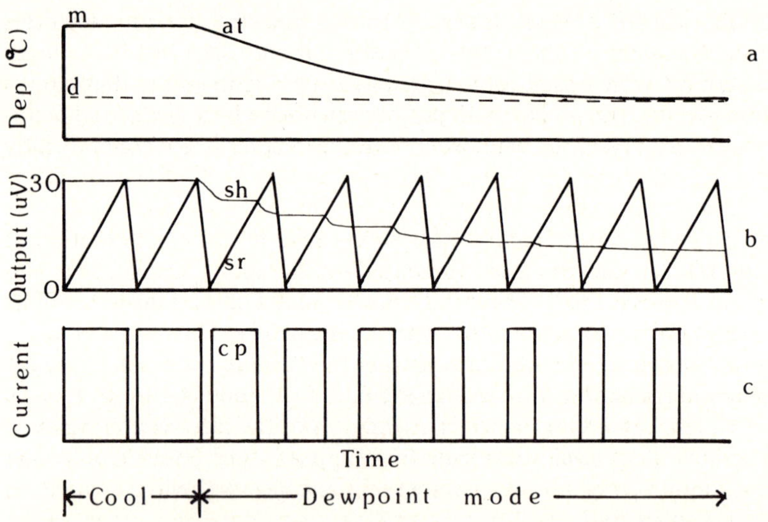

Fig. 7 a–c. Graphical representation of different aspects of the pulsed dew point system during cool and dew point cycles. **a** Average temperature depression (*at*) of the junction reaches a maximum (*m*) during cooling, declining to a stable dew point (*d*) with time. **b** Output from the hygrometer sample is "held" (*sh*) and compared with a sawtooth ramp (*sr*) function (after amplification) to determine the duration of cooling pulses. When the sawtooth voltage equals that from the sample hold circuit the pulse is turned off. It is turned on again at the foot of each sawtooth. **c** Current pulses last for 95% of each cycle during the "cool" phase. The interval between cooling pulses (*cp*) is constant but the pulse duration contracts until at the dew point each pulse length is the same. Hygrometer output is read between the pulses. (After Campbell et al. 1973)

erned by the π_v gain adjustment (Fig. 7b). The output from the sensing thermocouple, after amplification, is compared with this sawtooth and when greater, cooling current is applied. During this period the output to the meter is held constant even though no actual measurement is occurring.

Apparatus. For in situ plant measurements the L-51 leaf hygrometer is normally used, with various modifications of the holder depending on the part of the plant to which it is attached. Other sensors are also possible, such as the ones used for in situ soil work (Fig. 9a) or osmotic pressure determinations.

The electronic measuring and control equipment is housed in a robust aluminium case that is easily portable. The output is displayed in analogue form with a precision microvoltmeter. Provision is also made for output to a chart recorder. No special insulation is provided although most components are not thermally active. An exception can be the posts to which the hygrometer lead wires are connected. For fieldwork the unit should be kept in a well-insulated box so that the instrument panel is not exposed to direct solar radiation (Brown and Tanner 1981).

Operation. Before any measurements can be made each hygrometer must be tested to determine the cooling required to balance the heat input from the environment to the sensing junction. This is done by assembling the hygrometer without any sample material so that the junction remains dry. The hygrometer is now allowed to come to thermal equilibrium (about 4 min) and the microvoltmeter is zeroed with the input shorted out. The instrument is put into the READ mode in which the thermocouple output is measured. This gives a guide to temperature differences among sensing and reference junctions. Ideally, this should be zero or at least less than 0.3 μV (approx. 0.05 MPa). This is important as this "offset signal" will form part of that used in the feedback control in the dew point mode. The thermocouple is now Peltier cooled briefly (approx. 5–10 s) and then put into dew point mode. At this point the reading will usually rise or fall. The π_v setting is adjusted so that no further drift continues. Net heat flow into the junction at this point is zero and the temperature is therefore constant. The procedure is repeated by returning to READ mode followed by a further cooling/dew point cycle. If the setting is correct, a constant output should be obtained in dew point mode that should persist for at least 2 min (Savage and Cass 1984). A second, fine tuning might be necessary at this stage. Once accomplished this setting is assumed to remain constant for the hygrometer and apply over the whole of the working dew point range of temperatures. For larger scale changes in the general ambient temperature, π_v varies by 0.7 μV °C^{-1}. It is also assumed that the presence of the sample does not influence the thermal environment of the junction beyond that due to latent heat exchange.

Plant material is prepared and the hygrometer, e.g. L-51, attached (see above). Thermal equilibration is allowed to take place and small deviations (<0.3 μV) in the READ position are eliminated with the zero offset adjustment. The junction is moistened by Peltier cooling condensation (approx. 10 s with preset current) and the instrument turned to dew point mode. The output falls rapidly and then levels out more slowly to approach the dew point. With calibration solutions a steady value might be achieved within 90 s, with abraded plant material 3 min is more typical (Schaefer et al. 1986).

Calibration. Like the wet bulb psychrometer, dew point instruments are often calibrated against solutions of known osmotic strength. However, unlike the wet bulb psychrometer, output in the dew point mode should always be close to that expected theoretically, i.e. 7.5 μV MPa^{-1} at 25° C (Campbell et al. 1973). In some cases different calibration slopes are found (Schaefer et al. 1986). This is partly due to the fact that the heat transfer properties of the wet thermocouple appear to be different to those when dry (Shackel 1984, see below). The original π_v setting is hence in error and likely to cause the dew point output to drift. Setting π_v to obtain steady outputs for more than a few minutes with a dry thermocouple is usually a difficult task, and the value chosen may not be applicable over the whole microvolt range (Shackel 1984). It is perhaps somewhat surprising that the heat balance can be maintained over long periods (e.g. 16 h) and one suspects the presence of some non-linearity in the feedback control mechanism that allows this to be possible, perhaps relating to the change in heat characteristics with change in thermocouple droplet size. R. D. Briscoe (Wescor, pers. commun.) suggests using a slightly lower π_v (i.e. greater cooling) to maintain a wet junction, even though this is likely to increase the calibration slope.

Increasing the initial cooling time condenses more water on the junction and this appears to influence the output in the dew point mode (Shackel 1984). By turning to psychrometric mode after dew point it is possible to assess the degree of wetness of the junction by integrating under the microvolt output curve. Different cooling times can be used to allow an extrapolation to a theoretical zero junction wetness. This method produces a calibration curve close to that expected (intercept origin slope, 7.5 $\mu V\ MPa^{-1}$).

4.4 Continuous Monitoring

In principle, provided the dew point is maintained, it should be possible to monitor in situ ψ continuously for several hours. Maize leaf ψ's were tracked with the Wescor dew point system by Wiebe and Prosser (1977). McBurney and Costigan (1984) attached a modified L-51 leaf hygrometer (and Wescor HR-33T microvoltmeter) to the stem of a Brussel sprout in a controlled environment cabinet and logged cyclic fluctuations over 5 h on a microcomputer. Schaefer et al. (1986) used the same instrument with a chart recorder but could only achieve reliable long-term readings by electronically filtering the power supply.

4.5 Comparison of Dew Point Methods

There are few if any reports of direct comparisons of the two dew point techniques described here. The question of whether the heat exchange characteristics are the same for wet and dry junctions applies to both methods (see calibration, Sect. 4.3). However, for some hygrometers of both types this problem does not appear to arise as the dew points measured are very close to those expected theoretically. The pulsed system with continuous output would appear superior to the four-wire version, as longer times should be possible to re-equilibrate the chamber atmosphere after the initial condensation of moisture on the junction. It is, in addition, an automatic method, whereas the four-wire device is not.

4.6 Dew Point Versus Psychrometric Methods

From the point of view of water vapour exchange at the wet junction, dew point methods have an advantage over psychrometric (wet bulb) ones because they operate at the equilibrium point and are therefore not influenced by kinetic factors. Good corroboration is obtained between dew point and other methods such as the Scholander pressure bomb even in the field (Brown and Tanner 1981; Savage et al. 1983). Psychrometric techniques, on the other hand, necessarily disturb any vapour equilibrium that has been established and this can lead to errors despite abrasion of the plant surface (Turner et al. 1984). Whilst psychrometric procedures can be automated they do not offer the same intensity of measurement that is available with the pulsed dew point technique. On the other hand, close tracking of ψ at different sites would require replicate sets of expensive pulsed dew point meters.

5 In Situ Measurement at Particular Sites

5.1 Leaf

The abaxial (under) side is usually chosen for attachment to the leaf as stomata here are likely to offer a lower resistance to vapour movement, although in several species the additional removal of the cuticle will still be necessary (Sect. 2.3). For some leaves without upper stomata, the top surface might be preferable (after abrasion), as this will alter transpiration far less. In addition, some photosynthesis can still take place and hence there is less metabolic disruption. However, this will only be true for those hygrometers which attach to one surface only of the leaf, e.g. the silver foil psychrometer. Chambers made of translucent Teflon are also useful and Neumann and Thurtell (1972) made a transparent hygrometer specially for leaves. Admission of light, however, usually also allows entry of heat radiation and this can give rise to temperature gradient problems. For this reason additional shielding and insulation on the other side of the leaf is also advisable, at least during the actual measurement (Calissendorf 1970). Thermal gradients along the leaf do not appear to upset ψ measurements where the temperature under the hygrometer can either be buffered (the L-51, Sect. 3.3.4) or equilibrated rapidly (the silver foil psychrometer, Sect. 3.3.5; Wiebe and Prosser 1977).

Leaf hygrometers will necessarily stop transpiration beneath them as well as disrupt local water relations to some extent (Sects. 2.3 and 3.3.3). This is particularly true of designs that use large holders covered in insulation such as the Wescor L-51 (Sect. 3.3.4). Smaller hygrometers attached to only one side of the leaf, e.g. the silver foil psychrometer, would cause less interference.

In the extreme case the whole of the leaf may be covered so that there is no transpiration. Under these circumstances the hygrometer plus covered leaf monitor the xylem ψ of the stem. However, when ψ is varying in the stem, e.g. oscillations, damping or delays in response may occur at the hygrometer because of the resistance and capacitance of the leaf. This can be partly overcome by trimming away the excess leaf, leaving a minimum attached to the stem.

5.2 Stem

By and large, leaf hygrometers can also be used for stems, with some modification to the method of attachment. McBurney and Costigan (1982) used a Wescor L-51 fixed to the stem of a cabbage with quick setting silicone cement (Fig. 8a). The epidermis and outer cortex were removed with a scalpel blade to expose the vascular tissue, just before attachment to the stem. On the other hand, Wiebe et al. (1970) implanted a 2-mm-diameter ceramic cup soil psychrometer into a stem to measure ψ in situ. A more sensitive version without ceramic shielding was installed in a 4-mm-diameter hole bored into a soybean stem (Michel 1977). Because only a small proportion of water exchanges across the stem, whilst most travels up it, attachment of the hygrometer is less likely to upset plant water relations, providing the vascular elements have not been too badly damaged. Some idea of the local resistances should be known so that anatomical features such as hypo-

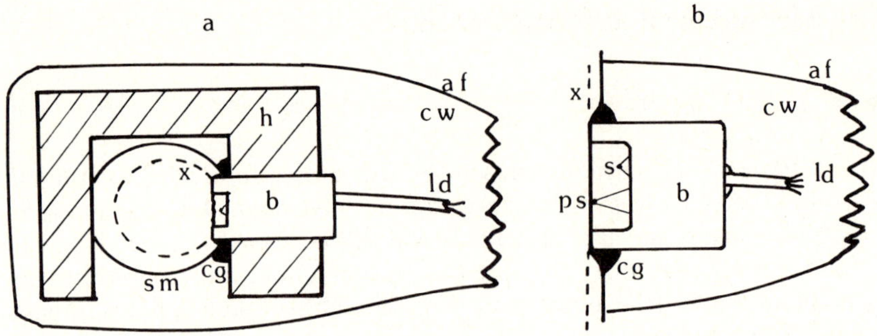

Fig. 8. a Cross-sectional view of the Wescor L-51 leaf hygrometer attached to a stem (*sm*). The barrel of the hygrometer (*b*) is held up against an exposed part of the xylem in the stem with an aluminium holder (*h*). A vapour seal is effected with silicone caulking compound (*cg*). The assembly is clad in cotton wool wadding (*cw*) and wrapped in aluminium foil (*af*) and extends at least 300 mm along the output lead (*ld*). **b** Side view of a thermocouple hygrometer with wetted sensor (*s*) and additional plant sensor (*ps*) to monitor stem temperature. Other symbols as in **a**

dermis or suberized layers do not interfere with the plant to sensor communication. There is an advantage in using the stem, particularly if the sensor is directly over the xylem, because the transpiration stream can wash away osmotically active solutes that might be released from wounded cells. However, water moving up the stem from the roots can also introduce temperature fluctuations that can disrupt measurements for 20 min or so (Michel 1977). Such perturbations may not be eliminated with the water-jacketed psychrometer of McBurney and Costigan (1987) as this system does not regulate the stem temperature. It would be wise to monitor the temperature of the stem directly under the hygrometer, in order to detect thermal gradients (Sect. 2.3, Fig. 8 b). The covered leaf technique does not suffer this problem because little water travels to the site of the sensor (Sect. 5.1).

5.3 Roots

As with leaves, ψ will be significantly altered if the hygrometer interrupts a substantial proportion of the total water flow. Unlike leaves, active roots usually have low resistances to water entry. This should allow the hygrometer to be attached without the need to scarify or dissolve the outer surface.

In older, larger roots (> 3-cm-diameter) a ceramic cup soil psychrometer can be put into an incision that reaches the xylem, (Fig. 9 a; Nnyamah and Black 1977). For younger roots a three-piece Teflon chamber can be used (Fiscus 1972). Here, sections with opposing grooves come apart so that the chamber can be slipped around an attached root (Fig. 9 b). Root hygrometers are operated like those used for soil measurements, with particular care for eliminating any adverse temperature gradient problems. Small size, spherical geometry, centrally located sensor, reference junctions placed horizontally and burial of an adjacent lead at the same depth (i.e. temperature) as the sensor, all favour better psychrometer per-

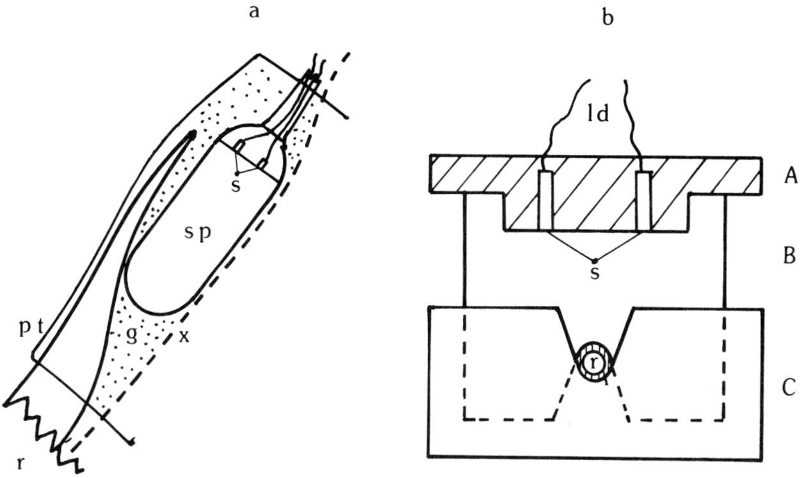

Fig. 9. a A ceramic soil psychrometer (*sp*, 20-mm-long, 6-mm diameter) placed axially into a slit extending down to the xylem (*x*) in the root (*r*). The thermocouple sensor is shown (*s*). Gypsum (*g*) has been packed into the wound to absorb gums and resin. The hygrometer is held in place with plastic tape (*pt*) wrapped around the root, with an outer coating of silicone rubber sealant (not shown). **b** A hygrometer for young roots. Three parts (*A, B, C*) fashioned from Teflon come apart to allow the root to be placed in the grooved slots. It is sealed in place with stopcock grease or an equivalent (*vertical hatching*). A chromel/constantan thermocouple embedded in the lid (*A*) acts as the sensor (*s*) (After Fiscus 1972)

formance. An independent thermometer to check general psychrometer temperature is also important.

6 Conclusion and Final Recommendation

Many of the measurements of plant ψ are on a somewhat large scale, with no attempt to pinpoint the site that is actually being observed. This is really a question about the size of resistances at an anatomical level, but needs to be considered carefully when taking measurements. Often the techniques are looking at the extracellular fluid and it is assumed that ψ will be similar inside the cell. For cells that are not changing in size this may be so. Shackel (1987) has demonstrated good agreement between ψ obtained with the dew point hygrometer and that found by summing pressure and osmotic components determined independently using a microcapillary tube at zero transpiration rates. In other cases, where there is a flux of water $\Delta\psi$ is thermodynamically not the appropriate driving force (see Eq. 4). However, for many cell membranes and physiological solutes σ is close to unity so that Eq. (4) reduces to $J_v = L_p \Delta\psi$. Similarly, for long-distance transport in the xylem $\sigma = 0$ so that $J_v = L_p \Delta p$. As the osmotic component of xylem fluid is usually small $\psi = p$ and $J_v = L_p \Delta\psi$ again. Thus, ψ measurements are still relevant to transport studies provided the assumptions about σ and π are correct.

For this purpose the pulsed dew point technique with a thermocouple hygrometer seems to be the best option to date. Some care will still be needed with those hygrometers that do not exhibit the expected calibration, and further explanatory work is required here (perhaps by the manufacturer). Nevertheless, this technique, with suitable precautions, can be used to continuously monitor water potential at various sites in the plant under laboratory or field conditions. Future goals for in situ measurement of ψ need to focus on the tissue and cell level.

Appendix

Useful constants

R	Universal gas constant	8.31	$MPa\ cm^{-3}\ mol^{-1}\ K^{-1}$
g	Acceleration due to gravity	980.6	$cm\ s^{-2}$
M_W	Molar weight of water	18.0	$g\ mol^{-1}$

Temperature-dependent properties

T (°C)	L_V (MPa)	V_W ($cm^3\ mol^{-1}$)	γ (kPa)	e_0 (kPa)	c_W ($\mu g\ cm^{-3}$)
0	2497	18.018	0.065	0.611	4.85
10	2474	18.021	0.065	1.277	9.40
20	2449	18.048	0.066	2.337	17.30
25	2438	18.069	0.066	3.167	23.05
30	2426	18.094	0.067	4.243	30.38
40	2402	18.157	0.067	7.378	51.19

L_V Latent heat of vapourization (volumetric)
V_W Partial molar volume of water
γ Psychrometric constant
e_0 Saturated vapour pressure of water
c_W Specific saturated humidity

References

Barrs HD (1964) Heat of respiration as a possible cause of error in the estimation by psychrometric methods of water potential in plant tissue. Nature 203:1136–1137

Barrs HD (1965a) Comparison of water potentials in leaves as measured by two types of thermocouple psychrometer. Aust J Biol Sci 18:36–52

Barrs HD (1965b) Psychrometric measurement of leaf water potential: lack of error attributed to leaf permeability. Science 149:63–65

Baughn JW, Tanner CB (1976a) Leaf water potential: comparison of pressure chamber and in situ hygrometer on five herbaceous species. Crop Sci 16:181–184

Baughn JW, Tanner CB (1976b) Excision effects on leaf water potential of five herbaceous species. Crop Sci 16:184–190

Black CR (1979) The relationship between transpiration rate, and water potential, and resistances to water movement in sunflower (*Helianthus annuus* L.). J Exp Bot 30:235–243

Boyer JS (1968) Relationship of water potential to growth in leaves. Plant Physiol 43:1056–1062

Boyer JS (1972) Use of isopiestic techniques in thermocouple psychrometry II, construction. In: Brown RW, Haveren BP van (eds) Psychrometry in water relations research. Utah Agric Exp Stn, Utah State Univ, Logan, Utah, pp 98–102

Boyer JS, Knipling EB (1965) Isopiestic technique for measuring leaf water potentials with a thermocouple psychrometer. Proc Natl Acad Sci USA 54:1044–1051

Brown PW, Tanner CB (1981) Alfalfa water potential measurement: A comparison of the pressure chamber and leaf dew point hygrometers. Crop Sci 21:240–244

Brown RW, Haveren BP van (1972) Psychrometry in water relations research. Utah Agric Res Stn, Utah State Univ, Logan, Utah

Brunini O, Thurtell GW (1982) An improved thermocouple hygrometer for in situ measurements of soil water potential. Soil Sci Soc Am J 46:900–904

Calissendorf C (1970) An in situ leaf and soil water psychrometer having low temperature sensitivity. MS Thesis, Washington State Univ, Pullman, Washington

Campbell EC, Campbell GS, Barlow WK (1973) A dew point hygrometer for water potential measurement. Agric Meteorol 12:113–121

Campbell GS, Campbell MD (1974) Evaluation of a thermocouple hygrometer for measuring leaf water potential in situ. Agron J 66:24–27

Dalton FN, Rawlins SL (1968) Design criteria for Peltier effect thermocouple psychrometers. Soil Sci 105:12–17

Dixon MA, Tyree MT (1984) A new stem hygrometer corrected for temperature gradients and calibrated against the pressure bomb. Plant Cell Environ 7:693–697

Fiscus E (1972) In-situ measurement of root water potential. Plant Physiol 50:191–193

Hoffman GJ, Herkelrath WN (1968) Design features of intact leaf thermocouple psychrometers for measuring water potential. Trans Am Soc Agric Eng 11:631–634

Hoffman GJ, Rawlins SC (1972) Silver foil psychrometer for measuring leaf water potential in situ. Science 177:802–804

Hsieh JJC, Hungate FP (1970) Temperature compensated Peltier psychrometer for measuring plant and soil water potentials. Soil Sci 110:253–257

Ike IF, Thurtell GW (1981) Water relations of cassava (*Manihot esculenta*), water content, osmotic and turgor potential relationships. Can J Bot 59:956–964

Katchalsky A, Curran PF (1975) Non-equilibrium thermodynamics in biophysics. Harvard Univ Press, p 123

Kitchen JH, Thames JL (1972) Pulsed thermistor psychrometer for measuring vapour pressure transducer. In: Brown RW, Haveren BP van (eds) Psychrometry in water relations research. Utah Agric Exp Stn, Utah State Univ, Logan, Utah, pp 113–119

Klepper B, Barrs HD (1968) Effects of salt secretion on psychrometric determinations of water potential of cotton leaves. Plant Physiol 43:1138–1140

Lambert JR, Schilfgaarde J van (1965) A method of determining the water potential of intact plants. Soil Sci 100:1–9

Lang ARG (1967) Osmotic coefficents and water potentials of sodium chloride solutions from 0 to 40 degrees centigrade. Aust J Chem 20:2017–2023

Lang ARG, Trickett ES (1965) Automatic scanning of Spanner and droplet psychrometry having output up to 30 μV. J Sci Instr 42:777–780

McBurney T, Costigan PA (1982) Measurement of stem water potential of young plants using a hygrometer attached to the stem. J Exp Bot 33:426–431

McBurney T, Costigan PA (1984) Rapid oscillations in plant water potential measured with a stem psychrometer. Am Bot 54:851–853

McBurney T, Costigan PA (1987) Plant water potential measured continuously in the field. Plant Soil 97:145–150

Meeuwig RO (1972) A low-cost thermocouple psychrometer recording system. In: Brown RW, Haveren BP van (eds) Psychrometry in water relations research. Utah Agric Exp Stm, Utah State Univ, Logan, Utah, pp 131–135

Michel BE (1977) A miniature stem thermocouple hygrometer. Plant Physiol 60:645–647

Millar AA, Lang ARG, Gardener WR (1970) Four terminal Peltier type thermocouple psychrometers for measuring water potential in non-isothermal systems. Agron J 62:705–708

Monteith JL (1973) Principles of environmental physics. Arnold, London

Monteith JL, Owen PC (1958) A thermocouple method for measuring relative humidity in the range 95–100%. J Sci Inst 35:443–446

Neumann HH, Thurtell GW (1972) A Peltier cooled thermocouple dew point hygrometer for in situ measurement of water potentials. In: Brown RW, Haveren BP van (eds) Psychrometry in water relations research. Utah Agric Exp Stn, Utah State Univ, Logan, Utah, pp 103–112

Nnyamah JV, Black TA (1977) Field performance of the dew point hygrometer in studies of soil-root water relations. Can J Soil Sci 57:437–444

Nulsen RA, Thurtell GW (1978) Recovery of corn leaf water potential after severe water stress. Agron J 70:903–906

Nulsen RA, Thurtell GW, Stevenson KR (1977) Response of leaf water potential to pressure changes at the root surface of corn plants. Agron J 69:951–954

Pallas JE, Michel BE (1978) Comparison of leaf and stem hygrometer for measuring changes in peanut plant water potential. Peanut Sci 5:65–67

Peck AJ (1968) Theory of the Spanner psychrometer. I. The thermocouple. Agric Meteorol 5:433–447

Peck AJ (1969) Theory of the Spanner psychrometer. 2. Sample effects and equilibration. Agric Meteorol 6:111–124

Rawlins SL (1966) Theory of thermocouple psychrometers used to measure water potential in soil and plant samples. Agric Meteorol 3:293–310

Rawlins SL (1972) Theory of thermocouple psychrometers for measuring plant and soil water potential. In: Brown RW, Haveren BP van (eds) Psychrometry in water relations research. Utah Agric Exp Stn, Utah State Univ, Logan, Utah, pp 43–50

Richards LA, Ogata G (1958) Thermocouple for vapour pressure measurement in biological and soil systems at high relative humidity. Science 128:1089–1090

Ritchie GA, Hinckley TM (1975) The pressure chamber as an instrument for ecological research. In: MacFayden A (ed) Advances in ecological research. Academic Press, New York London, pp 165–254

Savage MJ, Cass A (1984) Measurement of water potential using in situ thermocouple hygrometers. Adv Agron 37:73–126

Savage MJ, Wiebe HH, Cass A (1983) In situ field measurement of leaf water potential using thermocouple psychrometers. Plant Physiol 73:609–613

Savage MJ, Wiebe HH, Cass A (1984) Effect of cuticular abrasion on thermocouple psychrometric in situ measurement of leaf water potential. J Exp Bot 35:36–42

Schaefer NL, Trickett ES, Ceresa A, Barrs HD (1986) Continuous monitoring of plant water potential. Plant Physiol 81:45–49

Scholander PF, Hammel HT, Bradstreet ED, Hemmingsen EA (1965) Sap pressure in vascular plants. Science 148:339–346

Scotter DR (1972) The theoretical and experimental behaviour of a Spanner psychrometer. Agric Meteorol 10:125–136

Shackel KA (1984) Theoretical and experimental errors for in situ measurements of plant water potential. Plant Physiol 75:766–772

Shackel KA (1987) Direct measurement of turgor and osmotic potential in individual epidermal cells. Plant Physiol 83:719–722

Slatyer RO (1967) Plant-water relationships. Academic Press, New York London

Slavik B (1974) Methods of studying plant water relations. In: Ecological studies, vol 9. Chapman & Hall, Springer, Berlin Heidelberg New York

Spanner DC (1951) The Peltier effect and its use in the measurement of suction pressure. J Exp Bot 2:145–168

Tetens O (1930) Über einzige meteorologische Begriffe. Z Geophys 6:297–309

Turner NC (1981) Correction of flow resistances of plants measured from covered and exposed leaves. Plant Physiol 68:1090–1092

Turner NC, Long MJ (1980) Errors arising from rapid water loss in measurement of leaf water potential by pressure chamber technique. Aust J Plant Physiol 7:527–537

Turner NC, Spurway RA, Schulze ED (1984) Comparison of water potentials measured by in situ psychrometry and pressure chamber in morphologically different species. Plant Physiol 74:316–319
Wenhert W, Lemon ER, Sinclair TR (1978) Changes in water potential during pressure bomb measurement. Agron J 70:353–355
Wiebe HH (1984) Water condensation on Peltier-cooled thermocouple psychrometers: a photographic study. Agron J 76:166–168
Wiebe HH, Prosser RJ (1977) Influence of temperature gradients on leaf water potential. Plant Physiol 59:256–258
Wiebe HH, Brown RW, Daniel TW, Campbell E (1970) Water potential measurements in trees. Bioscience 20:225–226
Wylie RG (1962) Psychrometry. In: Thewlis J (ed) Encyclopedic dictionary of physics. Pergamon, Oxford New York, pp 692–693

Dehydration and Rehydration During Pollen Development, Pollination, and Fertilization

J. F. Jackson

1 Introduction

Sexual reproduction in plants involves some of the most dramatic developmental changes that plants ever undergo. Meiosis itself brings about enormous ultrastructural changes within the cell, the microspores so formed divide into generative and vegetative cells. These are both contained in the pollen grains that subsequently develop. The development of the pollen grain involves considerable loss of water vapor, so that by anthesis when pollen is finally shed the water content of the pollen may be as low as 9% and rarely more than 60%, depending on the species. Grass pollens normally have a higher water content at maturity than the pollen from most dicotyledonous plants. An exception is the pollen from sea grasses, which, because of the aqueous environment in their habitat, do not suffer the dehydration seen in the land plants.

It is well known that drought and associated high temperature can have enormous effects on seed set in many crop plants, much of it due to effects on pollination and ensuing fertilization. In crops such as maize, drought may put anthesis and style (silk) emergence out of synchrony and have deleterious effects this way, or of course seed development itself could be adversely affected. However, the effects of drought can also be partly attributed to such factors as the excessive loss of water vapor from pollen leading to inviability, and dehydration of stigmas which may also result in reduced seed set.

The pollen grain when shed at anthesis is virtually in a state of dormancy because of its dehydrated state. It remains in this dormant state until it comes in contact with a receptive stigma. At this point there is rehydration of the pollen grain, presumably at the expense of the stigma; this rehydration sets in motion the swelling of the pollen grain and the emergence of the pollen tube. The tube carries the sperm cells derived from the generative cell down through the stigma and style to the ovule, where fertilization takes place. The act of fertilization itself may need adequate hydration of the tissue involved. It is apparent then that the state of hydration of many parts of the flower is of vital importance for successful fertilization and subsequent seed set, and of course is the "raison d'être" for this chapter.

The chapter is organized in such a way as to, in the first place, describe flower development, after which the topic of dehydration of pollen during development will be taken up, followed by a consideration of rehydration of pollen during pollination. Then follows a description of the measurement of water potential, humidity, and the various procedures for determining water content and the interaction of water with various tissues of the flower, the various means of analyzing the biology of dehydration and hydration having been dealt with in the preceding sections.

2 Flower Development

Flowering plants produce spores. As in animals, certain cells of the plant undergo meiosis giving clusters of cells with haploid chromosome content. In the angiosperms the organ that gives rise to the male spores, or microspores as they are known, is called the anther. The female spores, or megaspores, arise in the ovary, again as a result of meiosis (Fig. 1). Both anther and ovary are specialized tissues of the flower. In gymnosperms, including the pines and some other species, the male spores are formed on the microsporophylls, while the female or megaspores are produced in the megasporophylls (Stanley and Linskens 1974). In both gymnosperms and angiosperms, during the meiotic events that produce microspores and megaspores, dramatic ultrastructural changes take place. Included in these changes are alterations to Golgi bodies, and severe regression in the various plastids resulting, in most cases, in unrecognizable structures within the spores. However, the mitochondria are not degraded to such an extent at this time and some remain functional during meiosis (Vijayaraghavan and Bhatia 1985).

The microspore once formed may undergo one, two, or even three mitotic divisions, depending on the plant species, followed by a dormant or resting period when the pollen grain, as the microspore has now become, is shed from the anther at anthesis. It is during the formation of this pollen grain that there is a large water loss from this tissue. The pollen grain is therefore a dehydrated entity. It has long been known that premature dehydration can of itself induce division of the generative cell in certain species (Poddubnaya-Arnoldi 1936; Geitler 1942), so it seems to be an important part of the sequence of events leading to mature pollen grain formation. During the first mitotic division of the microspore, two

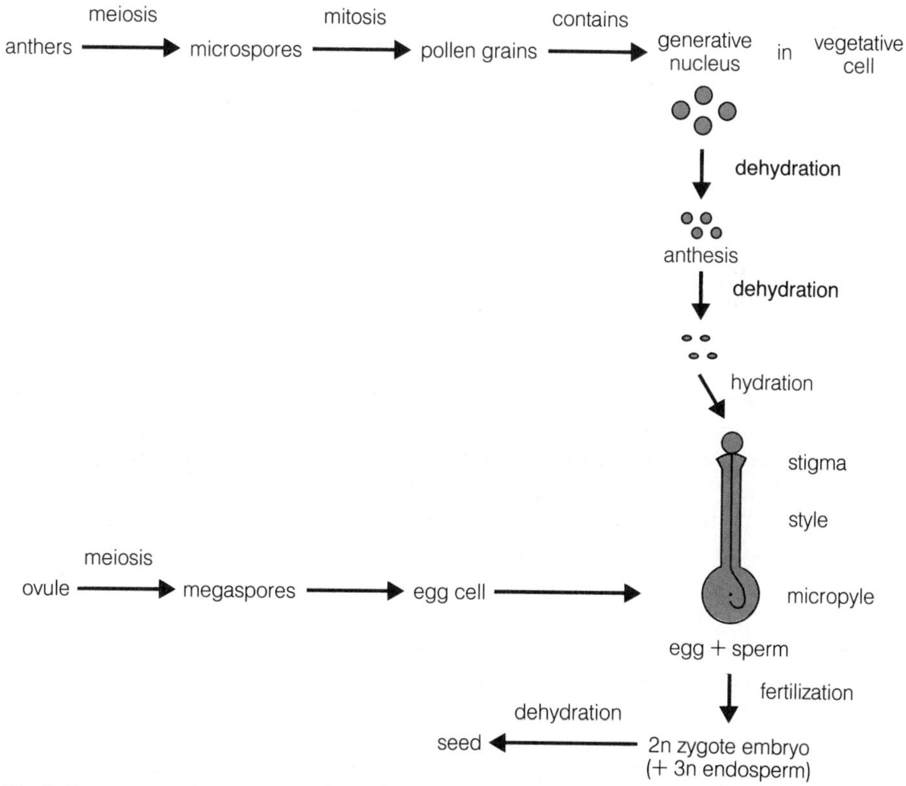

Fig. 1. Diagrammatic representation of reproduction in angiosperms

unequal cells are produced. One is the generative cell which ultimately gives rise to two sperm cells and which is embedded in the other cell to be produced at this first mitosis, the vegetative cell. The pollen grain after anthesis is therefore correctly termed a multicellular male gametophyte. This association is known as the male germ unit (Dumas et al. 1984). Most of the microspore organelles are incorporated into the vegetative cell. The two male sperm cells form in the pollen grain or in the pollen tube produced from the pollen grain at the time of germination of pollen. In angiosperms the pollen grain alights on the receptive surface or stigma of the female portion of the flower and there germinates. The stigma is connected by the style to the ovary, which is within an enlarged tissue at the base of the style. The ovary contains the ovules, each with an embryo sac containing several cells. One of these cells is the egg cell with which the male cell or sperm must fuse for successful fertilization (Fig. 1). The male cells or sperm are conveyed down the style toward the egg cell by the pollen tube which emerges from the pollen grain. There is considerable interaction between the pollen grain and/or pollen tube and the stigma and stylar tissue (Heslop-Harrison 1975, 1978). One of the effects of this interaction is a rehydration of the pollen grain on the receptive stigma, before the pollen tube emerges, presumably at the expense of contained water on or in the stigmatic tissue. Once the male sperm cells carried within the pollen tube reach the base of the style, the sperm enter the ovary through the micropyle.

In gymnosperms the pollen is transferred directly (e.g., by wind, etc.) to the micropyle of the ovule, instead of being transported there by pollen tube penetration of the stylar column following transfer to stigma by wind, insect, or other vectors as takes place in angiosperms. In both angiosperms and gymnosperm plants, there are two sperm cells within or arising from the pollen grain. An exception is in cycad pollen where there may be as many as 24 sperm cells within one pollen grain (Favre-Duchartre 1963). The sperm cells participate in double fertilization in angiosperms, one of the sperm cells forming the 2n zygote, the other giving rise to the 3n endosperm (Fig. 1). In gymnosperms, however, one sperm cell usually disintegrates leaving only one which produces a 2n zygote on fertilization.

3 Dehydration of Pollen

3.1 Dehydration During Development

Pollen grains are mobile plant spores in a state of extreme dehydration. At the time pollen is shed at anthesis, water content can be as low as 10% or less, a figure quoted for *Populus* pollen, to as high as 50–60% as seen in many grass pollens. Many species have a pollen water content of between 15 and 30% (Table 1). Dehydration of the microspores giving rise to pollen grains takes place over a period of several days at a time of many changes, morphologically and biochemically speaking. It may be that the very survival of pollen grains during its mobile phase in an often dry atmosphere is dependent on this dehydrated state. In this context it should be noted that the pollens with highest water content (e.g., grass pollens) have a very short survival time of an hour or so (Kerhoas and Dumas 1986), while the dry pollens have a much longer survival time of at least several days, or even years if kept frozen as in the case of certain *Pinus* species. After being shed at anthesis, the drier pollens lose little further moisture, presumably because of the effects of a plasma membrane or the thick outer cell wall with its often viscous covering.

According to Kerhoas and Dumas (1986), there are three states in which the plasma membrane can be found. The first of these is a porous-type membrane to

Table 1. Water content of pollen (% fresh weight)

Species	(%)	Ref.
Zea mays	57–58	Kerhoas et al. (1987)
Wheat	55	Kerhoas and Dumas (1986)
Cucurbita pepo	45	Gay et al. (1987)
Brassica spp.	20	Kerhoas and Dumas (1986)
Typha spp.	20	Stanley and Linskens (1974)
Pinus spp.	20	Stanley and Linskens (1974)
Populus spp.	9	Kerhoas and Dumas (1986)

be found in the shorter-lived grass pollens. The second type covers those with a continuous membrane, and is to be found in pollens with an intermediate water content (e.g., *Brassica*). The third category has a discontinuous plasma membrane, possessed in general by pollens with a normally low water content (e.g., *Populus*). Electron microscope studies suggest that there is a vesicular structure to be found in pollen with this type of discontinuous plasma membrane. The first and third of these categories are shown by pollens dispersed by wind, while the second type is typical of pollen transferred by animal or insect vectors; the wall is thick and covered by a coating of sticky pollen kit as in *Brassica* for example.

Humidity can have quite large effects on the metabolism of developing pollen grains. Thus, early work has shown that flowers of *Corylus* spp., *Cornus* spp., or *Poa* spp. when developing in high humidity contain less starch than when the same flowers reach anthesis at low humidity (Stanley and Linskens 1974). The maturation period, when storage reserves such as starch are synthesized, is also a stage when much desiccation takes place. Low humidity can bring on the first mitosis of the generative cell of microspores (see above).

A biological analysis of water loss has been approached by Heslop-Harrison (1979a), who has identified the routes by which water vapor is lost during anther dehydration. He found that different types of pollen grains can have quite different sealing devices for preventing water loss or controlling water-vapor flow (in or out). Heslop-Harrison (1979a) classifies sealing devices according to the exine type. It should be first noted that there are two domains in pollen grain walls (Heslop-Harrison 1975); the exine or outer layer with "patterning" on the very outermost surface made up of sporopollenins, and the intine, which is an inner, smooth layer predominantly of polysaccharide. Those pollens with *colpate or sulcate* type exines, which in general have a furrow-type aperture through which water vapor (or liquid) may come or go, have specific mechanisms for dehydration, e.g., infolding with buckling, folding (*Gladiolus*), or interleaving shutters, and may have lipid seals as on *Lilium*. A second type is the *porate type* exine, which may contain either a single pore with operculum as in the grasses, or have multiple pores with either operculum with or without lipid seals (Caryophyllaceae) or occlusion with granules and lipid seal (Malvaceae). In the third or *polyporate pollen grains*, the exine is usually massive and there is usually present a thick lipid seal. Knox (1984) presents scanning electron micrographs of such pollen grains showing these apertures in *Eucalyptus, Amyema, Ricinus, Datura, Cos-*

mos, and *Crossandra.* This third type is common among the dicotyledonous plants. The fourth type have *no apertures*, and the exine is reduced but with increased intine. It includes *Populus* with a very low water content (<10%), and the sea grasses which exist in an aqueous environment. In both of these types movement of water vapor is either not desirable or irrelevant. An aperture at pollen germination in this type is synthesized de novo at a site near contact with the stigma (Knox 1984).

As indicated previously dehydration of the microspore begins during maturation, several days before anthesis. Just before anthesis, pollen grains actually decrease in size. This probably represents an intense period of desiccation (Banerjee et al. 1965; Vithanage and Knox 1980; Willemse and Reznickov 1980). It should be mentioned while discussing the movement of water in and out of pollen that there is an allergen present on the surface and in the cytoplasm of rye pollen which is in a position to readily induce allergic reactions in the upper respiratory tract of susceptible human beings (Heslop-Harrison 1979 b). As pointed out by Knox (1984), this response is probably an unfortunate accident of evolution. The allergen is released very rapidly when the pollen is moistened, the mature and partly desiccated rye pollen grain does not have an intact plasma membrane to regulate the entry of water so that rapid release of allergens from cytoplasmic sites takes place. The lipid micelles reform plasma membranes soon after rehydration, but not soon enough to stop outflow of some allergens.

3.2 Dehydration of Pollen After Anthesis and Some Consequences of Dehydration

The mobile phase in pollen development can involve many transfer vectors, including wind. Some windborne pollen may travel great distances before alighting on a receptive stigma, influenced by the size and buoyancy of pollen (some gymnosperm pollens possess air sacs), wind velocity, and uplifting currents of air (Linskens 1982). The conditions encountered during the mobile phase may well then lead to further dehydration, the consequences of which are discussed by Jackson (1987). It is suggested that dehydration in many of the pollens has potential to lead to gamete DNA damage, necessitating repair of some sort before fertilization occurs. DNA repair has indeed been described in germinating pollen from *Petunia hybrida* (Jackson and Linskens 1978, 1979, 1980, 1982).

In pointing out the implications of dehydration for pollen and gamete DNA and the importance therefore of monitoring desiccation, it should be mentioned that ultraviolet irradiation of certain bacterial spores gives rise to an unusual thymine dimer not of the usual cyclobutane type, but rather of an azatene type called "spore product." It is considered that this arises because of the supposed dehydrated state of DNA within bacterial spores (Varghese 1970), since the same spore product arises from UV irradiation of dry DNA (Smith and Hanawalt 1969) and from UV irradiation of vegetative bacterial cells which have first been frozen to −80° C in order to reduce the amount of liquid water around the contained DNA (Gould 1983). Like pollen, many bacterial and fungal spores are considered to be dehydrated, although uncontroversial measurements of the water content of these spores have not been made. Gould (1983) suggests that spores from *N. crassa* can have a water content of between 5 and 65% depending on the humidity, while spores of *B. cereus* in an aqueous environment may have approximately 50% water content, compared to about 75% for the vegetative cell. Certainly dielectric and NMR data suggests that water molecules in spores lack rotational mobility and/or exchange motions when compared with vegetative cells. It seems likely then that like many pollens, bacterial and fungal spores are extensively dehydrated compared to their vegetative counterpart and that the contained spore DNA has an altered "dry" conformation (Wang et al. 1983; Saenger et al. 1986), possibly of an A type (Setlow and Setlow 1987) or even Z type. It seems reasonable to suppose that some pollen could also have such a DNA conformation. Such a structure has implications for increased damage to DNA, as dehydration tends to lead to some unwinding of DNA (Lee et al. 1981), resulting in increased ability to bind mutagens, metal ions, etc. It also gives an increased yield of the azatene thymine dimer compared to the quantum yield of normal thymine dimer arising from UV irradiation of B DNA, while spontaneous deamination of cytosine to uracil may also be increased (Jackson 1987).

4 Pollination and Rehydration of Pollen

Before discussing the rehydration of pollen that occurs on pollination, mention should first be made of the work of Gilissen (1977) who observed the effect of hydration of *Petunia hybrida* pollen grains on subsequent swelling of pollen in liquid culture medium. Gilissen showed that prior hydration (i.e., pretreatment at high relative humidity) of pollen grains gives a threefold increase in volume of pollen after placing in culture medium, compared with a twofold increase with desiccated pollen. He attributes the difference in swelling ability to the different rigidities associated with the different hydration states. It appears that water molecules from air are able to penetrate and leave the pollen quite easily.

Prior hydration of *Petunia hybrida* pollen also increases germination and pollen tube elongation (Gilissen 1977), so it would seem important for adequate seed set, at least for *Petunia hybrida*, that there be sufficiently high humidity at the time of pollination. Shivanna and Heslop-Harrison (1981) also observed increased pollen germination after hydration of grass pollens.

Biological analysis of changes in structure in and around the aperture of grass pollen during hydration following pollination has been studied by Heslop-Harrison and Heslop-Harrison (1980). They showed that in *Poa annua* pollen there is a lens-shaped oncus beneath the operculum which is composed of acidic polysaccharides (pectins) which becomes gellike when the pollen is hydrated, causing the operculum to lift off to open up the aperture and which dissolves in front of the emerging pollen tube.

Pollen germination in vitro or on the stigma in vivo, is triggered by hydration. The pollen grain swells, and a pollen tube emerges, which penetrates the stigma and makes its way toward the ovule.

5 Water Potential and Its Measurement in Reproductive Tissues

The water stress that is experienced by a particular tissue can be estimated by measuring the water potential of that plant tissue. These measurements are made with thermocouple psychrometers. The tissue and thermocouple are enclosed in the same small container maintained at constant temperature and the degree of cooling of the thermocouple observed as water evaporates from it and is absorbed by the tissue. The use of the Richards and Ogata psychrometers (Richards and Ogata 1958) and Spanner's psychrometer (Spanner 1951) assumed that the rate of vapor transfer is proportional to the difference in potential between the thermocouple and plant material. However, the work of Boyer and Knipling (1965) showed this assumption to be in error because of so-called leaf resistance (leaf being the plant tissue most often examined). These authors devised a variation of the basic method by using a Richards-Ogata-type thermocouple to determine the rate of water vapor movement between the thermocouple and the leaf when solutions of various potentials are present on the thermocouple. No vapor movement occurs when the solution on the thermocouple has a potential equal to that of the tissue and therefore "leaf resistance" or resistance of other tissue does not affect the measurement at this point. The rate of vapor transfer from the drop in which the thermocouple is placed may be given as:

$$\frac{dm}{dt_d} = \frac{-c_0 \bar{V} La_m a_p}{RT(La_m r_p + a_p r_a)} (\Psi_0 - \Psi_p), \qquad (1)$$

where $(dm/dt)_d$ is the rate of vapor transfer from the drop (g s^{-1}), c_0 is the saturation vapor concentration of water at the bath temperature, V is the partial molal volume of water (liters $mole^{-1}$), R is the ideal gas constant (liters bars $mole^{-1}$ deg^{-1}), T is absolute temperature, L is the proportionality constant, a_m is the geometric mean area for flow (cm^2), r_p is the resistance of plant tissue to vapor diffusion, a_p the area of the plant tissue, r_a is the resistance of the air to vapor transfer (sec cm^{-1}), ψ_0 is the water potential of the droplet at the thermocouple, and ψ_p is the water potential of the plant tissue. Equation (1) describes a straight line with a slope of $-c_0VLA_ma_p/RT(La_mr_p+a_pr_a)$. The tissue resistance r_p will affect the rate of vapor transfer at all points except where ψ_0 equals ψ_p and dm/dt is zero. This isopiestic point may be determined by measuring thermocouple output when ψ_0 is changed. Then a thermocouple output of zero indicates no net transfer of vapor.

Water potential measurements have recently been used as an aid to the study of the effects of water stress on pollen viability, stigma receptivity, fertilization, and seed set in maize. Thus, Schoper et al. (1986), knowing that water stress (drought) and associated high temperatures have a depressing effect on maize productivity in the field (Boyer 1982), investigated maize pollen viability and ear receptivity in plants under water stress and at high temperatures. They measured ear-leaf water potential to monitor the degree of water stress each plant was subject to, and found that the number of kernels (i.e., seed set) was not decreased when pollen from water-stressed plants was used to pollinate normal plants.

However, when pollen was used to pollinate water-stressed plants, there was a decided reduction in the number of kernels. It was deduced from this and other experiments that pollen viability is not affected by water stress on the plants, but that stigma receptivity leading to seed set certainly is. High temperature affected both pollen and stigma, however (Schoper et al. 1986), and actually reduced the amount of pollen shed from the anthers.

Sexual reproduction in maize has also been investigated by Westgate and Boyer (1986a, b). They went further than Schoper et al. (1986) and actually measured the water potential of the various parts of maize flowers under varying degrees of water stress to the plant. They measured the water potential of pollen, silk, and leaf, using two sets of plants – one set being well watered and the other set having water withheld. In plants supplied with water, the leaf-water potential varied diurnally between -0.15 and -0.17 MP_a, while silk changed less (from -0.3 to -0.6 MP_a). Fresh pollen varied initially from -1.2 MPa to an extremely low -12.5 MP_a as the day progressed. In plants which had water withheld, pollen water potential was observed to be as effectively measured as above, but leaf decreased to -1.7 MP_a and silk to -1.2 MP_a. Thus, silk followed the water stress of the leaf while pollen did not, reflecting reports that water-stressed plants produced pollen with apparently normal viability. The data of Westgate and Boyer (1986) also shows that since pollen water potential is always lower than that of the silk, water will always move from stigma to pollen during pollination. They deduce that pollen desiccation should not be a factor limiting grain production in the field, as far as maize is concerned, although Schoper et al. (1986) suggest that any effect on the amount of pollen actually shed should not be overlooked. The importance of the work of Westgate and Boyer (1986) lies in the measurement of the water potential of pollen for the first time, and they did this using the isopiestic point determination corrected for the heat of respiration. The thermocouple chambers were coated with melted and resolidified petrolatum to reduce sorption effects, and the accuracy of measurements depended on sealing the pollen or silk samples rapidly within the chamber and protecting samples from dehydration during sampling procedures. Freshly collected pollen from anthers that dehisced the same morning was collected by shaking the tassel at various times during the day into a bag and transferred immediately to a shoot bag to reduce evaporation and separated from anthers and debris. Pollen was then transferred to a psychrometer chamber directly from a hole in the corner of the bag. In this way shed pollen was exposed to the air a minimum time (about 10 s) and approximately 30 to 45 s were required to transfer the pollen from plant to sealed chamber.

In a companion paper, Westgate and Boyer (1986a) measured losses in grain yield as a result of varying water stress to maize plants. At high water potential in pollen and stigma, approximately 550 grains/ear were produced, a figure which was also produced at low (-12.5 MP_a) water potential in pollen. In contrast, at low silk water potential (-1.2 MP_a) grain set was reduced to zero. Examination of the silks under the latter conditions showed that they were still receptive to pollen, that the pollen tubes grew down the silks, and in fact fertilization also took place. However, the embryo, endosperm, and seed coat did not develop after 2 or 3 days. It seemed then that fertilization was successfully achieved on silks with low water potential from plants in drought, but that factors within the female portion of the plant did not allow development of the embryo, perhaps due to starvation of "substrate" in some way (e.g., photosynthate).

Westgate and Boyer (1986a) suggest that decreased grain production in maize at reduced water potential at the time of anthesis could be considered to be the result of (1) disruption of megasporogenesis; (2) the tassel may not emerge, the anther may not exert, silk may not elongate, or there may be asynchrony in flower development; (3) embryos may not grow in flowers that otherwise had developed normally.

6 Humidity Measurement

In view of the dehydration/rehydration events that take place in the course of flower development, it follows that the relative humidity in and around the flower at this time could be important. Gay et al. (1987) have recently reported on their investigations with the effect of humidity on the quality of *Cucurbita pepo* pollen through the various stages of flower development. Relative humidity can be measured with an hygrometric probe; such an instrument is available from Hygrocor, Bioblock, Strasbourg, France. Gay et al. (1987) placed a probe 2 mm from the stigma and another "control" probe outside the flower. The first probe close to the stigma is therefore within the corolla. In *Cucurbita pepo* the flowers open the corollas at the end of the night, and gradually close them again as the sun rises. During hot summer days the corollas are fully closed before midday. Gay et al. (1987) found that as the corolla closes, the relative humidity (RH) within the flower actually rises from approximately 40% RH to more than 70% RH after 18 h. Meanwhile, the RH outside the flower was maintained at approximately 46% by fresh weight if the corolla was intact. If, however, the corolla was first excised, *Cucurbita pepo* pollen water content dropped to 15% by fresh weight, and was no longer viable as confirmed by the fluorochromatic-reaction test (FCR) of Heslop-Harrison and Heslop-Harrison (1970). When enclosed within the corolla, 100% of the pollen was scored as viable. These results show the importance of relative humidity for viability of pollen and therefore seed set on this type of plant. It is of interest to note the contrasting result described above with maize. Thus, we have in *Cucurbita pepo* a water-stress sensitive pollen which cannot tolerate the stress of a water content below approximately 25% water by fresh weight. This same pollen will not survive storage at 4° C for more than 4 days.

Cucurbita pepo therefore has two strategies for overcoming water stress leading to relatively inviable pollen: (1) humidity kept high by enclosure of pollen within closed corolla, (2) parthenocarpy results with poor quality of pollen, so that at least a few seed may result rather than none at all. The latter could occur under stress conditions.

7 Measurement of Water Content

7.1 ^{1}H-NMR

The use of proton-NMR to reveal the complexity of water and membrane behavior during dehydration of pollen has the advantage that it is a nondestructive method and can discriminate between different types of water molecules in biological tissues. The principle of the technique involves the resonance of hydrogen nuclei when placed in an intense magnetic field. These nuclei absorb radiation at characteristic frequencies and the resulting spectral lines are measured as line positions, intensities, widths in transient and line-dependent experiments. These results can be interpreted in terms of the structure of the molecule containing these nuclei, conformation and molecular motion, etc. (Cohen 1983). The protons can be grouped according to energy levels; transitions between these states and absorption frequencies due to hydrogen in water can be observed by NMR.

Kerhoas and Dumas (1986) have described the use of NMR in two experiments on the dehydration of pumpkin pollen after dehiscence from the anther. In the first, the kinetics of water loss was monitored both by gravimetric means and by NMR. Both methods showed a curve of water loss over time with three discernible stages: an initial rapid dehydration from 46% water content to about 40%, with minimal loss in viability using the FCR test of Heslop-Harrison and Heslop-Harrison (1970) until approaching 40% water content. Then a second stage of slower water loss associated with a rapid decrease in viability, followed by a third stage of even slower water loss and with very little viability. The second experiment using NMR attempts to explain the existence of the three stages through the use of nuclear relaxation phenomena. In this approach a radiofrequency is applied to the pollen, inducing a transverse magnetization which declines when the radiofrequency is stopped. Transverse magnetization decays exponentially with relaxation time T_2, and provides us with a means of studying water mobility in the pollen, since relaxation time is considered to be related to interactions between water and contents of the cell. Pollen grains were examined following the Meiboon Carr Purcell spin echo method (Kerhoas and Dumas 1986) and T_2 estimated for each of the stages seen above in the kinetic experiments. Results were interpreted in terms of two types of cellular water-bound (with low T_2 values) and free or "bulk" water (high T_2). The first, rapidly dehydrating stage represented the loss of water from the "free water" compartment. As free water approaches exhaustion the plasmalemma is considered to begin breaking down and viability drops. In the second stage, Kerhoas and Dumas (1986) consider that the plasmalemma and internal membranes lose water, while the third stage represents the freezing of all water from the now lifeless pollen grain.

Controlled dehydration of *Zea mays* pollen has been studied by Kerhoas et al. (1987) using ^{1}H-NMR transverse relaxation time (T_2) measurements. These authors observed a steadily decreasing T_2 until about 15% water content when it began to increase again, a result which was interpreted as a steadily increasing proportion of bound water as dehydration proceeds until 15% water content, and a sudden increase in water mobility from this point. It was considered that the latter represented water replacement at the membrane level, with carbohydrate stabilizing membrane structure down to a water content as low as 3%.

7.2 ^{1}H-NMR Imaging

Spatially localized magnetic resonance was first demonstrated by Lauterbur (1974), and its use in obtaining magnetic resonance imaging in plants has since been demonstrated by several laboratories (Lauterbur 1974; Hinshaw 1976; Mansfield and Pykett 1978; Omasa et al. 1985; Bottomley et al. 1986). Previously, sample volumes exceeded 10 mm^3; now, however, resolution is increasing and the method extended into the microscopic area as shown by Johnson et al. (1987). These workers examined stem tissues by *Pelargonium hortorum* and obtained ^{1}H images with a resolution of 10 μm transversely and 1250 μm thickness. While this is still much too coarse for examination of single pollen grains, it could presumably be used for packed, mature pollen grains. Of more immediate interest would be imaging of anthers, where information could be gained on the dehydration of pollen grains that occur before anthesis, or the imaging of stigma, pistils, or even the ovule, where, as seen in the sections above, dehydration in these tissues as occurs in drought can have a severely depressing effect on seed set.

Johnson et al. (1987) used a prototype magnetic resonance system designed for clinical imaging, modified for microscopy by the addition of a small set of gradient coils to produce the high gradients (0.47 mT cm^{-1}) necessary for microscopy with three-dimensional spin-warp imaging, images with individual elements of $100 \times 100 \times 1250$ μm was obtained. In principle, externally applied radiofrequency pulses at the Larmor frequency manipulate the processing protons in the magnetic field away from their equilibrium position. The protons absorb energy in doing this, energy which is later reemitted and localized in space to give a digital image by application of magnetic gradients. The signal changes resulting from changes in water content can be interpreted in terms of proton density (N_H) and spin lattice relaxation time (T_1). The former gives the apparent water content and the latter gives the degree of water binding, that is water that is hydrogen bonded to larger macromolecules (Johnson et al. 1987).

7.3 ^{31}P-NMR for Membranes

Theoretically, polymorphic phases that may arise in phospholipids making up biological membranes could be monitored by ^{31}P-NMR, and certainly ^{31}P-NMR studies of *Typha latifolia* pollen at anthesis suggest that the membrane lipids are arranged in a bilayer (Priestly and DeKruijff 1982) even down to 11% water content. These studies were carried out especially because of the dehydration that occurs during pollen development. However, a severe limitation to further ^{3}P-NMR investigation is the inability to discriminate between membranes of subcellular components.

7.4 Freeze Fracture Replicas for Membranes

Cytological studies of pollen after anhydrous fixation have been carried out using freeze fracture replicas (Kerhoas ct al. 1987). This has enabled observation of membrane structure from 57% water content, corresponding to normal anthesis in *Zea mays* pollen, down to 3% water content, when the pollen is no longer viable. At 57% water content the vegetative plasma membrane is continuous with a very low density of intramembranous particles on the extraplasmic fracture face. At 28% water content, maize pollen viablity has dropped considerably and it is considered that there is formation of gel phase domains with greatly altered permeability of the membranes. At 15–13% water content all pollen is nonviable, gel phase microdomains more numerous but membranes still have a bilayer structure.

These studies using freeze fracture replicas were carried out following fixing of maize pollen in glutaraldehyde vapors (1 h) and osmium tetroxide vapors (1 h) to preserve water content. Samples were then incubated for 1 h in 3% glycerol-0.1 *M* cacodylate buffer pH 7.4. Fractures were achieved in a CF250 Jung Reichert cryofract, and replicas were prepared as described by Escaig and Nicolas (1976). Carbon and platinum were used for replica shadowing for electron microscopy.

7.5 Calorimetric Analysis

A differential scanning calorimeter is marketed by Mettler of Giessen, FRG. Freezing rate is $-5°$ C min^{-1}, pollen grains and an inert material such as aluminum are cooled in two different cells of the calorimeter so that a zero temperature difference is maintained between them. As cooling takes place, exothermal flux related to the freezing of all water, induces a temperature difference between the two cells. The transient temperature difference is compensated by a supplementary cold flow which is recorded as a peak, the area under which relates to the enthalpy change of the transition of pollen water from liquid to solid state.

Kerhoas et al. (1987) have used this technique to determine the proportion of freezable water in pollen from maize, as the pollen undergoes dehydration following anthesis. They found that the pollen when shed at 57% water content has large amounts of freezable "unbound" water, but that by 28% total water content, the pollen grain contains no unbound water which is crystallizable.

7.6 Other Methods

Total water content can be determined by gravimetric means before and after drying in, for example, an infrared desiccator, as marketed by Sartorius (1265 MP) in Göttingen, FRG. Kerhoas et al. (1987) use 5 min at 85° C for this determination.

The fluorochromatic reaction test of Heslop-Harrison and Heslop-Harrison (1970) has been used as an adjunct to desiccation studies, since it is a measure of viability of pollen depending on membrane integrity. The test is based on the penetration of fluorescein diacetate (nonfluorescent and nonpolar) into the pollen grain and subsequent hydrolysis by esterase to yield the brightly fluorescent fluorescein. The latter is quite polar and cannot pass through the plasma membrane as freely as the ester coming in. A viable pollen accumulates fluorescence within the pollen, a nonviable pollen may not produce fluorescence at all.

8 Summary

The various stages of flower development are described and the steps involving dehydration and hydration identified. A biological analysis of the dehydration and rehydration of pollen follows, gathered from various published sources, and some consequences of dehydration pointed out. One of these is the possible production of "dry" DNA structures, such as A or Z DNA, as in bacterial spores, giving rise to a potential for increased DNA damage and mutation in the sperm.

The measurement and use of water potential and humidity, and estimation of water content by NMR and differential scanning calorimetry are presented and discussed, together with other parameters linked with water vapor loss or gain, such as membrane integrity and the fluorochromatic test. The potential for further development of the ^{1}H-NMR imaging technique is recognized, especially for use in the microscopic domain. In the light of the findings already made with the effects of drought and heat stress on the maize reproductive system and the effects on seed production as described herein, it is considered that there is potential for gain with similar studies on reproductive systems in the various dryland crop plants.

References

Banerjee VC, Rowley JR, Alessio ML (1965) Exine plasticity during pollen grain maturation. J Palynol 1:70–89

Bottomley PA, Rogers HH, Foster TH (1986) NMR imaging shows water distribution and transport in plant root systems in situ. Proc Natl Acad Sci USA 83:87–89

Boyer JS (1982) Plant productivity and environment. Science 218:443–448

Boyer JS, Knipling EB (1965) Isopiestic technique for measuring leaf water potentials with a thermocouple psychrometer. Proc Natl Acad Sci USA 54:1044–1052

Cohen JS (ed) (1983) Magnetic resonance in biology, vol 2. Wiley, New York

Dumas C, Knox RB, Gaude T (1984) Pollen recognition: new concepts from electron microscopy and cytochemistry. Int Rev Cytol 90:239–272

Escaig J, Nicolas G (1976) Cryo-fractures de material biologique realisees a tres basses temperatures en ultravide. C R Acad Sci 283:1245–1248

Favre-Duchartre M (1963) Structure of cycad pollen. Ann Sci Nat Bot 12th Ser 5:233–239

Gay G, Kerhoas C, Dumas C (1987) Quality of a stress-sensitive *Cucurbita pepo* L. pollen. Planta 171:82–87

Geitler L (1942) State of hydration influences division of sperm cells in pollen. Planta 32:187–195
Gilissen LJW (1977) The influence of relative humidity on the swelling of pollen grains in vitro. Planta 137:299–301
Gould GW (1983) Resistance and dormancy of bacterial endospores. In: Hurst A, Gould GW (eds) The bacterial spore, vol 2. Academic Press, New York London, p 173
Heslop-Harrison J (1975) Physiology of the pollen-grain surface. Proc R Soc London Ser B 190:275–300
Heslop-Harrison J (1978) Cellular recognition systems in plants. Studies in biology, 100, Arnold, London
Heslop-Harrison J (1979a) Pollen walls as adaptive systems. Ann MO Bot Gard 66:813–829
Heslop-Harrison J (1979b) Aspects of the structure, cytochemistry, and germination of the pollen of rye (*Secale cereale* L.). Ann Bot Suppl 1:1–47
Heslop-Harrison J, Heslop-Harrison Y (1970) Evaluation of pollen viability by enzymatically induced fluorescence, intracellular hydrolysis of fluorescein diacetate. Stain Technol 45:115–120
Heslop-Harrison J, Heslop-Harrison Y (1980) Cytochemistry and function of the Zwischenkörper in grass pollen. Pollen Spores 22:5–10
Hinshaw WS (1976) NMR images of whole fruit. J Appl Phys 47:3709
Jackson JF (1987) DNA repair in pollen – a review. Mutat Res 181:17–29
Jackson JF, Linskens HF (1978) Evidence for DNA repair after ultraviolet irradiation of *Petunia hybrida* pollen. Mol Gen Genet 161:117–120
Jackson JF, Linskens HF (1979) Pollen DNA repair after treatment with the mutagens 4-nitroquinoline-1-oxide, ultraviolet and near-ultraviolet irradiation, and boron dependence of repair. Mol Gen Genet 176:11–16
Jackson JF, Linskens HF (1980) DNA repair in pollen: range of mutagens inducing repair, effect of replication inhibitors and changes in thymidine nucleotide metabolism, during repair. Mol Gen Genet 180:517–522
Jackson JF, Linskens HF (1982) Metal ion induced unscheduled DNA synthesis in *Petunia* pollen. Mol Gen Genet 187:112–115
Johnson GA, Brown J, Kramer PJ (1987) Magnetic resonance microscopy of changes in water content in stems of transpiring plants. Proc Natl Acad Sci USA 84:2752–2755
Kaku S, Iwayainove M, Gusta LV (1984) Relationship of nuclear magnetic resonance relaxation time to water content and cold hardiness in flower buds of evergreen azalea. Plant Cell Physiol 25:875–882
Kerhoas C, Dumas C (1986) Nuclear magnetic resonance and pollen quality. In: Linskens HF, Jackson JF (eds) Modern methods of plant analysis, New Series, vol 2. Springer, Berlin Heidelberg New York, pp 169–190
Kerhoas C, Gay G, Dumas C (1987) A multidisciplinary approach to the study of the plasma membrane of *Zea mays* pollen during controlled dehydration. Planta 171:1–10
Knox RB (1984) The pollen grain. In: Johri BM (ed) Embryology of angiosperms. Springer, Berlin Heidelberg New York, pp 212–215
Lauterbur PC (1973) Image formation by induced local interactions: examples employing nuclear magnetic resonance. Nature 242:190–191
Lauterbur PC (1974) Nuclear magnetic imaging of fruits. Pure Appl Chem 40:149–155
Lee C-H, Mizusawa H, Kapepuda T (1981) Unwinding of double-stranded DNA helix by dehydration. Proc Natl Acad Sci USA 78:2838–2842
Linskens HF (1982) Pollen collection during a balloon trip. Incompat Newslett 14:116–121
Mansfield P, Pykett IL (1978) Biological and medical imaging by NMR. J Magn Reson 29:355–360
Omasa K, Onoe M, Yamada H (1985) Nuclear magnetic imaging of intact plants. Environ Control Biol 23:99–102
Poddubnaya-Arnoldi VA (1936) Water availability effects division of sperm cells in pollen grains. Planta 25:502–510

Priestly DA, DeKruijff B (1982) Phospholipid motional characteristics in a dry biological system. A ^{31}P-nuclear magnetic resonance study of hydrating *Typha latifolia* pollen. Plant Physiol 70:1075–1078

Richards LA, Oagata G (1958) Thermocouple for vapor pressure measurement in biological and soil systems at high humidity. Science 128:1089–1090

Saenger W, Hunter WN, Kennard O (1986) DNA conformation is determined by economics in the hydration of phosphate groups. Nature 324:385–388

Schoper JB, Lambert RJ, Vasilas BL (1986) Maize pollen viability and ear receptivity under water and temperature stress. Crop Sci 26:1029–1033

Setlow B, Setlow P (1987) Thymine-containing dimers as well as spore photoproducts are found in ultraviolet-irradiated *Bacillus subtilis* spores that lack small acid-soluble proteins. Proc Natl Acad Sci USA 84:421–423

Shivanna KR, Heslop-Harrison J (1981) Membrane state and pollen viability. Ann Bot 47:759–770

Smith KC, Hanawalt PC (1969) Molecular photobiology. Academic Press, New York London

Spanner DC (1951) Thermocouple psychrometer for leaf water potential. J Exp Bot 2:145–149

Stanley RG, Linskens HF (1974) Pollen biology, biochemistry, management. Springer, Berlin Heidelberg New York

Varghese AJ (1970) 5-Thyminyl-5,6-dihydrothymine from DNA irradiated with ultraviolet light. Biochem Biophys Res Commun 38:484–490

Vijayaraghavan MR, Bhatia K (1985) Cellular changes during microsporogenesis, vegetative and generative cell formation: a review based on ultrastructure and histochemistry. Int Rev Cytol 96:263

Vithanage HIMV, Knox RB (1980) Periodicity of pollen development and quantitative cytochemistry of exine and intine enzymes in the grasses *Lolium perenne* and *Phalaris tuberosa*. Ann Bot 45:131–142

Wang AHJ, Fujii S, Boom JH van, Rich A (1983) Right-handed and left-handed double-helical DNA: structural studies. In: Watson JD, Owen D, Brown D (eds) Structure of DNA. Cold Spring Harbor Symp Quant Biol 47:33–34

Westgate ME, Boyer JS (1986a) Reproduction at low silk and pollen water potentials in maize. Crop Sci 26:951–956

Westgate ME, Boyer JS (1986b) Silk and pollen water potentials in maize. Crop Sci 26:947–951

Willemse MTM, Reznickov SA (1980) Formation of pollen in the anther of *Lilium*. Development of the pollen wall. Acta Bot Neerl 29:127–140

Exchange Determination of Water Vapor, Carbon Dioxide, Oxygen, Ethylene, and Other Gases of Fruits and Vegetables

S. BEN-YEHOSHUA and A. C. CAMERON

1 Introduction

The problem of gas exchange in plants in general and in fruits in particular, is appreciated by considering the fact that plants lack the blood circulatory system which functions in animals to provide gas exchange. Still, fruit tissues are usually adequately ventilated. This accomplishment is especially demonstrated considering the ventilation required for the bulkiest fruits, such as the pumpkin that reached the size of 612 lb. with a radius of over 60 cm (this pumpkin was grown by N. Gallagher from Chelan, Washington in the USA). According to physical laws, if fruit would be of a uniform water phase, then its oxygen would be depleted in a depth of around 0.5 cm. The explanation for the adequate ventilation is in the gas phase that exists in the intercellular spaces.

The gas phase in the intercellular spaces acts as a continuum, which extends throughout the fruit. This gas phase is responsible for the adequate gas exchange within bulky organs and any action that results in the clogging of this space by a liquid leads to inadequate gas exchange and fermentation (Ben-Yehoshua et al. 1963; Sacher 1973). Most, if not all, cells of a fruit are in direct contact with the gaseous phase in the intercellular spaces; this internal atmosphere is generally very different in composition from that outside of the fruit.

Plants have evolved their systems of gas exchange by adjusting to conflicting demands: provisions must exist for an effective route for the exchange of CO_2 and O_2, while minimizing transpiration to prevent desiccation. Thus, the mechanism for gas exchange represents a compromise between maintaining an adequate flux of O_2 and CO_2 and minimizing flux of water vapor. Particularly relevant to this organization of gas exchange is the control of the level of the gaseous phytohormone, ethylene, which has such a strong and versatile effect on the physiological processes of plants (Burg and Burg 1965).

In discussing the interrelation between moisture loss and gas exchange in biology, one is tempted to cite the marvelous coordination of the water loss that allows for the essential gas exchange of the embryo in the eggs of various birds (Rahn et al. 1979).

A thorough knowledge of gas exchange in various fruits and vegetables is essential, since modern practices of handling fruit are based on changing the composition of the fruit's atmosphere by use of controlled atmosphere, or on altering its natural gas exchange characteristics by modified atmosphere packaging or waxing.

2 Physical Laws of Gas Diffusion

Much of the research on gas exchange in bulky plant organs has been restricted to the study of the influence of various external factors on rate of gas flux and internal gas compositions, without much regard for the underlying laws of gas diffusion. Ideally, when there is no pressure-driven mass flow, all gases should behave independently and move at a rate dependent on the diffusive properties of the gas molecule, the magnitude of the gradient, and the physical properties of the intervening barrier (Barrer 1951). This relationship can be described mathematically by a simple form of Fick's first law for flat surfaces, which has often been applied to the study of gas exchange in bulky organs (Trout et al. 1942; Ben-Yehoshua et al. 1963; Marcellin 1963, 1974; Burg and Burg 1965; Burton 1974, 1978; Sastry et al. 1978; Cameron 1982; Cameron and Reid 1982) and in leaves (see Nobel 1974):

$$\mathrm{Ji} = \mathrm{Pi}\ \mathrm{A}\ \Delta \mathrm{X}^{-1}\ (\Delta \mathrm{Ci})\ ,$$

where:

Ji = rate of flux for species i ($cm^3\ s^{-1}$);
Pi = permeability coefficient of gas species i($cm^2\ s^{-1}\ atm^{-1}$);
A = surface area (cm^2);
$\Delta \mathrm{X}$ = barrier thickness (cm);
$\Delta \mathrm{Ci}$ = concentration gradient for gas species.

Cameron (1982) has shown mathematically that this form of Fick's law is valid only if (1) the internal tissue has high permeability relative to the skin, and (2) the barrier at the skin is very thin relative to the radius of the bulky organ. If these conditions are not met, a three-dimensional version of Fick's law may be required (Cameron 1982; Solomos 1987).

In reality, the skin is not homogeneous and its thickness is seldom known. Thus, usually in plant organs, an apparent permeability is measured and reported. This includes the thickness term:

$$\mathrm{Ji} = \mathrm{Pi}'\ \mathrm{A}\ (\Delta \mathrm{Ci})\ ,$$

where:

Pi' = apparent permeability ($cm\ s^{-1}\ atm^{-1}$).

The permeability coefficient is dependent on the physical and molecular properties of the skin of bulky organs and hence is of basic interest in the study of gas diffusion. Often, resistance coefficients are reported in the literature. These are simply the inverse of Pi or Pi′, depending on the measurement. Several approaches have been reported to determine the numerical value of the permeability or resistance (the inverse of the permeability) coefficient. These all fall into two categories: steady state and nonsteady state determinations.

3 Steady State Determination of Parameters of Gas Exchange

3.1 Theoretical Basis

Trout et al. (1942) recognized that permeability coefficients are a basic property of bulky plant organs which could be estimated using Fick's law for flat surfaces. The formulae for calculation are given in Table 1. It should be emphasized that these equations are valid for estimation of permeability coefficients only if the

Table 1. Formulae for steady state estimation of permeability coefficients for oxygen, carbon dioxide, ethylene, and water vapor using measured values of flux, surface area, and partial pressures of the respective gases

$P'_{O_2} = J_{O_2} A^{-1} [(O_2)_{external} - (O_2)_{internal}]$
$P'_{CO_2} = J_{CO_2} A^{-1} [(CO_2)_{internal} - (CO_2)_{external}]$
$P'_{H_2O} = J_{H_2O} A^{-1} [(H_2O)_{internal} - (H_2O)_{external}]$

rate of gas consumption or production by the plant organ is equal to the rate of escape or entry through the skin: a condition defined as "steady state." Steady state determination of Pi′ using the formulae in Table 1 is dependent on accurate measurement of surface area, rate of flux, and the concentration gradient of the gas of interest. Temperature has a profound effect on the measured values and must be carefully controlled in all cases.

3.2 Determination of Surface Area

The easiest method for estimating surface area is to assume the plant organ has a regular shape, such as a sphere, ellipsoid, cylinder, etc., and to calculate the area using standard formulae. This approach works relatively well for fruit such as tomato and apple (spheres), bell pepper (cylinder), and potato (ellipsoid), but is not universally appropriate. Turrell (1946) has prepared tables from which the volume and surface area of various fruits can be calculated by measuring their axes.

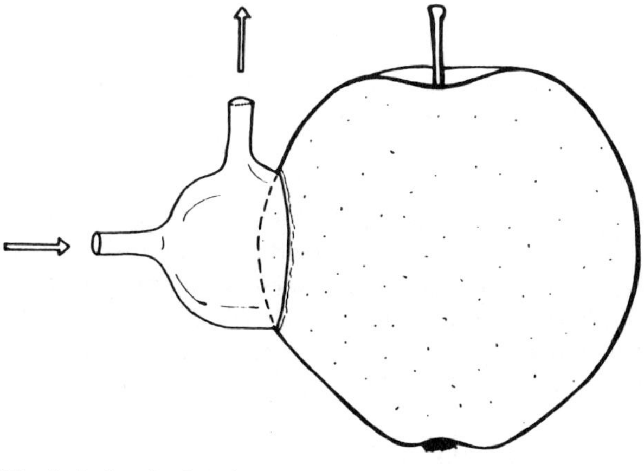

Fig. 1. A simple chamber designed to measure the flux of gases through an isolated portion of the skin of the fruit such as apple. The rim of the chamber is sealed to the skin with a small amount of Vaseline and the fruit and chamber are held in place by clamps. The composition of gases can be quickly and easily changed without altering the normal respiration of the whole fruit. For instance, when nitrogen is used, the flux of oxygen from the fruit to the chamber can be measured with a high degree of accuracy (Cameron 1982)

Some workers have peeled the skin, photocopied it, and measured the area with a leaf area meter. With this procedure there could be problems with shrinkage, as excised peels dry up.

Another option is to limit the area of gas exchange by the use of a small exchange chamber sealed with a given surface area (Fig. 1, Cameron 1982). In this case, the surface area is simply equal to the area under the chamber and the composition of gas in the external chamber can be altered without significant impact on the internal atmosphere of the organ under investigation. This method is analogous to the use of leaf porometers in the study of gas exchange in leaves during photosynthesis.

3.3 Determination of the Rate of Flux

For steady state determination of the rate of flux, it is common practice to place the plant organ in a chamber through which a known rate of gas flow is passed. The appearance or disappearance of a given gas species can usually be measured and the rate of flux calculated on the basis of the flow rate. Most researchers determine the rate of flux on a weight basis (i.e., ml h^{-1} kg^{-1}), but for the purposes of calculating permeability coefficients it is preferable to base the value on the surface area (i.e., ml h^{-1} cm^{-2}) as estimated by the techniques outlined above (Sect. 3.2).

The flow system is especially useful for the measurement of carbon dioxide and ethylene flux since these gases can be scrubbed from the incoming gas flow so that only the amounts produced by the organ are present in the effluent stream of air. This approach can also be used for measuring water flux if the vapor pressure or dew point is measured in both the inlet and outlet streams. Measurement of oxygen flux using this approach is more difficult, since it is necessary to measure accurately the difference between the inlet (ca. 20.5%) and the outlet (20.0–20.4%) following the relatively small amount of oxygen uptake by the product. It may be necessary to use very slow flow rates or even a closed system for a given time interval to monitor oxygen flux into the organ.

Burton and Wigginton (1970) developed a unique steady state approach for measuring oxygen flux into potato tubers. For this method, the tubers are held under nitrogen until the internal oxygen levels are depleted to concentrations just above what is required by cytochrome oxidase. Then, small amounts of oxygen are added to the chamber and the rate of uptake with time is measured manometrically. The permeability is calculated, in this case, by assuming that the internal concentration of oxygen is zero. The risk of damage due to anaerobic conditions is a drawback of this method.

Cameron (1982) developed a simple method for measuring rate of oxygen flux for permeability estimation using the system shown in Fig. 1. When the carrier gas is nitrogen, the rate of oxygen diffusing from the fruit into the chamber can easily be measured on a continual basis. The concentration gradient in this case equals the internal concentration of oxygen minus zero (since the external gas is nitrogen) and the surface area is simply that of the skin under the chamber. This method has been shown to provide reliable estimates of permeability (Cameron 1982).

The rate of water loss from fruits can be accurately measured as weight loss. In this case, the volume of water vapor lost per unit time can be calculated when the temperature is known using the ideal gas law (PV = nRT).

3.4 Determination of the Concentration Gradient

The concentration gradient of a given species is measured as an estimate of the chemical potential or driving force of gas diffusion. The primary objective is to measure accurately, both the internal and external concentrations without altering the composition by the methodology employed. Measurement of the internal gas concentration is by far the more tricky and several different approaches have been utilized, as summarized in the following sections. The actual methods for gas analysis are relatively standard and are not covered in this review.

3.4.1 Direct Sampling

An easy, rapid, and straightforward method for obtaining gas samples from the internal atmosphere of various bulky organs consists of inserting a hypodermic needle under the skin and slowly withdrawing a sample. The point of entry can be sealed with wax or Vaseline (Smith 1947; Hulme 1951) or cement (Williams and Patterson 1962) to prevent contamination from the air during sampling. An even easier method is to hold the entire organ under water during sampling (Lyons et al. 1962; Lyons and Pratt 1964; Burg and Burg 1965; Ben-Yehoshua 1969; Maxie et al. 1974). Direct sampling is easiest for plant organs such as cantaloupe, pumpkin, and papaya which contain large internal cavities, but it can also be used with care for a number of fleshy organs such as orange, tomato, apple, and pear. In the latter cases it often requires trial and error to locate an area within the tissue for sampling so that juice does not clog the needle.

It should be recognized that most 1 ml disposable syringes have 0.1 ml or more dead space at the tip and in the needle. This can cause severe contamination problems if only 0.1 to 0.2 ml samples are taken. Purging with nitrogen prior to sampling does not solve the problem. When only very small volumes of gas are available for sampling, glass syringes with a minimal dead space volume should be used for best possible accuracy. Generally, if tissue sap clogs the needle or enters the syringe during sampling, the sample should be discarded.

3.4.2 Extraction Using Artificial Cavities

3.4.2.1 Internal Cavities

Devaux (1891) appears to have been the first to have created an artificial internal cavity from which repeated gas samples could be withdrawn for use with organs which cannot be directly sampled, such as potato, banana, and avocado. In this method, a cylinder of tissue is removed usually with a cork borer. One end of a short piece of glass tubing can be inserted part of the way, into the newly formed "cavity", and the other end sealed with a septum. Trout et al. (1942) examined this method critically and concluded that equilibrium was established in apples within 24 h after each sampling. Ben-Yehoshua et al. (1963) also utilized this method for avocado, after showing that the injury involved in establishing the cavity did not affect respiration and gas exchange during the period of measurement. A similar method was used by Wardlaw (1936), Kidd and West (1949), And Ekambaram (1922) in which a small section of skin was removed and the tube attached to the outside of the organ. Another alternative is to insert a slightly larger syringe needle into the tissue (rather than glass tubing), which can be covered with a septum and sampled (Smith 1947; Hulme 1951; Vendrell 1970; Sfakiotakis and Dilley 1973). The use of the syringe needle permits repeated sampling from a given depth below the skin.

The greatest disadvantage of any of the internal cavity methods is the unknown factor of wounding, since wounding has the potential to increase the rate of respiration, the rate of ethylene production, and the degree of water soaking (Kahl 1974), any one of which can change diffusion behavior markedly. These factors should be considered in experiments where internal cavities are utilized.

3.4.2.2 External Cavities

The use of external cavities to avoid problems encountered with internal cavities was first proposed by Devaux (1891). Using gelatin or soft wax, a small, closed chamber is attached to the skin of the organ without wounding the tissue. Cameron (1982) modified the technique using the apparatus shown in Fig. 2. The chamber (approx. 5 ml volume) is sealed to the lower surface of the fruit using a small amount of Vaseline and both fruit and chamber are held in place by a ring stand and clamps. Samples are withdrawn through the septum. As the plunger of the syringe is moved back and forth, the water in the arm of the chamber is drawn up and down. This ensures a tight seal, prevents a significant drop in chamber

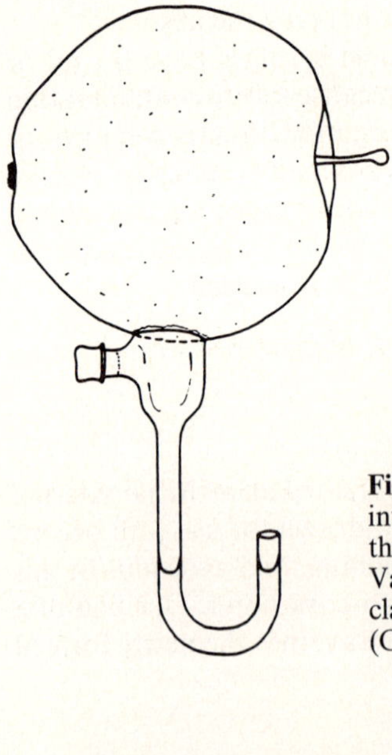

Fig. 2. External chamber apparatus developed for measuring internal gas composition of bulky fruits. The upper rim of the chamber is sealed to the skin with a small amount of Vaseline and the fruit and chamber are held in place by clamps. Water is used as the liquid in the arm of the chamber (Cameron 1982)

pressure (which could cause mass flow from the fruit), and equilibrates the gas in the syringe with that in the chamber. After the sample is withdrawn, the water level remains elevated in the arm, drawing a very slight vacuum (1–2 cm water pressure) on the skin of the fruit exposed to the chamber. For fruits with lenticels or other "holes", this slight vacuum slowly dissipates by net movement of gas from the tissue to the chamber. For fruits such as tomato, which contain no holes, a quantity of gas (i.e., nitrogen) equal to that removed can be injected into the chamber after sampling. Cameron (1982) found that sampling could be initiated about 8 h after placement of the chamber on apples and every 2 h thereafter.

3.4.3 Vacuum Extraction

The general technique of vacuum extraction of internal gases for analysis was developed and employed by several early workers. An extremely versatile and convenient system for vacuum extraction was developed for fruit by Bussel and Maxie (1966) and for vegetative tissue by Beyer and Morgan (1970). The organ or tissue is placed in a pressure cooker or desiccator jar half filled with degassed, saturated salt solution. An inverted funnel with a septum placed over its tip is then placed over the tissue and all air from the surface of the tissue and the interior of the funnel is removed (a very small amount of surfactant will help). The apparatus is then closed and a vacuum applied. As the gases escape from the tissue, they accumulate in the neck of the inverted funnel. After a short time, the vacuum is released and samples are taken directly through the septum with a hypodermic needle for gas analysis. For best results, one should use as little vacuum for as short a time as possible, to avoid extraction of dissolved gases (Gorter and Nadort 1941; Beyer and Morgan 1970; Ben-Yehoshua and Aloni 1974). Specific conditions for the degree and time of vacuum need to be established on a tissue-by-tissue basis.

3.5 Calculation of Permeability Coefficients

The calculation of permeability coefficients is relatively straightforward using the formula given in Table 1, once the parameters of flux, surface area, and concentration gradient have been accurately measured. The most common mistakes revolve around the use of inappropriate units.

4 Nonsteady State Methods for Determination of Resistance to Gas Diffusion

Cameron and Yang (1982) developed a nonsteady approach based on the kinetic analysis of the efflux of preloaded inert gases from plant tissues. Ethane was chosen since it is neither produced nor metabolized under normal conditions, it has diffusional properties similar to those of ethylene, and it can be measured quickly and accurately at low concentrations by gas chromatography.

To start an experiment, the plant organ to be studied is placed in a chamber ventilated with a constant flow of air containing 500–1000 ppm ethane. The length of time for the internal atmosphere of the organ to reach equilibrium with the ethane in the flow stream is a function of the permeability and size of the organ, but is usually less than 24 h. To initiate an efflux experiment, a single preloaded plant organ is transferred to a second ethane-free chamber which is quickly sealed. The volume of the chamber should be at least ten times larger than the internal air space volume of the organ under investigation (Cameron and Yang 1982; Banks 1985). To ensure proper mixing, a diaphragm-type or peristaltic pump should be incorporated. The volume of the chamber/pump system can be easily predetermined by injecting known quantities of 500 ppm ethane and measuring the extent of dilution (i.e., $C_1V_1 = C_2V_2$). Leaks are readily detected if the level of ethane drops with time. To monitor ethane efflux from plant organs, 1 ml gas samples are withdrawn at regular intervals (1–2 min) through a septum attached to the chamber. After a sufficient number of samples (usually 20–30) is taken, the pump should be turned off and the system allowed to reach equilibrium (several hours). The concentration of ethane is then remeasured.

Cameron and Yang (1982) have presented the mathematical analysis for calculation of $R = P^{-1}$ from the data and have shown close agreement between values obtained by ethane efflux and by steady state methods.

Cameron (1982) showed that ethane efflux from apples and tomatoes conformed well to the model using first-order efflux analysis. However, plots of the transformed data for potatoes were nonlinear, presumably due to significant tissue resistance caused by the small intercellular volume. Banks (1985) has shown that the efflux method can be adapted for use with organs such as potato by linear analysis of the initial phase of efflux during which time the decline in internal ethane is presumably negligible.

5 Morphology and Other Gas Exchange Methodologies

A complete range of methods has been developed for measurements of external morphology, texture, and gas permeability of plant organs. Special methods had to be elaborated with respect to circulation across pores, as well as across cuticle and cells. Among these were the methods of Marcellin and his group (1963, 1974) relating to the identification of the degree of opening of lenticels by oiling and by successive pressure levels, and the measurement of porosity by gaseous expansion. Measurement of the resistance of the internal and peripheral pores to the passage of gases was carried out by comparing the pore resistance to convection gas flow with that of a capillary with known properties, permeametry. Similarly, gas movement could be studied by causing interdiffusion between the gases in the intercellular spaces and gases of distinct molecular weights (CO_2-air or H_2-air combinations). This method, which was coined by Marcellin (1963, 1974) as the DEVAUX effect, refers to the rapid replacement of air in contact with the fruit by hydrogen (as an example) at the same temperature and pressure, thus causing the rapid introduction of hydrogen into the fruit and a slower exit of air from the intercellular spaces. Similarly, gas movement was measured by creating interdiffusion between gases of comparable molecular weights such as C_2H_4-N_2 or O_2-N_2 pairs.

Studies of the degree of opening of the stomata or other apertures involved in gas exchange have been reported using the technique of computerized image analysis. For example, differences in aperture area and frequency of stomata on fruits of two muskmelon (*Cucumis melo* L.) genotypes were determined by computerized image analysis of photomicrographs obtained by microrelief techniques (Altman et al. 1987). Acetate impressions of surface cellular features on polar and equatorial regions of the fruit were viewed by phase contrast microscopy and photomicrographs of random fields of stomata were made. a minicomputer-based image processor scanned each photomicrograph and digitized the image of an individual stoma. The image was displayed on a monitor and a digitizing tablet was used to mark end points on the axes of an ellipse circumscribing the effective aperture. A FORTRAN image processing system calculated the area of each ellipse. Resulting data showed a significantly lower stomatal aperture area and stomatal frequency on the surface of fruits of the netted genotype.

6 Applications of Methodology

6.1 Studying Paths of Gas Exchange Through Stem Scar, Stomata, Cuticle, and Lenticels

A critical issue for the study of gas exchange in bulky fruits is the relative contribution of each of the following components: stomatal, lenticular, stem end, and cuticular paths for gas exchange. The results vary for different commodities. Pieniazek (1944) reported that by plugging each of the lenticels of apples with Vaseline, he reduced the water vapor flux by 8–20%. However, Burg and Burg (1965) found that CO_2 flux was greatly enhanced in helium or hydrogen atmospheres and suggested that since hydrogen or helium enhances only gas diffusivity and not the diffusion rate through the skin, most of the diffusion of carbon dioxide occurred through the lenticels. In Burton's view (1982), lenticels and stomata have only minor importance in water loss because of their sparse distribution in fruit. He based this conclusion on many years of serious research on potato tubers. Burton stated that potato tubers have one lenticel cm^{-2} and that the rate of flow through each lenticel is 3×10^{-4} mg cm^{-2} $mbar^{-1}$ h^{-1}. These data were based on his measurement of CO_2 flow, possibly because of lack of data on water flow. This flow, which presumably is the same for water, accounts for only 3% of the transpiration of potatoes. The other 97% migrates through cell walls to the periderm, where it evaporates. The same holds true, suggests Burton, for other organs with lenticels, such as taproots and pome fruits.

The contribution of the stem scar as an avenue for gas exchange was investigated by comparing fruit with plugged and open scars. Burg and Burg (1965) found that sealing the stem scars of peppers reduced CO_2 emanation by 60%. Cameron (1982) showed that the contribution of the calyx to the passage of different gases varied in different fruits. In Golden Delicious apples, the calyx provides for the diffusion of 42% of the ethylene, 24% of the CO_2, and only 2% of the water. In tomatoes, the respective percentages are 94, 81, and 67. In oranges, the exchange of CO_2 and ethylene through the stem scar is only twice that through the peel (Barmore and Biggs 1972). Cameron (1982) showed that the peel of tomato has 1227-fold more resistance to ethane than the stem scar per unit surface area.

The relative contribution of stomata to gas exchange of oranges is not clear. As stated previously, the stomata of orange, particularly their upper vestibular chambers, are plugged by various materials such as wax deposits (Albrigo 1972), hyphal growth, and even unidentified spheroid and irregular objects (Turrell and Klotz 1940; Scott and Baker 1947; Albrigo 1972). All these reports have proposed that this plugging inhibited water loss and gas exchange. However, since stomata of harvested fruit are, at least intuitively, presumed to be closed, this outcome may not necessarily be true. These "plugs" may even prevent the closure of the stomatal pore, like a wedge. If this is so, then the plugs may enhance transpiration and gas exchange by preventing the effective closure of the stomata.

Moreshet and Green (1980) studied the functioning of stomata in orange fruit on and off the tree. In spite of being occluded by natural wax before harvest (Albrigo 1972), stomata still opened and closed in response to light and were highly effective in conducting water and CO_2. The resistance to water ranged from approximately 13 s cm^{-1} when they were open, to 50 s cm^{-1} when they were closed. However, their data showed clearly that the stomata stopped functioning after harvest.

In a recent study of stomata of Hamlin oranges and Duncan grapefruits, Ben-Yehoshua et al. (1983, 1985) showed with scanning electron microscope photomicrographs that although most stomata were closed, some stomatal pores may be seen as a dark, open slit between the two guard cells on fruit stored in the dark (Fig. 3). Thus, it appears that the stomata of harvested oranges are partially open and allow some gas exchange.

Stomata of fully mature harvested banana fruit open in high relative humidity and light and close in low relative humidity and in darkness, whether the bananas are attached to the plant or are being shipped under regular commercial conditions from the tropics (Johnson and Brun 1966).

It appears that a partial explanation for the discrepancy between different fruits and different reports may be obtained by treating various gases separately. This possible explanation was shown when the diffusion paths of water vapor and other gases were compared. Thus, the resistance of various fruits to water vapor is less than 100-fold that to CO_2, O_2, or ethylene (Cameron and Reid 1982; Ben-Yehoshua et al. 1983, 1985). Burg and Kosson (1983) and Ben-Yehoshua et al. (1983, 1985) have proposed that, unlike water, ethylene and CO_2 pass through apple peel in the air phase of a limited area of that peel. They based this proposal on the fact that the rate of movement of water out of the fruit is inversely proportional to the atmospheric pressure and also dependent on the density of the constituents of the ambient atmosphere. If passage were limited by a liquid phase,

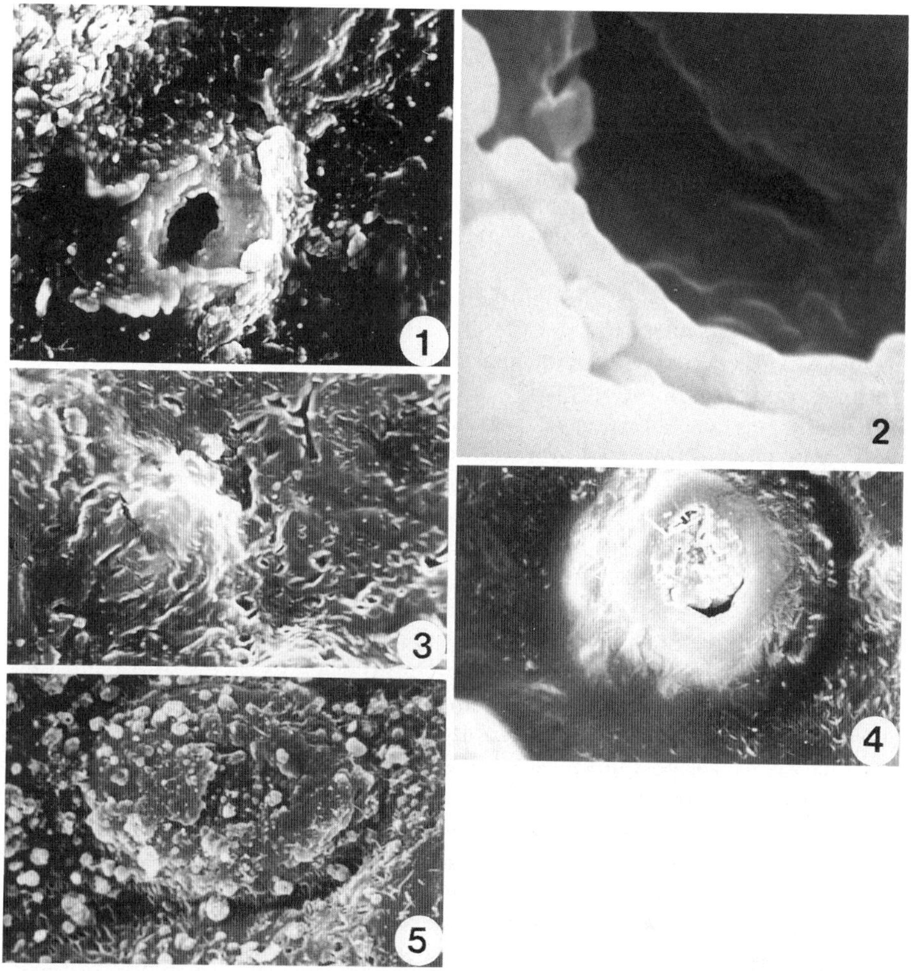

Fig. 3. *1* Scanning electron microscope (SEM) view of fruit surfaces of untreated grapefruit showing a stomata, wax platelets, and other irregular bodies of natural wax deposited over the cuticular surface (x 1600). *2* Stomatal pore. A greater magnification probes deeply into the pore, showing its partial opening, the various protrusions into the pore, as well as the cuticular walls at the surface opening of the pore (x 10000). *3* Wax surface formed after waxing with FMC solvent wax (x 1600). *4* Stomatal pore partially clogged by the applied wax (x 1600). *5* Stomatal pore completely covered by the new wax layer (x 1600) (Ben-Yehoshua et al. 1985)

resistance to CO_2 and ethylene would be inversely proportional to their solubility in that phase. Thus, resistance to ethylene would be much higher than it actually is, if the phase were water and much higher to CO_2 if it were lipid. In no event would the resistance be similar to both gases, which, however, is the case. It has been proposed that the different permeabilities to CO_2 and ethylene, as compared to that of water, are the result of differences in pathways (Ben-Yehoshua et al. 1983, 1985). Ethylene and CO_2 pass through an air phase and water runs through a water phase. The skin resistance to the passage of ethylene, CO_2, and O_2 of untreated Valencia oranges is similar and very high (6000 s cm^{-1}), although its resistance to water is only one-sixtieth as great. These results strengthen the argument for separate pathways for various gases. The similarity of resistance to CO_2, O_2, and ethylene supports the concept that all these gases diffuse through an air phase. Since diffusivity in air depends on the square root of the molecular weight, for O_2, CO_2, and ethylene, it cannot differ by more than 12%. These gases have widely differing air/water and air/oil partition coefficients. Consequently, it is difficult to conceive of a route, other than a passage through the air phase, which could transfer these gases through the fruit's surface with equal ease. Based on diffusivity, the resistance to O_2, CO_2, and ethylene would be 21 s cm^{-1} when the stomata are open, compared with 6000 s cm^{-1} after harvest. Clearly, the stomata are shut after harvest, for only 0.4% of the initial, fully open, pore area is needed to account for the residual gas-exchange capacity. The slightly opened stomata on harvested citrus fruit could account for this 0.4% opening.

6.2 Effects of Individual Seal-Packaging and Waxing on Gas Exchange of Fruits

The fruit and vegetable industries have, for the past 50 years, used wax and other skin coatings to restore or enhance gloss and to reduce shrinkage. Recently, a special adaptation of film packaging was developed whereby each individual fruit is sealed in plastic film and then passed through a hot-air tunnel to shrink the film (Ben-Yehoshua 1978, 1985). The various effects that seal-packaging and waxing have on gas exchange and keeping quality are not easily explained by morphological studies concerning the distribution of applied waxes (Ben-Yehoshua 1967, 1969, 1985), nor by most current theories of gas mass transport in citrus and other fruits. The commercial practice of waxing fruits does not reduce transpiration rate adequately and yet it restricts O_2 and CO_2 transport so that alcohol, aldehyde, and off-flavors are sometimes produced (Davis 1974). Conversely, sealing fruits individually in HDPE (about 10 μm thick) reduces water loss by a factor of 10 without changing the fruit's endogenous O_2, CO_2, or ethylene content (Ben-Yehoshua et al. 1979). Consequently, seal-packaging is more effective than waxing in preventing shrinkage and in extending the storage life of citrus and certain other fruits. this difference can be explained by studying the effects of waxing on the surface of citrus fruit with a scanning electron microscope and by computation of the gas exchange. Commercial waxing results in a new surface layer with a structure different from the natural extracuticular wax platelets (Ben-Yehoshua et al. 1985). Although the synthetic layer has many pits and breaks, it is far more effective than natural extracuticular wax and other occlusions in clogging the stomatal pores, presumably because it flows into them as a liquid.

The waxing for the tests discussed above was carried out with FMC solvent wax (product of Food Machinery Co.). This coating is a coumarone indene resin (a polymerization product of crude heavy coal tar of naphtha) dissolved in a petroleum-base solvent. Microscope observation showed that other waxes give similar results. An explanation for the difference between the effects of waxing and sealing was found by computing the resistance to diffusion of the various gases involved (Ben-Yehoshua et al. 1985). Waxing decreases water conductance by only 25%, but it increases the resistance to ethylene, O_2, and CO_2 by 100, 250, and 140%, respectively. Waxing hardly affects transpiration because the new surface layer has many pits and breaks, but it specifically retards gas exchange by plugging the stomatal pores. In contrast, seal-packaging increases resistance to water vapor by 1375%, and to ethylene, O_2, and CO_2 by 25, 233, and 72%, respectively. This result does not depend on the film's selective permeability because polyethylene is more permeable to H_2O than to CO_2, O_2, and ethylene. Instead, the success of HDPE in preventing water loss without substantially hindering gas exchange is due mainly to the fruit's selective permeability. Valencia orange and Duncan grapefruit have relatively high resistance to CO_2, O_2, and ethylene (6000 s cm^{-1}), but rather low resistance to water (100 s cm^{-1}). Thus, the thin film's resistance to water provides a much larger barrier to transpiration than the resistance of the fruit's surface to the passage of water vapor. The study of Ben-Yehoshua et al. (1985) illustrates the usefulness of visualizing separate pathways for gas and water vapor transport in harvested fruit. This concept, discussed in Sect. 6.1, helps to explain the observation that the 1-μm-thick skin coating formed by commercial waxing was more effective in impeding transport of O_2 and CO_2 than was a 10-μm-thick film of HDPE.

Supporting evidence for this theory regarding the different pathways of water and other fixed gases is derived from the measurements of the levels of ethanol and acetaldehyde in fruit sealed by either HDPE or Cryovac D-950 film or waxed with Broshar wax. Both ethanol and acetaldehyde are good indicators of the efficiency of gas exchange, that is, high levels of these materials suggest that the gas exchange is impeded. In three cultivars of citrus – Valencia and Shamouti oranges and Marsh grapefruit – the levels of acetaldehyde and, even more conspicuously, of ethanol, are significantly higher in juice of waxed fruit than of nonwaxed. However, sealing fruit with either of two different plastic films, 0.01-mm-thick HDPE or 0.015-mm-thick Cryovac D-950 per se, did not affect the levels of these metabolites (Ben-Yehoshua et al. 1985).

In summary, the following observations suggest that the mass transport of water and fixed gases is executed by different mechanisms in fruits: (1) the resistances to CO_2, O_2, and ethylene mass transport are similar, but the apparent resistance to water is 60- to 100-fold lower (Cameron 1982; Ben-Yehoshua et al. 1983, 1985), suggesting that water moves preferentially in a liquid phase in the cuticle (Schonherr 1981), and (2) waxing inhibits the transport of CO_2, O_2, and ethylene but not of water, whereas the 10–15-μm-thick film restricts mainly the transport of water (Ben-Yehoshua et al. 1985). This conclusion is in agreement with previous morphological observations which showed the lack of a direct relationship between the number of stomata and the rate of transpiration in oranges.

6.3 Resistance Network Approach

Nobel (1974) has recognized and applied the analogy of resistance to gas movement and resistance in electrical circuits. Cameron and Reid (1982) have utilized this approach for the study of gas diffusion in harvested fruits. The resistance network approach, as it is called, is straightforward in application. It is demonstrated in Fig. 4, which shows the various barriers to diffusion encountered by ethylene as it leaves a nonstomatal fruit which is waxed, wrapped in plastic, and placed in a carton. The total resistance can be calculated as for an electrical circuit:

$$R_j^{\text{total}} = R_j^{\text{tissue}} + \frac{R_j^{\text{skin}} \cdot R_j^{\text{stem scar}}}{R_j^{\text{skin}} + R_j^{\text{stem scar}}} + R_j^{\text{war}} + R_j^{\text{plastic}} + R_j^{\text{carton}},$$

note that the net resistance for a system in parallel, such as the stem scar and the skin (Fig. 4), is calculated exactly as for two resistors in parallel in an electrical circuit. The advantage of the resistance network approach is that it permits the segregation of the total resistance into its many components, thereby enabling investigation of how a change in the resistance of any one component might affect the total resistance. An important consequence of the resistance network approach is an understanding of the concentration profile of gas species j from the atmosphere to the tissue at steady state. The steady state condition for any gas species is met when the mass flux of that species is constant throughout the entire system under study. For example, when diffusion of oxygen is at steady state, it is utilized at a constant rate of x mol s^{-1}, precisely x moles moves across the plastic film every second, x moles per second crosses the wax barrier, and x moles per second crosses the stem scar and skin. However, whereas the *flux* of oxygen is

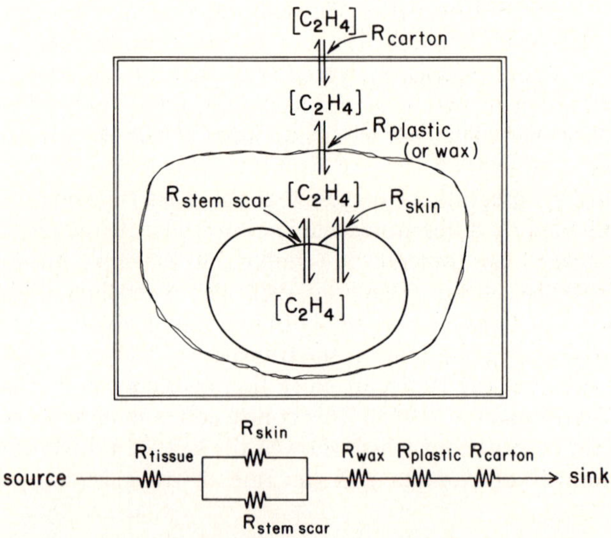

$$R_{\text{total}} = R_{\text{tissue}} + \frac{R_{\text{skin}} \cdot R_{\text{stem scar}}}{R_{\text{skin}} + R_{\text{stem scar}}} + R_{\text{wax}} + R_{\text{plastic}} + R_{\text{carton}}$$

Fig. 4. The resistance network approach applied to diffusion from bulky organs. The barriers to diffusion of ethylene from a tomato fruit are shown diagramatically and as a resistance network. The total resistance is calculated as for an electrical circuit constant, the *concentration* of oxygen drops from the atmosphere to the site of respiration. The concentration difference across any barrier for a given steady state flux will depend only on the resistance of the barrier and its surface area.

Cameron and Yang (1982) have studied the resistance of unwrapped and shrink-wrapped cucumbers. The ethane efflux method was utilized to investigate the effect of a plastic shrink wrap on ethane diffusion from English cucumbers. The film increased the resistance by a factor of 20 and provided about 95% of the resistance. It should be noted that the diffusion of gas through the cucumber skin and the plastic film is in series. Thus, the overall resistance coefficient should be the summation of the resistance of each of these components.

Acknowledgments. The senior author wishes to thank Zipora Minz for her help in the collection of literature.

This chapter was written with partial support of the U.S.-Israel Binational Agricultural Research and Development Fund. Contribution No. 2336-E, 1988 series, from the ARO, The Volcani Center, Bet Dagan, Israel, and MSU, East Lansing, MI, USA.

References

Albrigo LG (1972) Distribution of stomata and epicuticular wax on oranges as related to stem and rind breakdown and water loss. J Am Soc Hortic Sci 57:220–223

Albrigo LG, Syvertsen JP, Costa JTA (1982) Some stomatal characteristics of citrus and their implications to gas exchange. Abst Int Hortic Congr, Hamburg 2:1364

Altman SA, Corey KA, Hruschka WR (1987) Stomatal aperture determination of muskmelon fruits by microrelief image analysis. HortScience 22:629–631

Banks NH (1985) Estimating skin resistance to gas diffusion in apples and potatoes. J Exp Bot 36:1842–1850

Barmore CR, Biggs RH (1972) Ethylene diffusion through citrus leaf and fruit tissue. J Am Soc Hortic Sci 97:24–27

Barrer RM (1951) Diffusion in and through solids. Cambridge Univ Press, pp 464

Ben-Yehoshua S (1967) Some physiological effects of various skin coatings upon orange fruit. Isr J Agric Res 17:17–27

Ben-Yehoshua S (1969) Gas exchange, transpiration and the commercial deterioration of stored orange fruit. J Am Soc Hortic Sci 94:524–528

Ben-Yehoshua S (1978) Delaying deterioration of individual citrus fruit by seal-packaging in film of high density polyethylene. I. General effects. Proc 3rd Int Citrus Congr, Sydney, Aust, pp 110–115

Ben-Yehoshua S (1985) Individual seal-packaging of fruit and vegetables in plastic film – a new postharvest technique. HortScience 20:32–37

Ben-Yehoshua S (1987) Transpiration and water stress and gas exchange. In: Weichmann J (ed) Postharvest physiology of vegetables. Dekker, New York, pp 113–170

Ben-Yehoshua S, Aloni B (1974) Endogenous ethylene and abscission of orange leaf explants. Bot Gaz 135:41–44

Ben-Yehoshua S, Eaks IL (1970) Ethylene production and abscission of fruit and leaves of orange. Bot Gaz 131:144–150

Ben-Yehoshua S, Nahir D (1977) Seal-packaging of comestibles with high density polyethylene, Isr Patent No 52177

Ben-Yehoshua S, Robertson RN, Biale JB (1963) Respiration and internal atmosphere of the avocado fruit. Plant Physiol 28:194–201

Ben-Yehoshua S, Kobiler I, Shapiro B (1979) Some physiological effects of delaying deterioration of citrus fruit by individual seal-packaging in high-density polyethylene. J Am Soc Hortic Sci 104:868–972

Ben-Yehoshua S, Burg P, Young R (1983) Resistance of citrus fruit to C_2H_4, O_2, CO_2, and H_2O mass transport. Proc Plant Growth Regul Soc Am, East Lansing, Michigan, 145–150
Ben-Yehoshua S, Burg SP, Young R (1985) Resistance of citrus fruit to mass transport of water vapor and other gases. Plant Physiol 790:1048–1053
Beyer EM Jr., Morgan PW (1970) A method for determining the concentration of ethylene in the gas phase of vegetative plant tissues. Plant Physiol 46:352–354
Burg SP, Kosson R (1983) Metabolism, heat transfer and water loss under hypobaric conditions. In: Lieberman M (ed) Postharvest physiology and crop preservation. Plenum, Oxford New York, pp 399–424
Burg SP, Burg EA (1965) Gas exchange in fruits. Physiol Plant 18:870–884
Burton WG (1974) Some biophysical principles underlying the controlled atmosphere storage of plant material. Ann Appl Biol 78:149–168
Burton WG (1978) Biochemical and physiological effects of modified atmospheres and their role in quality maintenance. In: Hultin HO, Milner M (eds) Postharvest biology and biotechnology. Food and Nutrition Press, Westport, CT, pp 97–110
Burton WG (1982) Postharvest physiology and food crops. Longman, London
Burton WG, Wigginton MJ (1970) The effect of a film of water upon the oxygen status of a potato tuber. Potato Res 13:180–186
Bussel J, Maxie EC (1966) Gas exchange in Bartlett pears in relation to gamma irradiation. J Am Soc Hortic Sci 88:151–159
Cameron AC (1982) Gas diffusion in bulky plant organs. Ph D Diss, Univ California, Davis
Cameron AC, Reid MS (1982) Diffusive resistance: importance and measurement in controlled atmosphere storage. In: Richardson DG, Meheriuk M (eds) Controlled atmosphere for storage and transport of perishable agricultural commodities. Oregon State Univ, School Agric, Symp Ser 1, pp 171–178
Cameron AC, Yang SF (1982) A simple method for the determination of resistance to gas diffusion in plant organs. Plant Physiol 70:21–23
Davis PL (1974) Biochemical changes in grapefruit stored in air containing ethylene. Pro Fla St Hortic Soc 87:222–227
Devaux M (1891) Etude expérimentale de l'aération des tissus massifs. Introduction à l'étude des mécanismes des exchanges gazeux chez les plantes aériennes. Ann Sci Nat Bot 14:279–395
Ekambaram T (1922) The internal atmosphere and gas exchange of the respiring apple. Ph D Diss, Cambridge
Gorter A, Nadort W (1941) Composition of gas in the intercellular spaces of potatoes. Proc Acad Sci Amst 44:1112–1116
Grierson W, Ben-Yehoshua S (1986) The storage of citrus fruits. In: Wardowsky WF, Nagy S, Grierson W (eds) Fresh citrus fruits, chap 20. Publ Co, Westport, CT, pp 470–509
Hulme AC (1951) An apparatus for the measurement of gaseous conditions inside an apple fruit. J Exp Bot 2(4):65–85
Johnson BE, Brun WA (1966) Stomatal density and responsiveness of banana fruit stomates. Plant Physiol 41:99–103
Kahl G (1974) Metabolism in plant storage tissue slices. Bot Rev 40:263–314
Kidd F, West C (1949) Resistance of the skin of the apple fruit to gaseous exchange. Rep Food Invest Bd 1939, pp 59–64
Lyons JM, Pratt HK (1964) Effect of stage of maturity and ethylene treatment on respiration and ripening of tomato fruits. Proc Am Soc Hortic Sci 84:491–500
Lyons JM, McGlasson WB, Pratt HK (1962) Ethylene production, respiration and internal gas concentrations in cantaloupe fruits at various stages of maturity. Plant Physiol 37:31–36
Marcellin P (1963) Mesure de la diffusion des gaz dans les organes végétaux. Bull Soc Fr Physiol Veg 9:29–45
Marcellin P (1974) Conditions physiques de la circulation des gaz respiratoires à travers la masse des fruits et maturation. In: Coll Int CNRS. Facteurs et regulation de la maturation des fruits, 238:241–251

Maxie EC, Mitchell FC, Sommer NF, Synder RG, Rae HL (1974) Effect of elevated temperature on ripening of "Bartlett" pear, *Pyrus communis* L. J Am Soc Hortic Sci 99:344–349

Moreshet S, Green GC (1980) Photosynthesis and diffusion conductance of the Valencia orange fruit under field conditions. J Exp Bot 31:15–27

Nobel PS (1974) Biophysical plant physiology and ecology. Freeman, San Francisco, CA, pp 608

Pieniazek SA (1944) Physical characteristics of the skin in relation to apple fruit transpiration. Plant Physiol 18:529–536

Rahn H, Ar A, Paganelli CV (1979) How bird eggs breathe. Sci Am 240:38–43

Sacher J (1973) Senescence and postharvest physiology. Annu Rev Plant Physiol 24:197–224

Sastry SK, Baird CD, Buffington DE (1978) Transpiration rates of certain fruits and vegetables. ASHRAE 84:237–255

Schonherr J (1981) Resistances of plant surfaces to water loss: transport properties of cutin, suberin and associated lipids. In: Lange DL, Nobel PS, Osmond CB, Ziegler H (eds) Encyclopedia of plant physiology, vol 8. Physiological plant ecology. Springer, Berlin Heidelberg New York, pp 153–179

Scott FM, Baker KC (1947) Anatomy of Washington navel orange rind in relation to water spot. Bot Gaz 108:459–475

Sfakiotakis EM, Dilley DR (1973) Internal ethylene concentration in apple fruit attached to or detached from the tree. J Am Soc Hortic Sci 98:501–503

Smith WH (1947) A new method of determining the composition of the internal atmosphere of fleshy plant organs. Ann Bot 11:363–368

Solomos T (1987) Principles of gas exchange in bulky plant tissues. HortScience 22:766–771

Trout SA, Hall EG, Robertson RN, Hackney FMU, Sykes SM (1942) Studies in the metabolism of apples. I. Preliminary investigations on internal gas composition and its relation to changes in stored apples. Aust J Exp Biol Med Sci 20:219–231

Turrell FM (1946) Tables of surfaces and volumes of spheres and of prolate and oblate spheroids and spheroidal coefficients. Univ California Press, Berkeley

Turrell FM, Klotz LJ (1940) Density of stomata and oil glands and incidence of water spot in the rind of Washington navel orange. Bot Gaz 101:862

Vendrell M (1970) Relationship between internal distribution of exogenous auxins and accelerated ripening of banana fruits. Aust J Biol 23:1133–1142

Wardlaw CW (1936) Studies in tropical fruits. I. Preliminary observations on some aspects of development, ripening and senescence with special reference to respiration. Ann Bot 50:621–653

Wardlaw CW, Leonard ER (1940) Studies on tropical fruits. IX. The respiration of bananas during ripening at tropical temperatures. Ann Bot 4:269–316

Williams MW, Patterson ME (1962) Internal atmosphere in Bartlett pears stored in controlled atmosphere. Proc Am Soc Hortic Sci 81:129–136

Nitrogen

Methods for Measurement of Dinitrogen Fixation in Microorganisms and Symbiotic Systems

D. J. D. NICHOLAS

1 Introduction

Biological fixation of dinitrogen is an important event in nature since it contributes over 90% of the nitrogen turnover in the biosphere estimated to be 10^9 tons per annum. The contribution from fertilizer nitrogen via the Haber-Bosch industrial process is only about 5%. The remainder is produced by the conversion of N_2 gas into the oxides of nitrogen (N_2O and NO) and thence to nitrates under the influence of lighting and industrial processes.

Nitrogen gas is relatively inert and can be utilized for growth by relatively few microorganisms (prokaryotes) either free living or in symbiotic association with plants or even animals.

The nitrogen-fixing enzyme (nitrogenase) which activates dinitrogen and reduces it to ammonium (six electrons) has a similar mechanism of action in all N_2-fixing microorganisms. Thus, techniques described in this chapter apply to all known dinitrogen fixing systems. These procedures vary from the relatively insensitive method for determining increases in total nitrogen, to the use of the stable isotope ($^{15}N_2$) and the radioactive isotope ($^{13}N_2$) to follow the incorporation of the gas into intact systems and into preparations of nitrogenase.

2 Determination of N_2 Fixation by Increases in Total Nitrogen

The total N_2 fixed by a microorganism or a symbiotic system was (before the advent of the isotopes of nitrogen) determined by chemical analysis. Unfortunately, small amounts of N_2 fixed are often within experimental error of the method. Thus, stable and radioactive isotopes, $^{15}N_2$ and $^{13}N_2$, were subsequently developed to determine quantitatively biological N_2 fixation.

Before the development of these tracer techniques the determination of total N was the only procedure available to study increases in cell-nitrogen derived from N_2 fixation. The procedure described here is based on a hot acid digestion of microbial or plant material, whereby the organic and mineral nitrogen are reduced to ammonia in the presence of a catalyst. Many such methods have been described in detail (Umbreit and Bond 1936; Burris and Wilson 1957; Parker 1961; Bremner and Edwards 1965; Burris 1972).

2.1 Digestion of Samples by a Microkjeldahl Procedure

Plant material should be dried in a well-aerated oven and then ground, milled and thoroughly mixed into a homogeneous sample. About 250 mg subsamples are weighed for digestion; the total N content should be between 2 and 20 mg. When microorganisms are to be analyzed for total N, then washed samples containing about 1 mg N can be digested without preliminary drying. It is always advisable to digest replicate samples for analysis.

Digestion is done in microkjeldahl flasks (100 ml) in the presence of 5 ml 36 N H_2SO_4 (Analar grade) and 1.5 g of a catalyst, K_2SO_4/HgO (100:7 w/w). The HgO component is included to ensure that methylamine produced during the digestion of some plant material, e.g. grain legumes, is completely degraded to ammonia. Digestion is continued on a thermostatically controlled series of electric coil heaters at 300° C for 2 h after the solution had cleared. The flasks must be shaken and rotated periodically during digestion and it is advisable to add small glass beads to avoid bumping. After cooling, glass distilled water (freshly distilled) is added and the digest is then dispensed to an appropriate volume in a conical flask. The size of the flask will depend on the N content of the sample.

2.2 Analysis of Ammonia by Distillation Followed by Titration

Many distillation units have been described for the recovery of NH_3 from acid digests (Humphries 1956; Burris and Wilson 1957; Bremner and Edwards 1965; Bergersen 1980). The most extensively used distillation apparatus is that of Markham, where NH_3 passing from a condenser is trapped into 50 ml 2% w/v boric acid containing 200 ml 95% v/v ethanol and 20 ml indicator mixture (0.033% w/v bromocresol green, 0.066% w/v methyl red in 100 ml ethanol). The water used to generate steam should be acidified with 1 ml l^{-1} H_2SO_4 to trap NH_3. The apparatus should be steamed for about 15 min before use.

When steam is passing freely through an aliquot of the digest in the condenser then 5 ml 40% w/v NaOH is added. The tip of the condenser is immediately immersed into a 100 ml Erlenmeyer flask containing the boric acid indicator mixture. The collection of about 20 ml distillate is usually adequate to recover all the ammonia in the digest sample.

To determine the total N in the digest it is first made up to 100 ml with freshly distilled water in a volumetric flask. A suitable aliquot is then taken (10 ml) for titration with 1/140 N H_2SO_4; each litre of acid containing 5 ml of bromocresol green/methyl red indicator in ethanol (described above). Since 1 ml of the titration acid is equivalent to 0.1 mg N the total N in the digest can be readily calculated.

3 Use of $^{15}N_2$ to Determine Dinitrogen Fixation

Thode and Urey (1939) were the first to produce adequate amounts of compounds labelled with the stable isotope of nitrogen (^{15}N) for biochemical work.

The tracer was used to follow the incorporation of ^{15}N-labelled amino acids into cell-nitrogen compounds in animals (Schoenheimer and Rittenberg 1939).

Pioneer work on the use of $^{15}N_2$ techniques to follow the fixation of dinitrogen into microbial and symbiotic systems was carried out by the Wisconsin group (Burris and Wilson 1957; Burris 1972; as described by Bergersen 1980).

3.1 Preparation of $^{15}N_2$ from ^{15}N-Labelled Ammonium Salts

3.1.1 Oxidation with Hot Copper Oxide

The best source of the gas is ^{15}N-labelled ammonium salts which can be readily oxidized to $^{15}N_2$. The traditional method involves the oxidation of ^{15}N-labelled ammonium salts to $^{15}N_2$ in the presence of hot copper oxide in an evacuated apparatus illustrated in Fig. 1. The $^{15}N_2$ generated is collected in a carrier gas such as helium or argon in an evacuated 1 litre glass flask. Labelled ammonia, gener-

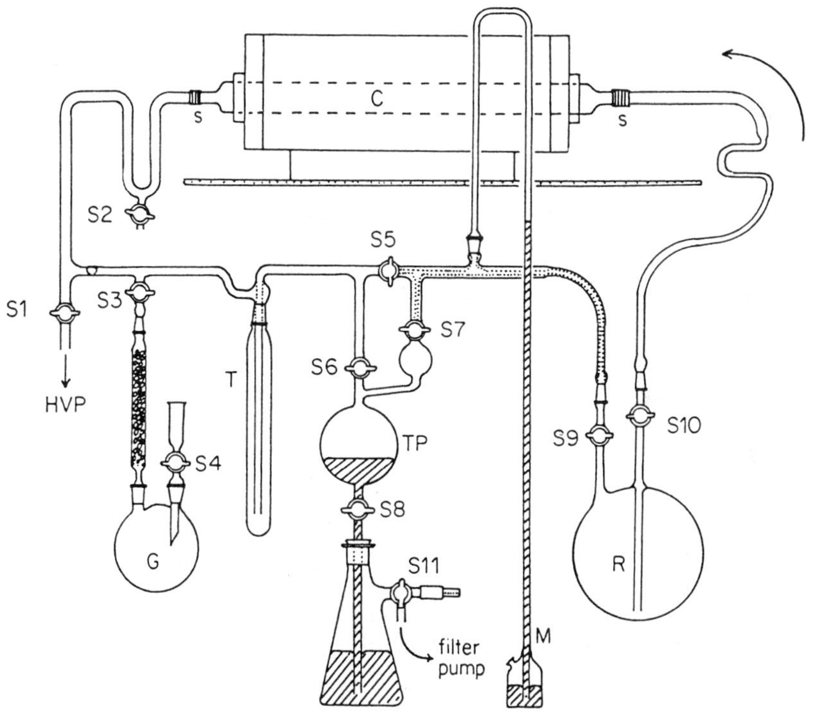

Fig. 1. Apparatus for production of $^{15}N_2$ gas from a $^{15}NH_4^+$ salt. It consists of a quartz combustion tube (*C*), filled with CuO granules, and joined through graded seals (*S*) to a Pyrex vacuum line as shown; a rotary vacuum pump (*HVP*) gives a vacuum of about 0.01 Torr. *G* is an NH_4 generator in which the salt is placed and NH_3 liberated by addition of alkali through *S4*. *T* is a liquid nitrogen-cooled trap for N impurities, *TP* a simple Toepler pump for circulation of the gas in the system and *R* is the gas reservoir into which the $^{15}N_2$ is finally pumped. A mercury manometer (*M*) is also provided. For details of operation, see text (Bergersen 1980)

ated from the ^{15}N-ammonium salt by adding sodium hydroxide, is passed over copper oxide heated to 600° C. The reaction is as follows:

$$2\,^{15}NH_3 + 3\,CuO \rightarrow {}^{15}N_2 + 3\,Cu + 3\,H_2O\,.$$

This method has been described in detail by Bergersen (1980).

The apparatus (Fig. 1) consists of an ammonia generator (G) connected through an NaOH filled tube to an evacuated system for circulating the NH_3 over CuO in a silica combustion tube (C) which can be heated in an electric furnace. The gas is circulated by means of a simplified Toepler pump (TP). A mercury manometer (M) and a gas reservoir vessel (R) are components of the system.

The procedure is as follows: The CuO is regenerated before each use by heating tube (C) with the system filled with O_2. While (C) is cooling the sample of $^{15}NH_4^+$, salt is placed in (G) and the entire apparatus evacuated by a vacuum pump (HVP). The vacuum is maintained at 0.01 torr for at least 1 h to ensure that the contents of the system are well out-gassed and at this stage the absence of leaks should be checked. The pump is then disconnected by closing S_1. The mer-

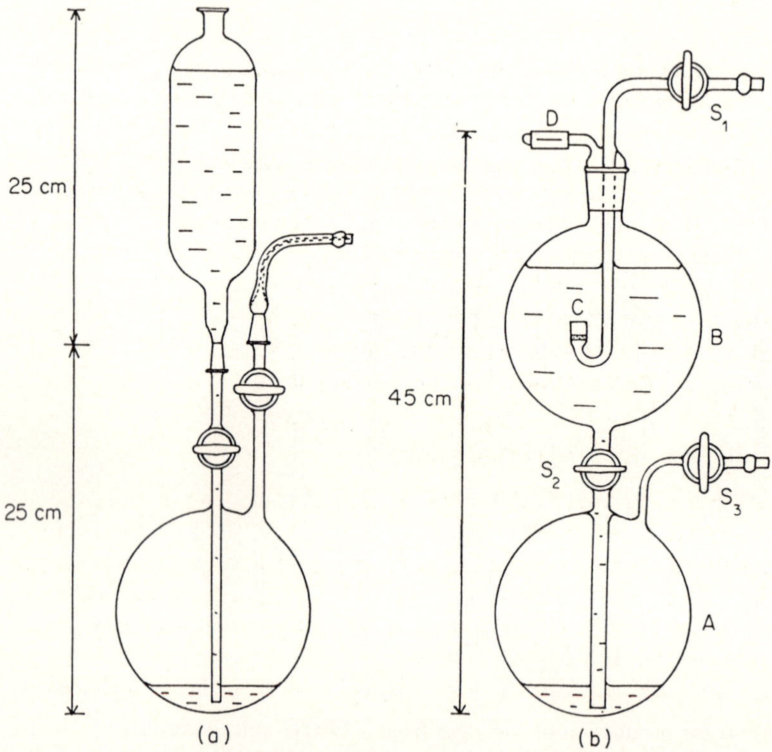

Fig. 2 a, b. $^{15}N_2$ reservoirs. **a** The gas reservoir shown in Fig. 1 has been fitted with a reservoir for displacement fluid and an attachment for a rubber connection to a gas manifold. **b** A gas reservoir for the preparation of ^{15}N gas mixtures and for anaerobic mixtures. The $^{15}N_2$ is kept in the lower bulb (*A*) under a displacement fluid in *B* which can be purged by passing argon or helium through *C; D* is a rubber Bunsen valve. S_1, S_2, and S_3 are high-vacuum stopcocks (Bergersen 1980)

cury in (TP) should be raised up to S_6 and S_7. A solution of 40% w/v NaOH is then run into G from the funnel and G is then heated gently. The NH_3 gas is then displaced into the system by gentle boiling of the liquid in G until only about 2 cm of the solid NaOH pellets remain in the tube (these prevent water entering the system). The mercury in TP is then lowered to draw the last of the NH_3 into the system and S_3 is closed (the generator should immediately be rinsed because the corrosive contents etch the glass). The furnace is then heated to 600° C and the NH_3 gas circulated in the system in the direction of the arrow by means of the Toepler pump for 1 h after the manometer (M) indicates that a constant volume has been reached. This ensures completion of the reaction. Finally, the trap (T) is cooled in liquid N_2, and the gas is circulated to remove impurities, then S_{10} is closed and the N_2 gas pumped into (R). The Toepler pump is operated as follows: with the mercury lowered to S8, S5, and S6 are closed, S7 is opened, and the mercury raised to S7, which is then closed. The mercury is then lowered and S6 opened, thus again charging the pump with gas from the system. The mercury is raised by connecting S11 to the atmosphere (or a slight positive air pressure) through a capillary, and lowered by connecting S11 to a vacuum provided by a filter pump.

After collection of the $^{15}N_2$, the pressure in the container will be less than 1 atm. A displacement fluid reservoir (Fig. 2a) can be added to the gas reservoir to provide a useful "gasometer" from which the $^{15}N_2$ can be dispensed. The displacement fluid should be acidified to trap any residual NH_3 or that present in the air. The addition of K_2SO_4 will also reduce the solubility of the $^{15}N_2$ in the fluid. The gas in this apparatus becomes contaminated with O_2 from air dissolved in the displacement water. This is of no concern for aerobic systems but for anaerobic N_2 experiments a storage container shown in Fig. 2b is used. In this case the water in the upper flask can be sparged with argon or helium to remove O_2.

Gas mixtures can be conveniently prepared for biological samples by using a manifold mercury manometer and a vacuum pump or by injecting $^{15}N_2$ through suitable serum caps into evacuated vials containing the N_2 fixing system.

3.1.2 Oxidation with Alkaline Hypobromite

A simpler method involves the oxidation of ^{15}N-labelled ammonium salts to $^{15}N_2$ with alkaline sodium or lithium hypobromite. Impurities produced during this reaction include the oxides of nitrogen which can be removed by passing the generated gas through a liquid nitrogen trap at −180° C when N_2O and NO gases are frozen out of the gas mixture leaving pure $^{15}N_2$. The apparatus used to generate N_2 gas is shown in Fig. 3.

The production of N_2 gas by this method is represented by the following equation:

$$2\,NaOBr + 2\,NH_3 \rightarrow N_2 + 3\,NaBr + 3\,H_2O\,.$$

A weighed amount of $^{15}N_2$-labelled ammonium salt, e.g. $(^{15}NH_4)_2SO_4$ (1.5 g), is placed in a 10-ml flask (A) which is attached to another 200-ml round-bottomed flask (B) via a conical joint (B_{10}). Flask (B) contains 100 ml sodium or lithium hypobromite (preparation described below). Before joining flask (B) to the rest

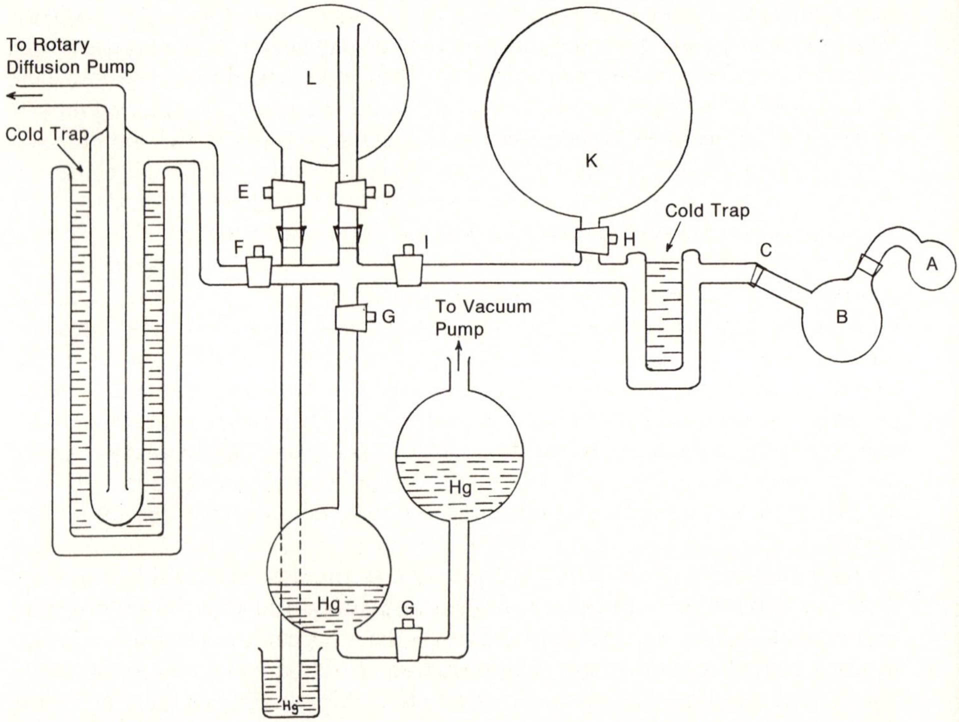

Fig. 3. Apparatus for generating $^{15}N_2$ from $^{15}NH_4$-labelled salts. (Details of operation given in the text)

of the apparatus a cylinder of helium or argon is attached at (C). Stopcocks D, E, and G are closed and F, H, and I are opened and the apparatus is evacuated via rotary and diffusion pumps to at least 0.01 Torr. Then stopcock F is closed and H opened so that the 5-litre reservoir flask (K) is filled with either helium or argon from the cylinder. Then stopcock H is closed, the gas cylinder removed and flask (B) is now attached to the apparatus via the conical joint C. Stopcocks D, E, I, and F are opened and the apparatus is evacuated as before to 0.01 Torr. The stopcock F is closed and G opened and the $(^{15}NH_4)_2SO_4$ is now transferred slowly from flask (A) to the hypobromite in flask (B) to generate $^{15}N_2$ gas which is passed through the cold trap (a Dewar flask containing liquid nitrogen) to remove moisture and the oxides of nitrogen. The gas is collected in a litre flask (L) by means of the Hg pump system. Then stopcock H is opened slowly so that the carrier gas either argon or helium from flask (K) can be transferred into flask (L) to the extent of 80% v/v of carrier gas.

Alkaline hypobromite is prepared by dissolving 100 g NaOH in 150 ml distilled water in a wide-necked Erlenmeyer flask (200 ml) which is then cooled in an ice-salt bath for 15 min before titrating slowly (dropwise) with bromine (30 ml) from a burette. The flask which is shaken after each addition of bromine must be kept below 2° C. This operation must be carried out in a fume hood fitted with an efficient extracting fan. After the addition of all the bromine the reaction mixture is allowed to stand overnight at 2° C and then filtered through a sintered glass funnel (porosity 1). The filtrate is diluted 1:1 with 0.2% v/v aqueous KI. About 1 ml of this solution will oxidize 12–16 mg NH_4^+ N. When larger amounts of N_2 (200 ml) are generated from 1.5 g $(^{15}NH_4)_2SO_4$, the hypobromite is diluted (2:1) with 0.4% w/v KI resulting in a more concentrated solution.

3.2 Exposure of Samples to $^{15}N_2$ Gas Mixtures

The apparatus shown in Fig. 4 is used to dispense the $^{15}N_2$ gas mixture into the biological samples. The flask (L) (see also Fig. 2) containing a $^{15}N_2$/He or Ar mixture is now attached to a gas manifold via a three-way tap A. The apparatus including flask (L) as well as the six 20 ml Erlenmeyer flasks containing the biological samples, attached to the manifold by B_{10} cones, are evacuated with a rotary pump to 0.01 Torr. By adjusting the three-way tap at A, the gas mixture is now passed by water displacement into the six flasks from flask (L). The distilled water in flask (K) is acidified with H_2SO_4 to trap any ammonia present in the air. The six 10 ml Erlenmeyer flasks are each fitted with a stopcock and a sidearm closed with a rubber septum as shown in Fig. 4. Solutions can be injected through the septa via gas-tight syringes into the sidearms before evacuation and subsequent gassing with the $^{15}N_2$ gas mixture. After gassing, each flask is closed off by turning the stopcock and the six flasks are transferred into a reciprocating water bath

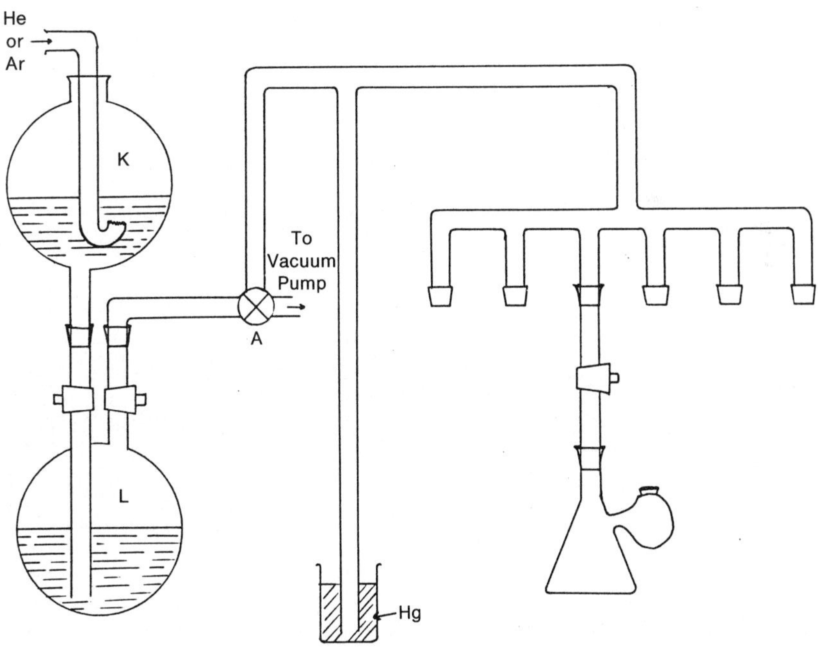

Fig. 4. Apparatus for dispensing ^{15}N/He or Ar gas mixture by water displacement into sample flasks containing the biological material to be exposed to the stable isotope. (Details of operation given in the text)

at 30° C and incubated for about 20 min. Then the content of each flask is transferred into a microkjeldahl flask and digested in 36 N H_2SO_4 plus HgO catalyst as described in Sect. 2.1. The ammonia produced is distilled into boric acid as described in Sect. 2.2.

A simpler procedure for exposing biological samples to suitable gas mixtures containing $^{15}N_2$ involves the use of serum bottles (5 ml) fitted with rubber serum caps. Hypodermic needles are used to insert or remove gases or liquids from the bottles. The bottle is first evacuated with a two-stage pump with a hypodermic needle inserted through the serum cap. Appropriate gas mixtures can be introduced via hypodermic needles into the serum bottles. The pN_2 of the gas mixture is related to the Km of the biological fixation sample. For most aerobic systems, e.g. cells of *Azotobacter*, 0.3 atm N_2 and 0.1 atm O_2 in either 0.6 atm He or Ar should be adequate. For anaerobic samples, O_2 which is omitted, is made up with the appropriate camer gas (argon or helium).

After exposure to the $^{15}N_2$ gas mixture for about 20 min in a reciprocating water bath at 30° C, about 0.5 ml 11 N H_2SO_4 is added to inactivate the samples. They are then transferred into 100-ml microkjeldahl flasks and 5 ml, 36 N H_2SO_4 is added plus the HgO catalyst and digestion continued as described in Sect. 2.2. The ammonia in the digest is distilled into boric acid in a 100-ml Erlenmeyer flask as described in Sect. 2.2. More 11 N H_2SO_4 (0.5 ml) is added to each flask and the contents evaporated to a small volume by heating on a hotplate. After cooling the solution is dispensed into a suitable volume in a graduated flask (10 ml) and appropriate aliquots (containing about 1 mg N) are taken to generate $^{15}N_2$ for analysis in a mass spectrometer.

3.3 Conversion of $^{15}NH_4^+$ to $^{15}N_2$ for Analysis in a Mass Spectrometer

3.3.1 Rittenberg Tubes

$^{15}N_2$ is generated from the ammonia by oxidation with alkaline hypobromite so that the gas can be analyzed in a mass spectrometer. A well-established procedure involves the use of Rittenberg tubes; in one limb is placed the sample of ammonia in boric acid (sufficient to generate between 0.5 and 1 mg $^{15}N_2$) and in the other arm, 1 ml alkaline hypobromite (see Sect. 3.1). The Rittenberg tube is attached to the mass spectrometer via a greased glass joint fitted to a copper tubing in the form of a U-tube which then links to a taper joint attached to the manifold of the mass spectrometer. The Rittenberg tube is rigorously evacuated to 0.01 Torr and the alkaline hypobromite is mixed in with the ammonia containing sample to generate $^{15}N_2$. The gas is passed into the mass spectrometer for analysis via the copper tubing, which is immersed in liquid nitrogen, to remove moisture and the oxides of nitrogen.

3.3.2 Glass Vials

A simpler procedure for the in situ generation of $^{15}N_2$ gas from the ammonia samples has been described by Ross and Martin (1970, see Fig. 5a, b). An aliquot of the ammonia sample (1 mg N) is dispensed into a clean glass vial (5 ml) fitted

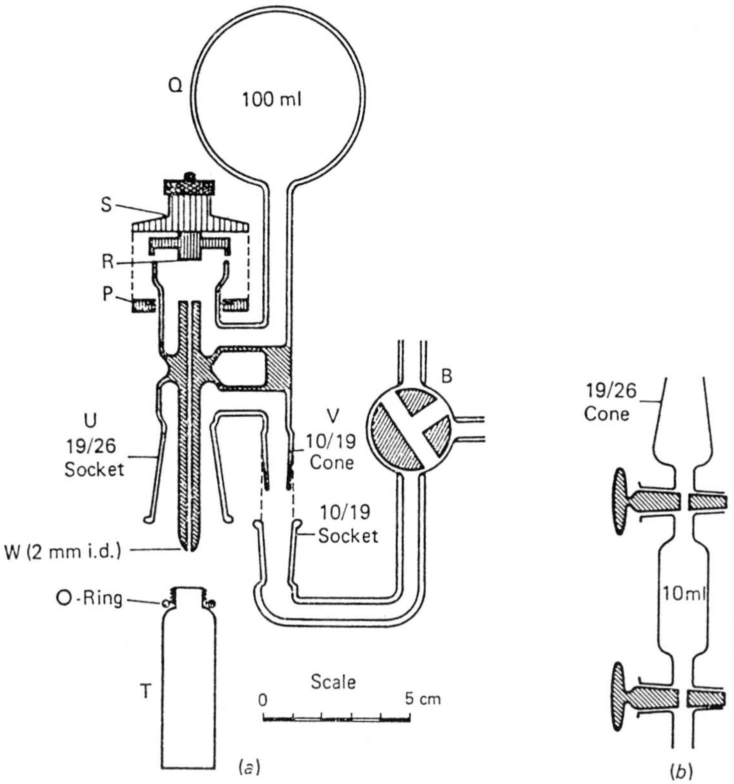

Fig. 5. a Conversion assembly for preparing nitrogen gas from ammonium sulphate. *B* 3-way glass vacuum stopcock; *P, R*, and *S* Springham valve assembly; *Q* hypobromite reservoir; *T* vial; *U* 19/26 socket (Quickfit or Clearfit); *V* 10(19 cone; and *W* capillary delivery tube. **b** Helium vessel (Ross and Martin 1970)

with an O-ring. The vial is attached to the glass assembly shown in Fig. 5a. The reservoir (Q) contains air-free hypobromite solution under an atmosphere of argon or helium. A fitting S (available from Springham and Co Ltd., Harlow, Essex) is attached to the upper portion of the assembly. Normally S is bolted to the retaining ring P, these components are separated in Fig. 5a for clarity. The vial T containing the ammonia sample is coupled to the lightly greased 19/26 socket U by using a neoprene O-ring (11 mm inner diameter; 16 mm outer diameter). With stopcock S closed and on evacuation of the assembly through the 10/19 cone, V, the vial is forced into the socket by atmospheric pressure to give a tight vacuum seal. Hypobromite solution can then be admitted into the vial by opening stopcock S, thus generating $^{15}N_2$ gas.

To remove spent hypobromite from the reservoir of the conversion assembly (Fig. 5a), admit air by opening stopcock S and suck the hypobromite solution out via the central capillary tube W with a water pump. Evacuate the reservoir with the pump, close S, and dip the end of the capillary into distilled water contained in an evaporating basin. Open S so that water is forced into the reservoir for rinsing. Remove the rinse water and suck up the freshly prepared hypobromite solution by the same procedure. As the hypobromite is forced up into the evacuated space by atmospheric pressure it is effectively degassed. Close stopcock S before all the solution is removed from the evaporating basin, so that no air enters the reservoir.

Pass helium from a cylinder through the glass assembly shown in Fig. 5b and trap 10 ml by closing the stopcocks. Lightly grease the 19/26 cone and attach it to the conversion assembly at U. Invert the conversion assembly, making sure that all of the hypobromite solution runs out of the well of the greaseless stopcock. Evacuate the assembly in this position through the cold trap C in Fig. 5a. Open the stopcock S (Fig. 5a) and continue to evacuate for 2 min or until the hypbromite solution begins to boil. Shut off the vacuum and open the stopcock on the helium fitting, to admit the helium into the reservoir, then close S. Remove the conversion assembly and turn it the right way up, making sure that the well S contains no trapped bubbles of helium or argon. The assembly is now ready for use.

Whichever method is used to evacuate the assembly in the above procedure, the volume between the assembly and the stopcock to the vacuum system should not be more than 10 to 20 ml, otherwise the final pressure of helium or argon in the reservoir may be too low, in which case N_2 gas produced in the sample vial may be forced into the reservoir where it will contaminate the hypobromite.

The preparative unit for converting ammonia to $^{15}N_2$ gas and admitting the gas into the mass spectrometer is illustrated in Fig. 6a. A is the conversion assembly shown in detail in Fig. 6a, B is a three-way glass stopcock used to regulate the vacuum manipulations and C is a 100-ml cold trap immersed in a dry ice-acetone freezing mixture to remove water during evacuation of the assembly. D is a cold trap consisting of a 300-mm stainless steel tube (1 mm inner diameter; 1.5 mm outer diameter) wound into a helix which is immersed into liquid nitrogen just before the $^{15}N_2$ gas sample is introduced into the mass spectrometer to remove moisture and the oxides of nitrogen. D is connected via 2 mm (inner diameter) stainless steel tubing E and the 3 mm polythene diaphragm valve 2 (G.E.C.-A.E.I., Manchester, UK) to the 500-ml mass spectrometer expansion vessel F, whence the gas sample can be admitted to the ion source by opening valve 3. Epoxy resin (Araldite A.W. 106 adhesive with HV 953 hardener, Ciba Ltd. Basle) is satisfactory for constructing glass-to-metal seals.

Between conversions, valve 1 is open while valves 2 and 3 are closed (Fig. 6a); stopcock B is in position 1 (Fig. 6b). Proceed as follows:

Attach a sample vial to the conversion assembly, close valve 1 and turn B anticlockwise to position 2 to evacuate the sample; allow 1 min for evacuation. During this time focus the mass spectrometer on the peak at mass 28 so that it can be used as a vacuum gauge and open valve 3 to check that the expansion vessel F is thoroughly evacuated. When the 1-min period has elapsed, open valve 1 to check for leaks in the conversion assemby. If there is no appreciable rise in the 28 peak the vacuum is satisfactory. Immerse the sample vial to a depth of 5 to 10 mm in a dry ice-acetone freezing mixture, taking care that no acetone contaminates the grease on the 19/26 socket U. Turn B to position 3 and by opening S, quickly admit into the vial sufficient hypobromite solution (0.5 to 1 ml) to oxidize

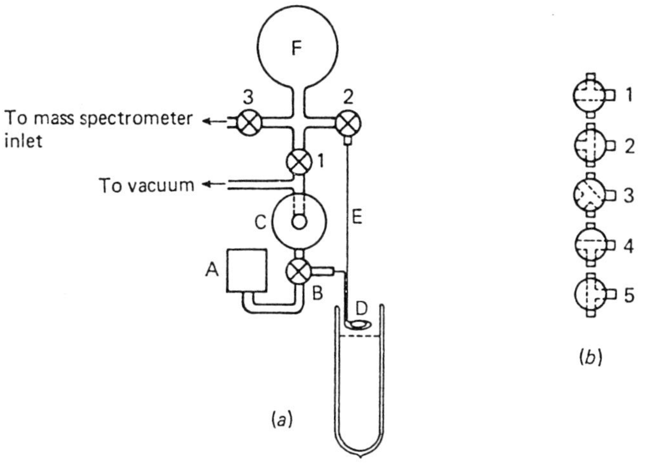

Fig. 6. a Diagrammatic lay-out of conversion assembly in relation to the mass-spectrometer inlet system. *A* Conversion assembly as in Fig. 1; *B* 3-way glass vacuum stopcock as in Fig. 1; *C* dry ice-acetone cold trop; *D* stainless steel helical cold trap; *E* stainless steel tubing; *F* expansion vessel; and *1, 2,* and *3* inlet valves. **b** Positions of the 3-way stopcock *B* during vacuum manipulations (see text; Ross and Martin 1970)

all the ammonium sulphate. Immerse the stainless steel helix D in liquid nitrogen and wait until all the hypobromite solution is frozen. Then close valve 1 and turn B to position 4. By using valve 2 as a throttle, allow the required amount of nitrogen to leak into F; this will register on the mass spectrometer. Turn B to position 1, remove the liquid nitrogen from D and remove the dry ice-acetone from the sample vial.

Carry out isotope-ratio analysis of the nitrogen gas. When this is complete close valve 3 and open valve 1. Remove the conversion assembly and place it upright in a clamp. Insert a 1 mm (outer diameter) polythene tube, attached to a water pump, into the capillary tube W as far as the Viton seat. Rinse the outside of the latter tube with distilled water from a plastic wash bottle; this water will be sucked into the capillary, thus rinsing it. Occasionally some of the solution will splash out of the vial during oxidation of the ammonium sulphate. If this occurs, rinse the upper part of the socket U also. Withdraw the polythene tube carefully so that no droplets of water remain to block the capillary during evacuation. Replace the conversion assembly and repeat the procedure with the next sample. The entire operation including isotope-ratio analysis takes about 5 min.

^{15}N-labelled ammonium salts are usually included as standard with each batch of samples so that memory effects can be readily checked.

3.4 Analysis of $^{15}N_2$ Data

The measurement of the nitrogen peak heights at mass numbers 28, 29, and 30 and the one for oxygen at 32 is made in the mass spectrometer. In addition to determining the N and O peaks, it is also advisable to measure the one for argon (mass 40) to confirm the absence of air from the samples. The percent enrichment fo ^{15}N in the samples is calculated as follows:

$$\frac{N_2^{(29)}-2(N_2^{30})}{2(N_2^{28}+N_2^{29}+N_2^{30})}.$$

From this value deduct 0.3663 which is the $^{15}N_2$ enrichment in air. Then calculate the μg N fixed as follows:

$$\frac{\text{Measured enrichment}}{\text{Initial enrichment}} \times \frac{\text{Total N } (\mu g)}{1}.$$

3.5 Analysis of ^{15}N Abundance by Emission Spectrometry

This method which measures the ^{15}N-^{14}N ratios in biological samples by means of emission spectrometric analysis is claimed to detect $^{15}N_2$ in amounts that are 100 times smaller than those by mass spectrometer procedures (Persche and Proksch 1971; Fiedler and Proksch 1975; Kano et al. 1975; Blackburn 1979; Yamamuro 1987).

The technique involves the analysis of $^{15}N_2$ gas in electrode-less quartz tubes at a pressure of 2 Torr by exciting the system with a 100-ME generator (Leichnam et al. 1968) operating at 50 W. The light from the tube is focussed and resolved in a modified quartz spectrograph (Hilger Watts Model E742 adapted with an RCA 1P28 photomultiplier tube). The band heads ^{14}N-^{14}N at 2977 Å, ^{14}N-^{15}N at 2983 Å and ^{15}N-^{15}N at 2989 Å are used for spectral determination of the $^{14}N/^{15}N$ ratio. The light corresponding to the N_{29} and N_{28} bands is collected by a photomultiplier, amplified and then recorded. The ^{15}N abundance is calculated from the peak heights of N_{29} and N_{28}.

The precision of the method has been checked with natural $(NH_4)_2SO_4$ generating 4 μg N using ten measurements. The average abundance was found to be 0.366% ^{15}N with a standard deviation of ± 0.011 which corresponds to about 3% of the mean.

There are a few problems associated with this method. Thus, a correction has to be applied to the ^{28}N-peak (which varies from 0.10 to 0.15%) to take into account the impurities (CO_2, SO_3^-, and Cl^-) which are present in varying amounts in biological samples and affect the N-bands.

When sampling microgram quantities of N, the thorough homogenization of the biological materials is of paramount importance to achieve reproducible samples. The amount of carbon in the samples should be known since the quantity of CaO + CuO in the briquette (normally 1 : 1) in the quartz capillary tube has to be adjusted accordingly. Too high amounts of CaO + CuO will absorb N_2 and then not enough will remain for excitation. Care must be taken to avoid contamination of the biological samples with air.

4 Use of $^{13}N_2$ to Determine Dinitrogen Fixation

Since the ^{15}N method is time-consuming some 2 days are required to complete an experiment from the initial exposure of the sample to the final analysis in the mass spectrometer, a technique employing radioactive $^{13}N_2$ (β^+ 1.24 MeV, half-life 10.05 min) has been developed by Nicholas et al. (1961).

4.1 Cyclotron Methods

$^{13}N_2$ is produced continuously in a cyclotron by bombarding coarsely granulated charcoal retained behind a stainless steel mesh with 15-MeV deuterons, beam current at 40 μA (Nicholas et al. 1961). The $^{13}N_2$ is produced by the reaction of ^{12}C (d.n.)^{13}N using a deuteron beam. The carrier-free gas is flushed from the target area in a stream of pure argon through small-bore polythene tubing to the adjacent laboratory where it is passed through combustion tubes packed with copper at 750° C and then through a Dreshel bottle containing 2 N H_2SO_4 to remove ammonia and then via a cryogenic unit containing liquid nitrogen to remove the oxides of nitrogen. The activity of the gas is continuously monitored and its half-life checked at intervals to confirm its identity. With a deuteron beam current of 40 μA and an argon flow rate of 0.5 l min^{-1}, a nitrogen-13 activity of between 30 and 60 mCi^{-1} is produced contaminated with about 1% of 1.8 h argon-41.

The biological samples contained in eight 50 ml Erlenmeyer flasks, connected in series, are exposed to the nitrogen 13 gas by bleeding off a portion of the gas from the main polyethylene line. The flasks suspended from a shaker arm in a water bath at 30° C are fitted with Quickfit (Biocones) with inlet and outlet glass tubes for gas transport. The inlet tube is drawn out to a fine jet which is just clear of the sample (usually 2 ml) contained in each flask. The eight flasks are connected in series with sufficient polyvinyl chloride tubing to allow for a thorough reciprocating action (80 oscillations per min) to effect a good exchange between gas and sample. The rate of flow of the gas into this line of flasks is controlled by a pinch clip and is estimated by observing the rate of bubbling as the gas passes through a Dreschel bottle containing water at the end of the line. From this point the gas rejoins the main line and is swept into a large polythene container on the roof of the cyclotron building where it is allowed to decay before being discharged into the atmosphere.

The target material is separated from the high vacuum system of the cyclotron by a thin aluminium window. This enabled the active gas to be collected by blowing a suitable carrier gas (Ar or He) over the target area and thence via appropriate traps (as described previously) into the biological samples. This method is about a 1000 times as sensitive as the ^{15}N procedure. Since the half-life of the $^{13}N_2$ is around 10 min, it can only be used in experiments conducted adjacent to the cyclotron.

Another procedure for generating ^{13}N in a cyclotron involves the 18 MeV proton bombardment of distilled water as substrate $^{16}O(p\alpha)^{13}N$ in a nuclear reaction, as described by Parks and Krohn (1978) and Meeks et al. (1985). A 60 ml recirculating target system is used generating about 0.5 Ci (ca. 1.9×10^{10} Bq) of ^{13}N primarily as $^{13}NO_3^-$ with trace amounts of $^{13}NO_2^-$ and $^{13}NH_4^+$ after a 20-min irradiation. The radioactive anions are concentrated by HPLC onto an anion exchange resin column (Partisil-10 SAX Whatman, Inc.) eluted with phosphate buffer and collected in an appropriate volume (Chasko and Thayer 1981). The concentrated $^{13}NO_3^-$ solution is then transferred to a reaction flask containing saturated NaOH and Devarda's alloy for its reduction to ammonia. The $^{13}NH_3$ is vacuum distilled and trapped into 3 ml of 0.35 M formic acid. About 150 mCi of $^{13}NH_4^+$ is recovered in this volume. The oxidation of $^{13}NH_4^+$ plus carrier $^{14}NH_4^+$ (15 μM) is catalyzed by hypobromite as described in Sect. 3.1.2. This reaction is carried out under vacuum with the $^{13}N_2$ swept from the liquid by gentle sparging with pure CO_2. Water vapour is removed by passage over anhydrous $CaSO_4$ and carrier CO_2 trapped in liquid N_2. The $^{13}N_2$ is collected, compressed and transferred to a container by means of a Toeppler pump (Meeks et al. 1985).

The flow scheme for preparing $^{13}N_2$ is as follows:

1. Generation: $H_2O \xrightarrow[\text{20 MeV 20μA}]{^{16}O(p,\alpha^{13}N)} {}^{13}NO_3^-$ and trace amounts of $^{13}NO_3^-$ and $^{13}NH_4^+$;

2. Concentration: 60 ml $^{13}NO_3^- \xrightarrow[\text{anion exchange column}]{\text{HPLC on}}$ 1 to 3 ml $^{13}NO_3^-$;

3. Reduction: $^{13}NO_3^- \xrightarrow[\text{65° C, saturated NaOH}]{\text{Devarda's alloy (Cu/Al) Zn}} {}^{13}NH_3$;

4. Oxidation: $^{13}NH_4 \xrightarrow[^{15}\text{μmol } ^{14}NH_4^+]{\text{Na/KOBr}}$.

4.2 Linear Accelerator

In collaboration with the Physics Division at the Australian Atomic Energy Commission's Research Establishment at Lucas Heights, Sydney, the 3 MeV Van de Graaff linear accelerator is used to generate $^{13}N_2$ (Ritchie 1968). The target ($^{12}Cd, n^{13}N$) is made of reactor grade graphite which is stable at high temperatures under beam bombardment. The increase in yield of gas is associated with the fact that the diffusion coefficient of gases in most materials increases about six-fold when temperature is increased to 1500° C. To overcome problems associated with the use of an aluminium window to separate the target material from the high vacuum system as in the cyclotron, a small aperture of 0.5 cm is used. Both sides of the aperture is pumped, but the pump speed on the target side is about ten times that of the high vacuum side. The yield of active gas increases with pressure; a suitable working pressure in the target chamber is about 0.1 mmHg.

Helium or argon is used as the carrier gas and the $^{13}N_2$ is flushed from the target area through copper tubing to a convenient shielded laboratory about 50 ft. from the target chamber. The yield of $^{13}N_2$ using 200 μA of 2.5 MeV deuteron beam and a target chamber pressure of 0.2 mmHg is about 80 mCi l^{-1} at a flow rate through the system of about 0.1 l min^{-1}. These values are comparable to those obtained with conventional cyclotrons.

References

Bergersen FJ (ed) (1980) Measurement of nitrogen fixation by direct means. In: Methods for evaluating biological nitrogen fixation. Wiley, New York, pp 65–110

Blackburn TH (1979) Method for measuring rates of NH_4^+ turnover in anoxic marine sediments using ^{15}N-NH_4^+ dilution technique. Appl Environ Microbiol 37:760–765

Bremner JM, Edwards AP (1965) Determination of isotope-ratio analysis of different forms of nitrogen in soils: I Apparatus and procedure for distillation and determination of ammonium. Soil Sci Soc Am Proc 29:504–507

Burris RH (1972) Nitrogen fixation, assay methods and techniques. In: Colowick SP, Kaplan NO (eds) Methods in enzymology, vol 24. Academic Press, New York, London, pp 415–431

Burris RH, Wilson PW (1957) Methods for measurement of nitrogen fixation. In: Colowick SP, Kaplan NO (eds) Methods in enzymology, vol 4. Academic Press, New York, London, pp 355–366

Chasko JH, Thayer JR (1981) Rapid concentration and purification of ^{15}N-labelled anions on high performance anion exchanger. Int J Appl Radiat Isotopes 32:645–649

Fiedler R, Proksch G (1975) The determination of nitrogen-15 by emission and mass spectrometry in biochemical analysis: a review. Anal Chim Acta 78:1–63

Humphries EC (1956) Mineral components and ash analysis. In: Paech K, Tracey MV (eds) Modern methods of plant analysis, vol 1. Springer, Berlin Göttingen, pp 468–502

Kano H, Yoneyama T, Kumazawa K (1975) Emission spectrometric ^{15}N analysis of the amino acids and amides in plant tissues separated by thin layer chromatography. Anal Biochem 67:327–331

Leichmann JP, Figdor HC, Keroe EA, Muehl A (1968) Transformation simple d'un spectrographe à plaques photographiques in spectromètre enrégistreur utilisable notamment pour le dosage isotopique de l'azote. Int J Appl Radiat Isotopes 19:235–247

Meeks JC, Enderlin CS, Joseph CM, Steinberg N, Weeden YM (1985) Use of ^{13}N to study N_2 fixation and assimilation by cyano bacteria – lower plant associations in nitrogen fixation. In: Evans HJ, Bottomley PJ, Newton WE (eds) Nitrogen fixation research progress. Nijhoff, Dordrecht Lancaster, pp 301–307

Nicholas DJD, Silvester DJ, Fowler JF (1961) Use of radioactive nitrogen in studying nitrogen fixation in bacterial cells and their extracts. Nature 189:634–636

Parker CA (1961) A method for the measurement of total nitrogen in microgram quantities. Aust J Exp Biol 39:515–520

Parks NJ, Krohn KA (1978) The synthesis of ^{13}N labelled ammonia, dinitrogen, nitrite and nitrate using a single cyclotron target system. Int J Appl Radiat Isotopes 29:754–756

Persche H, Proksch G (1971) Analysis of ^{15}N abundance in biological samples by means of emission spectrometry. In: Nitrogen-15 in soil-plant studies. IAEA, Vienna, pp 223–225

Ritchie AIM (1968) The production of radioisotopes $^{11}C^{13}N$ and ^{15}O using the deuteron beam from 3 MeV Van de Graaff accelerator. Nucl Instrum Meth 64:181–187

Ross PJ, Martin AE (1970) A rapid procedure for preparing gas samples for nitrogen-15 determination. Analyst 95:817–822

Schoenheimer R, Rittenberg D (1939) Studies in protein metabolism 1. General considerations in the application of isotopes to the study of protein metabolism. The normal abundance of nitrogen isotopes in amino acids. J Biol Chem 127:285–290
Thode HG, Urey HC (1939) The further concentration of ^{15}N. J Chem Phys 7:34–39
Umbreit WW, Bond VS (1936) Analysis of plant tissue. Appl Semi Micro Kjeldahl method 8:276–278
Yamamuro S (1987) The accurate determination of nitrogen-15 with an emission spectrometer. Soil Sci Plant Nutrit 27:405–419

Methods for Uptake and Assimilation Studies of Nitrogen Dioxide

H. S. SRIVASTAVA, D. P. ORMROD, and B. H. MARIE

1 Introduction

Nitrogen dioxide is a major air pollutant, discharged into the environment from both natural and anthropogenic sources, although its background concentration in most localities is well below the concentrations reported to produce visible damage and death of plants (National Academy of Sciences 1971). The control of industrial NO_2 emissions to the atmosphere has lagged behind that of other pollutants such as SO_2. Several scientists have suggested the creation of green belts in urban and sub-urban areas to reduce the air pollution load, as plants have been found to be an efficient sink of air pollutants including NO_2 (Hill 1971). The pollutants can diffuse into plant tissues through open stomata, as do CO_2, O_2 and water vapour, although cuticular absorption also accounts for some pollutant removal from the atmosphere. Plants play a major role in regulating the concentration of CO_2 and O_2 in the air; they may also play an important role in removing air pollution.

Nitrogen dioxide is soluble in cold water and so, after reaching the cell sap, may dissolve to produce nitrate and nitrite ions:

$$2NO_2 + H_2O \rightarrow 2H^+ + NO_3^- + NO_2^- .$$

The nitrate and nitrite ions can be reduced and assimilated by the plants and thus the air pollutant can indirectly act as a source of nutrient nitrogen. However, the foliar uptake of nutrient nitrogen is not the predominant route, and may cause some disturbance in the physiology and biochemistry of plants. Therefore, the potential role of NO_2 as a nitrogen nutrient will depend upon a suitable balance between its assimilation and toxic effects on other physiological processes. The methodological approaches to studying these questions are described in the present chapter.

2 Nitrogen Dioxide Uptake

Numerous studies have been undertaken to monitor the absorption of NO_2. Even in those studies where the primary objective is to examine the effect of the pollutant on plants, the assessment of its uptake is desirable, to relate dose and effect. Basically three approaches have been taken to determine the rate of uptake. These are: gas flux studies (measuring the decrease in NO_2 concentration across plant surfaces); nutrient status studies (measuring the increase in inorganic/organic nitrogen during exposure to NO_2); and ^{15}N studies.

2.1 Gas Flux Studies

In this method, a known concentration of NO_2 is passed through a cuvette or chamber enclosing part of a plant, or an entire plant; the decrease in gas concentration by ad- and absorption is monitored. The methodological approach is similar to that used for CO_2 uptake studies in photosynthetic research. The uptake of NO_2 is via the stomata, and is governed by factors similar to those for CO_2. The essential components of NO_2 uptake studies are: an NO_2 supply system, a flow through cuvette or chamber for enclosing the plant or leaf and an NO_2 measuring device.

2.1.1 Nitrogen Dioxide Supply Systems

The most satisfactory source of NO_2 is a cylinder of compressed gas, which is now readily available from most dealers of rare gases. The gas cylinder is generally equipped with a two-stage regulator to control the rate of NO_2 emission from the cylinder. Since low concentrations are used in most biological experiments, and NO_2 is toxic to human beings, gas cylinders containing less than 1% NO_2 in nitrogen are desirable. To achieve experimental concentrations of less than 5 $\mu l\, l^{-1}$, the source gas (usually less than 5000 $\mu l\, l^{-1}$) can be diluted with air, either in the exposure chamber or in another vessel attached before the exposure chamber. Some investigators have used cylinders of liquid N_2O_4 instead of NO_2 (Maclean et al. 1968; Spierings 1971; Fuhrer and Erismann 1980); the cylinder in such cases must be maintained at or above 25° C to vapourize N_2O_4 to NO_2. The gas is delivered to exposure facilities through needle valves; by manipulating the needle valves, the rate of NO_2 injection can be controlled.

In some studies, NO_2 is generated in the laboratory by chemical methods and used instantaneously (Sinn et al. 1984). The three most common chemical reactions for laboratory production of NO_2 are: (1) by heating lead nitrate and by the action of nitric acid on either (2) copper chips or (3) sodium nitrite:

1. $2Pb(NO_3)_2 \longrightarrow 2PbO + 4NO_2 + O_2;$
2. $Cu + 4HNO_3(conc) \longrightarrow Cu(NO_3)_2 + 2NO_2 + 2H_2O;$
3. $NaNO_2 + 2HNO_3(dil) \longrightarrow NaNO_3 + 2NO_2 + H_2O.$

Oleksyn (1984) produced NO_2 in the laboratory for studying its effects on photosynthesis and respiration in scots pine by bubbling air through a solution of concentrated HNO_3 at 83° C:

$$2HNO_3 \rightarrow 2NO_2 + H_2O + \tfrac{1}{2}O_2.$$

Laboratory methods of generating NO_2 are least expensive and the simplest way of obtaining NO_2, especially in laboratories which are not well equipped and lack resources. However, it is often difficult to control the pollutant level with such methods, and the treatment levels vary considerably between replicate experiments.

2.1.2 Exposure Systems

When either a single leaf or a part of the plant is to be exposed to the pollutant, an exposure cuvette is used. Designs of some such cuvettes have been described by several investigators (Unsworth 1982). A cross-sectional view of the cuvette designed by Srivastava et al. (1975 a), which is well suited for enclosing either detached leaves or twigs or attached leaves with long petioles, is outlined in Fig. 1 A and B. In constructing a cuvette, care must be taken to select a material that minimizes the sorption of the pollutant. Further, the material must be transparent, as in most studies, the plant part is illuminated from outside. Teflon™ and Plexiglass™ are the most suitable materials for cuvette construction.

The cuvette is equipped with a small fan to keep the pollutant well stirred, and to minimize boundary layer resistance. Often a thermocouple is inserted in the cuvette so that temperature during exposure may be monitored. Temperature inside the cuvette can be maintained by circulating water of the desired temperature through the outer jacket of the chamber (Fig. 1 A). The cuvette should be conditioned for 10–15 min before the plant is positioned and exposure begins, by flushing the pollutant through the cuvette and the entire gas flow system. This ensures saturation of the cuvette material by the pollutant gas, stabilizing flux measurement. Cuvettes are suitable for measuring short-term rates of pollutant uptake by a single leaf or twig of the plant. However, care should be taken in extrapolating such data to the entire plant, as often the rate of uptake by a single leaf or plant part differs from that of a whole plant.

For exposing either a whole plant or a population of plants, a larger exposure chamber is required. The Plexiglass™ or Teflon™ chambers may be rectangular, cubic or cylindrical. An exposure chamber designed and described by Heck et al. (1968) has been used in many studies; a cubic chamber has been used by Srivastava and Ormrod (1984). The chambers are generally provided with a rotor fan for circulating and mixing gases. The chamber may be lined with transparent Tedler™ (PVF) film to minimize the gas sorption by the chamber. Many investigators have preferred to use a slightly modified exposure chamber, the continuous stirred tank reactor (CSTR), where air exchange is usually more frequent than in other exposure chambers (Jefferies et al. 1976; Heck et al. 1978; Rogers et al. 1979 b; Rogers and Aneja 1980). The details of the design of a CSTR have been described by Rogers et al. (1977).

The use of closed chambers for studying pollutant uptake also suffers from a disadvantage in the sense that the rate of uptake by plants in the chamber may be different from field conditions. There is vigorous air movement in the chambers, which decreases the leaf boundary layer, and leaf surfaces are supplied with a constant pollutant concentration. In order to obtain more realistic data on the responses of plants to air pollutants, some investigators have used open top chambers (Heagle et al. 1973; Mandl et al. 1973). Some other investigators have used completely open field exposure systems for studying pollutant effects, which

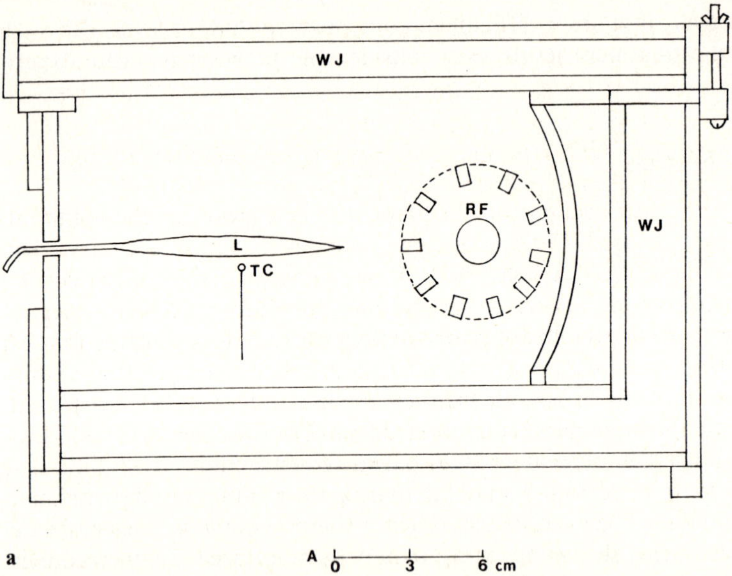

a

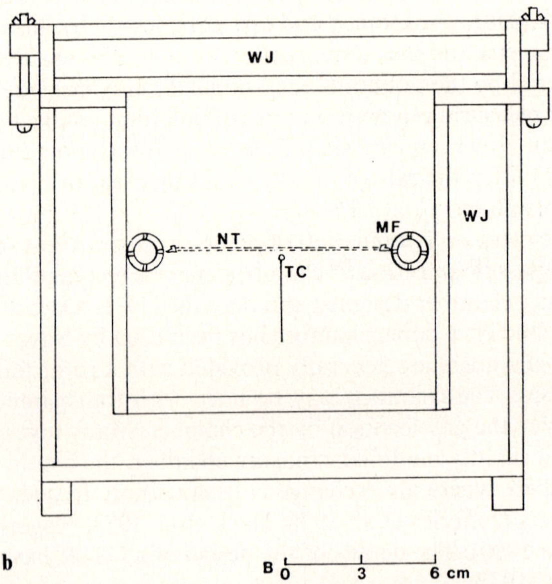

b

Fig. 1 a, b. Line diagram of the leaf chamber. **a** Median longitudinal (lengthwise) section; **b** Median transverse (widthwise) section. *L* Leaf; *MF* plexiglass manifolds for introducing and collecting air samples from the chamber; *NT* nylon thread to hold the leaf in position; *RF* rotory fan; *TC* thermocouple; *WJ* water jacket can also be used to determine the rate of NO_2 uptake. Networks of polyethylene tubing or pipes have been used for exposing large areas of fruit trees, natural grass or crops (Decormis et al. 1975; Lee and Lewis 1977; Muller et al. 1979). Although such exposure systems are closer to ambient situations than laboratory studies, the values obtained for pollutant uptake may be an approximation, as there may be non-ambient distribution of pollutant around the canopy.

2.1.3 Nitrogen Dioxide Monitoring Systems

At a given moment, the measurement of the concentration of NO_2 at inlet and outlet points in the exposure chamber or cuvette can give an idea of the rate of uptake by the plant or plant part enclosed inside the chamber/cuvette. The flow rate through the enclosure can be adjusted to obtain a gradient of concentration difference across the chamber which allows detection of treatment differences.

Nitrogen dioxide can be detected by various methods. In some earlier studies, the pollutant was measured by its chemical reaction, as described by Saltzman (1954). Sometimes its oxidizing property is also used to determine its concentration. The air containing the pollutant is blown into a chemical mixture and the potential developed due to the redox reaction is measured by a potentiometer. An NO_2 analyzer based on this principle is the Mast Meter (Mast Co., OH, USA). Dee et al. (1973) have described a chemical method of determining NO_2 concentration. The air stream containing NO_2 is passed over tubes containing PbO_2. The pollutant is absorbed by PbO_2 and the resultant nitrate is extracted from the tubes and estimated by a suitable colorimetric method:

$$PbO_2 + 2\,NO_2 \rightarrow Pb(NO_3)_2 \,.$$

Perhaps the most rapid and accurate method of NO_2 measurement is a chemiluminescent monitor. Several analyzers based on this principle are available (Benedix, Kimoto Electric, Meloy, Monitor Labs, Thermo-Electron); these in-

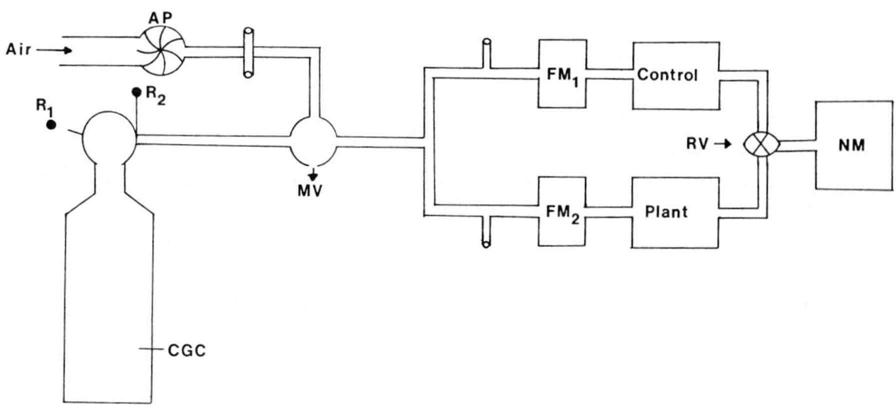

Fig. 2. Line diagram of the gas flow system to measure nitrogen dioxide uptake. *CGC* Compressed gas cylinder; R_1, R_2 regulators; *AP* aspirator pump; FM_1, Fm_2 flow meters; *Control/Plant* chambers; *RV* relay valve; *NM* NO_2 measuring instrument; *MV* mixing vessel

struments can measure different oxides of nitrogen and ammonia accurately in very small quantities.

A flow diagram of the essential components of an NO_2 exposure and measurement system is given in Fig. 2. The regulated gas stream coming from the cylinder is mixed with air to achieve a desired concentration of the pollutant. The rate of flow of the mixed air to the chamber is measured. It should be the same for the control chamber as for the chamber containing the leaf or plant (plant chamber). The NO_2 concentration of the stream coming from the control or the plant chamber is measured in turn by an NO_2 analyzer. The difference in NO_2 concentration between the control and plant chambers can be measured in ppm/pphm or $\mu g\ m^{-3}$. The rate of uptake can then be calculated according to the following equation:

$$r\ NO_2 = F\,\frac{(C_c - C_p)}{V},$$

where

$r\ NO_2$ is the rate of uptake of NO_2 in $\mu g\ NO_2\ m^{-3}\ s^{-1}$;

F is the flow rate of pollutant in $m^3\ s^{-1}$;

C_c is $[NO_2]$ in the empty chamber in $\mu g\ m^{-3}$;

C_p is $[NO_2]$ in the plant chamber in $\mu g\ m^{-3}$;

V is the volume of the chamber in m^3.

When only one chamber is to be used, the concentration of NO_2 before entering the chamber and just after leaving the chamber can be measured and the rate of uptake can be calculated as above, except that:

C_c is $[NO_2]$ at entry into the chamber;

C_p is $[NO_2]$ at exit from the chamber.

2.2 Nitrogenous Compound Extraction and Determination

As stated earlier, dissolution of NO_2 in the cell sap will produce nitrate and nitrite ions, which may be assimilated ultimately into various organic nitrogenous compounds. Thus, an increase in nitrate, nitrite, ammonium and organic nitrogenous compounds during NO_2 exposure may indicate NO_2 uptake by the plant. This response can be quantified in terms of the magnitude of the increase in nitrogenous compounds. Such approaches have been taken by several investigators (Spierings 1971; Yoneyama et al. 1979; Fuhrer and Erismann 1980; Sinn and Pell 1984). In the aquatic plant *Sphagnum cuspidatum*, the nitrate content of the tissue increased with NO_2 concentration in the air. Presumably, the atmospheric NO_2 was dissolved in the supporting water to produce nitrate, which was then absorbed by the aquatic plant (Preiss et al. 1986).

Nitrate and nitrite are usually extracted from dried plant samples in hot (70°–80° C) water and determined colorimetrically. Several models of nitrogen autoanalyzers are also available which can be used to determine nitrate, nitrite, ammonium and organic nitrogen contents. In most analyzers, nitrate is first reduced to nitrite by an activated cadmium column. Nitrite is then determined colorimetrically after diazotization with sulfanilamide and treatment with the color reagent N-(1-naphthyl) ethylenediamine dihydrochloride. Ammonium is also determined colorimetrically after treating the extract with Nessler's reagent. Total nitrogen is usually determined by the Kjeldahl/microKjeldahl method. The dried plant material is digested with concentrated H_2SO_4 and the ammonium produced is estimated either by distillation and titration or by colorimetric procedure. Nitrate and nitrite can be either excluded or included in the total nitrogen determination by the Kjeldahl method, by appropriate chemical treatment of the plant material during digestion (AOAC 1975).

The methods of determining nitrogenous compounds as indicators of NO_2 uptake are simple and inexpensive. However, the following limitations apply:

1. The increase in nitrogen as a result of short-term exposure to NO_2 may be small, below the reliable detection range of chemical methods;
2. Nitrate and nitrite ions are metabolized rapidly, so changes are difficult to detect;
3. In the case of partial plant exposure, translocation of nitrogenous compounds among stressed and unstressed plant parts may alter apparent effects.

2.3 ^{15}N Studies

Radioactive isotopes of essential elements such as C, P, and S have often been used to trace their uptake and metabolic conversions in the plants. However, ^{13}N, the radioactive isotope of nitrogen, has a half-life which is too short (10 min) to allow tracing of its entry and distribution in the plant, but investigations involving very short-term exposures can be carried on provided there is a readily available cyclotron.

Mass spectrometric determination of $^{15}NO_2$ has been used to assess the absorption of the pollutant in several studies (Matsumaru et al. 1979, 1981; Rogers et al. 1979a; Yoneyama et al. 1980; Okano et al. 1986). In the procedure adopted by Rogers et al. (1979a) dried plant material is mixed with oxidizing agents such as CuO, $KClO_4$ or elemental copper to reduce nitrate and nitrite to nitrogen gas, and CaO to absorb other generated gases (e.g. CO_2 and H_2O). The mixture is sealed in a glass ampule, and heated at 560° C for 10 h. The resultant nitrogen gas is passed through an ethanol-dry ice trap for analysis by mass spectrometry.

^{15}N can also be supplied to the plants in the form of fertilizer nitrogen in the soil. Its dilution with nitrogen derived from uptake of atmospheric NO_2 by the exposed plant can be determined to assess the rate of NO_2 uptake. Such an approach has been taken by Okano et al. (1986), who supplied ^{15}N-labelled KNO_3 as fertilizer to sunflower and maize plants. The fertilizer was applied in aqueous solution to ensure uniform labelling of the soil nitrogen pool. Plants growing in such a soil were exposed to NO_2 in a controlled chamber, and no additional fertilizer was applied during NO_2 exposure.

In such a situation, nitrogen originating from atmospheric NO_2 is equal to:

$$\left(1 - \frac{\text{at\% excess } ^{15}\text{N in NO}_2 \text{ exposed plants}}{\text{at\% excess } ^{15}\text{N in non-exposed plants}}\right) \times \text{total N in NO}_2 \text{ exposed plants} .$$

Analysis of ^{15}N in $^{15}NO_2$ exposed plants is the direct method of measuring NO_2 uptake, although it requires a mass spectrometer, which is an expensive apparatus.

2.4 Comparative Rates of Nitrogen Dioxide Uptake

The rates of NO_2 uptake measured by various methods are often comparable. In bean plants, the rate measured by direct analysis of ^{15}N content is about two-thirds of that measured by removal of NO_2 by the plant in an exposure chamber (Table 1). The rate of uptake varies according to the species, the morphophysiological status of the leaf and the environmental conditions. Since the primary sites of NO_2 uptake are stomata, any factor affecting the stomatal opening and closure and thereby the stomatal resistance for NO_2 (R_s NO_2) will affect NO_2 uptake. However, when stomata are fully open, the mesophyll resistance for NO_2 (R_m NO_2), which is an index of NO_2 concentration at its assimilatory/storage site inside the leaf, is of primary importance in its uptake (Srivastava et al. 1975a, b).

Table 1. Amount of NO_2 absorbed by bean leaves exposed to $^{15}NO_2$ for 3 h, as measured by removal of NO_2 from the exposure chamber (kinetic method) and by determining ^{15}N content, data of Rogers et al. (1979a)

Conc. of $^{15}NO_2$ (pphm)	Amount of ^{15}N absorbed (μmol g^{-1} dry wt.)	
	Kinetic method	Direct method
9.7	3.45	2.05
15.2	7.26	4.69
32.5	15.64	10.72

3 Nitrogen Dioxide Assimilation

The nutritive role of NO_2 has been noted in several studies, where exposure to low levels of the pollutant has been found to stimulate plant growth (Troiano and Leone 1977; Anderson and Mansfield 1979; Freer-Smith 1985; Okano and Totsuka 1986). The stimulation seems to be most apparent when the availability of soil nitrogen is limited (Rowland 1986; Srivastava and Ormrod 1986). Matsushima (1972), using ^{14}C, showed an increase in amino acid synthesis in citrus plants exposed to NO_2, and suggested that the nitrogen source for amino acids was NO_2. Nitrate and nitrite generated by the dissolution of NO_2 in the cell sap may be assimilated into amino acids, amides and other nitrogenous compounds by a process similar to that for soil nitrate and nitrite.

Two types of approaches have been taken to demonstrate the assimilation of NO_2 in plants. These are: increase in organic nitrogen content and increase in enzymes of nitrate/nitrite assimilation.

3.1 Increase in Organic Nitrogen

Significant increases in Kjeldahl and total nitrogen due to NO_2 exposure have been observed in kidney bean (Ito et al. 1985), tomato (Spierings 1971), tobacco leaves (Troiano and Leone 1977), spinach (Yoneyama and Sasakawa 1979) and several other plants (Zeevaart 1976). Exposure to 0.02 and 0.1 ppm NO_2 increased both ethanol-soluble and insoluble nitrogen in bean leaves (Srivastava and Ormrod 1984). An increase was also seen with 0.5 ppm NO_2 but only when the plants were supplied with inadequate soil nitrogen (Srivastava and Ormrod 1984). Amino acid content of root and shoot tissues of barley seedlings was also increased substantially by a 9-day exposure to 0.3 ppm NO_2 (Rowland 1986). An increase in root nitrogen indicates that NO_2 absorbed by the leaves is translocated to roots as well. By using $^{15}NO_2$, Rogers et al. (1979a) have shown that about 97% of the absorbed NO_2 is incorporated into organic nitrogen during a 3-h exposure period in bean. Yoneyama et al. (1980) have shown that nitrogen from NO_2 is first incorporated into the ethanol-soluble fraction and then gradually into the insoluble fraction. After 24 h of feeding, only 12% of the nitrogen incorporated was in the soluble fraction.

In most evaluations of NO_2 assimilation, total nitrogen is measured by the Kjeldahl method. The plant sample can also be fractionated into 80% ethanol-soluble and insoluble fractions before digestion and nitrogen determination. The soluble fraction contains small molecules such as amino acids, amides, etc., while the insoluble fraction contains macromolecules such as proteins and nucleic acids. Studies with bean have shown that the increase in the nitrogen content of the soluble fraction due to NO_2 exposure is higher than that of the insoluble fraction (Srivastava and Ormrod 1984). $^{15}NO_2$ feeding and mass spectrometric determination of ^{15}N have also been employed to demonstrate the assimilation of NO_2 in various organic nitrogenous compounds (Rogers et al. 1979b; Rowland 1986).

3.2 Increase in Nitrogen Pathway Enzymes

Nitrate derived from NO_2 is assimilated into organic nitrogenous compounds via nitrite and ammonium. Reduction of NO_3^- to NO_2^- involves the activity of the

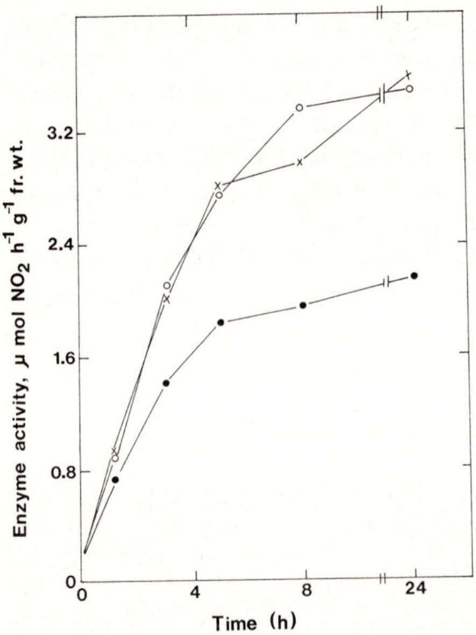

Fig. 3. Time course of increase in nitrate reductase activity during nitrate supply and nitrogen dioxide exposure in bean leaves. Bean plants grown with modified half-strength Hoagland's solution containing no nitrogen, for 10 days, were supplied with the same nutrient solution but containing either 10 m*M* KNO_3 as nitrogen source and/or exposed to 0.5 ppm NO_2 for up to 24 h. The enzyme activity was assayed in the leaf samples at different intervals by an in vivo method. *Filled circles*: $+NO_2$; *open circles*: +nitrate; *cross*: $+NO_2$, +nitrate (Srivastava and Ormrod, communicated)

enzyme nitrate reductase, which is readily induced by the supply of its substrate nitrate (Srivastava 1980). The increase in nitrate reductase activity has also been recorded with NO_2 in pea (Zeevaart 1974), bean (Zeevaart 1974; Srivastava and Ormrod 1984) and squash seedlings (Takeuchi et al. 1985). The time courses of increases in enzyme activity during 24-h exposure to either 0.5 ppm NO_2 or a supply of 10 mM nitrate in the nutrient solution are similar, although the magnitude of enzyme increase with NO_2 is generally lower than that with nitrate (Fig. 3). When both nitrate and NO_2 gas are supplied simultaneously, the enzyme increase is similar to that with nitrate alone. Nitrite reductase, which reduces nitrite to ammonium, is the second enzyme in nitrate assimilation. Its activity also increases during NO_2 exposure in some plants (Wellburn et al. 1981; Yoneyama et al. 1979).

Although several biochemical reactions for incorporating ammonium into organic nitrogen are known, the reductive amination of 2-oxoglutarate to produce glutamate is the most important route of ammonium assimilation. This reaction is catalyzed by the enzyme glutamate dehydrogenase (GDH). However, an alternate pathway of glutamate synthesis from ammonium involving the activity of the enzymes glutamine synthetase (GS) and glutamate synthase (GOGAT), has also been shown to operate under various conditions. Generally when ammonium salts are the primary nitrogen source, ammonium is assimilated by the GDH pathway and when nitrates are the nitrogen source, nitrate is assimilated by the GS/GOGAT pathway (Srivastava and Singh 1987). In bean leaves, exposure to NO_2 increases GOGAT activity significantly, while it has no consistent effect on GDH activity (Srivastava and Ormrod 1984). The increase is more pronounced in the absence of nutrient nitrate than in its presence. This observation has been taken as an indication of the operation of the GS/GOGAT pathway in the assimilation of NO_2.

The details of the methodology for extracting and assaying enzymes of nitrogen metabolism can be obtained from standard publications (Colowick and Kaplan 1980). Nitrate reductase, the first and rate-limiting enzyme in the pathway, is assayed either by in vivo or in vitro methods. In vitro measurements however, normally yield much higher values for nitrate reduction than actual in vivo values (Brunetti and Hageman 1976). All other enzymes of the pathway are assayed by in vitro methods.

3.3 Nitrogen Dioxide as a Plant Nutrient

By using adequate and appropriate techniques, it has been demonstrated that NO_2 is absorbed and assimilated by plants and thus it may act as a source of nutrient nitrogen, especially under conditions where soil nitrogen is limited. According to one estimate, based on a survey of absorption rates of NO_2 by ten species of herbaceous plants, a 0.1 ppm global level of NO_2 can satisfy up to 23% of the total nitrogen requirement of terrestrial plants (Srivastava 1974). However, the growth and nitrogen content of bean plants grown in NO_2 alone is not comparable to those of plants grown with adequate soil nitrate as a nitrogen source (Srivastava and Ormrod 1984, 1986). Evidently, NO_2 is not a replacement of soil nitrogen, although it is absorbed and asimilated by plants. The following considerations must be made when evaluating the role of NO_2 as a plant nutrient:

1. Perhaps there are other constraints, hitherto unidentified, on the assimilation of NO_2. A rigorous quantification of the absorbtion of NO_2 and the partitioning of its various assimilatory products should be made. Furthermore, the factors related to both plant and environment for optimum assimilation of NO_2 have yet to be identified.
2. The quality of the harvested plant part following NO_2 assimilation should be investigated. In crop plants, residue content of the seeds/fruits, their taste and aesthetic value and relative composition of nutrients such as protein, carbohydrate, vitamins, etc. should be determined. Literature on these aspects is very scarce.
3. Physiological and biochemical abnormality as a result of NO_2 assimilation should be considered. It is likely that the detrimental effects of NO_2 uptake may outweigh its nutritional role. The uptake and assimilation of the pollutant employ the normal pathways of gas uptake and of nitrate and nitrite assimilation in the plants. As such, the pollutant will cause changes in plant processes only when its intake is high enough to interfere with the normal function of these pathways. An excess of nitrate may not cause any metabolic abnormality, as most of the nitrate is inactivated by its compartmentalization in the storage pool. The nitrite produced, however, is toxic, unless it is rapidly metabolized. Even its rapid metabolism under optimum conditions can inhibit CO_2 assimilation and other processes requiring NADPH as a reductant, as this coenzyme is also utilized in nitrite assimilation. However, the most significant effect of NO_2 on plant processes is

likely to be due to the acidity (H^+) produced during its dissolution in the cell sap. In many plants, necrosis caused by NO_2 is ascribed to its acidic action in the sap (Zeevaart 1976).

References

Anderson LS, Mansfield TA (1979) The effect of nitric oxide pollution on the growth of tomato. Environ Pollut 20:113–121

AOAC (1975) Official methods of analysis of the association of the official agricultural chemists, 9th edn. Herwitz W (ed). AOAC, Washington, DC, pp 1094

Brunetti N, Hageman RH (1976) Comparison of in vivo and in vitro assays of nitrate reductase in wheat (*Triticum aestivum*). Plant Physiol 58:583–587

Colowick SP, Kaplan NO (1980) Photosynthesis and nitrogen fixation. In: San Pietro A (ed) Methods in enzymology, vol 69. Academic Press, New York London, p 894

Decormis L, Bonte J, Tisne A (1975) Technique expérimentale permettant l'étude de l'incidence sur la végétation d'une pollution par le dioxide de soufre appliqué en permanence et à dose subnecrotique. Pollut Atmosph 17:103–107

Dee LA, Martens HH, Merill CI, Nakamura JT, Jaye FC (1973) New manual method for nitrogen dioxide emission measurement. Anal Chem 45:1477–1481

Freer-Smith PH (1985) The influence of SO_2 and NO_2 on the growth, development and gas exchange of *Betula pendula* Roth. New Phytol 99:417–430

Fuhrer J, Erismann KH (1980) Uptake of NO_2 by plants grown at different salinity levels. Experientia 36:409–410

Heagle AS, Body DE, Heck WW (1973) An open top field chamber to assess the impact of air pollution on plants. J Environ Qual 2:365–368

Heck WW, Dunning JA, Johnson H (1968) Design of a simple plant exposure chamber. DHEW, National Center for Air Pollution Control Publications APTD-68-6 Washington, DC

Heck WW, Philbeck RB, Dunning JA (1978) A continuous stirred tank reactor (CSTR) system for exposing plants to gaseous air contaminants; principles, specifications, construction and operation. US Agric Res Ser s-181

Hill AC (1971) Vegetation: a sink for atmospheric pollutants. J Air Pollut Control Assoc 21:341–346

Ito K, Okano K, Kuroina M, Totsuka T (1985) Effects of NO_2 and O_3 alone and in combination on kidney bean plants (*Phaseolus vulgaris* L.): growth, partitioning of assimilates and root activities. J Exp Bot 36:652–662

Jefferies HE, Rodgers HH, Stahel EP (1976) Spatially uniform environment for the dynamic study of biological systems; application of the continuous stirred tank reactor concept. Sci Biol 2:180–182

Lee JJ, Lewis RA (1977) Zonal air pollution system. Design and performance. In: Preston EM, Lewis RA (eds) The bioenvironmental impact of a coal fired power plant. 3rd Interim Rep EPA-600/3-78-021, pp 322–344

Maclean DC, McCune DC, Weinstein LH, Mandl RH, Woodruff GN (1968) Effects of acute hydrogen fluoride and nitrogen dioxide exposures on *Citrus* and ornamental plants of central Florida. Environ Sci Technol 2:444–449

Mandl RH, Weinstein LH, McCune DC, Keveny M (1973) A cylindrical open top chamber for the exposure of plants to air pollutants in the field. J Environ Qual 2:372–376

Matsumaru T, Yoneyama T, Totsuka T, Shiratori K (1979) Absorption of atmospheric NO_2 by plants and soils. I. Quantitative estimation of absorbed NO_2 in plants by ^{15}N methods. Soil Sci Plant Nutrit 25:255–265

Matsumaru T, Yoneyama T, Totsuka T, Mutsuoka Y (1981) Absorption of atmospheric NO_2 by rice, wheat and barley plants. Estimation by the ^{15}N method. Soil Sci Plant Nutrit 27:255–261

Matsushima J (1972) Influence of SO_2 and NO_2 on assimilation of amino acids, organic acids and saccharoid in *Citrus nutsuidaidi* seedlings. Bull Fac Agric Mie Univ 44:131–139
Muller RN, Miller JE, Sprugel DG (1979) Photosynthetic response of field grown soybeans to fumigation with sulfur dioxide. J Appl Ecol 16:567–576
National Academy of Sciences (ed) (1971) Nitrogen oxides. Natl Acad Sci Washington, DC, pp 333
Okano K, Totsuka T (1986) Absorption of nitrogen dioxide by sunflower plants grown at various levels of nitrate. New Phytol 102:551–562
Okano K, Fukuzawa T, Tazaki T, Totsuka T (1986) ^{15}N dilution method for estimating the absorption of atmospheric NO_2 by plants. New Phytol 102:73–84
Oleksyn J (1984) Effects of SO_2, HF and NO_2 on net photosynthetic and dark respiration rates of Scots pine needles of various ages. Photosynthetica 18:259–262
Preiss MC, Woodin SJ, Lee JA (1986) The potential importance of an increased atmospheric nitrogen supply to the growth of ombrotrophic *Sphagnum* species. New Phytol 103:45–55
Rogers HH, Aneja VP (1980) Uptake of atmospheric ammonia by selected plant species. Environ Exp Bot 20:251–257
Rogers HH, Jeffries HE, Stahel EP, Heck WW, Ripperton LA, Witherspoon AM (1977) Measuring air pollutant uptake by plants: a direct kinetic technique. J Air Pollut Control Assoc 27:1192–1197
Rogers HH, Campbell JC, Volk JC (1979 a) Nitrogen-15 dioxide uptake and incorporation by *Phaseolus vulgaris* L. Science 206:333–335
Rogers HH, Jeffries HE, Witherspoon AM (1979 b) Measuring air pollutant uptake by plants: nitrogen dioxide. J Environ Qual 88:551–557
Rowland AJ (1986) Nitrogen uptake, assimilation and transport in barley in the presence of atmospheric nitrogen dioxide. Plant Soil 91:353–356
Saltzman BE (1954) Colorimetric microdetermination of nitrogen dioxide in the atmosphere. Anal Chem 26:1949–1955
Sinn JP, Pell EJ (1984) Impact of chronic nitrogen dioxide exposures on composition and yield of potato foliage and tubers. J Am Soc Hortic Sci 109:481–484
Sinn JP, Pell EJ, Decaria A (1984) A NO_2 generating system for use in air pollution research. Penn Agric Exp Stn Prog Rep 382
Spierings FHFG (1971) Influence of fumigation with NO_2 on growth and yield of tomato plants. Neth J Plant Pathol 77:194–200
Srivastava HS (1974) Effects of NO_2 on gas exchange in bean leaves. Ph D Thesis, Univ British Columbia, Vancouver
Srivastava HS (1980) Regulation of nitrate reductase activity in higher plants. Phytochemistry 19:725–733
Srivastava HS, Ormrod DP (1984) Effects of nitrogen dioxide and nitrate nutrition on growth and nitrate assimilation in bean leaves. Plant Physiol 76:418–423
Srivastava HS, Ormrod DP (1986) Effects of nitrogen dioxide and nitrate nutrition on nodulation, nitrogenase activity, growth and nitrogen content of bean plants. Plant Physiol 81:737–741
Srivastava HS, Singh RP (1987) Role and regulation of 1-glutamate dehydrogenase activity in higher plants. Phytochemistry 26:597–610
Srivastava HS, Jolliffe PA, Runeckles VC (1975 a) Inhibition of gas exchange in bean leaves by NO_2. Can J Bot 53:466–474
Srivastava HS, Jolliffe PA, Runeckles VC (1975 b) The effects of environmental conditions on the inhibition of leaf gas exchange by NO_2. Can J Bot 53:475–482
Takeuchi Y, Nihira J, Kondo N, Tezuka T (1985) Changes in nitrate reducing activity in squash seedlings with NO_2 fumigation. Plant Cell Physiol 26:1027–1035
Troiano JJ, Leone IA 81977) Changes in growth rate and nitrogen content of tomato plants after exposure to NO_2. Phytopathology 67:1130–1133
Unsworth MH (1982) Exposure to gaseous pollutants and uptake by plants. In: Unsworth MH, Ormrod DP (eds) Effects of gaseous air pollution in agriculture and horticulture. Butterworth, London, p 43

Wellburn AR, Higginson C, Robinson D, Walmsley C (1981) Biochemical explanation of more than additive inhibitory effects of low atmospheric levels of sulfur dioxide plus nitrogen dioxide upon plants. New Phytol 88:223–237

Yoneyama T, Sasakawa H (1979) Transformation of atmospheric NO_2 absorbed in spinach leaves. Plant Cell Physiol 20:263–266

Yoneyama T, Sasakawa H, Ishizuka S, Totsuka T (1979) Absorption of atmospheric NO_2 by plants and soils, II: Nitrite accumulation, nitrite reductase activity and diurnal changes of NO_2 absorption in leaves. Soil Sci Plant Nutrit 25:267–275

Yoneyama T, Arai K, Totsuka T (1980) Transfer of nitrogen and carbon from a mature sunflower leaf – $^{15}NO_2$ and $^{13}CO_2$ feeding studies. Plant Cell Physiol 21:1367–1381

Zeevaart AJ (1974) Induction of nitrate reductase by NO_2. Acta Bot Neerl 23:345–346

Zeevaart AJ (1976) Some effects of fumigating plants for short periods with NO_2. Environ Pollut 11:98–108

Immunological Detection of Nitrogenase

G. SARATH and F. W. WAGNER

1 Introduction

Biological nitrogen fixation involves the catalytic reduction of atmospheric nitrogen to ammonia by the enzyme complex nitrogenase, which is normally detected by monitoring the reduction of the synthetic substrate acetylene (Hardy et al. 1968). Nitrogenase proteins are exceedingly oxygen-labile, and in vivo are protected from free oxygen by several mechanisms (Gallon 1981). Consequently, strict anaerobic conditions are required to assay nitrogenase in extracts. Other means of detecting nitrogenase are required when experimental treatments result in the destruction or modification of enzyme activity without affecting its synthesis or turnover. Immunochemical methods allow the estimation of nitrogenase proteins under ambient oxygen concentrations, and are frequently used.

The nitrogenase complex is composed of two separate enzymes, dinitrogen reductase (MoFe protein, Component 1) and nitrogenase reductase (Fe-protein, Component 2). To date nitrogenase proteins have been detected only in prokaryotic organisms. These include both free-living and associative organisms (Bothe et al. 1983). The free-living organisms are important ecologically because they account for a substantial amount of the total nitrogen fixed annually. The associative organisms can either form complex symbiotic relationships such as those found between legumes and *Rhizobia*, or are found in less complex associations such as those between grasses and *Azospirillum* species. Most aspects of biotic nitrogen fixation have been extensively studied and reviewed (Phillips 1980; Subba Rao 1980; Muller and Newton 1983; Bothe et al. 1983; Ludden and Burris 1984; Shah et al. 1984; Veeger and Newton 1984; Evans et al. 1985; Elkan 1987; Hallenbeck 1987; Haaker and Klugkist 1987).

2 Characteristics of the Nitrogenase Complex

Dinitrogen reductase is a tetramer composed of two equivalents each of two nonidentical polypeptides (α and β). The α subunit is about 55000 daltons and the β subunit is about 60000 daltons (Bothe et al. 1983). Dinitrogenase reductase also has a MoFe cofactor which is thought to be involved in the catalytic reduction of nitrogen to ammonia (Burgess 1984). Nitrogenase reductase is composed generally of two identical subunits of approximately 30000 daltons each. Variations in subunit mass of the Fe-protein have been documented (Bothe et al. 1983). Both components of nitrogenase are extremely oxygen-liable with a $t_{1/2}$ of 10 min for the MoFe protein and a $t_{1/2}$ of 30–45 s for the Fe-protein at ambient oxygen levels. The physical properties of the nitrogenase components purified from several organisms have been recently reviewed (Bothe et al. 1983; Hallenbeck 1987).

In addition to the three polypeptides that comprise nitrogenase, there is a collection of proteins that are involved in the regulation of nitrogenase synthesis and in the synthesis of the Mo-Fe cofactor (Dixon 1984). Immunological methods to quantitate some of these proteins have been reported (Klugkist et al. 1985). Genes coding for the various proteins associated with the production and regulation of nitrogenase are collectively termed *nif* genes. There are several polypeptides synthesized from this gene cluster. Much of the information on the *nif* cluster is derived from detailed studies using *Klebsiella pneumoniae*, and have been the subject of some excellent reviews (Roberts and Brill 1981; Brooks et al. 1984; Dixon 1984). Only a highly abbreviated outline will be presented here.

In *Klebsiella* the *nif* gene cluster is about 24 kb and is composed of 18 genes, organized into 7 operons, all aligned trancriptionally in the same orientation. Nitrogenase proteins are the gene products of the *nif* H, *nif* K, and *nif* D genes. The *nif* H gene codes for the Fe-protein, while *nif* D and *nif* K code for the α and β subunit of the MoFe protein, respectively. Products of the other genes in this cluster are either regulatory or are involved with the production of the MoFe cofactor and correct processing of the nitrogenase proteins. Two genes in this cluster code for proteins essential for electron transport to the nitrogenase complex (Brooks et al. 1984).

The organization of *nif* genes in *Rhizobium* appears to be somewhat different. In fast-growing *Rhizobium* species the nitrogenase protein genes are present on plasmids with a common promoter for the *nif* DHK genes, and can be activated by the *Klebsiella nif* A gene product (Sundaresan et al. 1983). A characteristic feature of the *Rhizobium nif* region is the presence of reiterated DNA sequences (Palacios et al. 1985). In slow-growing *Bradyrhizobium* species *nif* K, D, and H genes are present in one copy per genome on the central chromosome. Regions similar to *nif* A, B, and E, and sharing extensive homology with *Klebsiella*, have also been mapped on the *Bradyrhizobium* genome (Hennecke et al. 1985).

In all organisms oxygen is a potent repressor of nitrogenase synthesis and activity (St. John et al. 1974; Roberts and Brill 1981; Arp and Zumft 1983). *Azotobacter*, an obligate aerobe, expresses nitrogenase at atmospheric oxygen concentrations; however, this organism shows very high rates of metabolism, which drastically reduces the oxygen levels within the cells (Gallon 1981). In *Klebsiella* the *nif* genes are regulated by combined nitrogen (Brooks et al. 1984; Dixon 1984), whereas combined nitrogen has no effect on the synthesis of nitrogenase in free-living *Rhizobium* cultures (Roberts and Brill 1981), but inhibits synthesis of nitrogenase proteins in *Rhizobia*-legume symbioses (Bisseling et al. 1978). Nitrogenase activity in *Rhodospirillum rubrum* is modulated by covalent modification of the Fe-protein (Kanemoto and Ludden 1984). Various aspects of regulation of nitrogenase have been reviewed recently (Arp and Zumft 1983).

3 Purification of Nitrogenase for Antibody Production

Immunological assay systems which are to detect the presence of single enzymes or proteins should employ antibody preparations made to a single antigen. Consequently, the first step in assaying nitrogenase or any other protein by immunological techniques is to purify the protein and prepare antibody.

Nitrogenase proteins are irreversibly denatured by molecular oxygen and require anaerobic conditions for their purification (Lowe et al. 1980). Purification is normally performed under an inert atmosphere of either argon or nitrogen. Commonly, harvested cells or washed bacteroids are ruptured by passage through a French Press, by sonication, by repeated freeze-thaw cycles in the presence of lysozyme, or by osmotic shock. Subsequent purification involves salt precipitation, ion-exchange and gel-filtration chromatography. Final purification is achieved by preparative polyacrylamide gel electrophoresis (PAGE). Excellent protocols for the purification of nitrogenase proteins from several organisms have been published (Evans et al. 1972; Hallenbeck et al. 1982; Shah 1986; see Lowe et al. 1980 for a compilation of methods used for other organisms).

Nitrogenase, whether in situ or in purified preparations, is most conveniently assayed by the acetylene reduction method (Hardy et al. 1968; Shah 1986). Using this assay in conjunction with immunodetection is often helpful in both physiological and biochemical studies. Other methods of assaying nitrogenase do exist and the reader is referred to Burris (1972) for more detailed procedures.

When preparing protein for immunization, it is often preferable to subject the purified proteins to SDS-PAGE, and electroelute the proteins from the gel. This procedure results in the separation of component subunits, and provides for the removal of contaminating protein. In cases where antibodies are required toward native protein, protein isolated by preparative PAGE can be used. An advantage of using SDS-PAGE purified protein is the development of antibodies to the different subunits. Antigenic properties are not impaired in SDS-PAGE purified nitrogenase proteins (Berman et al. 1985; Klugkist et al. 1985).

3.1 Immunological Techniques

Immunological procedures used to detect nitrogenase proteins thus far have utilized polyclonal antibodies. Development of antibodies requires the reaction of an antigen with the immune system of a suitable host (Barrett 1983). Rabbits have been used almost exclusively in developing antibodies to nitrogenase. Polyclonal antibodies are separated from the animal blood serum and subsequently used for immunodetection. The choice of the animal host is predicated upon the resources available for their care and by the amount of antibodies needed. Since larger animals require injections with greater amounts of purified proteins, the choice should be determined by the availability of protein and the nature of the usage of the antibodies. For most applications the amount of serum obtained from rabbits is adequate.

Purity of the injected proteins is critical for generating specific antibodies, since this minimizes the chance of generating antibodies toward very antigenic trace contaminants. Ideally, the polyclonal antibodies should be specific toward the various antigenic sites on the intact parent antigen. However, some preparations cross-react with other proteins when crude extracts of cellular proteins are immunodetected. Minimizing this nonspecific cross-reactivity is important.

Purified nitrogenase components prepared by electroelution from SDS gels can be dialyzed against buffered saline (Appendix 1), and are conveniently stored cold at a concentration of 1–2 mg ml^{-1} in 50–100 μg aliquots. A 50–100 μg aliquot of protein is emulsified with an equal volume of Freund's complete adjuvant and injected subcutaneously into one or two sites on the animal's back (New Zealand white rabbits). A second similar injection is administered after a period of 2 weeks. The animals are then reinjected two times at 2-week intervals with protein emulsified with Freund's incomplete adjuvant. Antibody titer can then be measured after 10–14 days after the last injection. The animal can be bled through an incision of a major vein in the ear. Usually, 10–15 ml of blood will yield sufficient serum for initial testing of titer. If strong cross-reaction is observed at the first bleeding, the animal can be bled a second time. A final injection in incomplete adjuvant is then made and the animal is bled (30 to 40 ml of blood) after an additional 10–14 days. If the antibody titer is low at this stage, it is usually best to immunize a new animal. Several other immunization protocols for production of antibodies to nitrogenase have been reported (Bishop et al. 1975; Rennie 1976; Nicholas et al. 1979; Scott et al. 1979; Maurer and Callahan 1980; Voordouw et al. 1982).

Collected blood is allowed to coagulate for 30 min at room temperature, the pellet of red blood cells is then gently loosened from the sides of the collection tube with a spatula and allowed to incubate for another 30 min at 37° C. The entire solution is centrifuged at 1000–2000 × *g* for 10 min and the serum supernatant fluid is removed with a Pasteur pipette. The serum can be used directly, although it is preferable to precipitate the immunoglobulin fraction (Ig), with ammonium sulfate (Hurn and Chantler 1980). The Ig fraction can then be redissolved and dialyzed against buffered saline containing 0.1% sodium azide and stored at 4° C or frozen in aliquots.

The easiest first check of titer strength is to perform an Ouchterlony double diffusion in agarose (Oudin 1980) using pure nitrogenase proteins in the outer wells and crude serum in the center well. The intensity of the precipitin lines should allow for an approximate estimation of titer strength. A semi-quantitative assay can then be performed using a "dot blot" apparatus (e.g., Bio-Rad Lab Products). The antigen-antibody complex can be visualized using protein A conjugated to an enzyme. Western blotting techniques will be discussed in detail in Sect. 3.4. Appendix 1 outlines some protocols for initial screening of antibody titer.

3.2 Immunological Relationships of Nitrogenases

Nitrogenases isolated from different organisms show varying degrees of sequence homology at the gene and protein levels. This is especially true for the Fe-protein. The MoFe protein shows less homology between organisms (Lowe et al. 1980; Ruvken and Ausubel 1980; Burgess 1984). Combinations of purified dinitrogen reductase and nitrogenase reductase from a number of different organisms will form active hybrid molecules (Eady and Postgate 1974; Emerich and Burris 1978). It is not surprising then, that antibodies raised against nitrogenase protein isolated from one organism cross-react with nitrogenase proteins extracted from other organisms. This feature has been exploited to immunodetect Fe-protein in *Bradyrhizobium japonicum* bacteroids using antibodies to *Rhodospirillum rubrum* Fe-protein (Sarath et al. 1986). Antibodies to *Klebsiella* MoFe protein have been used to measure the rate of synthesis of the MoFe protein in the cyanobacterium *Gleothece* (Maryan et al. 1986). Meesters et al. (1985) utilized antibodies to *Rhizobium leguminosarum* MoFe protein and Fe-protein to detect cross-reactive protein in the actinomycete *Frankia*. Using immunoblotting techniques they showed that nitrogenase components are enriched in vesicles as compared to the hyphae.

Rennie (1976) used fluorescein conjugated antibodies to *Klebsiella pneumoniae* nitrogenase components to study the degree of cross-reaction with purified nitrogenases from different organisms. Strong reaction occurred to nitrogenase isolated from *Bacillus polymyxa*, a trace reaction with *Azotobacter chroococcum*, and no reaction to nitrogenase from *Clostridium pasteurianum* or *Rhizobium japonicum*. The lack of cross-reaction of these antibodies with nitrogenase isolated from *Rhizobium japonicum* is surprising, since cross-reactivity has been observed in other laboratories (Maier and Brill 1976; Scott et al. 1979; Sarath and Wagner, unpublished data). Screening of toluene-treated bacteria actively reducing nitrogen revealed that most organisms tested showed at least a trace reaction to *Klebsiella pneumoniae* nitrogenase antibodies (Rennie 1976). Immunological relationships of nitrogenases isolated from slow- and fast-growing *Rhizobium* species have been investigated using radioimmunoassay techniques (Bisseling et al. 1982). With the exception of the protein isolated from *Rhizobium lupinii*, their results showed that the MoFe protein isolated from four fast-growing species were very similar to each other, in contrast to the MoFe protein isolated from slow growers. Much lower affinity was observed with assays utilizing antibodies to the MoFe protein isolated from *Azotobacter* or *Klebsiella*. Antibodies raised against *Azotobacter vinelandii* dinitrogen reductase cross-react with bacterial nitrate reductases and vice versa, but not with nitrate reductases isolated from *Anabaena* or higher plants (Nicholas et al. 1979). As pointed out by these authors, simple diffusion tests in agar do not imply a specific cross-reaction to nitrogenase, especially when crude bacterial extracts are being analyzed.

3.3 Immunodetection of Nitrogenase

Any of the numerous methods employed in immunochemistry are applicable to detecting nitirogenase. Double diffusion in agar has provided initial data on the capacity of free-living *Rhizobium japonicum* to synthesize nitrogenase (Bishop et al. 1975). Soo et al. (1979) used double diffusion to show that nitrogenase is synthesized by free-living *Rhizobia* only under microaerophyllic conditions in the absence of cyclic guanosine monophosphate. Immunoelectrophoresis has been used to quantitate nitrogenases in *Klebsiella* (Kahn et al. 1982). Radiolabeled nitrogenase proteins have been analyzed by immunoprecipitation (Scott et al. 1979; Maryan et al. 1986) and by radioimmunoassay (Bisseling et al. 1980). Ferritin-antibody conjugates have been used to immunolocalize nitrogenase in the heterocysts of *Anabaena cylindrica* (Murry et al. 1984).

3.4 Immunodetection by Western Blotting

Western blotting as a technique was first introduced by Towbin et al. (1979), with subsequent modifications by Burnette (1981). Numerous aspects of this technique and its applications have been reviewed (Gershoni and Palade 1983; Towbin and Gordon 1984). Western blotting offers numerous advantages: (1) the identification of nitrogenase on gels is facile and unequivocal; (2) proteins transferred to nitrocellulose may be stored for future analysis; (3) several samples can be analyzed at any one time under identical conditions; (4) a small amount of antibody can be used; (5) amplification of the antigen-antibody complex can be achieved by using secondary proteins that are specific for the primary antibodies. Commonly, either a secondary antibody or protein A, conjugated to an enzyme such as peroxidase or alkaline-phosphatase, is used. Still greater amplification is afforded by using ^{125}I-labeled protein A; and (6) quantitation can be performed from the blots (Towbin and Gordon 1984). A primary disadvantage of this method is its cost. The advent of mini-gel systems and less expensive electroblotting apparatus should help in alleviating these problems.

Hames and Rickwood (1981) provide pertinent information on the theoretical and practical aspects of electrophoresis in polyacrylamide gels. The most common gel system used is the SDS gel system originated by Laemmli (1970). Commonly, SDS gels containing 10% acrylamide monomer are used to fractionate dinitrogen reductase. When nitrogenase reductase is to be detected, 12% gels yield better resolution (Sarath and Wagner unpublished data). Analysis of nitrogenase proteins on gradient gels from 8–14% monomer concentration should result in good separation of both components (Berman et al. 1985). Optimum protein concentrations applied to the gels have to be determined by experimentation and depend on the nature of the extract and the antibody preparation. A good first step is to perform a "dot blot" assay (Appendix 1) using serial dilutions of both the antigen and the antibody, prior to gel electrophoresis. Once methods have been optimized, it is possible to analyze several samples under the same conditions. Development times for the gels are not critical. Generally, longer running times at lower current provide better resolution.

Gels should be electroblotted immediately after electrophoresis to avoid diffusion. The buffers used for electroblotting are determined by the gel type (Burnette 1981; Towbin and Gordon 1984). Bulletins available from most makers of electroblotting apparatus also provide useful data on both buffer types and blotting conditions. Normally, SDS-acrylamide gels are washed for 30 min with two changes of cold transfer buffer (25 mM Tris, 192 mM glycine, 20% methanol v/v), to remove excess salts prior to electroblotting. The gel is then placed on two sheets of blotting paper wetted with transfer buffer, care should be exercised to exclude air bubbles from being trapped between the filter paper sheets and between the gel and the blotting paper. Next, a sheet of nitrocellulose, precut to gel dimensions, is wet with transfer buffer and gently placed on the gel. Uneven transfer can occur if air bubbles are present between the gel and the nitrocellulose sheet. Thus, it is important to remove all trapped air bubbles from the gel-nitrocellulose interface by carefully rolling a test tube over the exposed surface of the nitrocellulose sheet. This sandwich is placed into the electroblotter holder with one to two sheets of prewet blotting paper sheets cut to the gel dimensions being placed over the nitrocellulose. When proteins are being transferred from SDS-containing gels in alkaline transfer buffers, the gel should face the cathode and the nitrocellulose should face the anode, since most proteins are negatively charged under these conditions and will migrate toward the anode. Transfer times are dependent on the nature of the gel, the type of electroblotting apparatus, and whether a cooling system is available. Information on transfer times and transfer voltages are normally available from the manufacturers of the electroblotting apparatus, e.g., see the Bio Rad Laboratories instruction manual for their transblot cell; and have also been reviewed (Towbin and Gordon 1984). Some modifications of the generally used transfer buffers and transfer conditions have been published recently (Dunn 1986).

Once transfer is complete, the nitrocellulose sheet is removed from the blotting apparatus, and rinsed twice in Tris-buffered saline (25 m*M* Tris-HCl, 0.5 *M* NaCl, pH 7.5) (TBS). The sheet is then immersed in either 3% gelatin or bovine serum albumin (defatted) solution in TBS (blocking solution) with gentle rocking, to block sites on the nitrocellulose not containing protein. The nitrocellulose sheet can be stored at 4° C in blocking solution for at least 1 month. If needed, the blocking solution can be made to 0.1% with sodium azide to retard microbial growth. Blocking times of at least 1 h are normally recommended. If stored in blocking solution in the cold, the gelatin solution should be thawed before removing the nitrocellulose sheet. The nitrocellulose sheet is then washed a few times for 10 min each with TBS and washed twice with TBS containing 0.05% Tween-20 (TTBS). The sheet is immersed in a solution of 1% gelatin in TBS containing the primary antibody (see Appendix 1; 0.2 to 1.5% v/v) and allowed to react for 1 h with shaking. The antibody concentration can be adjusted by experimentation. The sheet is then washed five times for 10 min each in TTBS, and allowed to react with protein A either ^{125}I-labeled or conjugated to an enzyme. Alternately, a secondary antibody conjugated to an enzyme can also be used. Protein A-enzyme conjugate is also made up in 1% gelatin solution in TBS (the amount of conjugate used per detection is dependent on the commercial source of the conjugate). This reaction is essentially complete in 45–60 min, at which time the nitrocellulose sheet is washed three to four times in TTBS, and twice in TBS. The final TBS wash is necessary if protein A is conjugated to peroxidase. Peroxidase is detected by incubation with 60 µl H202/100 ml TBS in the presence of 4-chloronaphthol (60 mg dissolved in 20 ml ice-cold methanol and added to peroxide-containing TBS solution) (Bio Rad Bulletin No. 84-0039). Incubation is carried out in the dark for 30–45 min, if no reaction is observed both the antigen and antibody concentrations need to increased. Once the reaction is complete, the nitrocellulose sheet is washed with water and stored in the dark. It is preferable to photograph the sheet as soon as it is dry, since the reaction product fades and the background darkens with time. When ^{125}I-labeled protein-A is used, the nitrocellulose sheet is air dried and an autoradiogram is developed. The 3% gelatin and primary antibody solution in 1% gelatin can be reused at least three times and should be stored with a suitable bactericidal agent.

3.5 Quantitation of Nitrogenase on Western Blots

Depending on the assay utilized to detect the antigen-antibody complex, quantitation methods will vary. The underlying principle in all the quantitation methods is to construct a standard curve using known amounts of antigen under similar experimental conditions to those of the main study. Quantitation is then performed by comparison to a standard curve.

The most common methods of quantitation of electroblots are densitometry and scintillation counting. When enzyme-based assays are used, densitometry would be the method of choice. Chart tracings of densitometric scans of nitrocellulose sheets are either cut out and weighed, or if possible the area corresponding to the nitrogenase proteins is computed from the tracings (Towbin and Gordon 1984). It is necessary to standardize the method using pure nitrogenase proteins, and also to fractionate known amounts of pure protein during every electrophoresis run. Usually 0.3 to 5 μg of pure protein yield linear standard curves. Radiochemical methods are normally employed when ^{125}I-labeled protein A is used for detection. While it is possible to perform densitometry on the autoradiograms, errors can be introduced when polyclonal antibodies are used. The density of the exposed silver grains in the X-ray film is not representative of the actual amount of protein detected (Klugkist et al. 1985). However, the autoradiogram can be used to delimit the bands of interest on the nitrocellulose sheet. These bands can then be cut out and solubilized for scintillation counting. Quantitation is performed by plotting the amount of radioactivity recovered in each sample against the log 10 of the amount of protein applied to the gel. For *Azotobacter vinelandii* cells this plot is linear from 5 to 25 pmol of pure protein (Klugkist et al. 1985). Haaker and Wassink (1984) applied this protocol to calculate the amounts of nitrogenase proteins in *Rhizobium leguminisarum* bacteroids. Approximately 30% of the total cell protein was nitrogenase, with a calculated intracellular concentration of 149 and 372 μM for the MoFe protein and Fe-protein, respectively.

3.5.1 Other Methods of Quantitation

Radiochemical quantitation can be utilized when radioactively labeled nitrogenase proteins are precipitated from crude extracts with specific antibodies. An aliquot of radioactively labeled proteins is first incubated with nitrogenase specific antibodies, the incubation time and amounts of extract and antibodies used need to be defined experimentally. The antigen-antibody complex is then incubated with an excess of protein A immobilized on Sephadex (Pharmacia Fine Chemicals), or with an immobilized secondary antibody. After a suitable incubation time the immunoprecipitated proteins are sedimented by centrifugation. Immunoprecipitates are washed and counted for radioactivity directly or fractionated by SDS-PAGE and then quantitated. These types of studies quantitate nitrogenase on a relative basis and are used primarily when enzyme synthesis or regulation are being investigated (Scott et al. 1979; Bisseling et al. 1980; Meesters et al. 1985; Maryan et al. 1986). Rocket immunoelectrophoresis (Laurell 1972) has been used to quantitate nitrogenase proteins in *Klebsiella pneumoniae* (Kahn et al. 1982), and in *Rhodospirillum rubrum* (Triplett et al. 1982). This technique is useful when antibodies show strong cross-reaction. A drawback of rocket immunoelectrophoresis is that when cross-reaction is low, reproducible data are difficult to obtain. Further, no reaction might be evident when using crude extracts or heterologous systems (Sarath and Wagner unpublished observations).

4 Conclusions

Immunodetection is a powerful tool for the study of proteins. This is particularly true when a protein cannot be detected based on an intrinsic activity. Thus, immunodetection becomes the method of choice in studies aimed at understanding regulation or the turnover of nitrogenase, when the amount of enzyme present in a cell is not reflective of the fraction that is active. In genetic studies, where expression of nitrogenase protein is being evaluated, immunochemical methods are useful to verify expression.

Several methods in immunochemistry are still to be applied to the study of nitrogenase. Reports are not available on the generation of monoclonal antibodies to any nitrogenase component. Monoclonal antibodies will be useful in probing not only enzyme structure and function (Rennie et al. 1978), but also in fully understanding the immunological relationships of nitrogenase. Krchnak et al. (1987) have developed computer software for detecting antigenic sites of a polypeptide. It might be interesting to apply their analyses to those nitrogenases for which the gene and amino acid sequences are known. The simultaneous detection of all three polypeptides of the nitrogenase complex, using purified Ig conjugated to different enzymes or generated in different animals, would also be worth pursuing. Such Ig will be useful in studies that result in the preferential synthesis or turnover of one component.

Appendices

1. Double Diffusion in Agarose

A 1% agarose solution made in Tris-buffered saline [25 m*M* Tris-HCl, 0.5 *M* NaCl, 0.1% azide (optional), pH 7.5]. The agarose is dissolved by warming, then poured onto clean glass slides or onto squares of hydrophilic nylon sheets (Gel-Bond, FMC Bioproducts, Rockland, ME), and allowed to gel at room temperature. The gel is then hardened at 4° C for a few hours. Wells are punched in the gel using a plastic pipette tip cut to the required size. A small drop of warm agarose is carefully pipetted into the bottom of each well to seal the edges. Once this agarose is gelled, the solutions to be tested are dispensed into the wells. For initial screening the center well should have the serum (20–50 μl) and the outer wells the purified proteins (1–10 μg in 20–50 μl). The gel is then placed in a moist chamber at 37° C overnight. Cross-reaction is evident if precipitin lines form.

Double diffusion can also be used to obtain an approximate idea of the titer strength. Reciprocal slides, one containing undiluted serum in the center well and the other undiluted antigen in the center well, are tested against serial dilutions of the protein and serum, respectively. The lowest dilutions resulting in a precipitation gives an approximation of the titer strength.

2. Dot Blot Analysis

A dot plot analysis is in many ways similar to the Western blotting method (Towbin and Gordon 1984). A sheet of nitrocellulose is placed in the dot-blot apparatus and serial dilutions of the antigen are pipetted into wells. Each row has the same concentration of protein. The protein solution is allowed to bind to the membrane (45–60 min). Each well is then treated with a 3% gelatin solution in TBS to block the unreacted sites. Excess solution is removed by gravity flow initially and after 45 min by gentle suction. The wells are washed a few times in TBS followed by TTBS. The antibody solution is then pipetted into the wells with the serial dilutions across each column. Binding of the antibody to the antigen is allowed to proceed for 1 h. Excess solution is removed by suction and the wells washed with TTBS solution. A solution of protein-A conjugated peroxidase (Protein A conjugated to other enzymes or ^{125}I-labeled protein A can also be used) in 1% gelatin is placed in the wells and allowed to bind for 45 min. The wells are then washed with TTBS followed with TBS (100 µl each wash). Peroxidase activity is assayed in the presence of H_2O_2 and 4-chloronaphthol in TBS 30–45 min. The nitrocellulose sheet is then washed with water and removed from the dot-blot apparatus. The intensity of enzyme reaction is proportional to the amount of antibody bound to the antigen.

3. Buffered Saline

When buffered saline is required for diluting and dialyzing antibodies or for preparing antigen for injection into an animal, either phosphate-buffered saline or Tris-buffered saline can be used. The compositions of these two buffers is given below.

A) Phosphate-Buffered Saline (10 mM, pH 7.5)

Component	$g\,l^{-1}$
Na phosphate (monobasic)	0.221
Na phosphate (dibasic)	1.193
NaCl	8.000
KCl	0.200

B) Tris-Buffered Saline (20 mM, pH 7.5)

Component	$g\,l^{-1}$
Tris base	2.42
NaCl	8.00
KCl	0.20 to pH 7.5 with HCl

4. Selection of Titer Dilutions for Immunodetection

When antibodies generated toward nitrogenase proteins from a given organism are used to immunodetect nitrogenase from the same organism, a homologous system is defined. In these cases the affinity of the antibodies to the antigens is strongest. Thus, smaller quantities of proteins can be immunodetected. In a heterologous system, where antibodies raised against nitrogenase from another species are used for immunodetection, cross-reaction will generally be much weaker (Bisseling et al. 1982; Rennie 1976). In such cases greater amounts of antigen will be needed. The least amount of Ig that can be detected by peroxidase-conjugated proteins is about 1 fmol (Towbin and Gordon 1984). However, higher concentrations of detecting reagents and antibody are generally needed in Western blot analyses. Sensitivity of detection is enhanced 10- to 100-fold when using ^{125}I-labeled protein A (Towbin and Gordon 1984). Thus, when purified nitrogenase is used it should be possible to detect 0.01–10 μg protein. Protein concentrations of crude extract can be then adjusted such that the amount of nitrogenase proteins fractionated by SDS-PAGE falls in this range.

Acknowledgments. We would like to thank all of our colleagues who made reprints available. The invaluable assistance of Dr. Dwane E. Wylie in preparing antibodies to nitrogenase components is gratefully acknowledged. This work was supported by a grant from the Nebraska Soybean Development and Utilization Board.

References

Arp DJ, Zumft WG (1983) Regulation and control of nitrogenase activity. In: Muller A, Newton WE (eds) Nitrogen fixation: the chemical-biochemical-genetic interface. Plenum, New York, pp 149–179

Barrett JT (1983) Textbook of immunology, 4 edn. Mosby, St. Louis

Berman J, Zilberstein A, Salomon D, Zamir A (1985) Expression of nitrogen-fixation gene encoding a nitrogenase subunit in yeast. Gene 35:1–9

Bishop PE, Evans HJ, Daniel RM, Hampton RO (1975) Immunological evidence for the capability of free-living *Rhizobium japonicum* to synthesise a portion of a nitrogenase component. Biochim Biophys Acta 381:248–256

Bisseling T, Bos RC van den, Kammen A van (1978) The effect of ammonium nitrate on the synthesis of nitrogenase and the concentration of leghemoglobin in pea root nodules induced by *Rhizobium leguminosarum*. Biochim Biophys Acta 539:1–11

Bisseling T, Bos RC van den, Moen L, Hontelez JGJ, Kammen A van (1982) An immunological comparision of nitrogenase proteins of fast and slow growing rhizobia. FEBS Lett 145:45–48

Bisseling T, Straten J van, Houwaard F (1980) Turnover of nitrogenase and leghemoglobin in root nodules of *Pisum sativum*. Biochim Biophys Acta 610:360–370

Bothe H, Yates MG, Cannon FC (1983) Physiology, biochemistry and genetics of dinitrogen fixation. In: Lauchli A, Bieleski RL (ed) Inorganic plant nutrition. Springer, Berlin Heidelberg New York, pp 241–285

Brooks SJ, Imperial J, Brill WJ (1984) Biochemical genetics of nitrogen fixation in *Klebsiella pneumoniae*. In: Ludden PW, Burris JE (eds) Nitrogen fixation and CO_2 metabolism. Elsevier, New York, pp 65–74

Burgess BK (1984) Structure and reactivity of nitrogenase – an overview. In: Veeger C, Newton WE (eds) Advances in nitrogen fixation research. Nijhoff/Junk, The Hague, pp 103–114

Burnette WN (1981) Western blotting: electrophoretic transfer of proteins from sodium dodecyl sulfate-polyacrylamide gels to unmodified nitrocellulose and radiographic detection with antibody and radioiodinated protein A. Anal Biochem 112:195–203

Burris RH (1972) Nitrogen fixation-assay methods and techniques. Meth Enzymol 24:415–430

Dixon RA (1984) The genetic complexity of nitrogen fixation. J Gen Microbiol 130:2745–2755

Dunn SD (1986) Effects of the modification of transfer buffer composition and the renaturation of proteins in gels on the recognition of proteins on Western blots by monoclonal antibodies. Anal Biochem 157:144–153

Eady RR, Postgate JR (1974) Nitrogenase. Nature 249:805–810

Elkan GH (1987) Symbiotic nitrogen fixation technology. Dekker, New York

Emerich DW, Burris RH (1978) Complementary functioning of the component proteins of nitrogenase from several bacteria. J Bacteriol 134:936–943

Evans HJ, Koch B, Klucas R (1972) Preparation of nitrogenase from nodules and separation into components. Meth Enzymol 24:470–476

Evans HJ, Bottomley PJ, Newton WE (eds) (1985) Nitrogen fixation research progress. Nijhoff, Dordrecht

Gallon JR (1981) The oxygen sensitivity of nitrogenase: a problem for biochemists and micro-organisms. Trends Biochem Sci 6:19–23

Gershoni JM, Palade GE (1983) Protein blotting: principles and applications. Anal Biochem 131:1–15

Haaker H, Klugkist J (1987) The bioenergetics of electron transport to nitrogenase. FEMS Microbiol Rev 46:57–71

Haaker H, Wassink H (1984) Electron allocation to H^+ and N_2 by nitrogenase in *Rhizobium leguminosarum* bacteroids. Eur J Biochem 142:37–42

Hallenbeck PC (1987) Molecular aspects of nitrogen fixation by photosynthetic prokaryotes. CRC Crit Rev Microbiol 14:1–48

Hallenbeck PC, Meyer CM, Vignais PM (1982) Nitrogenase from the photosynthetic bacterium *Rhodopseudomonas capsulata*: purification and molecular properties. J Bacteriol 149:708–715

Hames BD, Rickwood D (eds) (1981) Gel electrophoresis of proteins: a practical approach. IRL, Oxford

Hardy RWF, Holsten RD, Jackson EK, Burns RC (1968) The acetylene-ethylene assay for measurement of nitrogen fixation: laboratory and field evaluation. Plant Physiol 43:1185–1207

Hennecke H, Alvarez-Morales A, Betancourt-Morales M, Ebeling S, Filser M, Fischer HM, Gubler M, Hahn M, Kaluza K, Lamb JW, Meyer B, Regensburger B, Struder D, Weber J (1985) Organisation and regulation of symbiotic nitrogen fixation genes from *Bradyrhizobium japonicum*. In: Evans HJ, Bottomley PJ, Newton WE (eds) Nitrogen fixation research progress. Nijhoff, Dordrecht

Hurn BAL, Chantler SM (1980) Production of reagent antibodies. Meth Enzymol 70(Pt A):104–142

Kahn D, Hawkins M, Eady RR (1982) Nitrogen fixation in *Klebsiella pneumoniae*: nitrogenase levels and the effect of added molybdate on nitrogenase derepressed under molybdate deprivation. J Gen Microbiol 128:779–787

Kanemoto RH, Ludden PW (1984) Effect of ammonia, darkness and phenazine methosulfate on whole-cell nitrogenase activity and Fe protein modification in *Rhodospirillum rubrum*. J Bacteriol 158:713–720

Klugkist J, Haaker H, Wassink H, Veeger C (1985) The catalytic activity of nitrogenase in intact *Azotobacter vinelandii* cells. Eur J Biochem 146:509–515

Krchnak V, Mach O, Maly A (1987) Computer prediction of potential immunogenic determinants from protein amino acid sequence. Anal Biochem 165:200–207

Laemmli UK (1970) Cleavage of structural proteins during assembly of the head of bacteriophage T4. Nature 227:680–685

Laurell CB (1972) Electroimmunoassay. Scand J Clin Lab Invest 124:21–37

Lowe DJ, Smith BE, Eady RR (1980) The structure and mechanism of nitrogenase. In: Subba Rao NS (ed) Recent advances in nitrogen fixation. Oxford & IBH, New Delhi, pp 34–87

Ludden PW, Burris JE (eds) (1984) Nitrogen fixation and CO2 metabolism. Elsevier, New York

Maier RJ, Brill WJ (1976) Ineffective and non-nodulating mutant strains of *Rhizobium japonicum*. J Bacteriol 127:763–769

Maryan PS, Eady RR, Chaplin AE, Gallon JR (1986) Nitrogen fixation by the unicellular cyanobacterium *Gleothece*. Nitrogenase synthesis is only transiently repressed by oxygen. FEMS Microbiol Lett 34:251–255

Maurer PH, Callahan HJ (1980) Proteins and peptides as antigens. Meth Enzymol 70(Pt A):49–70

Meesters TM, Genesen ST van, Akkermans ADL (1985) Growth acetylene reduction and localisation of nitrogenase in relation to vesicle formation in *Frankia* strains Ccl.17 and Cpl.2. Arch Microbiol 143:137–142

Muller A, Newton WE (eds) (1983) Nitrogen fixation. The chemical-biochemical-genetic interface. Plenum, New York

Murry MA, Hallenbeck PC, Beneman JR (1984) Immunochemical evidence that nitrogenase is restricted to the heterocysts in *Anabaena cylindrica*. Arch Microbiol 137:194–199

Nicholas DJD, Ferrante JV, Clarke GR (1979) Immunological studies with nitrogenase from *Azotobacter* and bacterial nitrate reductases. Anal Biochem 95:24–31

Oudin J (1980) Immunochemical analysis by antigen-antibody precipitation in gels. Methods Enzymol 70(Pt A):166–198

Palacios R, Flores M, Martinez E, Quinto C (1985) *Rhizobium phaseoli*: nitrogen fixation genes and DNA reiteration. In: Evans HJ, Bottomley PJ, Newton WE (ed) Nitrogen fixation research progress. Nijhoff, Dordrecht

Phillips DA (1980) Efficiency of symbiotic nitrogen fixation in legumes. Ann Rev Plant Physiol 31:29–49

Rennie RJ (1976) Immunofluorescence detection of nitrogenase proteins in whole cells. J Gen Microbiol 97:289–296

Rennie RJ, Funnell A, Smith BE (1978) Immunochemistry of nitrogenase as a probe for the enzyme mechanism. FEBS Lett 91:158–161

Roberts GP, Brill WJ (1981) Genetics and regulation of nitrogen fixation. Annu Rev Microbiol 35:207–235

Ruvken GB, Ausubel FM (1980) Interspecies homology of nitrogenase genes. Proc Natl Acad Sci USA 77:191–195

Sarath G, Pfeiffer NE, Sodhi CS, Wagner FW (1986) Bacteroids are stable during dark induced senescence of soybean root nodules. Plant Physiol 82:346–350

Scott BD, Hennecke H, Lim ST (1979) The biosynthesis of nitrogenase MoFe protein polypeptides in free-living cultures of *Rhizobium japonicum*. Biochim Biophys Acta 565:365–378

Shah VK (1986) Isolation and characterization of nitrogenase from *Klebsiella pneumoniae*. Meth Enzymol 118:511–519

Shah VK, Ugalde RA, Imperial J, Brill WJ (1984) Molybdenum in nitrogenase. Annu Rev Biochem 53:231–257

Soo LT, Hennecke H, Scott DB (1979) Effect of cyclic guanosine 3′,5′ monophosphate on nitrogen fixation in *Rhizobium japonicum*. J Bacteriol 139:256–263

St. John RT, Shah VK, Brill WJ (1974) Regulation of nitrogenase synthesis by oxygen in *Klebsiella pneumoniae*. J Bacteriol 119:266–269

Subba Rao NS (ed) (1980) Recent advances in biological nitrogen fixation. Oxford & IBH, New Delhi

Sundaresan V, Jones JDG, Ow DW, Ausubel FM (1983) *Klebsiella pneumonia nif*A product activates the *Rhizobium meliloti* nitrogenase promoter. Nature 301:728–732

Towbin H, Gordon J (1984) Immunoblotting and dot immunoblotting – current status and outlook. J Immunol Meth 72:313–340

Towbin H, Staehelin T, Gordon J (1979) Electrophoretic transfer of proteins from polyacrylamide gels to nitrocellulose sheets: procedure and some applications. Proc Natl Acad Sci USA 76:4350–4354

Triplett EW, Wall JD, Ludden PW (1982) Expression of activating enzyme and Fe protein of nitrogenase from *Rhodospirillum rubrum*. J Bacteriol 152:786–791

Veeger C, Newton WE (eds) (1984) Advances in nitrogen fixation research. Nijhoff/Junk, The Hague

Voordouw J, de Haard H, Timmermans AM, Veeger C, Zabel P (1982) Dissociation and assembly of pyridine nucleotide transhydrogenase from *Azotobacter vinelandii*. Eur J Biochem 127:267–274

Analysis of Volatile Nitrogen (NO and NO_2) Release from Plants

J. V. Dean and J. E. Harper

1 Introduction

There is currently little direct evidence that higher plants evolve appreciable amounts of N oxides under normal physiological conditions. Under experimental conditions, however, the emission of large amounts of N oxides from soybean leaves has been reported. The question of where these volatile N compounds originate, and the significance of this evolution, remains to be confirmed. Under normal field conditions, NO_3^- is the predominant form of N available to most cultivated plants (Beevers and Hageman 1980). Before NO_3^- can be incorporated into amino acids and subsequently protein, it must first be reduced to the level of ammonia. The reduction of NO_3^- to ammonia in higher plants involves the nitrate reductase (NR) and nitrite reductase enzymes.

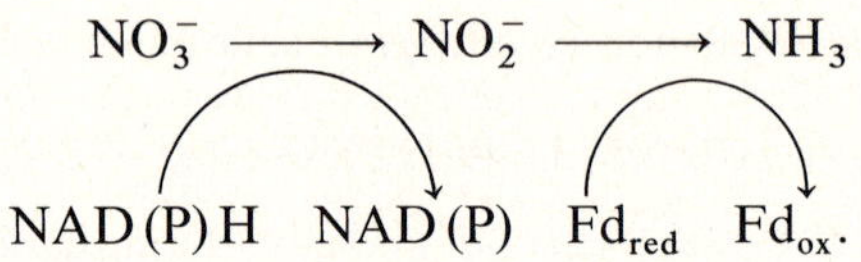

In the currently accepted pathway, NO_3^- reduction utilizes NAD(P)H as a reductant source and is thought to occur in the cytoplasm, while nitrite reductase utilizes ferredoxin reduced during photosynthetic electron flow and is thought to occur in the chloroplast (Beevers and Hageman 1980). The NO_3^- reduction pathway has been implicated in loss of volatile nitrogenous compounds.

1.1 $NO_{(x)}$ Emissions from Herbicide-Treated Soybean

Klepper (1979) reported that substantial amounts of $NO_{(x)}$ (collectively nitric oxide [NO] and nitrogen dioxide [NO_2]) could be evolved from soyben leaves treated with photosynthetic-inhibitory herbicides. These photosynthetic inhibitor herbicides block the light-dependent reduction of NO_2^-, while NO_3^- reduction remains unaffected, resulting in the accumulation of NO_2^- in the plant leaves (Klepper 1974, 1975). Application of 2,4-D to soybean is thought to promote NO_3^- reduction in the dark which also results in the accumulation of NO_2^- and subsequent emission of $NO_{(x)}$ (Klepper 1979). Klepper (1979) suggested that NO and NO_2 were formed by a chemical reaction of the accumulated NO_2^- with plant metabolites. There have been reports that NO, N_2O, and N_2 can be formed non-enzymatically when certain plant metabolites are treated with NO_2^- (Evans and McAuliffe 1956; Porter 1969). These reactions are typically favored by low pH and high NO_2^- concentrations. Klepper (1979) observed that NO appeared to be formed at lower NO_2^- levels, while both NO and NO_2 (predominantly NO) appeared to be formed when NO_2^- levels increased in the leaf.

1.2 Association of $NO_{(x)}$ Evolution with the NR Enzyme

Soybean leaves subjected to the purged in vivo NR assay evolve significant quantities of $NO_{(x)}$ (Harper 1981), predominantly NO (Dean and Harper 1986). Evolution of NO from soybean leaves was later confirmed by Klepper (1987) and Wei et al. (1987). $NO_{(x)}$ evolution from soybean was thought to be the result of an enzymic reaction since leaf disks that were infiltrated with NO_2^- (the substrate for $NO_{(x)}$ evolution) and boiled, did not evolve $NO_{(x)}$, whereas unboiled controls infiltrated with NO_2^- did evolve $NO_{(x)}$ (Harper 1981). Harper (1981) observed that the amount of $NO_{(x)}$ evolved was greater under anaerobic gas purging and increased flow rate conditions. Harper's study was undertaken in order to explain why N_2 purging of soybean leaves during the in vivo NR assay sometimes resulted in slight stimulations of NO_2^- accumulation, while at other times apparent decreases in NO_2^- accumulation were observed. The gaseous loss of $NO_{(x)}$ from the in vivo NR assay medium partially explained the decrease in NO_2^- accumulation during gas purging of young soybean leaves, but a stoichiometric relationship was not found (Harper 1981).

Further evidence that $NO_{(x)}$ evolution from soybean was enzymatic came from the isolation of a soybean mutant (designated nr_1) that lacked both constitutive NR activity and $NO_{(x)}$ evolution (Nelson et al. 1983; Ryan et al. 1983); an observation which led to the hypothesis that $NO_{(x)}$ evolution was in some way linked to constitutive NR activity in soybean. Subsequent enzyme purification indicated that soybean plants contain two constitutive NR isoforms (c_1NR and c_2NR) (Streit et al. 1985). This led to the question of whether $NO_{(x)}$ evolution was associated with one or both of the constitutive enzymes. Isolation of two additional soybean mutants (LNR-5 and LNR-6), both of which retained the c_1NR enzyme form and lacked the c_2NR form (Streit and Harper 1986) has provided evidence that the c_1NR enzyme was associated with $NO_{(x)}$ evolution. Recently, based on copurification of the c_1NR and $NO_{(x)}$ activities, it has been concluded that the c_1NR enzyme is capable of NO_3^- reduction and subsequent NO_2^- reduction to NO (Dean and Harper 1988). However, based on the a priori requirement that appreciable NO_2^- levels need to accumulate in the tissue before $NO_{(x)}$ evolution occurs, it does not appear likely that $NO_{(x)}$ evolution occurs in intact plants in situ. Further study is needed to clarify the role of constitutive NR enzyme activities in soybean and their possible role in N use economy; NO_3^- reduction vs gaseous loss of nitrogenous compounds.

This chapter will discuss the current status of knowledge on evolution of nitrogenous gasses from plants, with primary emphasis on N oxides. The techniques described will deal with N losses from intact plants, and with those techniques used in our laboratory to identify and quantify N oxides evolved from soybean during the purged in vivo NR assay. Hopefully, the methods described here will provide base techniques which can be adapted to measure N oxides produced from other plant systems of interest to the reader.

2 Volatile N Carried in Water Vapor from Intact Plants

Substantial loss of nonelemental N evolved from the foliage of a wide variety of crop and weed species has been demonstrated by Stutte and co-workers (Stutte and Weiland 1978; Stutte et al. 1979; Weiland and Stutte 1979; da Silva and Stutte 1981). The collection procedure involved circulating ambient air past leaves enclosed in a plastic bag and through a cold finger trap (dry ice, $-80°$ C) to condense the volatile N compounds. The collected compounds were then quantitatively determined using a pyro-chemiluminescent technique. Determination with this technique is based on the reactions of NO with oxygen atoms and ozone to give a metastable molecule of NO_2. Upon instantaneously returning to the ground state, the high energy NO_2 molecule emits a quantum of detectable light. Presumably, in an O_2-rich atmosphere at temperatures greater than 900° C, chemically bound N forms are pyrolyzed to NO. According to Weiland and Stutte (1979), if O_2 is removed from the reaction, then only the oxidized forms of nonelemental N will be converted to NO. Based on these studies, it was concluded that the majority of the chemically bound N was evolved in the reduced state, while only a small portion was in the oxidized state (Stutte et al. 1979; Weiland and Stutte 1979, 1980). It was suggested that at least 45 kg of N ha^{-1} could be lost over the course of a growing season from field-grown soybean (Stutte and Weiland 1978; Stutte et al. 1979). Wetselaar and Farquhar (1980) indicated that this figure might be an overestimation since the air recirculating over the leaf may contain partial pressures equal to zero for the unknown nitrogenous compounds which would result in the overestimation of effluxes from the leaf unless the leaf was incapable of metabolizing these gasses. A more recent study provides support that gaseous N products are evolved from intact seedlings of soybean (Mulvaney 1984). That study involved chemical trapping of volatiles from seedling soybean plants. The gas exchange system involved an acrylic plastic chamber (58 cm high, 20.4 cm i.d., 6.4 mm wall) which completely enclosed a pot containing four 24-day-old soybean seedlings. The root and shoot chambers were sealed separately. Compressed air was introduced into the bottom of the shoot chamber at the rate of 300 ml min^{-1}. In addition, the atmosphere within the chamber was recirculated at 5 l min^{-1}. The exiting gas (300 ml min^{-1}) was bubbled through a series of three 125-ml gas-washing bottles. The three traps (I, II, and III) contained 0.1 N H_2SO_4, 1 N KOH, and 1 N KOH: 0.1 M $KMnO_4$, respectively. The following compounds would be expected to be trapped, if present: trap I, basic compounds such as NH_3 and amines (Cheng and Bremner 1965); trap II, acidic compounds such as NO_2 and HCN (Cheng and Bremner 1965; Nahrstedt et al. 1981); and trap III, acidic compounds and those compounds oxidized to acidic products by the alkaline permanganate, such as NO (Cheng and Bremner 1965; Tedesco and Keeney 1972). Mulvaney (1984) reported some 30 to 40 μg total N $plant^{-1}$ h^{-1} was evolved from intact soybean seedlings, using the above chemical trapping system. Over 50% of the N trapped was found in trap II, indicating that acidic compounds were primarily evolved. It was further concluded that oxidized compounds were more prevalent, in contrast to the report of Weiland et al. (1982) that reduced compounds were more prevalent. It is obvious that additional work in needed before definitive conclusions can be drawn concerning the types of nitrogenous compounds evolved from intact plants.

3 Methods for Detecting N Oxides

3.1 Greiss-Saltzman Colorimetric Assay

Chemical methods for the detection of N oxides are designed almost exclusively for the detection of NO_2 and not NO. One of the most common methods for quantization of NO_2 is based on modifications of the reagent that Greiss (1879) (cited by Allen 1973) used for the detection of the NO_2^- ion. The Greiss reaction involves the diazotization of an aromatic amine by NO_2^- in an acid solution and coupling of the resulting diazo compound to a reactive aromatic amine or phenol to form an azo dye.

Saltzman (1954) analyzed many modifications of the Greiss reagent for use during continuous sampling of NO_2 in air. The final composition adopted consisted of sulfanilic acid and N-(1-napthyl)ethylenediamine dihydrochloride in dilute acetic acid.

The requirement for high-speed instrumentation capable of rapidly sensing pollutant levels of NO_2 led to the development of a colorimetric reagent for NO_2 that had faster color development, and greater color intensity (Lyshkow 1965). The original formulation of Lyshkow's (1965) NO_2 colorimetric reagent utilized sulfanilamide as the diazotization agent, N-(1-napthyl)ethylenediamine dihydrochloride as the coupling reagent, tartaric acid as the H^+ source, and 2-naphthol 3,6 disulfonate ("R salt") as a reaction promoter. The reaction promoter allowed rapid color development, improved color intensity, and longer shelf life of the solution (Lyshkow 1965).

Nitrogen dioxide is readily soluble in H_2O ($2\,NO_2 + H_2O \rightarrow NO_2^- + NO_3^- + 2\,H^+$), which makes it possible to detect it as NO_2^- ion. However, corrections should be made to account for the portion of NO_2 that is converted to NO_3^-. Theoretically, absorption of NO_2 by H_2O should yield equimolar amounts of NO_2^- and NO_3^-. Therefore, 0.5 mol of NO_2^- ion in water would be equivalent to 1.0 mol of gaseous NO_2; this represents an NO_2^- equivalence factor of 0.5. Saltzman (1954) and Saltzman and Wartburg (1965) showed that in the Greiss-Saltzman reagents, 1 mol of NO_2 gas was equivalent to 0.72 mol of a standard NO_2^- solution. This value varied with concentrations and combinations of the ingredients of the reagent. The NO_2^- equivalence factor for the Greiss-Saltzman reagent has been redetermined by several others, often with conflicting results (see Allen 1973). There still remains controversy over the exact value of this factor for the Greiss-Saltzman reagents and it is suggested that investigators will need to individually establish a factor for their specific experimental conditions.

3.1.1 Oxidation of NO to NO_2

As was stated earlier, colorimetric methods are not designed to detect NO, therefore, NO is usually first oxidized to NO_2. Although others have been used, solid oxidizers appear to be the most popular and convenient. Bethell et al. (1968) reported that a solid oxidizer prepared by drying a solution of potassium dichromate in sulfuric acid onto glass wool could convert 97% of the NO passing through it (100 ppm v/v in flue gas flowing at 140 ml min^{-1}) to NO_2. An adaptation of the solid oxidizer described by Bethell et al. (1968) was made by Klepper (1979) for use with plant tissue. This involved drying the H_2SO_4-dichromate solution onto glass beads rather than glass wool and has proven to be quite useful in determining evolution of N oxide compounds from plants.

3.1.2 Colorimetric Determination of $NO_{(x)}$ Produced During in Vivo NR Assays

The following system was used by Harper (1981) to measure $NO_{(x)}$ production during the purged in vivo NR assay of soybean leaves. The in vivo NR assay was conducted as described by Nicholas et al. (1976). The assay tubes were covered with aluminium foil to exclude light and capped with rubber stoppers through which inlet and outlet needles (16 gauge) were inserted. The N_2 purge gas was bubbled through the assay medium and then sequentially passed through the preoxidizer and a fritted glass gas dispersion tube submerged in the Greiss-Saltzman reagents (20 ml). The preoxidizer was prepared by a modification of the system used by Bethell et al. (1968), as described by Klepper (1979), and involved coating of glass beads (5 mm diameter) with a solution of 320 g sodium dichromate, 120 ml H_2SO_4, and 1 liter H_2O. The beads were dried at 80° to 90° C until their color turned to a dark brick red. The actual column consisted of a pyrex tube (30 cm long × 22 mm diameter) filled half-full with coated beads. Both ends of the tube were fitted with a single-hole rubber stopper and a glass wool filter to allow gas entry and exit past the coated beads. The trapping solution consisted of modified Greiss-Saltzman reagents as described by Lyshkow (1965). The exact composition was: 30 g tartaric acid; 3.0 g sulfanilamide; 0.10 g N-(1-napthyl)ethylenediamine dihydrochloride; 0.10 g 2-naphthol 3,6 disulfonic acid disodium salt; and deionized water to a final volume of 4 liters.

The efficiency of a single column and a single trapping solution have been shown to be greater than 95%, based on using multiple columns and solution traps in series (Harper 1981). The trapping solution used by Harper (1981) was calibrated with sodium NO_2^- standards. It is known that a portion of the NO_2 will be converted to NO_3^- in the trapping solution, therefore, a correction factor must be applied for quantitative analyses (see Sect. 3.1).

The method of $NO_{(x)}$ determination just described has also been automated. Klepper (1979) measured $NO_{(x)}$ evolution occurring from herbicide-treated soybean leaves with an H_2SO_4-dichromate solid oxidizer and an Aeron NO_2 analyzer (GCA/Precision Scientific, Chicago, I1). Automated wet chemical methods based on the Greiss-Saltzman reagents consist of a gas-liquid contact column, for mixing of gas sample and Greiss-Saltzman reagents, and a continuous flow colorimetric detector. This allows for continuous analysis of N oxides (Lyshkow 1965; Allen 1973).

Whatever method is employed, NO is determined by the difference between total $NO_{(x)}$ (presence of oxidizer column) and NO_2 determined alone (absence of oxidizer column).

3.1.3 Colorimetric Determination of $NO_{(x)}$ Produced During in Vitro NR Assays

It has recently been discovered that $NO_{(x)}$ evolution from soybean is associated with the constitutive NAD(P)H:NR (pH 6.5) EC 1.6.6.2 (c_1NR) enzyme (Dean and Harper 1988) (see Sect. 1.2). The $NO_{(x)}$ activity of this enzyme can be assayed in vitro using either a crude soybean extract or a purified preparation of the NR enzyme. Although in vitro NR assays use NO_3^- as the substrate, this approach did not produce sufficient NO_2^- to saturate the reaction producing $NO_{(x)}$, therefore, the assay was modified to include KNO_2 rather than KNO_3 as the substrate. The complete in vitro $NO_{(x)}$ assay medium (5 ml) consists of one drop of octyl alcohol, 20 m*M* K-phosphate (pH 6.75), 5 m*M* KNO_2, and 0.375 m*M* NAD(P)H. The assay is started by the addition of either the crude or purified enzyme. $NO_{(x)}$ is detected essentially by the same system used by Harper (1981) as described in Sect. 3.1.2 to detect $NO_{(x)}$ evolution during in vivo NR assays. A purge gas (N_2 at 150 ml min^{-1}) is passed sequentially through the in vitro $NO_{(x)}$ assay medium, a preoxidizer column, and into the Greiss-Saltzman reagents (10 ml). The octyl alcohol is included in the assay mix in order to decrease frothing during gas purging. Details for the preparation of the crude extract and purification of NR enzymes will not be given here, but are based on protocols used by Streit et al. (1985, 1987).

3.2 Gas Chromatography (GC)

Gas chromatography would appear to be the analytical method of choice for the quantization of both NO and NO_2, however, the high reactivity of these gases presents special problems when using this method. Two of the main problems are that (1) NO is oxidized to NO_2 in the presence of O_2 or air; and (2) in addition to materials used in obtaining and transferring samples, NO_2 also reacts with many of the column-packing materials used for GC analysis including Porapak Q, Chromosorb 102 (Trowell 1971), and moist molecular sieve (Greene and Pust 1958). Although NO might also react with GC column-packing materials, it is not as reactive as NO_2 (Bremner and Blackmer 1982).

Several column-packing materials as well as a variety of detectors have been used for the determination of N oxides (for reviews see Allen 1973; Fishbein 1973; Bremner and Blackmer 1982), however, usually only NO is eluted from the column, while NO_2 is permanently retained or chemically altered. Porapak has been as reliable as any of the column-packing materials used for GC determination of NO (Barbaree and Payne 1967; Bell 1968; Bailey and Beauchamp 1973) and the new thermal conductivity detectors (TCD) have adequate sensitivity for the detection of NO and N_2O produced during the purged in vivo NR assay of soybean and winged bean (Dean and Harper 1986). A recent paper (Wei et al. 1987) also reports detection of N oxides from plant tissues using a GC equipped with an alkali flame ionization detector. A rubidium sulfate flame tip was used.

The NO and NO_2 gas standards are available from Matheson Gas Products. Handling of standards requires some precautions due to the toxic nature of these gases. Working in a hood is highly recommended. Evacuated collection tubes (e.g. Vacutainer tubes, Vacutainer Systems, Rutherford, N.J., USA) provide a convenient system for handling gas samples withdrawn from gas cylinders until they are injected into the GC with a syringe.

3.2.1 Cryogenic Trapping of N Oxides

The system depicted in Fig. 1 has been used for the collection of volatile compounds produced during the purged in vivo NR assay of soybean and winged bean (Dean and Harper 1986). The system was constructed entirely of glass except for the sampling port and pressure gauge which were attached to the glass system with Kovar seals. For the assay, unifoliolate leaves (15 g) of soybean (10 days after planting) or winged bean (13 days after planting) were sliced perpendicular to the midrib into about 1-cm-wide strips. The strips were placed in a 1-liter flask containing 500 ml of standard in vivo NR assay mix composed of 0.10 M K_2HPO_4-KH_2PO_4 (pH 7.5) and 0.05 *M* KNO_3. The leaf strips were vacuum infiltrated twice with buffer (2 min each time) and the flask was covered with aluminum foil, placed in a 30° C water bath, and attached to the collection system (Fig. 1). The assay mix was subsequently purged with helium (He) at a flow rate of 350 ml min^{-1}. The purge gas stream then passed sequentially through trap A (250 ml cold finger held at −80° C to remove the bulk of the water vapor), trap B (75 ml cold finger held at 196° C to collect the volatile N compounds), a preoxidizer column (consisting of glass beads coated with an H_2SO_4-dichromate mixture), and finally through a fritted glass gas dispersion tube immersed in 20 ml of Greiss-Saltzman reagents. The preoxidizer and Greiss-Saltzman reagents (discussed in Sect. 3.1.2) were used to quantify the amount of $NO_{(x)}$ that was not collected in trap B. The assay mix was purged with He for 15 min before immersing trap B into the liquid N_2 in order to flush air from the system. After immersing trap B into the liquid N_2, the assay mix was purged with He for an additional 2 h. At the end of this time, stopcocks 1 and 2 (Fig. 1) were closed to isolate trap B (only trace amounts of NO and N_2O were collected in trap A). Trap B was removed from the liquid N_2 and allowed to warm to room temperature (about 1 h). The concurrent increase in pressure was registered on the pressure gauge (Fig. 1).

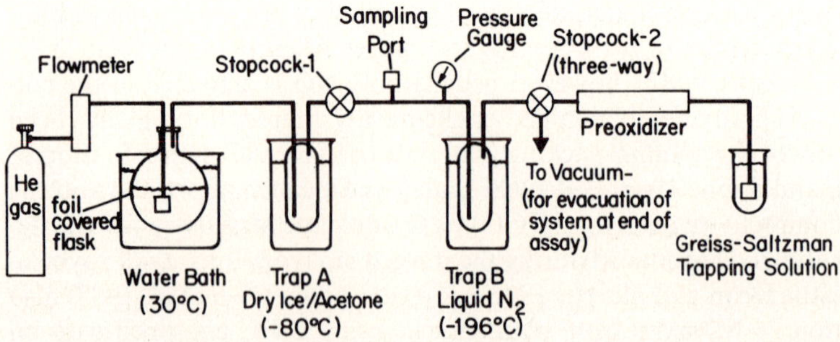

Fig. 1. Diagram of the system used for cryogenic trapping of NO and N_2O produced during the He-purged in vivo NR assay of soybean and winged bean leaflets (Dean and Harper 1986)

Immediately after removing trap B from the liquid N_2, a compound resembling bluish-white "snow" could be seen on the interior glass tube of the trap at a point just above the level of liquid N_2 contact with the trap. Further observation revealed that the "snow" turned to a blue fluid upon warming, and at room temperature the trap contained a gas that had a reddish-brown tint. It is known that NO can exist as a bluish-white solid, a blue liquid, or a colorless gas depending on temperature. It is believed that the reddish-brown color in trap B, following warming, was due to NO_2 since an aliquot of gas taken from trap B and injected directly into the Greiss-Saltzman reagents resulted in color formation. The NO_2 in trap B was most likely formed by the reaction of NO with O_2. Even though the assay was carried out under anaerobic conditions, it is possible that small amounts of O_2 (bp $-182.96°$ C) in trap B ($-196°$ C) could have resulted from impurities in the He purge gas or from dissolved O_2 in the assay mix or plant tissue that was not totally eliminated during the 15 min prepurge. If NO_2 had been formed during the assay, it is unlikely that it would be purged from the assay mix based on its high solubility in an aqueous medium. Even if it did escape the aqueous medium, NO_2 (bp 21.15° C) would have been collected in trap A ($-80°$ C). Analysis of water vapor in trap A with the Greiss-Saltzman reagents revealed the presence of only slight traces of NO_2.

3.2.2 Sampling

Gaseous compounds collected in trap B were sampled with a needle and syringe from the sampling port (Fig. 1). The sampling port contained a gas-tight septum through which a needle could be inserted and multiple samples taken. Before sampling, needles and syringes were thoroughly purged with He in order to remove residual air, however, despite exhaustive efforts, complete removal of air could not be accomplished. This is a problem when sampling with a syringe, especially if N_2 is a gas of interest, however, if this limitation is kept in mind, the speed and simplicity of this method make it attractive. Using the above conditions, a 0.5-cc gas sample is adequate for GC and GC/MS analyses. At the end of each assay, it was necessary to remove residual gases from the system. This was accomplished by several cycles of flushing the system with air and subsequent evacuation through stopcock 2 (Fig. 1). The flask, trap A, and trap B were all connected to the system with ground glass joints so that they could easily be removed for cleaning before the next assay.

3.2.3 Assay Conditions

For assay of gases cryogenically trapped, as noted above, a 0.5-ml aliquot taken from the sampling port was injected directly into a Hewlett-Packard Model 5890A GC fitted with a TCD and a 100/120 mesh Porapak N column (6.02 m long × 2 mm i.d. stainless steel). The oven temperature was programmed to hold an initial temperature of 60° C for 3 min and then increase 20° C min^{-1} to 120° C where the temperature was held. The injection temperature was 60° C and the detector temperature was 150° C. The carrier gas was He at a flow rate of 45 ml min^{-1}. Locating and quantifying peaks was simplified by using a Nelson analyti-

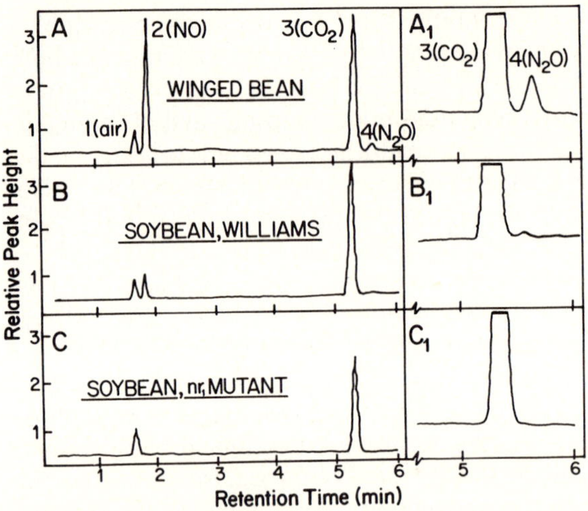

Fig. 2 A–C. Chromatogram tracings from GC analysis, using a TC detector, of compounds collected in trap B (Fig. 1) when leaf tissue either from **A** winged bean, **B** Williams soybean, or **C** the nr_1 mutant soybean was used in the He-purged in vivo NR assay. $\mathbf{A_1}$, $\mathbf{B_1}$, and $\mathbf{C_1}$ show magnified tracings of the 5 to 6 min retention time period of **A**, **B**, and **C**, respectively. The NR assay medium consisted of 15 g of leaf slices and 500 ml of buffer containing 0.1 *M* K_2HPO_4-KH_2PO_4 (pH 7.5) and 0.05 *M* KNO_3. The helium flow rate was 350 ml min^{-1}. Trap B was not cooled for the first 15 min of the assay in order to purge most of the air from the system (Dean and Harper 1986)

cal 3000 series chromatography data system (Nelson Analytical, Inc., Cupertino, CA) linked to an IBM personal computer for data reduction. The Nelson system is recommended over conventional integrators, since, among other advantages, data can be stored on computer diskettes and reexamined, or views can be magnified revealing small peaks that may otherwise go unnoticed.

This GC procedure resulted in the separation of air (which was a composite peak of N_2 and O_2 and considered a contaminant), NO, CO_2, and N_2O which were collected during the He purged in vivo NR assay of soybean (cv. Williams) and winged bean (cv. Lunita) (Fig. 2A, A_1, B, B_1). The nr_1 mutant (described in Sect. 1.2) of soybean did not evolve NO or N_2O as revealed by GC analysis (Fig. 2C, C_1).

Wei et al. (1987) also used a gas chromatography system to measure gaseous products evolved from plant leaves. Their system differed in that leaves (200 g) were placed in a foil-covered flask without any external aqueous media. The leaves were then subjected to vaccum distillation for 5 h at 20° C and gaseous volatiles were collected in a liquid N_2 cold finger trap. The gaseous sample (upon warming) was then transferred to a glass storage bulb for analysis by a Varian Model 2100 GC equipped with an alkali flame ionization detector. The GC column (2 mm × 180 cm glass) was packed with Porapak Q. The column temperature program was held at 75° C for 1 min and then programmed to increase at 6° C min^{-1}. Nitrogen was the carrier gas (20 cc min^{-1}). Analyses of volatiles from soybean leaves resulted in detection of four peaks (Fig. 3); identified as N

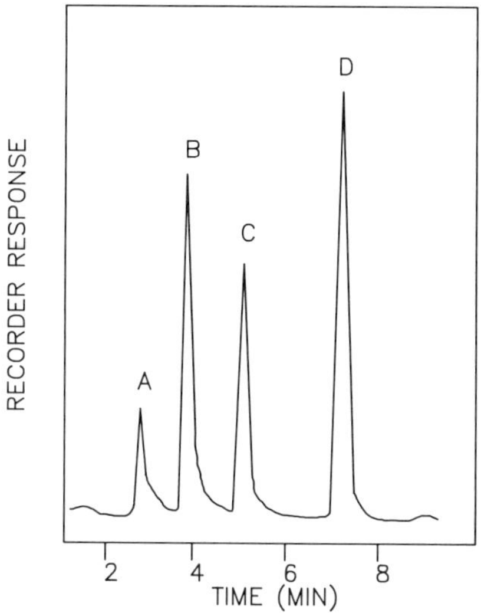

Fig. 3. Chromatogram tracings from GC analysis, using an alkali flame ionization detector, of compounds collected by vacuum distillation of volatiles from soybean leaf segments. Continuous vacuum was applied to the flask containing 200 g of leaves. Incubation was in the dark at 20° C without any external aqueous media. Peaks were matched by retention time to authentic standards of N oxides (**A**) (both NO and NO_2 resulted in one peak), methanol (**B**), acetaldehyde (**C**), and ethanol (**D**). Volatiles were collected in a liquid N_2 trap placed between the leaf flask and the vacuum system during a 5-h incubation period. (Results are unpublished data kindly supplied by Lester Wei, Section of Economic Entomology, Illinois Natural History Survey, University of Illinois)

oxides, methanol, acetaldehyde, and ethanol (based on retention times of authentic standards; both NO and NO_2 standards resulted in a peak which matched the retention time of peak A).

3.3 Gas Chromatography-Mass Spectrometry (GC-MS) Assay Conditions

Gas chromatography alone (described in Sect. 3.2) was used to tentatively identify NO, N_2O, and CO_2 by comparing sample retention times to retention times of authentic standards. Confirmation of compound identities were accomplished with GC-MS. With this analytical method, the MS essentially serves as a highly sensitive and selective GC detector. Inclusion of the MS to the GC system gave the added dimension of allowing detection of gaseous compounds that could be labeled in vivo with ^{15}N. Labeling with ^{15}N facilitated the identification of gaseous N compounds (NO and N_2O) (see Dean and Harper 1986).

For GC-MS analysis of compounds evolved during the purged in vivo NR assay of soybean, gaseous material was cryogenically trapped and sampled as described in Sects. 3.2.1 and 3.2.2. Samples were injected directly into a Hewlett-Packard Model 5985 GC-MS system. The GC column and operating conditions were exactly as described in Sect. 3.2.2. The mass spectrometer was operated in the electron impact mode. The electron energy equaled 70 eV and the source temperature was 200° C. Following separation of the compounds with GC, the effluent from the column was allowed to flow directly in the MS.

3.3.1 ^{15}N Labeling

The in vivo NR assay conditions used to generate ^{15}N-labeled NO and N_2O were the same as those used to generate unlabeled compounds (Sect. 3.2.1) except that (1) the leaf tissue was from soybean plants that were grown on a nutrient solution

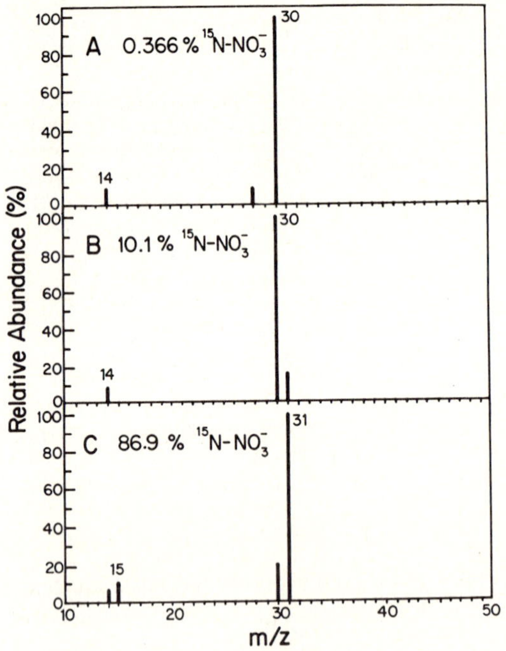

Fig. 4 A–C. Mass spectrum from GC/MS analysis of peak 2 (NO; Fig. 2) when either **A** 0.366, **B** 10.1, or **C** 86.9 at% $^{15}N\text{-}NO_3^-$ (10 m*M*) was included in the assay medium during the He-purged in vivo NR assay of soybean leaflets. The peaks at 14, 28, and 30 in **A** correspond to the ions $^{14}N^+$, $^{14}N^{14}N^+$, and $^{14}NO^+$, respectively. The peaks at 14, 30, and 31 in **B** correspond to the ions $^{14}N^+$, $^{14}NO^+$, and $^{15}NO^+$, respectively. The peaks at 14, 30, and 31 in **C** correspond to the same ions as in **B**, and the peak at 15 corresponds to $^{15}N^+$. (See Fig. 2 legend for experimental details; Dean and Harper 1986)

that lacked NO_3^- in order to eliminate interference by $^{14}N\text{-}NO_3^-$ in the tissue with the $^{15}N\text{-}NO_3^-$ supplied during the assay; and (2) the 10 m*M* KNO_3 supplied in the assay medium was enriched with either 0.366 (natural abundance), 10.1, or 86.9 at% ^{15}N.

Mass spectra following GC-MS analysis of peak number 2 (NO from GC analysis; Fig. 2) when the assays were done in the presence of either 0.366, 10.1, or 86.9 at% $^{15}N\text{-}KNO_3$ are shown in Fig. 4 A–C. The labeling pattern at each ^{15}N enrichment is consistent with the theoretical labeling pattern that would be expected for NO. GC-MS analysis revealed that the compound represented by peak 3 (CO_2 from GC analysis; Fig. 2) did not label with ^{15}N and that the mass spectrum was consistent with the theoretical mass spectrum of CO_2 (data not shown; see Dean and Harper 1986). Figure 5 A–C shows the mass spectra following GC-MS analysis of peak 4 (N_2O from GC analysis; Fig. 2) from the same ^{15}N experiments used to analyze peak 2. In the case of peak 4, the labeling pattern at each ^{15}N enrichment is consistent with what would be expected for N_2O. It is now known that NO, N_2O, and CO_2 (in addition to a few other organic compounds) are evolved from soybean during the purged in vivo NR assay (Dean and Harper 1986). In addition, both NO and N_2O were produced from NO_3^- during NO_3^- reduction since both were labeled with ^{15}N from $^{15}N\text{-}NO_3^-$.

Other methods involving cryogenic trapping and fractional distillation, and chemical trapping procedures, have been used to collect N compounds evolved during the purged in vivo NR assay of soybean leaves; collected compounds were identified using MS and ultraviolet spectroscopy (Mulvaney and Hageman 1984). However, these methods did not detect NO which has been shown by Dean and Harper (1986) to be the predominant compound evolved. It was postulated that

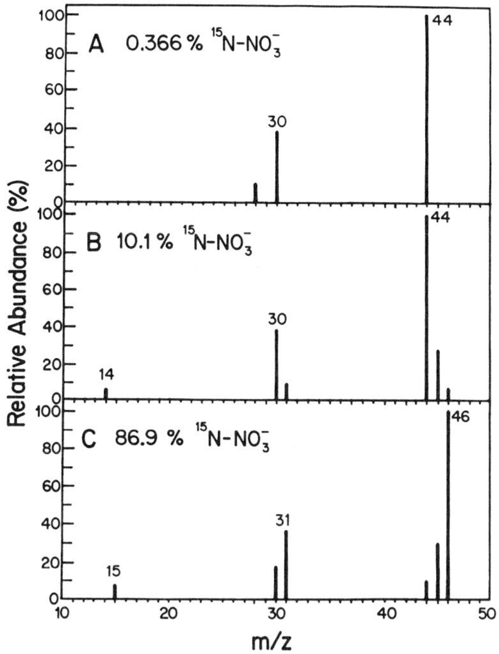

Fig. 5 A–C. Mass spectrum from GC/MS analysis of peak 4 (N_2O; Fig. 2) when either **A** 0.366, **B** 10.1, or **C** 86.9 at% $^{15}N-NO_3^-$ (10 m*M*) was included in the asssay medium during the He-purged in vivo NR assay of soybean leaflets. The peaks at 28, 30, and 44 in **A** correspond to the ions $^{14}N^{14}N^+$, $^{14}NO^+$, and $^{14}N^{14}NO^+$, respectively. The peaks at 14, 30, 31, 44, 45, and 46 in **B** correspond to the ions $^{14}N^+$, $^{14}NO^+$, and $^{15}NO^+$, $^{14}N^{14}NO^+$, $^{15}N^{14}NO^+$, and $^{15}N^{15}NO^+$, respectively. The peaks at 30, 31, 44, 45, and 46 in **C** correspond to the same ions as in **B**, and the peak at 15 corresponds to $^{15}N^+$. (See Fig. 2 legend for further experimental details; Dean and Harper 1986)

NO was not detected by Mulvaney and Hageman (1984) because it was either lost during sample manipulations or it chemically reacted with other compounds during the week-long incubation periods used in the previous study. GC and GC-MS allow immediate analysis of samples so that losses of the highly reactive NO are not encountered.

Acknowledgments. The authors thank J. C. Nicholas and D. J. Hendren for technical assistance with GC and GC/MS procedures, respectively. The authors also thank F. J. Stevenson and L. A. Klepper for their review and suggestions on the manuscript. The work described from our laboratory was supported by an American Soybean Association research grant (project No. 84953). The mention of firm names or trade products does not imply that they are endorsed or recommended by the U.S. Department of Agriculture over other firms or similar products not mentioned.

References

Allen JD (1973) A review of methods of analysis for oxides of nitrogen. J Inst Fuel 46:123–133
Bailey LD, Beauchamp EG (1973) Gas chromatography of gases emanating from a saturated soil system. Can J Soil Sci 53:122–124
Barbaree JM, Payne WJ (1967) Products of denitrification by a marine bacterium as revealed by gas chromatography. Mar Biol 1:136–139
Beevers L, Hageman RH (1980) Nitrate and nitrite reduction. In: Stumpf PK, Conn EE (eds) The biochemistry of plants, vol 5. Academic Press, New York London, pp 115–168

Bell RG (1968) Separation of gases likely to be evolved from flooded soils by gas chromatography. Soil Sci 105:78–80

Bethell KD, Shaw JT, Thomas AC (1968) An improved form of solid oxidizer for the conversion of nitric oxide to nitrogen dioxide. Chem Ind 20:91

Bremner JM, Blackmer AM (1982) Composition of soil atmospheres. In: Keeney DR (ed) Methods of soil analysis, pt 2. Chemical and microbiological properties. Agron Monogr 9:873–901

Cheng HH, Bremner JM (1965) Gaseous forms of nitrogen. In: Black CA (ed) Methods of soil analysis, 1st edn, pt 2. Am Soc Agron, Madison, pp 1287–1323

da Silva PRF, Stutte CA (1981) Nitrogen loss in conjunction with transpiration from rice leaves as influenced by growth stage, leaf position and N supply. Agron J 73:38–42

Dean JV, Harper JE (1986) Nitric oxide and nitrous oxide production by soybean and winged bean during the in vivo nitrate reductase assay. Plant Physiol 82:718–723

Dean JV, Harper JE (1988) The conversion of nitrite to nitrogen oxide(s) by the constitutive NAD(P)H-nitrate reductase enzyme from soybean. Plant Physiol (submitted)

Evans H, McAuliffe C (1956) Identification of NO, N_2O, and N_2 as products of the nonenzymatic reduction of nitrite by ascorbate or reduced diphosphopyridine nucleotide. In: McElroy WD, Glass B (eds) Inorganic nitrogen metabolism. Hopkins, Baltimore, pp 189–197

Fishbein L (1973) Chromatography of environmental hazards, vol 2. Elsevier, Amsterdam, pp 237–257

Greene SA, Pust H (1958) Determination of nitrogen dioxide by gas-solid chromatography. Anal Chem 30:1039–1040

Harper JE (1981) Evolution of nitrogen oxide(s) during in vivo nitrate reductase assay of soybean leaves. Plant Physiol 68:1488–1493

Klepper LA (1974) A mode of action of herbicides: inhibition of nitrite reduction. Nebraska Exp Stn Res Bull 259:1–42

Klepper LA (1975) Inhibition of nitrite reduction by photosynthetic inhibitors. Weed Sci 23:188–190

Klepper LA (1979) Nitric oxide (NO) and nitrogen dioxide (NO_2) emissions from herbicide-treated soybean plants. Atmosph Environ 13:537–542

Klepper LA (1987) Nitric oxide emissions from soybean leaves during in vivo nitrate reductase assays. Plant Physiol 85:96–99

Lyshkow NA (1965) A rapid and sensitive colorimetric reagent for nitrogen dioxide in air. J Air Pollut Control Assoc 15:481–484

Mulvaney CS (1984) Evolution of nitrogen compounds from soybean. Ph D Thesis, Univ Ill, Champaign-Urbana, pp 67

Mulvaney CS, Hageman RH (1982) Evolution of N compounds from soybean seedlings under ambient conditions. Agron Abstr, p 105

Mulvaney CS, Hageman RH (1984) Acetaldehyde oxime, a product formed during the in vivo nitrate reductase assay of soybean leaves. Plant Physiol 76:118–124

Nahrstedt A, Erb N, Zinsmeister HD (1981) Methods of liberating and estimating hydrocyanic acid from cyanogenic plant material. In: Vennesland B, Conn EE, Knowles CH, Westley J, Wissing F (eds) Cyanide in biology. Academic Press, New York London, pp 461–471

Nelson RS, Ryan SA, Harper JE (1983) Soybean mutants lacking constitutive nitrate reductase activity. I. Selection and initial plant characterization. Plant Physiol 72:503–509

Nicholas JC, Harper JE, Hageman RH (1976) Nitrate reductase activity in soybeans (*Glycine max* [L.] Merr.). I. Effects of light and temperature. Plant Physiol 58:731–735

Porter LK (1969) Gaseous products produced by anaerobic reaction of sodium nitrite with oxime compounds and oximes synthesized from organic matter. Soil Sci Soc Am Proc 33:696–702

Ryan SA, Nelson RS, Harper JE (1983) Soybean mutants lacking constitutive nitrate reductase activity. II. Nitrogen assimilation, chlorate resistance, and inheritance. Plant Physiol 72:510–514

Saltzman BE (1954) Colorimetric microdetermination of nitrogen dioxide in the atmosphere. Anal Chem 26:1949–1955

Saltzman BE, Wartburg AF Jr. (1965) Precision flow dilution system for standard low concentrations of nitrogen dioxide. Anal Chem 37:1261–1264
Streit L, Harper JE (1986) Biochemical characterization of soybean mutants lacking constitutive NADH : nitrate reductase. Plant Physiol 81:593–596
Streit L, Nelson RS, Harper JE (1985) Nitrate reductases from wild-type and nr_1-mutant soybean (*Glycine max* [L.] Merr.) leaves. I. Purification, kinetics, and physical properties. Plant Physiol 78:80–84
Streit L, Martin BA, Harper JE (1987) A method for the separation and partial purification of the three forms of nitrate reductase present in wild-type soybean leaves. Plant Physiol 84:654–657
Stutte CA, Weiland RT (1978) Gaseous nitrogen loss and transpiration of several crop and weed species. Crop Sci 18:887–889
Stutte CA, Weiland RT, Blem AR (1979) Gaseous nitrogen loss from soybean foliage. Agron J 71:95–97
Tedesco MJ, Keeney DR (1972) Determination of (nitrate + nitrite)-N in alkaline permanganate solutions. Commun Soil Sci Plant Anal 3:339–344
Trowell JM (1971) Reaction of nitrogen dioxide with Porapak Q. J Chromatogr Sci 9:253–254
Wei L, Kogan M, Fischer D (1987) Trapping and identification of nitrogen oxides from soybean leaves. Phytochemistry 26:2397–2398
Weiland RT, Stutte CA (1979) Pyro-chemiluminescent differentiation of oxidized and reduced N forms evolved from plant foliage. Crop Sci 19:545–547
Weiland RT, Stutte CA (1980) Concomitant determination of foliar nitrogen loss, net carbon dioxide uptake, and transpiration. Plant Physiol 65:403–406
Weiland RT, Stutte CA, da Silva PRF (1982) Nitrogen volatilization from plant foliage. Arkansas Agric Exp Stn Rep 266
Wetselaar R, Farquhar QD (1980) Losses of nitrogen from the tops of plants. Adv Agron 33:263–302

Other Gases

Hydrogen-Oxidizing Bacteria: Methods Used in Their Investigation

D. J. Arp

1 Introduction

H_2-oxidizing bacteria are of interest because of their roles in processes relevant to agriculture, the environment, and renewable energy resources. The literature on H_2-oxidizing bacteria continues to grow as a result of this interest. Several excellent reviews have covered the roles of hydrogen oxidation in the metabolisms of bacteria that express H_2-oxidizing enzymes (Mortenson and Chen 1974; Schlegel and Schneider 1978 b; Adams et al. 1981; Vignais et al. 1981, 1985; Odom and Peck 1984). Examples of H_2-oxidizing bacteria are found among the aerobes, autotrophs, phototrophs, anaerobes, diazotrophs, and facultative microorganisms.

With regard to plant metabolism, H_2-oxidizing bacteria have their greatest importance in the process of symbiotic N_2 fixation (Eisbrenner and Evans 1983; Arp 1985; Maier 1986; Evans et al. 1987). Many of the microorganisms (*Bradyrhizobium, Rhizobium, Frankeae* sp.) which fix N_2 in a symbiosis with plants are also capable of oxidizing H_2. The relevance of this to biological N_2 fixation stems from the fact that nitrogenase, the enzyme that reduces N_2 to ammonia, also reduces protons to H_2. As a minimum, 25% of the reductant and ATP consumed by nitrogenase are used in the production of H_2. This represents a considerable additional expenditure of energy in an already energy-intensive process. When the symbionts are capable of H_2 oxidation, the H_2 produced by nitrogenase can be recycled and the reductant recovered by the microorganism. H_2 oxidation also provides the O_2-sensitive nitrogenase a higher level of protection against inactivation by O_2 because the oxidation of H_2 is linked to the consumption of O_2. Because H_2 is a competitive inhibitor of N_2 reduction, a third potential benefit of H_2 oxidation to N_2 fixation is a reduction of this inhibition as the in situ H_2 concentration is lowered. In summary, H_2 oxidation is expected to lead to an increased efficiency of N_2 fixation.

The enzyme which catalyzes the oxidation of H_2 is hydrogenase. Stevenson and Stickland (1931) were the first to use this name to describe the presumably enzymatic activation of H_2. However, 40 years passed before Nakos and Mortenson (1971) reported the first purification to homogeneity of a hydrogenase. Hydrogenases have now been purified from a number of microorganisms and have proved to be a diverse group of enzymes (Adams et al. 1981). Molecular weights in the range of 60000 to 210000 have been reported for minimum catalytic units; larger aggregates with activity have also been described. Monomer, dimer, trimer, and tetramer subunit compositions have been reported for these minimum catalytic units (Adams et al. 1981; Hausinger 1987). All hydrogenases appear to have in common the presence of at least one iron sulfur center, although the number (one to four) and types (Fe_4S_4, Fe_3S_x, Fe_2S_2) vary with the source of the enzyme. Many hydrogenases also contain Ni (Hausinger 1987), especially those whose primary function is to oxidize H_2. Hydrogenases have been localized in the cytoplasm, membrane, and periplasm, again dependent upon the microorganism and hydrogenase in question. Some microorganisms express more than one hydrogenase, for example, *Alcaligenes eutrophus* H16 has a membrane-bound hydrogenase (electron transport system linked) and a soluble hydrogenase (NAD-linked). Reviews by Mortenson and Chen (1974), Krasna (1979), Adams et al. (1981), and Hausinger (1987) cover various aspects of the enzymology of hydrogenases. Volumes 60, No. 3 (1978) and 68, No. 1 (1986) of Biochimie are devoted entirely to reports dealing with hydrogenases as is a book entitled "Hydrogenases: their catalytic activity, structure and function" edited by Schlegel and Schneider (1978 b).

2 Methods for the Determination of H_2-Oxidizing Activity

Given the diversity of hydrogenases and the microorganisms that express these enzymes, it is not surprising that there is considerable diversity in the methods applied to their study. Therefore, a detailed consideration of all of the methods applicable to the study of H_2-oxidizing microorganisms would not fit within the confines of a single chapter of this volume. To focus the aim of this chapter, I have chosen to consider in detail only those methods that are pertinent to the actual measurement of H_2-oxidizing activity, whether it be in intact plant organs (e.g., nodules), microorganisms, cell-free extracts, or purified enzyme preparations. A later section provides a cursory treatment of a number of other techniques used in investigations of H_2-oxidizing microorganisms along with references to more detailed descriptions. With regard to the methods used in the measurement of H_2-oxidizing activity of hydrogenases, a number of reviews have given at least some coverage to assays for hydrogenase activity (e.g., Mortenson 1978; Krasna 1978; Aragno and Schlegel 1981; Adams et al. 1981). Some reports have addressed specific aspects of hydrogenase assays (van Dijk et al. 1981; Fernandez 1983; Bagyinka et al. 1984). While the intent of this review is to acquaint the newcomer to this field with some of the more widely used and generally useful methods for determining hydrogenase activity, it is hoped that the veteran investigator of hydrogenases will also find some of the information helpful. The most detailed coverage is given to those methods most likely to be useful to the largest number of laboratories.

2.1 Practical and Theoretical Considerations in the Use of H_2 as a Reagent

H_2 is a colorless, odorless gas of molecular weight 2.016. It has a diffusion coefficient into air of 0.634 $cm^2\ s^{-1}$ which compares to a value of 0.178 for O_2 (CRC Handbook 1970 b). In practical terms, this means that H_2 will diffuse through porous materials (e.g., rubber septa and plastic containers) and small leaks in closed vessels more rapidly than O_2 (and other light gases), but not dramatically so. Therefore, H_2 is handled, transferred, and contained much like any other light gas (e.g., N_2, O_2, CO_2, CH_4). Any system suitable for containing other light gases will probably also be suitable for H_2, e.g., vials stoppered with rubber septa will contain H_2 nearly as well as O_2 or N_2. Small amounts of H_2 are transferred by use of gas-tight syringes, while large amounts are generally transferred through copper, plastic, or rubber tubing with low permeability toward gases.

The diffusion coefficient for H_2 in water is 3.59×10^{-5} cm^2 s^{-1} which compares to the value for diffusion of N_2 into water of 1.62×10^{-5} (Jost 1960). Thus, one must be aware of the possibility that the rate of diffusion of H_2 is the rate-limiting step in a reaction, just as this possibility must be considered in reactions utilizing N_2, O_2, or other light gases moving between a gas and liquid phase. For example, diffusion of H_2 from the gas phase to the liquid phase containing H_2-oxidizing bacteria might well be rate-limiting if high densities of cells are present. Alternatively, the rate of diffusion of H_2 through soil or tissue could limit the determination of H_2 oxidation rates by soil cores or intact plant tissue.

When using H_2 gas as a reagent, one should consider whether the purity of the gas is sufficient for the application, just as would be the case for any other reagent. The high purity H_2 available from commercial suppliers is adequate for many studies, especially those utilizing intact H_2-oxidizing aerobic microorganisms. Generally, the only contaminant of consequence in H_2 is O_2. The traces of O_2 present in cylinders of H_2 can be removed by treatment of H_2 by one of the following three methods: (1) the gas stream is passed through a heated column (5 cm diameter × 50 cm length; 120° C) containing a copper-based catalyst (R3–11, Chemical Dynamics Corp., South Plainsfield, NJ). (2) The gas stream is passed through a Dreschel bottle (or similar gas-scrubbing bottle) that contains 500 ml of 0.1 *M* Tris HCl (pH 9), 0.02 *M* sodium dithionite, and 0.001 *M* methyl or benzyl viologen. The violet color of the reduced viologen indicates that the chamber still has the capacity to remove O_2. (3) The H_2 stream is passed through a commercially available column or cartridge designed to remove O_2.

As with any reagent, one must often be able to calculate the molar concentration or amounts of H_2 used in experiments. For H_2 in the gas phase, this can be readily accomplished by application of the ideal gas law assuming the temperature and partial pressure of H_2 are known. (For H_2, deviations from the "ideal" gas can be ignored under the conditions of temperature and pressure normally encountered.) For H_2 at 101 kPa (1 atm) and 297 K, the concentration of H_2 in the gas phase is 41 m*M*. It is often necessary to calculate the concentration of H_2 in the liquid phase where a gas phase containing a known partial pressure of H_2 is allowed to equilibrate with the liquid phase. The concentration of H_2 in the liquid phase will be proportional to the H_2 pressure in the gas phase. The proportionality constant, or Bunsen coefficient, is defined as the volume of gas in ml (reduced to 0° C and 101 kPa) dissolved in 1 ml of water when the gas pressure is 101 kPa (Dawson et al. 1986). For water at 30° C in equilibrium with 101 kPa H_2, the Bunsen coefficient is 0.017. Under these conditions, the molar concentration of H_2 in the water is 758 μ*M*. When the H_2 pressure is halved, so is the molar concentration of H_2 in the water, etc. The temperature of the water will also affect the partitioning of H_2 between the liquid and gas phases. For H_2, the Bunsen coefficient increases from 0.0164 at 40° C to 0.0182 at 20° C (Umbreit et al. 1972; Dawson et al. 1986).

When using H_2, one must also be aware of certain safety considerations. H_2 is not toxic, although it will act as a simple asphyxiant at high concentrations. The major safety consideration stems from the flammability of H_2. Mixtures of H_2 and O_2 are explosive. The upper and lower flammability limits of H_2 in air at 20° C and 101 kPa are 4 and 74.5% H_2, respectively (Aragno and Schlegel 1981). Care is therefore warrented in the use and handling of H_2. Explosive mixtures should be avoided or prepared in only small amounts as needed and adequate ventilation is essential when H_2 is used.

2.2 Gas Chromatographic Assay of H_2-Oxidizing Activity

Of the many methods available for the measurement of H_2-oxidizing activity of bacteria and cell-free extracts, perhaps the most readily available and one of the least ambiguous is based on the gas chromatographic determination of H_2 concentration in the gas phase. The gas chromatographic column separates H_2 from the other components of a gas sample of interest followed by the quantification of the H_2 at the detector. The gas phase over the biological sample of interest is sampled over a period of time and any decrease in the amount of H_2 added initially is determined. This method is simple, requires only a modest gas chromatograph, and provides a direct detection of the H_2. The disadvantages of the gas chromatographic method are that a fixed time point assay (rather than a continuous assay) is used and the sensitivity is not as great as with some of the other methods.

The gas chromatograph used for detection of H_2 should be fitted with a thermal conductivity detector. Because the sensitivity of detection is a function of the difference in the thermal conductivities of H_2 and the carrier gas, argon and N_2 are good choices, while helium is a poor choice because its thermal conductivity is too close to that of H_2 (CRC Handbook 1970a). With argon as carrier gas, N_2 (as well as O_2) can also be detected and thereby monitored in the sample. Typically, the detector is held at 130° C and the filament current is kept low (70 mA) to prevent filament burnout, even though this results in a somewhat lowered sensitivity. The separation of H_2 from other components of the gas is accomplished by passing the sample through a column ($5' \times {}^1/_8''$ OD copper tubing) packed with molecular sieve 5A. H_2 elutes first from this column, followed by O_2 and N_2. [CO_2 is adsorbed by this packing material, but Hanus et al. (1980) have described a tandem column procedure for measuring H_2, CO_2, N_2, and O_2]. The column should be maintained at a temperature between 25° to 120° C during operation. Lower temperatures result in longer retention times and some broadening of peaks. We generally use a carrier gas flow rate of 40 ml min^{-1}. A typical chromatogram is shown in Fig. 1. The column should be baked out before the first use and occasionally thereafter to remove water and other adsorbed compounds.

Gas sample sizes may vary from 10 µl to 1 ml. It is difficult to maintain accuracy with smaller samples and larger samples create a pressure peak which can

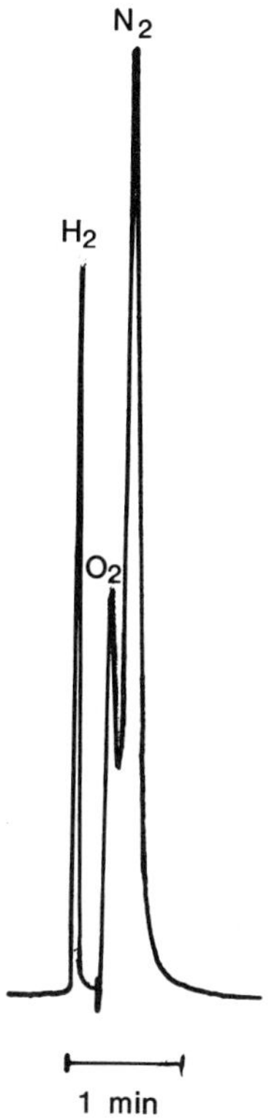

Fig. 1. Typical gas chromatographic separation of H_2, N_2, and O_2. A 0.1 ml sample was taken from a vial containing 7 ml air and 0.02 ml H_2 and injected onto a gas chromatographic column maintained at 70° C. All other column and detector conditions were as described in the text. Between the H_2 and O_2 peaks, the attention was increased from 1 to 8

interfere with the H_2 peak. Any gas-tight syringe of the appropriate size can be used for injections. For precise work, low dead-volume syringes are recommended. For routine analyses, disposable plastic, 1-ml tuberculin syringes are useful. A lower limit for detection is usually around 1 nmol of H_2 in a given injection. Calibration of the instrument is accomplished by recording the peak heights or peak areas obtained when known quantities of H_2 are injected onto the column. Additional considerations on the use of gas chromatography to detect and quantify H_2 may be found in the review by Hanus et al. (1980).

The material to be sampled may be intact microorganisms, cell-free extracts, purified enzymes, or plant organs such as nodules (see below). In a typical experiment, 1 ml of the solution or 1 g of the material to be analyzed is placed in a stoppered, 7-ml vial with an appropriate gas phase. Usually, the gas phase will be identical to that from which the sample was taken. H_2 oxidation requires an electron acceptor and with intact systems, this will usually be O_2. Other acceptors, either natural or artificial, will be required in some cases. For example, when working with purified *Azotobacter vinelandii* hydrogenase, the electron acceptor cannot be O_2, as this will inactivate the enzyme (Kow and Burris 1984). The reaction is initiated by addition of H_2 to the vial. A small amount (0.1 to 1 kPa) is added, because H_2 oxidation will be monitored as a decrease in the amount of H_2 and the larger the initial concentration, the more time and sample will be required to register a significant change in that concentration. Gas samples are then

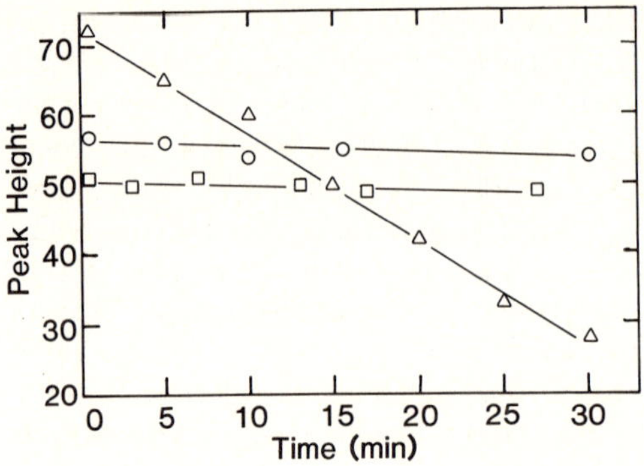

Fig. 2. Gas chromatographic determination of H_2 oxidation by soybean nodules. Vials with the contents described below were stoppered with a gas phase of air. Reactions were initiated by addition of 0.02 ml of H_2 to each vial. At the indicated times, 0.1-ml samples were removed from each vial and injected onto the gas chromatographic column. The peak height (in arbitrary units) for the H_2 peak is indicated on the figure. □, Control, no added material; ○, 1 g intact soybean nodules; △, 1 g crushed soybean nodules suspended in 1 ml buffer (100 m*M* potassium phosphate, pH 7.5). The different initial peak heights reflect the different amounts of material added to each vial

taken at appropriate intervals and analyzed. Throughout the assay time, samples with a liquid phase should be shaken vigorously (200 strokes min^{-1}) to ensure equilibration of the liquid and gas phases.

A typical result is shown in Fig. 2. The decrease in H_2 peak height for samples taken from the gas phase in contact with crushed nodules is indicative of H_2 oxidation. A control with no added biological material or with boiled material added should always be included as a check on the H_2 leak rate from the vial. An interesting problem associated with soybean root nodules harboring H_2-oxidizing bacteroids is revealed in this experiment. When the nodules remained intact, the rate of H_2 oxidation was not distinguishable from the leak rate. However, when the nodules were crushed and suspended in buffer, a readily measurable rate of H_2 oxidation was observed. Apparently, this is related to the limitation of respiration rates by the rate of O_2 supply in intact nodules such that H_2 oxidation does not add appreciably to or compete readily with the oxidation of carbon sources. In contrast, once crushed, O_2 is no longer rate-limiting for respiration, and H_2 oxidation can proceed much more rapidly.

In the example shown in Fig. 2, a rate of 0.41 μl H_2 consumed min^{-1} or 17.5 nmol min^{-1} was determined. Lower rates can be measured by decreasing the volume of the gas phase in the reaction vial, increasing the sample volume, and increasing the reaction times. This will provide adequate sensitivity for determination of H_2-oxidizing activity in most cases.

2.3 Spectrophotometric Assay of H_2-Oxidizing Activity

A very useful method for the determination of H_2-oxidizing activity in cell-free extracts is based on the coupling of H_2 oxidation to a suitable electron mediator. The electron mediator must either directly or indirectly accept electrons from hydrogenase and must afford a color change upon reduction. This color change, which is directly linked to H_2 oxidation, is monitored with a spectrophotometer. This assay, which is continuous and relatively simple, is particularly useful for routine assay of cell-free extracts and purified hydrogenase preparations where interfering reactions are minimal. The major disadvantage is that H_2 is not monitored directly, so other reactions which result in reduction of the electron mediator will interfere with measurement of H_2 oxidation. Furthermore, reoxidation of the electron mediator (e.g., by O_2) can result in an underestimate of the rate of H_2 oxidation. It is for this reason that any measurement of H_2-oxidizing activity which employs an autooxidizable electron mediator must be carried out under anaerobic conditions. However, elaborate apparatuses for maintenance of anaerobic conditions are not required, and with a minimum of effort a system can be established for preparing anaerobic cuvettes.

The assays are carried out in cuvettes closed with a rubber stopper. Glass cuvettes are recommended and double-stoppered cuvettes should be used for critical work (Arp and Burris 1981). Plastic cuvettes can be used (i.e., Sarstead #67.749), although gas diffuses readily through the plastic so the cuvettes must be used immediately after they are prepared. Cuvettes containing 1.5 ml of an appropriate buffer plus 0.05 *M* methylene blue (as electron acceptor) are stoppered and then purged for 7 min with H_2 to remove O_2 and provide the substrate. This is accomplished by inserting a long needle attached to an H_2 gas train through the stopper and into the buffer. A vent needle inserted into the stopper serves as the outlet for the H_2 stream. A flow rate of 100 ml min^{-1} is used. The H_2 should be as free from O_2 as possible (see above for methods to remove O_2 from H_2). As the cuvette is prepared, the sample of interest, which must be either a suspension or solution, is also made anaerobic by gentle purging with an anaerobic gas stream. The reaction is initiated by addition of an aliquot of the sample to the cuvette. Any color change is monitored continuously in the spectrophotometer. For methylene blue, which becomes colorless upon reduction, we use an extinction coefficient of 32.8 mM^{-1} at 600 nm (Arp and Burris 1981).

To be useful in this spectrophotometric assay, an electron acceptor must be able to accept electrons from hydrogenase, either directly or indirectly, and it must undergo a color change upon reduction. Additional properties that enhance the usefulness of acceptors are (1) high solubilities in aqueous buffers, (2) ability to permeate membranes (which is especially important when whole cells or membrane particles are assayed), and (3) a low apparent Km such that the concentrations required to saturate the reaction rate are reasonable low. Because it meets all of these criteria, methylene blue has been most generally useful in these assays. Other useful acceptors in certain circumstances include benzyl or methyl viologen, phenazine methosulfate, dichlorophenol indophenol, and ferricyanide. The ideal electron acceptor would also be specific for hydrogenase and would not be reduced by any other reaction other than H_2 oxidation. However, such an electron acceptor has not been identified.

In general, it is difficult to measure rates of H_2 oxidation in whole cells or bacteroids using the spectrophotometric technique. First, the electron acceptors may not readily penetrate the cell. Second, large amounts of cells as needed to measure low rates will result in considerable light scattering and increased initial optical densities, possibly beyond the useful limit of the spectrometer. Third, and most significant, the normal metabolic oxidation of endogenous respiratory substrates can also lead to reduction of artificial electron acceptors. As a result, comparison to controls lacking H_2 is essential. In an experiment with intact *A. vinelandii* whole cells, the rate of methylene blue reduction in the absence of H_2 was still 68% of the rate in the the presence of H_2, even though these cells have a substantial H_2-oxidizing capability. To limit the interference from endogenous substrates, inhibitors of their oxidation which have no effect on hydrogenase can be included. When we used potassium fluoride and EDTA to inhibit endogenous substrate respiration, as suggested by Postgate et al. (1982), the rate of methylene blue reduction in the absence of H_2 was decreased to 40% of the rate in the presence of H_2. For soybean bacteroids, iodoacetate and malonic acid are useful inhibitors of respiration which have little or no effect on hydrogenase (Emerich et al. 1979).

2.4 Amperometric Determination of H_2-Oxidizing Activity

In 1971, Wang et al. first described an amperometric method for continuously monitoring a change in the H_2 concentration in solution and applied the technique to measurement of H_2 evolution rates of algae. The method is a variation on the well-established use of a Clark-style electrode interfaced to a polarimeter to measure the concentration of O_2 in solution. When measuring H_2, the H_2 passes through the gas permeable membrane covering the platinum and silver electrodes and is oxidized at the platinum surface. For the oxidation to proceed, the polarity of the electrode is held at +600 mV with respect to the Ag reference electrode. As H_2 is oxidized to H_2O, a current is produced with a magnitude proportional to the concentration of H_2 in solution. In the reaction, Ag^+ is reduced to elemental Ag, therefore, the electrode must be "preconditioned" (see below) before use, a process which presumably involves coating the Ag electrode with AgCl.

The amperometric determination of H_2 oxidation is continuous and can provide excellent sensitivity under optimal conditions. The electrode can actually be used in either the liquid or gas phase. The disadvantage of this method is that the stability of the response to H_2 and reproducibility of the sensitivity from day to day can be problematic. However, we find that these problems can be kept to a minimum if the electrode is properly preconditioned.

The reaction vessel consists of a Clark-style electrode inserted into a chamber as described by Wang et al. (1971). Typically, the chambers will have a volume of 1 to 2 ml and are sealed by insertion of a ground glass fitting made of capillary tubing to allow additions to the chamber. (The use of capillary tubing eliminates the need for the ground glass stopper described by Wang et al. 1971.) Rapid stirring of the solution in the chamber is essential to avoid H_2 concentration gradients at the membrane surface. Wang et al. (1971) used a Keithley 150A microvolt-ammeter to polarize the electrode and measure the current which resulted from oxidation of H_2. Hanus et al. (1980) have published a schematic diagram of an inexpensive device used to provide the polarizing potential. A Keithley

602 solid state electrometer was used to measure the current. Sweet et al. (1980) have described and provided a schematic diagram for a device which provides both the polarizer and the amplifier.

"Preconditioning" the electrode is essential. Presumably, this step provides a coating of AgCl on the silver reference electrode. Several devices and methods for this preconditioning have been described (Wang et al. 1971; Hanus et al. 1980; Sweet et al. 1980). We have adopted the preconditioning methods described by Sweet et al. (1980). With this procedure, the electrode response is stable and reasonably reproducible from day to day.

Concentrations of H_2 in solution from as low as 0.1 μM to nearly 1 mM can be measured. The response is not always strictly proportional to H_2 concentration over this wide concentration range, and some correction for this nonlinearity may be necessary. The response to changes in H_2 concentrations in the chamber is rapid, though not immediate. For a large change in H_2 concentration, 90% of the response will occur in the first few seconds. To calibrate the electrode response, aliquots of H_2-saturated H_2O are injected into the chamber to bring the H_2 concentration to the desired level and the electrode response corresponding to this level is recorded. This is repeated at several concentrations as a check on the linearity of the electrode response.

A reaction may be initiated either by addition of H_2 (we typically add 50 µl of H_2-saturated H_2O to a 1.6-ml chamber) or addition of the enzyme source (cells, cell-free extract, etc.). The observed rate must be corrected for the rate which occurs in the absence of an enzyme source. The low rate of signal decrease in the absence of a hydrogenase is a result of three factors: leakage of H_2 from the electrode chamber, consumption of H_2 by the electrode, and loss of sensitivity by the H_2 electrode. The latter is usually only a problem if the preconditioning steps are not followed. One practical consideration in the use of an H_2 electrode is the elimination of all gas bubbles from the chamber during measurement of H_2 oxidation in the liquid phase. Because H_2 is about 50 times more soluble in the gas phase than in the liquid phase, even small bubbles clinging to the side of the chamber can provide a space for H_2 to concentrate and result in a decrease in the solution concentration.

2.5 Use of $^3H_2$ in the Measurement of Hydrogenase Activity

Because there is a useful radioisotope of hydrogen – tritium – it is not surprising that several hydrogenase assays have been developed that utilize this isotope. In two such assays, tritium incorporation from $^3H_2$ into H_2O is measured via liquid scintillation counting. In one variation, $^3H_2$ oxidation (i.e., in the presence of an electron acceptor) results in the formation of $^1H^3HO$. However, when reactions are carried out in the absence of an electron acceptor, tritium incorporation into water still occurs, but via an exchange mechanism where formation of $^1H^3HO$ is coupled to formation of $^1H^3H$ and H_2 (Krasna 1979). For H_2-oxidizing hydrogenases, exchange is usually much slower than H_2 oxidation. Therefore, it is important to make the distinction between the two assays and decide which reaction will be followed.

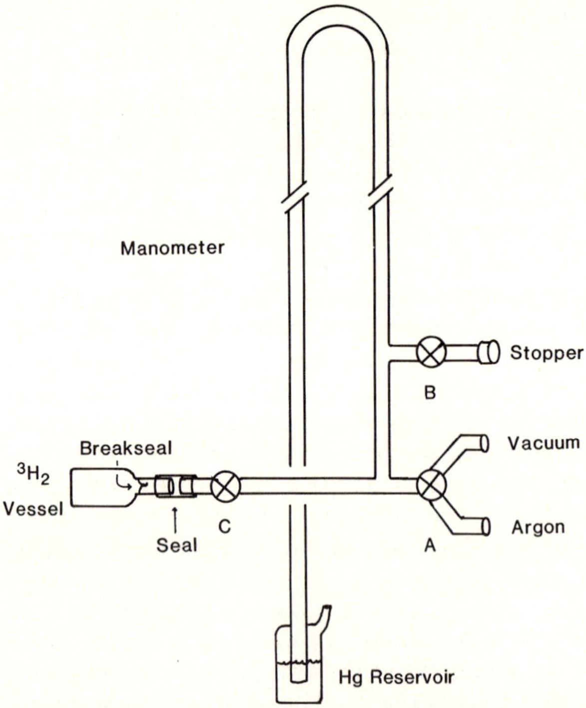

Fig. 3. Diagram of a manifold used for dispensing $^3H_2$ gas. Considerations on the use of the manifold are given in the text. Stopcock A can be positioned to a vacuum source or argon source or left in a closed position. Stopcock B opens to the stopper from which gas samples are removed. The stopper is replaceable and made of butyl rubber which has low permeability to gases and can accept a syringe needle. Needle valve C should be capable of fine flow regulation. The distance between the Hg reservoir and the top of the manometer should be 1 m

Gingras et al. (1963) first used the incorporation of tritium from $^3H_2$ into water to measure H_2 exchange in whole cells. Lim (1978) further developed the assay and used it to determine hydrogenase activity in free-living cultures of *Rhizobium japonicum*. Bethlenfalvay and Phillips (1979) adapted this assay for measurement of tritium exchange in whole nodules. Fallon (1982) measured $^3H_2$ uptake by soils, presumably mediated by H_2-oxidizing bacteria, and studied the influences of pH, temperature, and moisture on this uptake. Schink et al. (1983) applied the tritium exchange assay to viable cells in extreme environments. Anand and Krasna (1965) developed a variation of the exchange assay in which ^3H-H_2O was converted to $^1H^3H$ in the gas phase which was monitored in an ionization chamber.

Hydrogenase assays based on tritium usually have the advantages of high sensitivity and absence of interfering reactions. However, setting up the apparatuses to safely and economically handle small quantities of radioactive gases can be a particular challenge. Furthermore, some manufacturers who offer $^3H_2$ provide it only in lots of 1 Ci or more. Nonetheless, once these obstacles are overcome, tritium-based assays can be very useful.

Figure 3 is a diagram of a manifold that can be used to dispense small quantities of $^3H_2$ as required for hydrogenase assays. The manifold may be of metal and/or glass, but must be constructed such that it is gas and vacuum tight. The vessel in which the $^3H_2$ is supplied is sealed to the manifold upstream of needle valve C. The seal between the vessel and manifold must be gas and vacuum tight. Then, with C and B open, the entire manifold, up to but not including the $^3H_2$ vessel, is then placed under a vacuum by opening stopcock A to the vacuum. Stopcock B is opened to the septum stopper and needle valve C is opened to the break seal (or other seal) of the tritium vessel. Stopcock A and needle valve C are then closed and the seal on the tritium vessel is broken. The tritium gas will now fill the space up to needle valve C where it will reside as long as it lasts or the manifold is in use. A small amount of gas is then dispensed into the manifold by carefully opening needle valve C. We typically allow about 4 mm (0.5 kPa) to enter the manifold. Needle valve C is then closed and stopcock A is opened to the argon inlet to allow the manifold to just fill up to atmospheric pressure. After closing stopcock A, the manifold should be left for about 1 h to allow the $^3H_2$ and argon to reach an equilibrium mixture in the manifold. Then, gas can be dispensed through the stopper in front of stopcock B by use of a gas-tight syringe. When the manifold is not in use, stopcock B is closed to prevent leakage through the stopper, which will be the largest source of leakage into and out of the manifold. Also, with B closed, the stopper can be replaced when necessary. The space enclosed by Stopcock B and the stopper is simply flushed with argon before opening B to initiate re-equilibration. Only infrequent filling of the manifold from the original vessel should be necessary.

As an alternative to carrier-free tritium as supplied commercially, small amounts of $^3H^1H$ (in H_2) can be generated from ^3H-H_2O by treatment with lithium metal (Hallahan et al. 1986). This method has the advantage that smaller amounts of gas can be generated as needed. It has the disadvantage that carrier-free $^3H_2$ cannot be generated and any H_2 in the gas will competitively inhibit the binding of $^1H^3H$.

Any ^3H-H_2O vapor present in the $^3H_2$ gas will be trapped in the liquid phase when the assay is initiated, thereby producing a large background of radioactivity against which to measure an increase due to hydrogenase activity. Therefore, it is necessary to remove this water vapor prior to using the gas for the assay. A simple and effective method is to prepare a stock mixture of $^3H_2$ in a vial containing a small amount of water. The ^3H-H_2O gas will be trapped in the liquid phase. By including an O_2 trap in the liquid phase (e.g., $Na_2S_2O_4$ in buffer) this step can also serve to remove O_2 from the $^3H_2$. We normally prepare a stock mixture of $^3H_2$ and argon by removing 100 µl of gas from the manifold and injecting it into a vial (2 ml volume) containing argon and 0.2 ml of buffer that is 10 mM in $Na_2S_2O_4$. After incubation for a few minutes, the gas is ready for use.

The following is a typical protocol for a tritium assay. One ml of buffer or other reaction mixture suitable for the reaction to be measured is placed in a stoppered, 7-ml serum vial with an appropriate gas phase. From the $^3H_2$ stock mixture described above, 200 µl of gas is injected into the vial. The reaction is initiated by addition of the hydrogenase source. The vials must be shaken (about 200 cycles min^{-1}) during the assay to ensure equilibration of the gas and liquid phases. Samples (10 μl) of the liquid phase are taken every few minutes and injected into vials containing 5 ml of liquid scintillation cocktail. Vigorous shaking of the cocktail will cause the small amount of $^3H_2$ in the sample to escape the liquid phase such that it will not contribute to the count. The samples are counted in a liquid scintillation counter and the increase in counts with time provides an indication of the relative rates.

To convert the increase in counts to a rate in μmol min^{-1}, it is necessary to obtain a ^3H-H_2O sample of known specific radioactivity and determine the efficiency with which it is counted under the conditions of the assay. In the protocol described, the $^3H_2$ pressure in the assay vial will be about 10^{-5} atm, or 1 Pa, which corresponds to a solution concentration of $^3H_2$ near 7 n*M*. Clearly, at this concentration, the exchange and oxidation assays will not be kinetically saturated with respect to the $^3H_2$ concentration. If saturation is necessary, then the $^3H_2$ should be diluted with $^1H_2$ to the desired total H_2 concentration. However, it should be noted that $^1H_2$ will compete with $^3H_2$ in the tritium assays, thus the actual rate will be seen to decrease. Furthermore, an isotopic fractionation between $^1H_2$ and $^3H_2$ may occur, especially in the exchange assay. For this reason, the ratio of $^1H_2$ to $^3H_2$ should be kept constant.

2.6 Mass Spectrometric Measurements of H_2 Metabolism

Mass spectrometry provides a versatile method for the detection and quantitation of not only H_2, but of other gases in solution or in the gas phase. With mass spectrometry, the protocols developed will be specific to the investigators, the equipment available to them, and the questions they are attempting to answer, thereby making it difficult to provide any sort of generalized protocol or description of the technique. Therefore, the examples below were chosen to demonstrate the utility of mass spectrometry and to cite those publications which emphasized method development.

Lespinat et al. (1978) used a direct mass spectrometric determination to measure the relationship between hydrogenase and nitrogenase in a culture of *Azotobacter chroococcum*. They described the use of $^2H_2$ to monitor H_2 uptake simultaneously with the production of H_2 by nitrogenase. The ability to discriminate stable isotopes is one of the strengths of the mass spectrometric technique. Jouanneau et al. (1980) described a culture vessel which can be used for the direct and continuous monitoring of H_2 production or recycling. They applied the method to cultures and cell extracts of *Rhodopseudomonas capsulata*. These authors describe many of the considerations involved in the use of diffusion inlets to mass spectrometers and the simultaneous measurement of several gases. Berlier et al. (1985) and Berlier and Lespinat (1980) have described in detail a reaction cell they designed which provides a diffusion inlet from the chamber to the mass spectrometer. The use of this facility in measurements of the exchange, H_2 oxidation, and H_2 evolution reactions of hydrogenase were described, as were a number of kinetic considerations relevant to the measurements.

Many of the studies listed above have taken advantage of the stable isotope of hydrogen – deuterium. In a variation of the tritium exchange assay described above, one can monitor the exchange of deuterons from $^2H_2$ with protons from water to form $^1H^2H$ or $^1H_2$ in the gas phase. With the mass spectrometer, it is possible to monitor the rates of formation of each independently. This assay was first described by Farkas et al. (1934) and has since been used by a number of investigators (e.g., see detailed description by Krasna 1978). Experiments of this nature have provided evidence of a heterolytic, rather than homolytic, cleavage of H_2 during catalysis (Krasna 1979).

2.7 Other Methods for Measuring Activity of Hydrogenases

A number of other techniques have been developed for measurement of hydrogenase activities. Although these have not gained general acceptance as routine assays of hydrogenase activity, they are of interest and can often provide information that cannot be gained in any other way.

2.7.1 Catalysis of Para-H_2 Conversion

Normal H_2 at temperatures above 273 K is a mixture of two nuclear spin isomers, namely para-H_2 (about 25%) and ortho-H_2 (about 75%). However, a sample can be enriched in para-H_2 by incubation over a sutiable catalyst (e.g., finely divided palladium or platinum metals or charcoal) at low temperatures. When raised to room temperatures in the absence of the catalyst, the conversion to an equilibrium mixture will be slow. Hydrogenase can also catalyze this conversion and this provides the basis of another assay for hydrogenase activity. The determination of the amount of each isomer in a sample of H_2 is carried out in a thermal conductivity cell and is based on the different rotational, specific heats of para-H_2 and ortho-H_2. The method, apparatuses, and theory have been thoroughly discussed by Krasna (1978). This reaction and the isotope exchange reactions are considered to be "virtual" reactions of hydrogenase because they require only activation of the dihydrogen and interaction with the solvent protons. They do not require transfer of electrons to or from an electron mediator. They are also equally applicable to whole cells, cell-free extracts, or purified enzyme preparations.

2.7.2 Enzymatic Electrode Cell Method

Yagi et al. (1975) have described a method in which hydrogenase activity is measured in an enzymatic electric cell. The current density obtained as the H_2-H^+ equilibrium is approached is proportional to the amount of hydrogenase present. Basically, the cell consists of two chambers connected by a salt bridge. One chamber contains a calomel reference eletrode and the other cell contains a glassy carbon tube that serves as the measuring electrode and is the conduit through which H_2 is bubbled into the solution containing hydrogenase and the electron acceptor. As H_2 oxidation proceeds, electrons flow from the solution containing hydrogenase to the reference electrode. The current density of this electron flow is measured and is proportional to the amount of hydrogenase in solution.

2.7.3 pH-Stat Method

With the appropriate choice of conditions, either H_2 oxidation or H_2 evolution can be accompanied by release of protons into the solvent. Aguirre et al. (1983) have developed a method in which the protons produced are automatically titrated by a pH-stat device. By recording the amount of titrant required, one can monitor the level of hydrogenase activity. This method is limited to purified hydrogenase preparations where all pH changes can be attributed to hydrogenase catalysis. It has the advantage that the pH is maintained constant even in the presence of very low buffer concentrations.

2.7.4 Detection of Hydrogen by Conversion of Mercury Oxide to Mercury Vapor

Seiler et al. (1980) described a method for detection of H_2 which measures the reduction of HgO to Hg vapor coupled to the oxidation of H_2. The mercury vapor is quantified in an atomic absorption spectrometer. This method provides a remarkable level of sensitivity relative to gas chromatography. Concentrations of H_2 as low as 1 ppb can be detected. Conrad and Seiler (1979) used this technique to demonstrate that untreated soil could consume H_2 present at only 0.7 ppm in the gas phase and that this capacity was lost when the soil was autoclaved. Interestingly, the capacity to consume H_2 at these low levels could not be reconstituted by treatment of the soil with suspensions of common H_2-oxidizing bacteria, suggesting that as yet unidentified bacteria or soil enzymes are responsible for oxidation of H_2 at atmospheric levels of H_2.

3 Methods Other Than Activity Determinations

In this section, a number of methods applicable to the study of H_2-oxidizing organisms other than activity determinations are presented, along with references to more detailed discussions. With regard to isolation of microorganisms from the soil and other sources, Aragno and Schlegel (1981) have detailed the considerations necessary and provided a number of basal media useful in enrichment cultures of H_2-oxidizing microorganisms. They also provide a comprehensive discussion of how to grow these microorganisms in culture, including diagrams of culture vessels and apparatuses useful in preparing mixtures of gases used to support the growth of these gas-utilizing microorganisms.

Considerable progress has been made in the last few years in the area of the molecular biology of hydrogenases and H_2-oxidizing microorganisms. The only methods in these investigations unique to H_2 oxidation involve the methods for the selection of mutants which have lost the H_2-oxidizing phenotype (HUP-) or which are regulatory mutants. A number of publications have appeared which detail the selection methods used in the isolation of these mutants (Postgate et al. 1982; Haugland et al. 1983; Lambert et al. 1985; Tichy and Lotz 1985; Schlegel and Meyer 1985). All are based on colorimetric assays of hydrogenase activity and are applied to individual colonies on culture plates, individual nodules, or bacteroid suspensions.

A substantial number of hydrogenases have now been purified to homogeneity. Unfortunately, no general purification schemes have emerged which are applicable to all hydrogenases, nor is it at all likely that any such scheme will emerge. This stems in part from the different intracellular locations of hydrogenases. However, even for the membrane-bound hydrogenases which require treatment with a detergent for release from the membrane, no one detergent has been found useful for all hydrogenases. Schneider et al. (1983) prepared a Procion red-agarose affinity matrix and demonstrated its applicability in the purification of a number of hydrogenases. A number of publications have considered and reviewed the purification of hydrogenases. Kovacs et al. (1985) considered the purification of hydrogenase of *Thiocapsa rosepersicina* by a number of methods. Mortenson (1978) provided a detailed account of the purification of hydrogenase from *Clostridium pasteurianum* and Krasna (1978) described a purification scheme for *Chromatium* hydrogenase. Adams et al. (1981) provide a general accounting of the methods used and considerations pertinent to the purification of hydrogenases. One difficulty encountered with a number of purifications is the sensitivity of active hydrogenases to O_2. In many cases, this problem is circumvented by the purification of an O_2-stable but inactive form of the hydrogenase which can later be activated. In other cases, the hydrogenases must be purified strictly in the absence of O_2 to prevent irreversible loss of activity.

Because most H_2-oxidizing hydrogenases are linked to electron transport in the microorganisms that express them, there has been considerable interest in determining the pathway of electron flow from H_2 to the terminal oxidant, usually O_2 (see reviews cited in Sect. 1). One of the most useful techniques has been that of redox difference spectroscopy, coupled with the judicious choice of oxidant and reductant and with the use of various respiratory inhibitors to elucidate the pathway of electron flow. However, this technique is essentially limited to investigations of cytochromes, with some application to flavoproteins. Podzuweit and Arp (1985) developed a method for redox difference spectroscopy in which sedimented respiratory membranes are squeezed between two gas-permeable foils. These "sandwiches" are then placed in the light path of a spectrophotometer in a stoppered cuvette. Because both the reductant (H_2) and oxidant (O_2) are gases, one can alter the redox state of carriers in the membranes simply by changing the gas phase. An intermediate steady state can be obtained by using a mixture of H_2 and O_2. The great advantage of the sandwiches is that the optical signal to noise ratio is greatly enhanced, especially at lower wavelengths where light scattering is particularly problematic in membrane suspensions. In addition to cytochromes, this technique allows one to readily visualize the redox state (and extent of reduction) of ubiquinone in the membranes. Ubiquinone is an important branch point in the electron transport pathways found in many H_2-oxidizing microorganisms.

4 Summary

This chapter details some of the more commonly used methods for measurement of H_2-oxidizing activity associated with microorganisms and purified hydrogenases and provides references to several other methods used in investigations of H_2-oxidizing microorganisms. As the interest in H_2-oxidizing microorganisms and the hydrogenases which catalyze H_2 oxidation continue to increase, one can expect that the number of investigators studying these bacteria and enzymes will also increase. A natural consequence of this increased interest will be the adoption into many additional laboratories of the methods described here. Furthermore, we can expect new methods to be developed in support of continued investigations of H_2-oxidizing microorganisms.

Acknowledgments. Work in the author's laboratory pertaining to the development of methods for investigations of H_2-oxidizing microorganisms has been supported by grant No. DE-FG03-84ER13257 from the Department of Energy and by grant No. DMB-8506777 from the National Science Foundation.

References

Adams MWW, Mortenson LE, Chen J-S (1981) Hydrogenase. Biochim Biophys Acta 594:105–176

Aguirre R, Hatchikian EC, Monsan P (1983) Bidirectional measurement of hydrogenase activity by the pH-stat method. Anal Biochem 131:525–529

Anand SR, Krasna AI (1965) Catalysis of the H_2-HTO exchange by hydrogenase. A new assay for hydrogenase. Biochemistry 4:2747–2753

Aragno M, Schlegel HG (1981) The hydrogen-oxidizing bacteria. In: Starr MP, Stolp H, Truper HG, Balows A, Schlegel HG (eds) The prokaryotes: a handbook on habitats, isolation, and identification of bacteria, vol 1. Springer, Berlin Heidelberg New York, pp 865–893

Arp DJ (1985) H_2-oxidizing hydrogenase of aerobic N_2-fixing microorganisms. In: Ludden PW, Burris JE (eds) Nitrogen fixation and CO_2 metabolism. Elsevier, New York, pp 121–131

Arp DJ, Burris RH (1981) Kinetic mechanism of hydrogen-oxidizing hydrogenase from soybean nodule bacteroids. Biochemistry 20:2234–2240

Bagyinka NA, Zorin NA, Kovacs KL (1984) Unconsidered factors affecting hydrogenase activity measurement. Anal Biochem 142:7–15

Berlier YM, Lespinat PA (1980) Mass-spectrometric kinetic studies of the nitrogenase and hydrogenase activities in in-vivo cultures of *Azospirillum brasilense* Sp. 7. Arch Microbiol 125:67–72

Berlier YM, Dimon B, Fauque G, Lespinat PA (1985) Direct mass-spectrometric monitoring of the metabolism and isotope exchange in enzymic and microbiological investigations. In: Degn H, Cox RP, Toftlund H (eds) Gas enzymology. Reidel, Dordrecht Lancaster, pp 17–36

Bethlenfalvay GJ, Phillips DA (1979) Variation in nitrogenase and hydrogenase activity of Alaska pea root nodules. Plant Physiol 63:816–820

Conrad R, Seiler W (1979) The role of hydrogen bacteria during the decomposition of hydrogen by soil. FEMS Microbiol Lett 6:143–145

CRC Handbook of chemistry and physics (1970a) Weast RC (ed) Chemical Rubber Co., Cleveland, p E2

CRC Handbook of chemistry and physics (1970 b) Weast RC (ed) Chemical Rubber Co., Cleveland, p F47
Dawson RMC, Elliott DC, Elliott WH, Jones KM (1986) Data for biochemical research, 3rd edn. Clarendon, Oxford, pp 555–556
Dijk C van, Mayhew SG, Veeger C (1981) An analysis of activity determinations in a series of coupled redox reactions with special reference to hydrogenase. Eur J Biochem 114:201–207
Eisbrenner G, Evans HJ (1983) Aspects of hydrogen metabolism in nitrogen-fixing legumes and other plant-microbe associations. Annu Rev Plant Physiol 34:105–136
Emerich DW, Ruiz-Argueso T, Ching TM, Evans HJ (1979) Hydrogen-dependent nitrogenase activity and ATP formation in *Rhizobium japonicum* bacteroids. J Bacteriol 137:153–160
Evans HJ, Harker AR, Papen H, Russell SA, Hanus FJ, Zuber M (1987) Physiology, biochemistry, and genetics of the uptake hydrogenase in *Rhizobia.* Annu Rev Microbiol 41:335–361
Fallon RD (1982) Influences of pH, temperature, and moisture on gaseous tritium uptake in surface soils. Appl Environ Microbiol 44:171–178
Farkas A, Farkas L, Yudkin J (1934) The decomposition of sodium formate by *Bacterium coli* in the presence of heavy water. Proc R Soc London B Ser 115:373–379
Fernandez VM (1983) An electrochemical cell for reduction of biochemicals: its application to the study of the effect of pH and redox potential on the activity of hydrogenases. Anal Biochem 130:54–59
Gingras G, Goldsby RA, Calvin M (1963) Carbon dioxide metabolism in hydrogen-adapted *Scenedesmus.* Arch Biochem Biophys 100:178–184
Hallahan DL, Fernandez VM, Hatchikian EC, Hall DO (1986) Differential inhibition of catalytic sites in *Desulfovibrio gigas* hydrogenase. Biochimie 68:49–54
Hanus FJ, Carter KR, Evans HJ (1980) Techniques for measurement of hydrogen evolution. Meth Enzymol 69:731–739
Haugland RA, Hanus FJ, Cantrell MA, Evans HJ (1983) Rapid colony screening method for identifying hydrogenase activity in *Rhizobium japonicum.* Appl Environ Microbiol 45:892–897
Hausinger RP (1987) Nickel utilization by microorganisms. Microbiol Rev 51:22–42
Jost W (1960) Diffusion. Academic Press, New York London, p 475
Jouanneau Y, Kelley BC, Berlier Y, Lespinat PA, Vignais PM (1980) Continuous monitoring, by mass spectrometry, of H_2 production and recycling in *Rhodopseudomonas capsulata.* J Bacteriol 143:628–636
Kovacs KL, Tigyi G, Alfonz H (1985) Purification of hydrogenase by fast protein liquid chromatography and by conventional separation techniques: a comparative study. Prep Biochem 15:321–334
Kow YW, Burris RH (1984) Purification and properties of membrane-bound hydrogenase from *Azotobacter vinelandii.* J Bacteriol 159:564–569
Krasna AI (1978) Oxygen-stable hydrogenase and assay. Meth Enzymol 53:296–314
Krasna AI (1979) Hydrogenase: properties and applications. Enzym Microbiol Technol 1:165–172
Lambert GR, Hanus FJ, Russell SA, Evans HJ (1985) Determination of the hydrogenase status of individual legume nodules by a methylene blue reduction assay. Appl Environ Microbiol 50:537–539
Lespinat PA, Gerster R, Berlier Y (1978) Direct mass-spectrometric determination of the relationship between respiration, hydrogenase and nitrogenase activities in *Azotobacter chroococcum.* Biochimie 60:339–341
Lim ST (1978) Determination of hydrogenase in free-living cultures of *Rhizobium japonicum* and energy efficiency of soybean nodules. Plant Physiol 62:609–611
Maier RJ (1986) Biochemistry, regulation, and genetics of hydrogen oxidation in *Rhizobium.* CRC Crit Rev Biotech 3:17–38
Mortenson LE (1978) Purification and properties of hydrogenase from *Clostridium pasteurianum.* Meth Enzymol 53:287–296

Mortenson LE, Chen JS (1974) Hydrogenase. In: Nielands JB (ed) Microbial iron metabolism, a comprehensive treatise. Academic Press, New York London, pp 231–282

Nakos G, Mortenson L (1971) Purification and properties of hydrogenase, an iron-sulfur protein, from *Clostridium pasteurianum* W5. Biochim Biophys Acta 227:576–583

Odom JM, Peck HD Jr. (1984) Hydrogenase, electron-transfer proteins, and energy coupling in the sulfate-reducing bacteria *Desulfovibrio*. Annu Rev Microbiol 38:551–592

Podzuweit HG, Arp DJ (1985) Difference spectroscopy with respiratory membranes of an H_2-oxidizing microorganism layered between two gas-permeable, plastic foils: a procedure that allows measurements in the ultraviolet range. Anal Biochem 151:487–494

Postgate JR, Patricia Partridge CD, Robson RL, Simpson FB, Yates MG (1982) A method for screening for hydrogenase negative mutants of *Azotobacter chroococcum*. J Gen Microbiol 128:905–908

Schink B, Lupton FS, Zeikus JG (1983) Radioassay for hydrogenase activity in viable cells and documentation of aerobic hydrogen-consuming bacteria living in extreme environments. Appl Environ Microbiol 45:1491–1500

Schlegel HG, Meyer M (1985) Isolation of hydrogenase regulatory mutants of hydrogen-oxidizing bacteria by a colony-screening method. Arch Microbiol 141:377–383

Schlegel HG, Schneider K (eds) (1978 a) Introductory report: distribution and physiological role of hydrogenases in microorganisms. In: Hydrogenases: their catalytic activity, structure and function. Göltze, Göttingen, pp 15–44

Schlegel HG, Schneider K (eds) (1978 b) Hydrogenases: their catalytic activity, structure and function. Göltze, Göttingen, pp 452

Schneider K, Pinkwart M, Jochim K (1983) Purification of hydrogenases by affinity chromatography on procion red-agarose. Biochem J 213:391–398

Seiler W, Giehl H, Roggendorf P (1980) Detection of carbon monoxide and hydrogen by conversion of mercury oxide to mercury vapor. Atmosph Technol 12:40–45

Stephenson M, Stickland LH (1931) XXVII. Hydrogenase: a bacterial enzyme activating molecular hydrogen. I. The properties of the enzyme. Biochem J 25:205–214

Sweet WJ, Houchins JP, Rosen PR, Arp DJ (1980) Polarographic measurement of H_2 in aqueous solutions. Anal Biochem 107:337–340

Tichy HV, Lotz W (1985) Screening method for the detection of uptake hydrogenase activity of *Rhizobium leguminosarum* bacteroids. FEMS Microbiol Lett 27:107–109

Umbreit WW, Burris RH, Stauffer JF (1972) Manometric and biochemical techniques, 5th edn. Burgess, Minneapolis, p 62

Vignais PM, Henry MF, Sim E, Kell DB (1981) The electron transport system and hydrogenase of *Paracoccus dinitrificans*. Curr Top Bioenerget 12:115–196

Vignais PM, Colbeau A, Willison JC, Jouanneau Y (1985) Hydrogenase, nitrogenase, and hydrogen metabolism in the photosynthetic bacteria. Adv Microbiol Physiol 26:155–234

Wang R, Healey FP, Myers J (1971) Amperometric measurement of hydrogen evolution in *Chlamydomonas*. Plant Physiol 48:108–110

Yagi T, Goto M, Nakano K, Kimura K, Inokuchi H (1975) A new assay method for hydrogenase based on an enzymic electrode reaction: the enzymic electric cell method. J Biochem 78:443–454

Methane Estimation for Methanogenic and Methanotrophic Bacteria

M. R. SMITH and L. BARESI

1 Introduction

Methanogenic and methanotrophic bacteria frequently occur in the same habitats, the methanogens producing methane and the methanotrophs consuming the methane produced by the methanogens. The activities of both bacterial groups can be monitored by measuring methane in the atmospheres of cultures and ecosystem samples. However, there is a greater reliance on methane measurement for methanogenic than for methanotrophic bacteria. In this chapter, we cover methods for estimating methane and associated gases. A few specialized methods for each group will also be considered.

Except for methane and analytical methods for measuring gases, the two groups of bacteria have little in common (Table 1). Methanogens are strictly an-

Table 1. Some characteristics of methanotrophic and methanogenic bacteria

Attribute	Methanotrophs [a]	Methanogens [b]
Morphology	Rods, cocci, vibrios	Rods, cocci, spirilla, filaments, sarcinalike masses
Gram stain	Negative	Positive, negative or variable
Classification	Eubacteria	Archaebacteria
Cell wall types	Peptidoglycan (Eubacterial)	Pseudomurine, protein, heteropolysaccharide
Metabolism	Strictly aerobic, cytochromes	Strictly anaerobic, cytochromes in some species
Energy and carbon sources	Methane, methanol, dimethyl ether, methyl formate, dimethyl carbonate	H_2 plus CO_2, H_2 plus methanol, formate, methylamines, methanol, acetate
Other carbon sources	CO_2, acetate, some amino acids	CO_2, acetate, amino acids
Catabolic products	Carbon dioxide	Methane or methane plus carbon dioxide
TCA cycle	Incomplete (type I) or or complete (type II)	Incomplete, missing part varies with species
Carbon assimilation pathways	Ribulose monophosphate pathways (type I) or serine pathway (type II)	TCA cycle, gluconeogenesis
Resting cells	Cysts (type I) or exospores (type II)	

[a] Whittenbury et al. (1974); Wolfe and Higgins (1979); Whittenbury and Dalton (1981).
[b] Balch et al. (1979); Mah and Smith (1981); Jones et al. (1987).

aerobic, methanotrophs are strictly aerobic. The methanogens catabolize only a few C_1 substrates and acetate, methanotrophs may cometabolize a wide variety of substrates. Each group possesses unique catabolic enzyme systems and coenzymes; few catabolic enzymes are present in both groups.

In addition to the characteristics listed in Table 1, methanotrophic bacteria can oxidize (by cometabolism) carbon monoxide, n-alkanes, n-alkenes, and aromatic compounds to alcohols, acids, ketones, and organic oxides (Ferenci 1974; Ferenci et al. 1975; Wolfe and Higgins 1979; Dalton 1980; Hou et al. 1980; Imai et al. 1986). Methanogens may produce ethane, ethylene, and acetylene from bromoethane, dibromoethane, dichloroethane, and 1,2-dibromoethylene (Belay and Daniels 1987). They also anaerobically oxidize methane (at low rates, Zehnder and Brock 1979) or carbon monoxide (Daniels et al. 1977; Nelson and Ferry 1984) to carbon dioxide, and produce small amounts of carbon monoxide (Conrad and Thauer 1983) during methanogenesis.

Catabolic pathways used by methanogenic and methanotrophic bacteria are entirely different. Methanogens anaerobically reduce CO_2 or methyl groups to methane or cleave acetate to methane plus carbon dioxide. Methanotrophic bacteria use molecular oxygen to oxidize methane to carbon dioxide via methanol, formaldehyde, and formate. The intermediates are oxidized by the action of dehydrogenases, or by a dissimilatory ribulose monophosphate pathway.

2 Cultivation

Detailed methods for cultivating methanogenic and methanotrophic bacteria are given elsewhere (Whittenbury et al. 1970; Balch et al. 1979; Hanson 1980; Mah and Smith 1981; Whittenbury and Dalton 1981) and will be described only briefly here to give the reader an idea of the circumstances under which analytical procedures are performed.

Methanogenic bacteria are typically grown in small volumes in liquid media enclosed in an oxygen-free atmosphere in sealed serum bottles or test tubes. Balch et al. (1979) described a specially designed test tube and rubber stopper for holding gases under pressure and convenient for holding small (5–10 ml) culture volumes. It is available from Bellco Glass, Inc., Vineland, N.J. The tube is also useful for growing cultures on hydrogen, which is usually added under pressure to the gas space. Hungate screw caps and septa (also available from Bellco Glass, Inc.) can be used with ordinary screw-capped test tubes for cultivating methanogens.

Nearly all operations with methanogenic bacteria require exclusion of oxygen and are carried out in an anaerobic glove box or under a stream of oxygen-free gas. Needle and syringe methods are used for sampling culture gas spaces for gas composition, transferring cultures, and adding reagents to cultures, cell suspensions, and cell extracts because the methods are convenient for maintaining anaerobic conditions. The needles and syringes are flushed well with oxygen-free gas before performing operations requiring entry into the cultures.

Methanotrophic bacteria grow well on a gas mixture containing 30:70 methane:air and 1 to 2% CO_2 in stoppered flasks or bottles (Whittenbury et al.

1970; Whittenbury and Dalton 1981). Gas mixtures can be made by injecting methane and carbon dioxide into the gas space containing air. Silicone stoppers and septa (Suba-seal) are preferred over red rubber for sealing cultures because rubber contains inhibitory substances.

3 Methods for Estimating Methane

3.1 Sampling Procedures

Methane in the gas spaces of cultures, cell suspensions, cell extracts, and digester or ecosystem materials is most often monitored by gas chromatography. Isotopically labeled substrates may be incubated with cultures or ecosystem samples and the incorporation of radioactivity into methane and other gases, cell carbon, or cellular intermediates followed.

Gas space samples are taken with needles and syringes equipped with Teflon Mininert valves (Supelco, Inc., Bellafonte, Pa. or Pierce Chemical Company, Rockford, Ill.) or other gas-tight syringes. The syringe valve allows samples to be taken at a fixed volume for injection into a gas chromatograph. When using constant volume sampling, the quantity of gas in the gas space of a closed vessel is the product of the gas concentration ($\mu mol\ ml^{-1}$) and the volume of the gas space (ml). The vessel volume is measured before the vessel is used by filling the vessel with water and measuring the volume or weighing the water.

Methanogenic enrichment culture gas spaces are occasionally sampled at atmospheric pressure to prevent the gas pressure from methanogenesis from accumulating (Mah et al. 1978). The excess gas is first bled into a large capacity (50 ml) syringe and the volume recorded. The syringe should be lubricated with water or other low viscosity lubricant. A gas sample for gas chromatography is then taken by needle and syringe and injected into the gas chromatograph. The quantity of gas present is the sum of the gas space volume and volume of excess gas multiplied by the gas concentration. If multiple bleedings are performed, the total gas produced is the sum of the moles of excess gas and the moles of gas in the gas space at the last bleeding.

3.2 Gas Chromatographic Analysis of Gases and Substrates

Gas chromatographic methods are largely empirical; the choice of chromatograph configuration and operating parameters depends on the desired sensitivity of the analysis, the type of material to be analyzed, and the number of substances to be analyzed. For more detailed information on the theory, operation, and applications of gas chromatographs the reader is referred to the literature (Purnell 1962; Littlewood 1970; Brewer et al. 1974; Cramers and McNair 1983; Journal of Gas Chromatography, Journal of Chromatography, Gas Chromatography Abstracts).

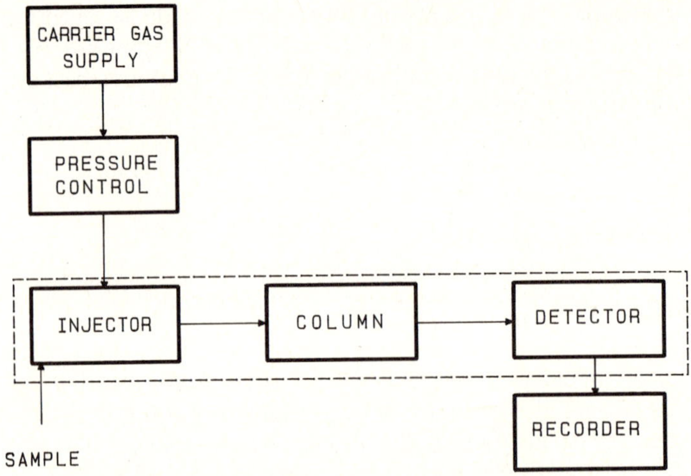

Fig. 1. Diagram of the components of a gas chromatographic system. Those components contained within the *broken-lined box* are part of the gas chromatograph

3.2.1 Apparatus

A gas chromatograph consists of an injector port, a column containing a medium for separating substances in samples, and a detector for detecting the separated substances as they elute from the column. A carrier gas from an external gas supply flows through the injector port, down the column, and through the detector where it exits (Fig. 1). The gas pressure and flow rates need to be regulated to achieve stable operation. The detector produces electrical signals in response to gases exiting the column and sends the signals to a chart recorder or other recording devices.

3.2.2 Operation

Substances are separated by partitioning between a mobile phase (the carrier gas stream) and a stationary phase (column-packing material). The column-packing material may be a solid (gas-solid chromatography, GSC) or a liquid coated on a solid support (gas-liquid chromatography, GLC). As substances in the carrier gas stream traverse the column, they separate, the amount of separation depending on the relative amount of time spent in the mobile phase compared to the stationary phase.

Samples are injected by needle and syringe through a septum at the injector port where they enter the carrier gas stream and are swept down the column to the detector. For common gases, the sample port temperature may be set to ambient temperatures; for nongaseous materials, the sample is converted to a gas by setting the injection port temperature to 25° to 50° C above the boiling point of the least volatile component.

An alternate method of introducing samples is loop injection, where a bypass loop, consisting of a fixed-volume chamber outside the carrier gas stream, is

Table 2. Absorbents used in gas chromatography traps[a]

Material		Substance absorbed at 20 °C
Drierite		Water
Molecular sieve	3 A	Water, ammonium
	4 A	Ethanol, hydrogen sulfide, carbon dioxide, C_2H_6, C_3H_6, water, methane
	5 A	Same as 4 A plus $n-C_4H_9OH$ and $n-C_4H_{10}$
	13 X	Same as 5 A plus mercaptans
Silica gel		Water, alcohols, phenols
Activated carbon		Volatile organics, vinyl chlorides, disulfides
Tenax-GC		Volatile organics

[a] Data from Breck (1964), Simmons (1972), Littlewood (1970), Bulletin 769 (1977), and NIOSH Manual (1974).

loaded with sample then brought into the carrier gas stream by opening and closing selected valves. The bypass loop method of injection is more cumbersome than the needle and syringe method but is also more accurate. Moreover, dilute samples can be concentrated by absorption onto a solid absorbent packed into the loop (absorption trap, see Table 2) or by condensation in the loop by cooling with liquid nitrogen (liquid nitrogen trap). The samples are then volatilized by heating the loop and using the valve system to discharge the samples into the carrier gas stream. Loop injection is used when quantities of methane or other materials are at low concentration, such as in marine anaerobic sediments (Reeburgh 1980; Alperin and Reeburg 1985).

Volatile substances injected into the carrier gas stream are separated by a gas-absorbent packing material in the column. Columns are constructed of glass, nickel, stainless steel, copper, or Teflon; the choice of material depends on requirements for resistance to corrosion, levels of absorption, and ease of handling. Glass columns are more inert than stainless steel or copper columns but are more fragile and difficult to handle. Teflon columns have many advantages of glass and stainless steel but are prone to deformation.

A large number of column-packing materials are available for separating simple gases (Table 3). Solid packing materials are most commonly used for gas analysis but their absorption characteristics give rise to asymmetrical peaks and nonlinear calibration curves. Calibration curves with solid absorbents should cover a broad, overlapping range of concentrations.

Column performance tends to deteriorate with the passage of time because of irreversible absorption of sample materials. Columns that have deteriorated (and also new columns) can be conditioned by increasing the temperature under a constant flow of gas to remove the absorbed substances.

Irreversible absorption may also be used to advantage; a precolumn of silica gel or molecular sieve (Table 2) can be used to absorb water, carbon dioxide, or other gases from the samples before they reach the separating column. This can shorten the analysis time for methane or hydrogen when using Porapak Q as the separating medium because there is no need to wait for the absorbed carbon dioxide (which elutes last) to elute.

Table 3. Examples of columns for separating H_2, O_2, N_2, CH_4, CO, and CO_2

Support[a]	Column type[b] and dimensions	Carrier gas and flow rate (cc min^{-1})	Column temperature (°C)
Molecular sieve 5 A (60/80 mesh)[c]	Gl; 16′ × 5 mm ID	He; 25	100
Chromosorb 102 (80/100 mesh)[d]	SS; 3′ × 1/8″	He; 20	60
Porapak Q (80/100 mesh)[c]	Cu; 40′ × 1/8″	N_2; 25	100
Carbosieve S (80/100 mesh)[f]	SS; 4.5′ × 18″	He; 40	35 to 175 25 min^{-1}
Carbosieve B (120/140 mesh)[f]	SS; 9′ × 1/8″	He; 60	100
Carbosphere (80/100 mesh)[g]	SS; 6′ × 1/8″	N_2; 45	225
Silica gel (60/120 mesh)[h]	SS; 5′ × 1/8″	N_2; 40	103

[a] Porapak Q and QS, Waters Associates, Framingham, Ma.; Molecular Sieve 5 A, Union Carbide Corp., Linde Div., Somerset, NJ; SP1200, FFAP, Carbosieve A&B and Carbowax, Supelco, Inc., Bellefonte, Pa.; Carbosphere and Silica Gel, Applied Science Labs., Deerfield, Il.; Chromosorb 101 and 102, Johns-Manville Corp., Denver, Co.
[b] SS stainless steel, Cu copper, Gl glass.
[c] Kyryacos and Boord (1957).
[d] Bulletin 760 A.
[e] Baresi et al. (1978).
[f] Bulletin 712B.
[g] Bulletin "Carbosphere".
[h] Taylor and Pirt (1977).

Column performance depends on the column dimensions, the type of packing material or concentration of liquid phase (GLC), the operating temperature, choice of carrier gas, and flow rates. These operating parameters are determined empirically, depending on the application, but some general rules apply:

1. Increasing the column length increases separation of components; the maximum length is limited by the maximum operating pressure. To some extent, the limit may be increased by using GLC capillary columns, narrow-bore tubes coated on the inside with a thin film of liquid phase material.
2. The capacity of a column is proportional to its cross-sectional area; larger diameters accommodate larger sample sizes.
3. Higher flow rates and temperatures shorten the analysis time but lower the resolution. Optimum performance is a compromise between the two.
4. Increasing carrier gas density (molecular weight) results in decreased flow rates. For rapid flows, use hydrogen or helium as the carrier gas.

3.2.3 Detectors

The choice of detector for an analysis depends on the type of material analyzed and the desired sensitivity of detection. The most commonly used detectors are thermal conductivity (TC), flame ionization, and electron capture (EC) detectors.

TC detectors compare the thermal conductivity of the carrier gas to that of a substance eluting from the column. This is accomplished by heated filaments maintained at constant temperature in two cells: a reference cell through which only carrier gas flows and a sensing cell through which column effluent flows. Gases passing over the filaments carry away heat, changing the electrical resistance of the filaments. The two filaments form part of a Wheatstone bridge circuit; a change in resistance of one of the filaments causes an imbalance in the bridge circuit and a flow of electrical current in the detection circuit.

TC detectors are less sensitive than ionization detectors but they can detect gases (e.g., CO_2, N_2, H_2, O_2, H_2O) not detectable by FI and do not destroy the samples. The choice of carrier gas is an important consideration with TC detection because the sensitivity of the detector depends on the difference between the thermal conductivity of the carrier and that of the separated component; methane analysis is more sensitive in helium or hydrogen carrier gas than in nitrogen. Carrier gases can be chosen to mask the presence of interfering substances in samples by selecting one that has a thermal conductivity similar to that of the interfering substances.

TC detection can also result in positive or negative peaks (e.g., above or below baseline), depending on the thermal conductivity of the substance relative to the carrier. In its extreme form, this bidirectional response may be manifested by "W"-shaped peaks, often seen when hydrogen is detected using a helium carrier (Keppler et al. 1957). This response is eliminated by reducing the detector temperature (Purnell 1962).

FI and EC detectors ionize the gas leaving the column; changes in ionization of the gas cause changes in the detector current, which are amplified and recorded. FI detectors ionize the gas sample by combustion in a hydrogen-oxygen flame; EC detectors use radioactive emissions to ionize sample gases. FI detection is used for analysis of methane, other combustible gases, and fatty acids or alcohols, where a broad range of sensitivity is required or where the substance is present at low concentration.

3.2.4 Calibration and Quantitation

Gas chromatographs are calibrated for gases by injecting varying volumes of a pure gas into the gas chromatograph then measuring the peak areas that appear on the chart recorder or other recording device. Alternately, the gas can be diluted in serum bottles full of carrier gas and injected at a fixed volume. A calibration curve is constructed by plotting moles of gas injected against peak area.

Many devices (digital and mechanical integrators, integrating amplifiers, computer systems) are available commercially for estimating peak areas. Other methods include cutting out peaks from the chart recording and weighing them, counting internal squares, using a planimeter, or triangulation. Estimates by triangulation are made using a triangle to approximate the sides of the peak then multiplying the width of the peak at half-peak height by the peak height.

Substances can also be calibrated by peak height rather than by peak area, especially if the peaks are sharp. This is more rapid than area determinations but usually produces nonlinear calibration curves.

Table 4. Gas chromatographic analysis of gases, methanol, and methyl amines[a]

Substance:	Methane Methanol	Methane Ethane	Methane Carbon dioxide	Methylamines Methanol
Temperature (°C):				
Injector	NS	145	NS	225
Column	125	100	100	55
Detector	NS	200	NS	250
Carrier gas:	Nitrogen	Helium	Helium	Nitrogen
Detector:[b]	FI	FI	TC	FI
Gas flow ($ml\ min^{-1}$)				
Carrier	40	40	50	20
Column type:	Glass		Copper	Glass
Size:	2.1 m × 4 mm		1 m × 2 mm	6 m × 2 mm
Packing:	Porapak Q (80/100)	Porapak Q	Carbosieve S (120/140)	Pennwalt 231 GC (120/140)
Sample size (μl):	NS	2 to 5	NS	2
Sample pretreatment:				25 μl 6 N KOH plus 200 μl cell-free culture
Reference:	Tonge et al. (1975)	Ribbons (1975)	Zinder et al. (1984)	Hippe et al. (1979)

[a] NS, not specified.
[b] FI flame ionization, TC thermal conductivity.

3.2.5 Measuring Gas Space Gases

Table 4 lists some examples of gas chromatograph configurations and operating conditions that have been used for the analysis of methane and other gases. Little or no sample preparation is required for gas space measurements. Samples up to 1 ml are injected for TC detection and about 10 to 50 μl for FI detection. Most of the common gases can be estimated simultaneously with methane using TC gas chromatographs set up for measuring methane. Dissolved methane, or methane in the gas space of an enzyme assay, is measured preferably by FI detection.

Some of the gas chromatographic systems given in Table 4 may be used for analysis of methanogenic substrates, such as methanol or methylamines in addition to methane. Analysis of methylamines requires adding a strong base to the solutions to convert the amines to their neutral forms before injecting samples of liquid into the gas chromatograph.

3.2.6 Measuring Dissolved Gases

Dissolved gases can be analyzed, provided gas concentrations are sufficiently high for detection, by directly injecting samples of liquid into a gas chromatograph. If gas concentrations are below the limit of detection, as in some ecosystem samples, the gases can sometimes be concentrated using loop injection (Sect. 3.2.2) or extraction with carbon dioxide followed by absorption. Other methods for dissolved gases include the use of gas-permeable membranes or tubing (Ohi et al. 1979), or gas-sensitive electrodes.

A syringe method for concentrating hydrogen and other gases by extraction with CO_2 followed by absorption of the CO_2 was described by Robinson et al. (1981):

A sample of rumen fluid (10 to 35 ml) containing a low concentration of dissolved hydrogen was drawn into a 50-ml syringe fitted with a one-way stopcock (Popper and Sons, Inc., New Hyde Park, N.Y.) and an 18-gauge needle. Carbon dioxide was drawn into the syringe, the syringe shaken vigorously for 1 min, then additional CO_2 was drawn in to replace that which dissolved. After shaking another minute, the gas phase was injected into a collection column containing a solution of 200 g NaCl plus 40 g NaOH per liter. The collection column (35 cm long, 6 mm ID, 25 ml volume) had a septum at the top and a sidearm on the side. The alkaline brine solution absorbed out the CO_2 leaving a small bubble (approx. 0.5 ml). Air was injected into the column to bring the bubble volume to 1 to 2 ml and a 1-ml syringe, with a Teflon Mininert valve and a 25 gauge needle, was inserted through the septum at the top. The pressure was brought to atmospheric by adding filling solution to the sidearm until the levels of solution in the sidearm and collection column were equal. The Mininert valve was then closed, the syringe and needle withdrawn, and the sample injected into a gas chromatograph for analysis.

Bunsen absorption coefficients for the dissolved hydrogen were calculated by performing double reciprocal plots (after taking several measurements at varying syringe gas to liquid phase ratios) using the following formula:

$$V_s/X = 1/N(V_s/V_1) + A/N ,$$

Table 5. Column materials for separating acetic, propionic, n-butyric, isobutyric, n-valeric, and isovaleric acid

Support[a]	Column type[b] and dimensions	Carrier gas and flow rate (cc min^{-1})	Column temperature (°C)
Chromsorb 101 (80/100 mesh)[c]	Gl; 6′ × 2 mm ID	N_2; 10	200
Porapak QS (80/100 mesh)[d]	Gl; 6′ × 2 mm ID	N_2; 20	200
10% Carbowax on Chromosorb W (40/60 mesh)[d]	Gl; 3′ × 2 mm ID	N_2; 40	125
10% SP-1200-1% H_3PO_4 on AW Chromosorb W (80/100 mesh)[d]	SS; 6′ × 1/8″ or Gl; 6′ × 2 mm ID	N_2; 40	125
10% FFAP on Chromosorb W (80/100 mesh)[d]	Gl; 6′ × 2 mm ID	N_2; 40	125

[a] Porapak Q and QS, Waters Associates, Framingham, Ma.; Molecular Sieve 5 A, Union Carbide Corp., Linde Div., Somerset, NJ; SP1200, FFAP, Carbosieve A&B and Carbowax, Supelco, Inc., Bellefonte, Pa.; Carbosphere and Silica Gel, Applied Science Labs., Deerfield, Il.; Chromosorb 101 and 102, Johns-Manville Corp., Denver, Co.
[b] SS stainless steel, Cu copper, Gl glass.
[c] Carlsson (1973).
[d] Ottenstein and Bartley (1971 a, b).

where N = mol of dissolved hydrogen/ml of extracted aqueous phase, V_1 = volume (ml) of aqueous phase in the 50-ml syringe, V_s = volume (ml) of gas phase in the syringe, and X = mol of hydrogen in the gas phase of the syringe (mol of hydrogen/ml bubble multiplied by the volume of the bubble).

3.2.7 Analysis of Volatile Fatty Acids

Volatile fatty acids and other fermentation intermediates may be directly (acetate, formate) or indirectly fermented to methane in digesters and other methanogenic systems. They are most frequently analyzed by gas chromatography with FI detection. The preceding discussion of gas chromatography of gases applies also to these substances; the principal differences are that liquid instead of gas samples are injected and some sample preparation is required.

Table 5 lists some column-packing materials and Table 6 some gas chromatography systems used for the analysis volatile fatty acids. The only sample prep-

Table 6. Analysis of VFA and alcohols by gas chromatography

Substance:	C_1 to C_7 VFA Lactic, succinic, fumaric acids	C_2 to C_6 VFA Methanol	C_2 to C_4 VFA Isobutyrate
Temperature (°C):			
Injector	230	250	180
Column	50 to 250 Programmed 10 deg min^{-1}	100 to 200 Programmed 5 deg min^{-1}	130
Detector	270		180
Carrier gas:	Nitrogen	Helium	Nitrogen
Detector:	FI	FI	FI
Flow rates (ml min^{-1}):			
Carrier	250	190	30
Air	260	570	
Hydrogen	84	60	
Column	Glass	Glass	Teflon
Size	6 ft. × 0.25 in.	10.2 × 0.6 cm	10.3 m × 2 mm or 0.5 m × 2 mm
Packing[a]	Chromosorb W (80/100) coated with Dexsil 300 G	Polypack-2 (80/120) uncoated	Porapak Q (80/100) or Chromosorb 101
Sample:			
Size (μl):	2	10	1
Preparation:	Derivatization to butyl esters	0.2 ml HCl/15 ml sample	Phosphoric acid to 0.15 *M*
Reference: Salanitro and Muirhead (1975)	Rogosa and Love (1968)	Zinder et al. (1984)	

[a] Chromosorb W plus Dexsil 300 G, Analabs, North Haven, Conn.; Polypak-2, Hewlett Packard F&M Scientific Division, Palo Alto, Calif.; Porapak Q, Supelco, Inc., Bellefonte, Pa.

aration (Table 6) required when using the method of Rogosa and Love (1968) or Zinder et al. (1984) for fatty acid analysis is acidification to convert fatty acid salts to their more volatile undissociated forms. Fatty acids sometimes absorb tightly to the columns giving rise to tailing peaks or "ghosting" effects. This problem can largely be circumvented by injecting formic acid into the gas chromatograph to dislodge the adsorbed acids between sample injections (Ackman 1972; Cochrane 1975).

Some fermentation products, such as lactic, succinic, and fumaric acids require a derivatization step to make them sufficiently volatile for analysis. Salanitro and Muirhead (1975) derivatized the acids to their butyl esters as follows:

Samples (1 ml) of supernatant liquid from centrifuged rumen bacterial cultures were adjusted to pH 9 to 10 with 10 N NaOH to convert the acids to their salts. The samples were frozen in a dry ice acetone bath and freeze dried. Chloroform (0.8 ml) plus 0.2 ml of 1-butanol, saturated with anhydrous HCl by bubbling until the pH was 1 or less, was added to the samples, mixed by vortexing and heated at 80° C for 2 h. An alternate method for producing butyl esters was thc addition of butanol (0.2 ml), sulfuric acid (0.05 ml), and boron trifluoride (14% wt/vol) to the samples before vortexing and heating. After heating, the samples were cooled and 0.2 ml of trifluoroacetic anhydride was added. The anhydride was allowed to react for 1 h, after which, the samples were washed with 1-ml aliquots of distilled water and the water layer discarded. The chloroform layer was adjusted to 1 ml and placed into vials for injection (2 μl) into a gas chromatograph (Table 5). Organic acid standards, subjected to the same treatment, were used to calibrate the gas chromatograph.

3.3 Isotope Methods for Gases

Liquid scintillation counting and gas proportional counting are the two most commonly used methods for estimating isotopically labeled methane and carbon dioxide in methanogenic studies. Mass spectrometry was, on occasion, used for analysis of deuterium-labeled methane but it is not used routinely.

The following methods will focus mainly on measuring radioactivity in gases. Liquid scintillation and gas proportional counting methods can also be combined with gas chromatography for analysis of volatile fatty acids or alcohols. However, analysis of radioactive volatile faty acids by gas chromatography presents problems because the acids tend to adsorb tightly to the columns and elute slowly. The problem can be circumvented somewhat by adding formic acid to the carrier gas, but it may be preferable to use high pressure liquid chromatography (HPLC) methods for separating the acids, followed by liquid scintillation counting of the separated acids.

3.3.1 Liquid Scintillation Counting

The principal advantages of liquid scintillation counting over other methods for measuring radioactivity in methane and other gases are the high counting efficiencies (>80%) and high reproducibility of results. The principal disadvantages are that the methods are generally slower and more cumbersome.

3.3.1.1 Direct Counting Methods

The simplest procedure for determining radioactive methane, if no other radioactive gases are present, is direct injection of gas samples into scintillation vials containing scintillation cocktails (McBride and Wolfe 1971; Ferry and Wolfe 1976; Zehnder et al. 1979). Zehnder et al. (1979) modified 24-ml liquid scintillation vials by drilling holes into the screw caps then plugging the holes with Teflon-Silicone septa (Pierce Chemical Company, Rockford, Ill.) to allow penetration by hypodermic needles. Toluene-based scintillation cocktail or Bray's solution (20 ml, Table 7) were placed into the vials after accurately measuring the volume. A 1-ml gas sample containing radioactive methane was injected into the gas space, the vial was shaken vigorously, allowed to equilibrate for 1 h at 4° C, then counted in a liquid scintillation counter. ^{14}C counting efficiencies of 80 to 90% were reported.

Methane injected into a vial head space distributes itself between the gas phase and liquid phase according to Henry's Law. Table 7 shows compositions of some liquid scintillation counting solutions and Table 8 gives their Bunsen coefficients for methane, from which the expected distribution of radioactivity between the gas space and liquid may be estimated. However, it is probably best to determine the distribution experimentally rather than use the values in Table 8.

The distribution is found by injecting a measured molar amount of nonradioactive methane into control vials containing liquid scintillation counting solution. The vials are shaken vigorously and allowed to equilibrate for 1 h or more in the liquid scintillation counter. A fixed volume of gas space sample is withdrawn and injected into a gas chromatograph to determine the fraction that did not dissolve in the cocktail. The difference between the quantity of methane in-

Table 7. Some liquid scintillation counting solutions

Solution	Composition	
Toluene-based [a]	2,5 Diphenyloxazole	0.375 g
	Dimethyl POPOP [b]	0.1 g
	Toluene	1000 ml
Bray's solution [a]	Naphthalene (scint. analyzed)	4 g
	2,5-Diphenyloxazole	4 g
	POPOP [c]	0.2 g
	Methanol	100 ml
	Ethylene glycol	20 ml
	1,4-Dioxane (scint. grade)	to 1 liter
$^{14}CO_2$ counting [d]	2,5-Diphenyloxazole	5 g
	POPOP	0.1 g
	Methanol	270 ml
	2-Phenylethylamine	270 ml
	Toluene	460 ml

[a] Zehnder et al. (1979).
[b] 1,4-bis-2-(methyl-5-phenoxazolyl)-benzene.
[c] 1,4-bis-2-(5-phenyloxazolyl)-benzene.
[d] Hash (1972).

Table 8. Absorption coefficients for methane in scintillation cocktails[a]

(Temperature (°C)	Toluene-based scintillation cocktail[b]	Bray's solution[b]	Pure toluene[c]
4	0.650	0.414	
10	0.638	0.395	
25	0.603	0.396	0.445
30			0.430
35			0.417
40			0.408
45			0.403
50			0.401
60			0.369

[a] Bunsen absorption coefficients.
[b] Data from Zehnder and Brock (1979).
[c] Data from Washburn et al. (1928).

jected into the gas space and the amount remaining after equilibration is the dissolved methane. The moles of methane injected into the control vials divided by the moles of methane that dissolved in the cocktail, when multiplied by the counts obtained in the sample vials, gives the total counts of methane in the sample vials.

If radioactive carbon dioxide is present with the radioactive methane, the carbon dioxide must be removed before the methane can be counted. This was done in the method of Zehnder et al. (1979) by absorbing out the CO_2 with NaOH; a vial was filled completely with 1 N NaOH, followed by withdrawal of 1 ml of the NaOH solution using a hypodermic needle and syringe. A second needle inserted into the septum allowed 1 ml of air to replace the NaOH solution removed. A gas sample containing a mixture of radioactive methane and carbon dioxide was then injected into the head space; the vial was vigorously shaken and allowed to equilibrate for 1 h. Following equilibration and absorption of the $^{14}CO_2$, 1 ml of the gas sample was withdrawn by needle and syringe, taking care to not allow contact of the needle with the radioactive alkali solution. the sample, containing only $^{14}CH_4$, was then injected into a scintillation vial containing the toluene-based cocktail as described above. With this method half of the original methane present actually gets counted.

3.3.1.2 Combustion and Entrapment Methods

Methods for radioactive methane analysis almost always employ some combination of combustion and/or absorption techniques. The steps are frequently carried out on a flowing stream of gas in tubes connected serially by glass or rubber tubing. These techniques can be used by themselves or in combination with gas chromatography. Some general considerations will be mentioned here together with some specific methods.

Methane is combusted by passing it over cupric oxide heated to glowing in quartz combustion tubes (Dennis and Nichols 1929); glass tubes are not used because they soften and melt. Several passes through the combustion tube may be required for the methane to oxidize completely. Adsorption of CO_2 by the hot copper oxide may also cause errors. The carbon dioxide formed by combustion can be estimated gravimetrically (as $BaCO_3$) or radiometrically after absorption in alkali. If carbon dioxide is initially present, the quantity must be estimated or absorbed out before combusting the methane.

In some cases, combustible gases such as hydrogen, carbon monoxide, or higher hydrocarbons may be present in addition to methane. These gases may be estimated using selective combustion techniques; carbon monoxide or hydrogen, but not methane, is completely oxidized by cupric oxide at 250° C (Dennis and Nichols 1929). Unsaturated hydrocarbons can be absorbed out with fuming sulfuric acid.

The CO_2 formed by combustion of the methane is trapped by bubbling the gas through solutions of hydroxides of sodium, potassium, or barium, or by absorbing in organic bases (ethanolamine, phenethylamine) (Hash 1972). If the trapping solution forms an insoluble carbonate with CO_2 (e.g., $BaCO_3$ from $Ba(OH)_2$], the samples can be counted by planchet counting or by liquid scintillation counting of a suspension in a cocktail containing a thixotropic agent (Hash 1972). Trapping agents, such as organic bases that give homogeneous solutions, can be incorporated directly into liquid scintillation cocktails and counted.

Laurinavichus and Belyaev (1979) used combustion and absorption methods to measure radioactive methane in culture gas spaces by passing a stream of oxygen through the cultures to which 0.5 ml of saturated KOH had been added to absorb carbon dioxide. A gas train was set up by inserting needles through the culture stoppers and attaching tubing to the needles. The head space gases were

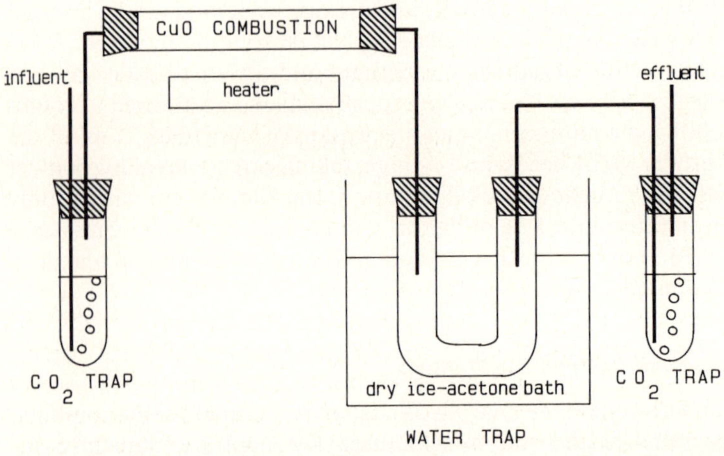

Fig. 2. Simplified example of gas train for trapping ^{14}C and ^{3}H from radioactive methane. A radioactive gas mixture containing $^{14}CO_2$, $^{14}C_4$, and $[^3H]CH_4$ enters with the carrier stream from the right. $^{14}CO_2$ is removed from the gas mixture by absorption in the first CO_2 trap. The remaining gas contains only ^{14}C- and ^{3}H-CH_4 which passes through a CuO combustion furnace where the methane is burned to produce $^{3}H_2O$ plus $^{14}CO_2$. $^{3}H_2O$ is trapped by condensation in a dry ice-acetone bath as it leaves the combustion furnace, while $^{14}CO_2$ continues on to the second absorption trap containing an alkaline solution

flushed into Dreschel wash bottles containing 0.1 N KOH to absorb additional carbon dioxide then led to a combustion tube containing copper oxide heated to 500° to 700° C. In the combustion tube, the methane was completely oxidized to CO_2. CO_2 leaving the combustion tube was then bubbled through three serially connected scintillation vials, each containing 2 ml of phenethylamine and 10 ml of a toluene-based scintillation cocktail. An oxygen flow rate of 50 to 60 ml min^{-1} was used and more than 97% of the methane was recovered as radioactive carbon dioxide.

Combustion methods can also be applied to counting tritium in gas samples if the gas sample after combustion is passed through a cold trap (a U-tube partly immersed in a dry ice-acetone mixture) to condense ^3H_2O (Hash 1972). The remaining gases may then be swept into an absorption solution for counting radioactive carbon (Fig. 2).

3.3.1.3 Gas Chromatography/Liquid Scintillation Counting

Methods for combining scintillation counting with gas chromatography have been described (Karmen et al. 1962; Popjak et al. 1962; Robbins and Bakke 1967; Zehnder and Brock 1979) and are available commercially. Zehnder and Brock (1979) sealed the cover of an FI detector with Teflon tape to force the gas chromatograph effluent out the exit hole of the detector and into three serially connected liquid scintillation vials. Each vial contained 2 ml of phenethylamine, 2 ml of methanol, and 10 ml of scintillation cocktail to absorb $^{14}CO_2$ exiting the gas chromatograph. Radioactivity in the vials were counted by liquid scintillation counting methods, achieving recoveries approaching 100%.

3.3.2 Gas Proportional Counting

Gas proportional counting is the most convenient method for estimating radioactive methane and carbon dioxide because it is easily combined with gas chromatography (Martin 1968). Carbon-14 and tritium may be determined simultaneously on multiple components of a single sample (Nelson and Zeikus 1974).

3.3.2.1 Description

A gas proportional counter consists of a hollow, gas-filled detector tube and its associated electronic circuitry (Fig. 3). The detector tube is filled with an inert detector gas (helium or argon) and a small quantity (10%) of a quench gas (usually propane) to permit the detection of pulses of electrical current from ionization of the detector gas. A thin tungsten wire runs through the middle of the detector tube and a high voltage (1400 to 1700 V) is applied between the wire and the metal outer tube; emissions from radioactive gas from the sample, flowing into the tube, cause the detector gas to ionize, resulting in a pulse of current from the tube to the central wire. The detector is enclosed in a lead shield to eliminate most of the stray background radiation.

The electronic circuitry for detecting the pulses of current includes an amplifier to amplify the pulses, a discriminator to select the energy levels detected, a

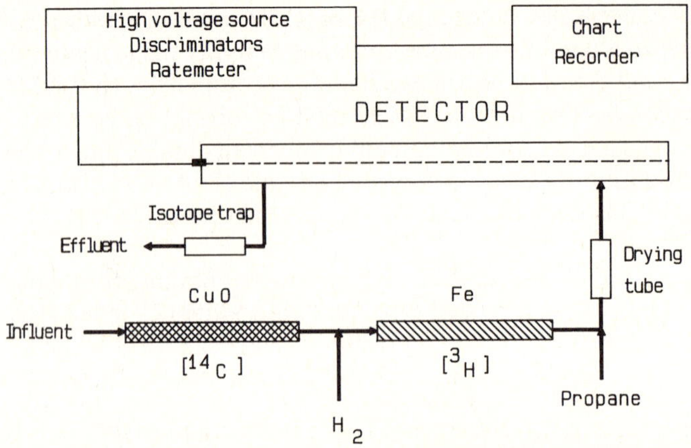

Fig. 3. Diagram of a gas proportional counter configured for counting tritium and carbon-14. Effluent from a gas chromatograph enters the gas proportional counter from the right then passes to a copper oxide combustion furnace. It is there burned to carbon dioxide and water. The mixture then enters a reducing furnace (*boxed area*) containing iron and hydrogen from an external source to keep the iron reduced. In the reducing furnace, ^3H_2O from the combustion of methane is reduced to $^3H_2$. The mixture passes through a drying tube on its way to the detector, where it is finally counted. The reducing furnace is usually omitted when only ^{14}C is to be counted. Propane serves as a quench gas and enters the detector tube from a point below the combustion furnaces

ratemeter to indicate counts min^{-1}, and scaling circuits to select the full-scale range of a chart recorder used for recording radioactive peaks. Setting the discriminator mode allows the detection of tritium or carbon-14. Radioactive emissions in the gas stream are sampled at intervals; the length of time spent sampling depends on the setting of a time constant.

Normally, the gas proportional counter detector tube is connected to the effluent line of a gas chromatograph TC detector. The combination gas chromatograph/proportional counter allows the detection of mass peaks and radioactive peaks on the same sample, from which specific activities may be calculated. Methane and other gases can cause quenching in the proportional counter so the gases are subjected to a combustion step to convert them to carbon dioxide before they are introduced into the detector.

The model 894 proportional counter from Packard Instrument Company (Downers Grove, Illinois) has combustion furnaces inserted between the detector and a gas chromatograph effluent line (Fig. 3). The carrier gas for the gas chromatograph (helium or argon) flows from the gas chromatograph, through the combustion tubes, to the detector. Quench gas (propane) is introduced into the detector tube from a separate line connected downstream from the combustion furnaces. A single combustion tube containing cupric oxide, to oxidize organic compounds to carbon dioxide, is used for counting carbon-14. If tritium is counted, a second furnace (dotted box area, Fig. 3) is connected between the combustion furnace and the detector. This second (reducing) furnace contains a quartz tube filled with iron filings or steel wool to reduce ^3H_2O to $^3H_2$; radioactive carbon dioxide can flow through the reducing furnace without reacting. Hydrogen is introduced just before the stream reaches the reducing furnace to maintain the iron in a reduced state. The furnaces are operated at a temperature of 750° C and a drying tube is inserted just in front of the detector tube to absorb water that may be produced by the combustion step.

3.3.2.2 Operation

The carrier gas flow rate from the gas chromatograph should be 40 to 120 ml min^{-1}. Quench gas and hydrogen (if tritium is counted) are mixed with the carrier gas at their respective positions in the gas train and the proportional counter is connected to a chart recorder to record radioactive emissions. The discriminator should be set to count carbon-14 or carbon-14 plus tritium. The quench gas flow rate is adjusted via a needle valve to give a background count of 30 to 40 counts min^{-1} on the chart recorder. Sufficient time (15 min) is allowed for the system to come to equilibrium before readjustments are made. When the system is in equilibrium and a proper range of background counts are detected, the proportional counter is calibrated by injecting samples from standards containing known amounts of radioactivity into the gas chromatograph. It is important to check the calibration each time the gas proportional counter is used; the sensitivity of the instrument varies with flow rates and other factors that are difficult to maintain at a constant value. Radioactive standards may be prepared from samples of radioactive methane counted by liquid scintillation counting.

3.3.2.3 Calculating Radioactivity

Counts per minute are proportional to the peak heights recorded on the chart recorder. The average background count should be subtracted from the peak height. Total counts within a peak are obtained by measuring the area of the peak, obtained by multiplying the peak height (in counts min^{-1}) by the width (in time units) of the peak at half the peak height. The peak width is measured in chart recorder units then multiplied by the speed of the chart recorder to obtain the width in units of time.

Corrections for quenching are made using quench curves constructed after using radioactive standards diluted into increasing quantities of nonradioactive methane. Counting efficiency is calculated from the following formula:

$$\% \text{ Counting efficiency} = \text{peak area} \times 100 \times \text{flow rate}/(\text{sample dpm} \times \text{detector volume}) .$$

For the Packard model 894 gas proportional counter, the detector volume is 20 ml and the flow rate is the sum of the flow rates of the carrier gas, quench gas, and any hydrogen added. The flow rate may be measured with a bubble flow meter connected to the outlet of the gas proportional counter detector tube.

Counts per minute (or counts) per ml of sample is calculated by dividing the counts min^{-1} (or counts) from a peak on the chart recorder by the sample volume to obtain cpm (or counts) ml^{-1} of sample. Counts in a culture head space are the product of the head space volume and counts ml^{-1} in the sample. Counts should be corrected to disintegrations per minute (dpm) by dividing by the counting efficiency. The specific activity of the gas is the dpm of the radioactive peak divided by the moles of gas obtained from the mass trace from the gas chromatograph. Other calculations (correction to standard temperature and pressure, etc.) are performed as for mass calculations.

3.3.2.4 Limitations

In spite of the speed and convenience of gas proportional counting, the method is limited by loss of accuracy at low (<1000 dpm) levels of radioactivity, possible adsorption of carbon dioxide in the cupric oxide combustion furnace, and problems resulting from excessive quenching.

Excessive quenching leads to underestimates of radioactivity and may be caused by fluctuations in the flow rates of the quench gas or carrier gas, lack of complete combustion of methane in the CuO combustion furnace and/or high concentrations of methane in the sample, incomplete absorption of water by the drying tube at the inlet of the detector, seepage of oxygen into the system, and gas leaks. The problems can be controlled by standardizing the equipment each time it used, frequently replacing the copper oxide oxidant and water absorbent and checking for and repairing gas leaks. The effects of high methane concentration and incomplete combustion on quenching is controlled by constructing quench curves as described in Sect. 3.3.2.3.

The flow rates of the quench and carrier gases are critical and are often difficult to adjust and maintain to the precision required for accurate reproducibility. They almost always vary each time the system is used. Frequent standardization will help to remedy the problem.

The proportional counter is best used for comparing the distribution of radioactivity among gases in a sample. Where counts from the proportional counter are compared with counts obtained by another method (e.g., liquid scintillation counting), special attention should be given to the total recoveries of radioactivity by the two methods. In our experience, recoveries and specific activities by gas proportional counting tend to be significantly lower and more variable than those from liquid scintillation counting (Smith and Mah 1980). In general, it is probably best to not mix counting methods. Comparison of specific activities in gases to specific activities in cellular intermediates or to assimilated carbon may best be made using one of the liquid scintillation counting methods for gases described above.

3.3.3 Gas Chromatography / Mass Spectrometry

Gas chromatography combined with mass spectrometry has had an important role in evaluating underlying biochemical mechanisms in methanogenesis and methane oxidation by measuring the fate of compounds labeled with nonradioactive isotopes. Thus, using deuterium-labeled substrates, Pine and Barker (1956), Walther et al. (1981), and Blaut and Gottschalk (1982) were able to observe the intact transfer of methyl groups from acetate or methyl amines to methane during methanogenesis. Daniels et al. (1980) showed that the hydrogen atoms in methane from reduction of CO_2 with hydrogen were derived from water rather than hydrogen, and Lovely et al. (1984) showed evidence that 2-mercaptoethanesulfonate (coenzyme M) was involved in methanogenesis from acetate. Fuchs et al. (1979) used the method to examine carbon isotope fractionation during methanogenesis and Higgins and Quayle (1970) showed evidence of mixed function oxygenase involvement in methane oxidation by observing that $^{18}O_2$ was incorporated directly into methanol. Nevertheless, the methods have been used only occasionally. Descriptions of the many types of mass spectrometers and their applications are given in detail elsewhere (Glover 1956; Caprioli 1972; Watson 1972).

4 Methods for Methanogenic Bacteria

Enzyme methods used with methanogenic bacteria require strict exclusion of oxygen throughout growing cultures, harvesting cells, and washing and breaking cells, if methanogenic activity is desired. All of these procedures are done under an inert or reducing atmosphere.

4.1 Preparing Methanogenic Cell Suspensions and Extracts

The two most indispensable items needed for preparing active cell suspensions and extracts are an outgassing manifold and an anaerobic glove box. The outgassing manifold is easily constructed from rubber tubing and connectors (which can be made by breaking off and using the wide end of a Pasteur pipette); it provides multiple streams of oxygen-free gas for sparging reagents in tubes or serum bottles to make them anaerobic by displacement of dissolved air with cylinder gas. The gas (hydrogen, nitrogen, argon, carbon dioxide, or mixtures of these gases) is delivered from a gas cylinder and made oxygen-free by passage through a reducing column filled with copper turnings and heated to 350° C. A suitable reducing column is available commercially from Sargent-Welch, Inc. or it can be made. The column is made by stuffing glass wool into the bottom of a chromatography column, filling the rest with copper turnings, then stuffing glass wool into the top to sandwich the copper turnings. A rubber stopper with a hole in it and a glass tube fitted into the hole is inserted into one or both ends and wired into place. The finished column is then wrapped with electrical heating tape or placed in an electric furnace controlled by a rheostat to heat it to the proper temperature.

The anaerobic glove box can be purchased from a commercial source. Sterile media, glassware, equipment (small spectrophotometers, colorimeters, pH meters), and other items can be stored in the glove box and routine operations requiring exposure of cultures to the atmosphere performed there. We normally keep an atmosphere of nitrogen with less than 5% (vol) hydrogen to lessen the risk of explosion. Palladium catalysts, available commercially, continually remove oxygen by reacting with the hydrogen present, requiring that the hydrogen be replaced at frequent intervals. Activated charcoal should be placed in the glove box to absorb sulfide, which may poison the catalyst. Items made of rubber or plastic should be stored in the glove box for about 24 h before use to eliminate adsorbed oxygen.

Cell suspensions of methanogenic bacteria may be prepared from small volume (< 500 ml) exponential phase cultures by transferring the cultures into an anaerobic glove box and dispensing them into metal centrifuge tubes with metal screw-on lids (Balch et al. 1979; Romesser and Balch 1980). The tubes are removed from the glove box, centrifuged, and returned to the glove box. The supernatant liquid from the centrifugation is decanted and the cell pellet resuspended in 20 m*M* potassium or sodium phosphate buffer (pH 7.0) with 1 to 3 m*M* mercaptoethanol, dithiothreitol, or other reducing agent except sulfide. Cells are washed by repeating the centrifugation and resuspension steps, after which, the final cell suspensions are dispensed inside the glove box into stoppered test tubes or serum vials. Anaerobic reagents or substrates may be added to the cell suspensions inside the glove box or by injection after removal from the glove box.

Cultures for cell extract preparation may be grown in 10 to 100 l volumes in large pyrex carboys (Smith and Lequerica 1985) or in a large fermenter modified to maintain an anaerobic atmosphere. To grow cultures in carboys, the media ingredients are added aerobically to the carboys containing distilled water, stoppered with cotton, then autoclaved. After autoclaving, the media are cooled and the carboys stoppered with sterile rubber stoppers. The atmospheres inside the carboys are replaced with nitrogen, argon, hydrogen, carbon dioxide, or a mixture of the gases by outgassing through sterile needles inserted through the stoppers. Argon may be substituted for nitrogen and is superior to nitrogen because its higher density slows the diffusion of oxygen from the air. After outgassing, reducing agent is added to the media by injection. Resazurin (0.0001% wt/vol) should be present in the media as an oxidation-reduction indicator (Mah and Smith 1981); when it becomes colorless, the media are ready for inoculation.

Cells are harvested from carboys by continuous flow centrifugation under a stream of inert gas. After harvesting, the cells are placed inside an anaerobic glove box, suspended in phosphate buffer with reducing agent and washed as described above for cell suspensions. The final cell pellets are placed into glass tubes and stoppered with rubber stoppers. The gas spaces may be replaced with hydrogen by outgassing, using an outgassing manifold like that described above. Cells may then be frozen by dipping the stoppered tubes containing them into a dry ice-acetone bath. They are then stored at $-20°$ C until ready to use.

Cell extracts are prepared by suspending cells in an equal volume of buffer such as 20 m*M* potassium phosphate, pH 7.0, plus 1 to 3 m*M* 2-mercaptoethanol, dithiothreitol, or other reducing agent. Cells are washed and suspended in buffer inside an anaerobic chamber. The suspended cells are usually broken using a French pressure cell at 137 MPa, loaded inside an anaerobic glove box or in the open atmosphere with a stream of hydrogen applied to the tube holding the cells. Before loading in the open atmosphere, the pressure cell should be flushed with oxygen-free gas. The tube holding the cells is stoppered after cell collection and transported back to the glove box where the cell suspension is dispensed into metal centrifuge tubes and centrifuged at $30\,000 \times g$ for 30 min. The supernatant fraction contains most of the methanogenic activity.

4.2 Enzymatic Methane Production

Cell extracts from methanogenic bacteria will convert the known methanogenic substrates to methane or methane plus carbon dioxide (Romesser and Balch 1980; van der Meijden et al. 1983; Naumann et al. 1984; Baresi 1984; Krzycki and Zeikus 1984). The final reaction in methanogenesis is the reduction of methylcoenzyme M (2-methylthioethanesulfonate) to methane and free coenzyme M (2-mercaptoethanesulfonate) by methylcoenzyme M methyl reductase:

$$CH_3SCH_2CH_2SO_3^- + [2\,H] \rightarrow CH_4 + HSCH_2CH_2SO_3^- \,.$$

This reduction step requires FAD, Mg^{2+}, and catalytic amounts of ATP (Jones et al. 1987).

Reducing equivalents for reduction of methyl coenzyme M are generated from the oxidation of molecular hydrogen, methanol, formate, or trimethylamine to carbon dioxide, or the carboxyl group of acetate to carbon dioxide. Methyl groups from methanogenic substrates containing them are transferred intact to coenzyme M by the action of methyltransferases to form methyl coenzyme M. CO_2 and formate are reduced to methyl groups bound to coenzyme M on the methylreductase complex via methanopterin derivatives (Jones et al. 1987).

Table 9 lists assay mixtures used in generating methane from methanogenic substrates by cell extracts. Ingredients are added to the reaction mixtures in 5-ml or smaller vials inside an anaerobic glove box. Methylcoenzyme M, for the methyl reductase assay, is not commercially available and may be synthesized from methyl iodide and 2-mercaptoethanesulfonate (Sigma Chemical Company) by the method of Romesser and Balch (1980). The vials are stoppered with red serum caps, rubber stoppers, or septa and placed on ice outside the glove box. The cell extract or substrate may be added to vials inside the glove box or added later by injection from anaerobic stock solutions. Addition of cell extract outside the glove box is by injection using a microliter syringe, made anaerobic by flushing with an anaerobic solution of phosphate buffer containing a reducing agent. Other additions, such as substrates, may also be made by injecting stock anaerobic solutions into the reaction vials. After adding the ingredients, the vial gas spaces are flushed with hydrogen for about 15 min, following which they are transferred to a water bath at 37° to 40° C. The reactions are started by adding cell extract or substrate. After starting the reactions, gas space samples of 50 μl are injected into a flame ionization gas chromatograph for analysis of methane. A flame ionization gas chromatograph is needed because of the small quantities of methane produced. If radioactive isotopes are used, the method of Zehnder and Brock (1979) can be used to trap and count carbon-14 from carbon dioxide in the gas chromatograph effluent (Baresi 1984) or headspace samples can be counted in a gas proportional counter (Krzycki and Zeikus 1984).

A large number of punctures, which can cause leakage and oxidation of the extracts, are made in the stoppers or septa of the reaction vials when adding reagents or removing gas samples from the reaction mixtures. These problems can be minimized by coating the surfaces of the stoppers with a thin layer of silicone grease and rubbing the thumb over the puncture holes to seal them each time a puncture is made.

Table 9. Reaction mixtures for enzymatic methanogenesis

Methanogenic substrate	Reaction mixture	Reference
CH_3SCoM[a] or H_2+CO_2	50 m*M* Potassium phosphate, pH 7.1 4.8 m*M* $MgSO_4$ 5.2 m*M* ATP 12 m*M* CH_3SCoM or HSCoM (H_2+CO_2) Cell extract: 2 to 4 mg protein Atm: H_2 or H_2+CO_2 Reaction vol: 0.25 ml	Romesser and Balch (1980)
Methanol	10 m*M* TES[b], pH 7.2 6.25 m*M* $MgCl_2$ 9.38 m*M* ATP 12.5 m*M* Methanol Cell extract: 0.4 to 1 mg protein Atm: H_2 followed by N_2 Reaction vol: 0.1 ml	van der Meijden et al. (1983)
Trimethylamine	50 m*M* TES, pH 7.2 2 m*M* Dithioerythritol 15 m*M* $MgCl_2$ 7.5 m*M* ATP 18 m*M* HSCoM 6 m*M* Trimethylamine Cell extract: 5.25 to 6.75 mg protein Atm: H_2 followed by N_2 Reaction vol: 1.95 ml	Naumann et al. (1984)
Acetate	54 m*M* Sodium phosphate, pH 6.6 15 m*M* Dithiothreitol 25 m*M* Sodium acetate Cell extract: 0.4 ml Atm: N_2 Reaction vol: 0.4 ml	Baresi (1984)
	10 m*M* ATP 10 m*M* $MgCl_2$ 50 m*M* Sodium acetate Cell extract: 8.8 mg protein Atm: H_2 Reaction vol: 0.56 ml	Krzycki and Zeikus (1984)

[a] 2-Methylthioethanesulfonate (methylcoenzyme M), HSCoM, 2-mercaptoethanesulfonate (coenzyme M).
[b] TES, N-tris(hydroxymethyl)-methyl-2-aminoethanesulfonate.

Some of the methanogenic substrates require an activation step for methanogenesis to occur in cell extracts. Methanogenesis from methanol by *Methanosarcina* extracts in a nitrogen atmosphere requires a brief exposure of the extracts to hydrogen before incubating them in nitrogen (van der Meijden et al. 1983). Methanogenesis from acetate may require activation of the acetate by the formation of acetyl coenzyme A (via acetate kinase and phosphotransacetylase, Krzycki and Zeikus 1984). This is supported (contrary to our initial opinion) by the isolation of a fluoroacetate-resistant mutant *Methanosarcina* strain, deficient in phosphotransacetylase and unable to use acetate as a carbon or methane source (Smith and Lequerica 1985).

5 Methods for Methanotrophic Bacteria

The gas chromatographic and isotopic methods discussed in the previous sections can be applied to estimating methane consumption by methanotrophic bacteria. For example, methods for measuring methane oxidizing activity in ecosystems, using absorption techniques with radioactive methane as substrate, were summarized by Hanson (1980). Other methods listed included measuring nonradioactive methane consumption by gas chromatography, performing colony counts on samples inoculated into media in which methane was the sole energy source, and measuring methane oxidation directly.

Methane-oxidizing activity was measured using radioactive methane by incubating ecosystem samples at 30° C in sealed containers with $^{14}CH_4$ in the gas space then following the formation of $^{14}CO_2$. The purity of the $^{14}CH_4$ used is important; radioactive methane of sufficient purity can be purchased or generated from methanogenic cultures by reducing $^{14}CO_2$ with molecular hydrogen. Sodium hydroxide solution was added to the samples at the end of the incubation to trap any $^{14}CO_2$ formed and the gas space was flushed with nitrogen to eliminate unreacted $^{14}CH_4$. Aliquots of liquid were then counted by liquid scintillation counting before and after acidification of the samples. The difference in radioactivity before and after acidification was the amount of $^{14}CO_2$ produced; the amount of radioactivity remaining after acidification was the quantity of radioactive methane assimilated into cell carbon.

Alternately, oxidation of radioactive methane to radioactive carbon dioxide can be followed by gas chromatography/gas proportional counting or gas chromatography/liquid scintillation counting methods.

5.1 Respirometric Analysis

Respirometric techniques are often used for measuring methane-oxidizing activity with methanotrophic cultures and cell suspensions because the bacteria are aerobic. Higgins and Quayle (1970) used conventional Warburg respirometry to estimate methane oxidation by cell suspensions of *Methanomonas methanooxidans* and *Pseudomonas methanica*. A description of Warburg methods may be found in Kenten (1956) or Umbreit et al. (1964).

Polarographic measurements of oxygen uptake, using an oxygen-sensing electrode, is another method used with cell suspensions and extracts (Ribbons and Michalover 1970; Ferenci 1974; Ferenci et al. 1975; Tonge et al. 1975). A full description of many types of oxygen-sensing electrodes and respirometers, their construction in the laboratory, and applications may be found in Gnaiger and Forstner (1983). Briefly, cultures, cell suspensions, or cell extracts (3.0 ml) are incubated at 30° C in a polarographic oxygen-sensing electrode. A low voltage applied to the leads of the electrode results in a current flow proportional to the fugacity of oxygen at the electrode-sample interface.

5.2 Methane Monooxygenase Activity

Another method for estimating methane-oxidizing activity in cell suspensions and extracts is by assaying for methane monooxygenase activity. Methanotrophic bacteria use molecular oxygen to sequentially oxidize methane to methanol, formaldehyde, formate, and carbon dioxide (Wolfe and Higgins 1979). Oxidation of methane to methanol is accomplished by methane monooxygenase, a mixed function monooxygenase that requires NADH for activity, acts on a broad spectrum of organic compounds, and occurs in a soluble and a particulate form (depending on the bacterial species and the availability of copper to the cultures) (Ribbons 1975; Wolfe and Higgins 1979; Stanley et al. 1983; McPheat et al. 1987). The particulate form can be sedimented by differential centrifugation (40 000 × *g* for 20 min, Ribbons 1975). The monooxygenase will also oxidize carbon monoxide to CO_2 (Ferenci 1974; Ferenci et al. 1975). Subsequent oxidation steps involve dehydrogenases for methanol, formaldehyde, and formate and the dissimulatory ribulose monophosphate pathway for formaldehyde (Colby et al. 1979; Dalton 1980; Higgins et al. 1981; Roitsch and Stolp 1985).

Several methods have been used for assaying methane-oxidizing activity by cell suspensions and cell extracts. Methane monooxygenase in cell extracts has been measured spectrophotometrically by monitoring methane-dependent oxidation of NADH (Ribbons 1975). Gas chromatography was employed for assaying the monooxygenase based on: (1) the conversion of methane to methanol in the presence of 0.15 *M* phosphate (which inhibits further metabolism of methanol but does not inhibit the monooxygenase) (Tonge et al. 1975); (2) oxidation and disappearance of bromoethane (Colby et al. 1975); and (3) epoxidation of propylene to propylene oxide (Best and Higgins 1981; Patel et al. 1982; Leak and Dalton 1983; McPheat et al. 1987). Because bromoethane was shown to be unstable at neutral pH, hydrolyzing spontaneously to methanol, it was suggested that the assay was unsuitable for monitoring monooxygenase activity (Meyers 1980).

The propylene oxide assay depends on the ability of methane monooxygenase to catalyze the oxidation of alkenes to their corresponding oxides (Colby and Dalton 1978; Hou et al. 1979; Patel et al. 1982; Leak and Dalton 1983; Imai et al. 1986). Propylene oxide formed during the incubation of cell suspensions or cell extracts with propylene and oxygen is not metabolized further.

The assay on whole cell suspensions (Hout et al. 1980) consisted in washing the cells in 50 m*M* phosphate buffer (pH 7.0) and resuspending cells in phosphate buffer to a final optical density (660 nm) of 0.5. Aliquots were distributed into tubes and the tubes capped with rubber caps. The gas space was replaced with a mixture (1 : 1) of propylene and oxygen and incubated in a rotary shaker at 30° C or propylene was injected into the gas space. Samples of liquid (2 to 3 μl) were removed at intervals and injected into a flame ionization gas chromatograph to detect formation of propylene oxide. Gas chromatographic methods for assay-

Table 10. Analysis of some methanotrophic oxidation products

Products:	Propane, propylene, propylene oxide, acetone, 2-propanol, allyl alcohol	Acetone, propylene, propylene oxide
Detector:[a]	FI	FI
Carrier gas:	Helium	Nitrogen
Flow rate (ml min^{-1}):	35	30 to 60
Column	Stainless Steel	
Size	20 ft. × 1/8 in.	2.1 m × 4 mm
Packing	10% Carbowax 20 M on 80/100 mesh Chromosorb W	Porapak Q or Tenax GC
Temp. (°C)	80–200 Isothermal	150–190
Sample size:	3 µl	5 µl
Reference:	Hou et al. (1980)	Leak and Dalton (1983)

[a] FI, flame ionization.

ing propylene oxide and other oxidation products of methanotrophic bacteria are given in Table 10.

Patel et al. (1982) prepared cell extracts of *Methylobacterium* by washing 250 g (wet wt.) of cells twice in 25 m*M* potassium phosphate buffer, pH 7.0 then suspending the cells in 250 ml of 25 m*M* of the buffer supplemented with 5 m*M* $MgCl_2$ and 0.05 mg ml^{-1} DNase. Cells were disrupted in a French pressure cell at 4° C and 20000 lb in^{-2}. The broken cells were centrifuged at 15000 × *g* for 15 min to remove cell debris, followed by centrifugation of the supernatant fraction at 40000 × *g* for 60 min. The 40000 × *g* supernatant liquid was centrifuged at 80000 × *g* for another 60 min. Methane monooxygenase was assayed on the supernatant fraction from the final centrifugation.

The reaction mixture consisted of 25 µmol of potassium phosphate, pH 7.0, 10 µmol of NADH and cell extract (in a total volume of 0.5 ml in 3-ml vials). Extracts were incubated at 35° C in a reciprocating shaker water bath (50 oscillations min^{-1}); the reactions were started by vacuum removal of the gas phase followed by replacement with 1:1 propylene plus oxygen.

6 Calculating Methane and Other Gases

Calculating the quantity of gas in the gas space of a closed vessel (Sect. 3.1) is simply a matter of multiplying the gas space volume (ml) by the concentration to the gas (µmol ml^{-1}, determined by gas chromatography). Often, methane production is compared to the production of gases with nonnegligible solubility in water (like carbon dioxide) in order to determine the stoichiometry of a methanogenic reaction or to obtain a carbon balance. In this case, the solubility of the

Table 11. Conversion factors for pressure units

Convert to \ Convert from (Multiply by)	Atm	kPa	mm Hg	Torr	Bar
Atm	1	0.00986923	0.00131579	0.00131579	0.986923
kPa	101.325	1	0.1333224	0.1333224	100
mm Hg	760	7.50061683	1	1	750.0616827
Torr	760	7.50061683	1	1	750.0616827
Bar	1.01325	0.01	0.00133322	0.0013332	1

Table 12. Henry's law[a]

1. Henry's law: $P = H\,X_g$
2. $S = A\,P$

Henry's law constant (Washburn et al. 1928):

3. $H = 22414\ d/(M\ A) + 1$

Gas absorption coefficients:

4. Bunsen's (Washburn et al. 1928): $A = 273.15\ L/T$
5. Ostwald's (Washburn et al. 1928): $L = C_1/C_g$
6. (Wilhelm et al. 1977): $L = [X/(1 - X\,P)]\ (R\ T/P)\ d/M$

[a] Abbreviations: *P* Partial pressure of pure gas (atm); *H* Henry's law constant (atm/mol frac); X_g mole fraction of dissolved gas; *S* solubility of gas (ml gas/ml liquid); *A* Bunsen's coefficient (ml of gas at STP/ml of liquid); *L* Ostwald's coefficient (ml gas/ml liquid); C_g molar concentration of gas in gas phase; C_1 molar concentration of gas in liquid phase; *T* temperature (K), *X* mole fraction of dissolved *R* gas law constant (82.06 ml atm K^{-1} mol^{-1}); *d* density (g ml^{-1}) of solvent; *M* molecular weight of solvent.

gas must be taken into account. Dissolved gases are frequently estimated by calculation rather than by measurement. Tables 10 through 15 have been included to facilitate estimating methane and other gases, taking their solubilities into account.

Table 11 gives conversion factors for interconverting pressure units. Pressures are usually expressed in kPa, but it is more convenient to use atmospheres for calculations. The tables assume pressures in atm unless indicated otherwise.

Henry's law [Table 12, Eq. (1)] of gas solubility states that the mole fraction of a pure gas dissolved in a pure liquid is proportional to the partial pressure of the gas above the liquid. The law is valid at low gas pressures; significant deviations occur at partial pressures above 1 atm. The constant of proportionality (H) is in units of pressure/mole fraction. Henry's law may be expressed in terms of the Bunsen absorption coefficient [A in Eq. (2)], the volume of pure gas at STP absorbed by a unit volume of a pure liquid. The solubility of the gas is in ml of gas at STP ml^{-1} liquid. The solubilities of individual gases are independent of other dissolved gases that might be present. Equations (1) and (2) assume there are no dissolved solutes other than gases, and that the gas does not react with the solvent. The Henry's law constant is related to the Bunsen coefficient through Eq. (3).

Gas solubilities may be expressed in terms of absorption coefficients other than Henry's law constants and Bunsen coefficients. The Ostwald absorption coefficient is useful because it can be expressed in terms of directly measurable quantities (the molar concentrations of gas in the liquid and gas phases) and can be used for calculating Bunsen coefficients [Eq. (4)]. The coefficient is defined as the volume (ml) of pure gas absorbed by a unit volume of pure liquid, the gas and liquid being at the same temperature and pressure. The gas volume is not reduced to STP. A consequence of the definition for the Ostwald coefficient is that it may be expressed as the ratio of the molar concentration of gas dissolved in the liquid phase to its molar concentration in the gas phase [Eq. (5), Ben-Naim 1972]. This ratio is independent of the partial pressure of the gas. As a result, gases at any partial pressure less than 1 atm, can be injected into the gas spaces of vessels with liquids, the concentrations of gas in the gas and liquid phases measured by gas chromatography, and the absorption coefficients calculated. Equation (6) expresses Ostwald's coefficient in terms of the mole fraction of dissolved gas.

Table 13 contains formulas for calculating gas quantities in closed vessels. Equation (1) is for the reduction of gas volumes at a given temperature and pres-

Table 13. Formulas for calculating gases in closed vessels[a]

Reduction of volume to STP (Dennis and Nichols 1929):
1. $V_0 = V\ P/(1+0.0037\ t)$

Sampling at atmospheric pressure (Mah et al. 1978):
2. $\mu mol = V_h\ C_g + \Sigma\ V_s\ C_g$

Fixed volume sampling:
3. $\mu mol = V_h\ C_g$

Volume of gas in a closed vessel (Umbreit et al. 1964):
4. ml gas at STP $= V_h\ (273.15/T)\ P + V_1\ A\ P$

Correction factor for dissolved gas in a closed vessel:
5. Total gas/gas space gas $= 1 + V_1/V_h\ (A\ T/273.15)$
6. $\quad = 1 + V_1/V_h\ L$

Total gas = gas in gas space plus gas dissolved in liquid

CO_2 dissolved in water:
Umbreit et al. (1964)[b]:
7. $pH = pK' + \log HCO_3^- - \log P_m\ (CO_2) - \log [A/(760 \times 2240)]$

Zehnder and Wuhrmann (1977):
8. $pH = pK' + pK_H + \log [HCO_3^-]/pCO_2$

Salinity correction (when $I > 10$ m*M*):
9. $pK' = pK_1 - I^{1/2}/[2\ (1 + 1.4\ I^{1/2})]$

[a] Abbreviations: V_0 volume at STP; V volume at given TP; P pressure (or partial pressure for a pure gas); t temperature (°C); V_h gas space volume; V_1 liquid volume; V_s gas volume bled into syringe; C_g molar concentration of gas in gas phase; T temperature (°K); A Bunsen coefficient; L Ostwald coefficient; HCO_3^- molar conc. bicarbonate; P_m partial pressure (mm Hg); (CO_2) % CO_2 (vol); pK' first dissociation constant for bicarbonate (corrected); pK_1 first dissociation constant for bicarbonate; $pK_H = -\log$ (Henry's law const.); pCO_2 partial pressure of CO_2 (atm); I ionic strength.

[b] pK′ values for CO_2 in water: 20 °C 6.392, 25 °C 6.365, 30 °C 6.348, 35 °C 6.328, 40 °C 6.322.

sure to standard temperature and pressure (STP). Ideal gases are assumed in all of the tables of formulas and is usually sufficiently accurate because the partial pressures involved with methanogenic systems are usually less than 1 atm. Higher accuracy can be achieved by assuming that the gases are van der Waal's gases and modifying some of the formulas accordingly.

Equations (2) and (3) are equations for calculating head space gases given in Sect. 3.1. They are repeated here for easy reference.

The remaining Eqs. (4) through (10) are for estimating gas solubilities or correcting head space gas calculations to account for dissolved gases.

The correction to apply to gas space gases to account for dissolved gases in a closed vessel is given by Eqs. (5) and (6). These equations were derived from Eq. (4), which estimates the total volume of gas at STP in a closed vessel containing a liquid. This total gas quantity (in units of volume, moles or dpm) can be calculated by multiplying the head space gas by Eq. (5) (using the Bunsen coefficient) or Eq. (6) (using the Ostwald coefficient).

If a gas reacts with the solvent, or if the solvent contains dissolved electrolytes or other nongas solutes, the gas solubilities will differ from those in a pure liquid. Electrolytes cause a "salting out" effect resulting in an overestimate of dissolved gas when using absorption coefficients for pure liquids. If the gas reacts with the liquid, the dissolved gas may be underestimated. Equations (7) through (9) are for estimating dissolved CO_2 concentrations when the pH of the solution is known [Eq. (7)] or when the pH and ionic strength [Eqs. (8) and (9)] are known. If samples are acidified to convert all of the bicarbonate to CO_2, then allowed to equilibrate with the gas space, CO_2 can be treated using Eqs. (1) through (6).

Table 14. Coefficients for Henry's law constants for gases in water[a]

Gas	$H=e^{-[a+b/T+c\ln(T)+dT]}$				Temp. range (K)
	a	b	c	d	
Helium	−177.332	4397.06	16.2365	−0.00602486	273–334
Argon	−169.464	8137.13	23.2547	−0.00306357	274–347
Hydrogen	−180.053	6993.51	26.3119	−0.0150431	274–339
Nitrogen	−164.980	8432.77	21.5580	0.00843624	273–346
Oxygen	−144.395	7775.06	18.3974	0.00944354	274–348
Carbon					
monoxide	−171.761	8296.75	23.3372	0	273–353
dioxide	−159.852	8741.55	21.6690	−0.00110259	273–353
Hydrogen					
sulfide	−149.536	8226.50	20.2307	0.00129405	273–333
Methane	−183.767	9111.66	25.0379	−0.000143434	275–353
Ethane	−268.413	13368.1	37.5523	−0.00230129	275–353
Propane	−316.458	15921.1	44.3241	0	273–347
Butane	−321.663	16498.4	44.8613	0	273–349
Propene	100.471	− 1983.14	−18.0322	0	294–361
Acetylene	−156.508	8160.12	21.4022	0	274–343

[a] Calculated from data of Wilhelm et al. (1977), H (atm/mol frac.), e=2.71828 (base of natural logarithms), T=Temperature (°K).

Table 15. Formulas for calculating gas absorption coefficients[a]

Density of H_2O:
$d=0.999868/C$
Coefficient of cubical expansion of water (Dean 1973):
For $0 \Leftarrow t \Leftarrow 25$ °C:
$C=1-6.4268\times10^{-5}t+8.50526\times10^{-6}t^2-6.78977\times10^{-8}t^3+4.01209\times10^{-10}t^4$
For $25 < t < =100$ °C:
$C=1-5.3255\times10^{-5}t+7.61532\times10^{-6}t^2-4.37217\times10^{-8}t^3+1.64322\times10^{-10}t^4$
Bunsen absorption coefficient for pure water (Washburn 1928):
$A=1241.54\ d/(H-1)$
Ostwald absorption coefficient for water (Wilhelm et al. 1977):
$L=[X/(1-X)]\ R\ T\ (d/M)$

[a] Abbreviations: *d* density of water (g ml^{-1}); *t* temperature (°C); *C* coefficient of cubical expansion; *A* Bunsen coefficient; *L* Ostwald coefficient; *X* mole frac. dissolved gas at 1 atm partial pressure (1/H); *M* molecular weight of solvent (water=18.0534); *R* gas constant (82.06 ml atm K^{-1} mol^{-1}).

Table 16. Sample calculation for CH_4 and CO_2 in a closed vessel

Initial information:
Cultures acidified and equilibrated at 23 °C (296.15 K)

Vessel volume: 160 ml	Gas space analysis:		
Culture (liq.) vol. (V_1): 50 ml		CH_4	CO_2
Gas space vol (V_h): 110 ml	μmol ml^{-1}	20	9
	dpm ml^{-1}	2000	900

Ostwald's coefficient:
Density of H_2O (23 °C): C=1.002307 $d=0.999868/1.002307=0.99757$

For CH_4:	For CO_2:
$x=-183.767+9111.66/296.15+25.0379\ \ln(296.15)$ $-0.000143434\ (296.15)=-10.5551$	$x=-7.32559$
$H=e^{-x}=38372.6$	$H=1518.67$
$A=1241.54\ (0.99757)/(38372-1)=0.03228$	$A=0.81779$
$L=(0.03228)\ (296.15/273.15)=0.03500$	$L=0.8867$

Gas in culture:
Correction for dissolved CH_4: $1+50/110\ (0.03500)=1.01591$
Correction for dissolved CO_2: $1+50/110\ (0.8867)=1.4030$
CH_4: 20 μmol ml^{-1} (110 ml) (1.01591)=2,235 μmol 223,500 dpm
CO_2: 9 μmol ml^{-1} (110 ml) (1.4030)=1389 μmol 138,900 dpm

Table 14 is a table of coefficients for calculating gas solubility constants (Henry's Law). This table was intended for estimating gas solubility constants without the need for interpolation, as is common with tables of solubility constants for discrete temperatures. The table may be conveniently used for programming a computer or programmable calculator to calculate dissolved gases. Simply substitute the temperature (K) and the coefficients for one of the gases into the expression at the head of the column to calculate the Henry's law constant.

Most of the above formulas use Bunsen or Ostwald coefficients, which are defined in terms of the volume of gas that will dissolve in a volume of liquid. To calculate these coefficients from Henry's law constants, the molar volume of the solvent (molecular weight/density) at specified temperatures must be known. These values can be found in handbook tables or estimated using the formulas in Table 15. Table 15 also gives formulas for calculating the Bunsen and Ostwald coefficients from Henry's law constants.

For clarity and to allow programmers to check their programs, a sample gas calculation, making use of the preceding tables, is given in Table 16. The starting conditions appear at the top of the table under the heading, initial information. From these conditions, the Bunsen coefficients for methane and carbon dioxide are calculated using the information in Tables 14 and 15. The Ostwald coefficient is calculated from the Bunsen coefficient using Eq. (4) in Table 12. The Ostwald coefficient is used to calculate the correction factor [Table 13, Eq. (6)] for gas space gases to estimate the total gas. Finally, the correction factor is applied to the total μmol and dpm in the gas space to estimate gas space plus dissolved gas (μmol or dpm) of gas present in the vessel. It is clear from the values of the correction factors, in the example, that dissolved methane contributes little (1.5%) to the total methane present, while dissolved carbon dioxide makes a sizable (29%) contribution to total carbon dioxide.

References

Ackman RG (1972) Porous polymer bead packings and formic acid vapor in the GLC of volatile free fatty acids. J Chromatogr Sci 10:560–565

Alperin MJ, Reeburgh WS (1985) Inhibition experiments on anaerobic methane oxidation. Appl Environ Microbiol 50:940–945

Balch WE, Fox GE, Magrum LJ, Woese CR, Wolfe RS (1979) Methanogens: reevaluation of a unique biological group. Microbiol Rev 43:260–296

Baresi L (1984) Methanogenic cleavage of acetate by lysates of *Methanosarcina* sp. J Bacteriol 160:365–370

Baresi L, Mah RA, Ward DM, Kaplan IR (1978) Methanogenesis from acetate: enrichment studies. Appl Environ Microbiol 36:186–197

Belay N, Daniels L (1987) Production of ethane, ethylene, and acetylene from halogenated hydrocarbons by methanogenic bacteria. Appl Environ Microbiol 53:1604–1610

Ben-Naim A (1972) Thermodynamics of dilute aqueous solutions of nonpolar solutes. In: Horne RA (ed) Water and aqueous solutions structure, thermodynamics, and transport processes. Wiley, New York London Sydney Toronto, p 430

Best DJ, Higgins IJ (1981) Methane-oxidizing activity and membrane morphology in a methanol-grown obligate methanotroph, *Methylosinus trichosporium* OB3b. J Gen Microbiol 125:73–84

Blaut M, Gottschalk G (1982) Effect of trimethylamine on acetate utilization by *Methanosarcina barkeri*. Arch Microbiol 133:230–235

Breck DW (1964) Crystalline molecular sieves. J Chem Ed 41:678–685

Brewer JM, Pesce AJ, Ashworth RB (eds) (1974) Experimental techniques in biochemistry. Prentice-Hall, Englewood Cliffs, NJ, pp 374

Bulletin 712B (1976) Carbosieve brand S-GSC packing. Supelco, Bellefonte, PA

Bulletin 760A (1976) Analysis of permanent gases. Supelco, Bellefonte, PA

Bulletin 769 (1977) Determination of organic vapors in the industrial atmosphere. Supelco, Bellefonte, PA

Bulletin (1981) Carbosphere. Appl Sci Lab, Deerfield, IL

Caprioli RM (1972) Use of stable isotopes. In: Waller RG (ed) Biochemical applications of mass spectrometry. Wiley, New York London Sydney Toronto, pp 735–779
Carlsson J (1973) Simplified gas chromatographic procedure for identification of bacterial metabolic products. Appl Microbiol 25:287–289
Cochrane GC (1975) A review of the analysis of free fatty acids [C_2–C_6]. J Chromatogr Sci 13:440–447
Colby J, Dalton H (1978) Resolution of the methane mono-oxygenase of *Methylococcus capsulatus* (Bath) into three components. Purification and properties of component C, a flavoprotein. Biochem J 171:461–468
Colby J, Dalton H, Whittenbury R (1975) An improved assay for bacterial methane mono-oxygenase: some properties of the enzyme from *Methylomonas methanica*. Biochem J 151:459–462
Colby J, Dalton H, Whittenbury R (1979) Biological and biochemical aspects of microbial growth on C_1 compounds. Annu Rev Microbiol 33:481–517
Conrad R, Thauer RK (1983) Carbon monoxide production by *Methanobacterium thermoautotrophicum*. FEMS Microbiol Lett 20:229–232
Cramers CA, McNair HM (1983) Gas chromatography. In: Heftmann E (ed) Chromatography fundamentals and applications of chromatographic and electrophoretic techniques, pt A: fundamentals and techniques. Elsevier, Amsterdam Oxford New York, pp A195–A224
Dalton H (1980) Oxidation of hydrocarbons by methane monooxygenases from a variety of microbes. Adv Appl Microbiol 26:71–87
Daniels L, Fuchs G, Thauer RK, Zeikus JG (1977) Carbon monoxide oxidation by methanogenic bacteria. J Bacteriol 132:18–126
Daniels L, Fulton G, Spencer RW, Orme-Johnson WH (1980) Origin of hydrogen in methane produced by *Methanobacterium thermoautotrophicum*. J Bacteriol 141:694–698
Dean JA (ed) (1973) Lange's handbook of chemistry, 11th edn. McGraw-Hill, New York, pp 1015–1017
Dennis LM, Nichols ML (1929) Gas analysis. MacMillan, New York, pp 138–259
Ferenci T (1974) Carbon monoxide-stimulated respiration in methane-utilizing bacteria. FEBS Lett 41:94–98
Ferenci T, Strom T, Quayle JR (1975) Oxidation of carbon monoxide and methane by *Pseudomonas methanica*. J Gen Microbiol 91:79–91
Ferry JG, Wolfe RW (1976) Anaerobic degradation of benzoate to methane by a microbial consortium. Arch Microbiol 107:33–40
Fuchs G, Thauer R, Ziegler H, Stichler W (1979) Carbon isotope fractionation by *Methanobacterium thermoautotrophicum*. Arch Microbiol 120:135–139
Glover J (1956) Methods involving labeled atoms. In: Paech K, Tracey MV (eds) Modern methods of plant analysis, vol 1. Springer, Berlin Göttingen Heidelberg, pp 325–374
Gnaiger E, Forstner H (eds) (1983) Polarographic oxygen sensors. Springer, Berlin Heidelberg New York, pp 370
Hanson RS (1980) Ecology and diversity of methylotrophic organisms. Adv Appl Microbiol 26:3–39
Hash JH (1972) Liquid scintillation counting in microbiology. In: Norris JR, Ribbons RW (eds) Methods in microbiology, vol 6 B. Academic Press, New York London, pp 109–155
Higgins IJ, Quayle JR (1970) Oxygenation of methane by methane-grown *Pseudomonas methanica* and *Methanomonas methanooxidans*. Biochem J 118:201–208
Higgins IJ, Best DJ, Hammond RC, Scott D (1981) Methane-oxidizing microorganisms. Microbiol Rev 45:556–590
Hippe H, Caspari D, Fiebig K, Gottschalk G (1979) Utilization of trimethylamine and other N-methyl compounds for growth and methane formation by *Methanosarcina barkeri*. Proc Natl Acad Sci Usa 76:494–498
Hou CT, Patel RN, Laskin AI, Barnabe N (1979) Microbial oxidation of gaseous hydrocarbons: epoxidation of n-alkenes by methylotrophic bacteria. Appl Environ Microbiol 38:127–134

Hou CT, Patel RN, Laskin AI (1980) Epoxidation and ketone formation by C_1-utilizing microbes. Adv Appl Microbiol 26:41–69

Imai T, Takigawa H, Nakagawa S, Shen S, Kodama T, Minoda Y (1986) Microbial oxidation of hydrocarbons and related compounds by whole-cell suspensions of the methane-oxidizing bacterium H-2. Appl Environ Microbiol 52:1403–1406

Jones JW, Nagle DP, Whitman WR (1987) Methanogens and the diversity of archaebacteria. Microbiol Rev 51:135–177

Karmen A, McCaffrey I, Bowman RL (1962) A flow-through method of scintillation counting of carbon-14 and tritium in gas-liquid chromatographic effluents. J Lipid Res 3:372–377

Kenten RH (1956) Gasometric analysis in plant investigation (Warburg, van Slyke, microdiffusion methods and ethylene). In: Paech K, Tracey MV (eds) Modern methods of plant analysis, vol 1. Springer, Berlin Göttingen Heidelberg, pp 415–451

Keppler JG, Dijkstron G, Schols JA (1957) In: Destry DF (ed) Vapour phase chromatography, proceedings of the first symposium. Academic Press, New York London, p 222

Krzycki JA, Zeikus JG (1984) Acetate catabolism by *Methanosarcina barkeri*: hydrogen-dependent methane production from acetate by a soluble cell protein fraction. FEMS Microbiol Lett 25:27–32

Kyryacos G, Boord CE (1957) Separation of hydrogen, oxygen, nitrogen, methane, and carbon monoxide by gas adsorption chromatography. Anal Chem 29:787–788

Laurinavichus KS, Belyaev SS (1979) Radioisotope method for determining microbial methane production rate. Mikrobiologiya (Engl Transl Plenum, New York) 47:1115–1116

Leak DJ, Dalton H (1983) In vivo studies of primary alcohols, aldehydes and carboxylic acids as electron donors for the methane mono-oxygenase in a variety of methanotrophs. J Gen Microbiol 129:3487–3497

Littlewood AB (1970) Gas chromatography, principle, techniques, and applications. Academic Press, New York London, pp 546

Lovely DR, White RH, Ferry JG (1984) Identification of methyl coenzyme M as an intermediate in methanogenesis from acetate in *Methanosarcina* spp. J Bacteriol 160:521–525

Mah RA, Smith MR (1981) The methanogenic bacteria. In: Starr MP, Stolp H, Truper HG, Balows A, Schlegel HG (eds) The prokaryotes and handbook on habitats, isolation, and identification of bacteria. Springer, Berlin Heidelberg New York, pp 948–977

Mah RA, Smith MR, Baresi L (1978) Studies on an acetate-fermenting strain of *Methanosarcina*. Appl Environ Microbiol 35:1174–1184

Martin RO (1968) Gas chromatograph-combustion-continuous counting system for analysis of microgram amounts of radioactive metabolites. Anal Biochem 40:1197–1200

McBride BC, Wolfe RS (1971) A new coenzyme of methyl transfer, coenzyme M. Biochemistry 10:2317–2324

McPheat WL, Mann NH, Dalton H (1987) Isolation of mutants of the obligate methanotroph *Methylomonas albus* defective in growth on methane. Arch Microbiol 148:40–43

Meijden P van der, Heythuysen HJ, Sliepenbeek HT, Houwen FP, Drift C van der, Vogels GD (1983) Activation and inactivation of methanol: 2-mercaptoethanesulfonic acid methyltransferase from *Methanosarcina barkeri*. J Bacteriol 153:6–11

Meyers AJ (1980) Evalutation of bromoethane as a suitable analogue in methane oxidation studies. FEMS Microbiol Lett 9:297–300

Naumann E, Fahlbusch K, Gottschalk G (1984) Presence of a trimethylamine: HS-coenzyme M methyltransferase in *Methanosarcina barkeri*. Arch Microbiol 138:79–83

Nelson DR, Zeikus JG (1974) Rapid method for the radioisotopic analysis of gaseous end products of anaerobic metabolism. Appl Microbiol 28:258–261

Nelson MK, Ferry JG (1984) Carbon monoxide-dependent methyl coenzyme M methylreductase in acetotrophic bacteria. J Bacteriol 160:526–532

Niosh Manual of analytical methods (1974) HEW Publ (NIOSH) 75-121 2nd edn, vol 1–7. Superintendent of documents, US Gov Print Off, Washington, DC (GPO No 1733-0041)

Ohi K, Nishimura T, Okazaki M, Miura Y (1979) Determination of dissolved hydrogen concentration during cultivation and assimilation of gaseous substrates by *Alcaligenes hydrogenophilus*. J Ferment Technol 57:203–209

Ottenstein DM, Bartley DA (1971 a) Separation of free acids C_2-C_5 in dilute aqueous solution column technology. J Chromatogr Sci 9:673–681

Ottenstein DM, Bartley DA (1971 b) Improved gas chromatography separation of free acids C_2-C_5 in dilute solution. Anal Chem 43:952–955

Patel RN, Hou CT, Laskin AI, Felix A (1982) Microbial oxidation of hydrocarbons: properties of a soluble methane monooxygenase from a facultative methane-utilizing organism, *Methylobacterium* sp. strain CRL-26. Appl Environ Microbiol 44:1130–1137

Pine M, Barker HA (1956) Studies on the methane fermentation XII. The pathway of hydrogen in the acetate fermentation. J Bacteriol 71:644–648

Popjak G, Lowe AE, Moore D (1962) Scintillation counter for simultaneous assay of H^3 and C^{14} in gas-liquid chromatographic vapors. J Lipid Res 3:364–371

Purnell H (1962) Gas chromatography. Wiley, New York, pp 441

Reeburgh WS (1980) Anaerobic methane oxidation; rate depth distribution in Skan Bay sediments. Earth Planet Sci Lett 47:345–352

Ribbons DW (1975) Oxidation of C_1 compounds by particulate fractions from *Methylococcus capsulatus*: distribution and properties of methane-dependent reduced nicotinamide adenine dinucleotide oxidase (methane hydroxylase). J Bacteriol 122:1351–1363

Ribbons DW, Michalover JL (1970) Methane oxidation by cell-free extracts of *Methylococcus capsulatus*. FEBS Lett 11:41–44

Robbins JD, Bakke JE (1967) Method for collecting $^{14}CO_2$ from a hydrogen flame detector. J Gas Chromatogr 5:525–526

Robinson JA, Strayer RF, Tiedge JM (1981) Method for measuring dissolved hydrogen in anaerobic ecosystems: application to the rumen. Appl Environ Microbiol 41:545⁵48

Rogosa M, Love LL (1968) Direct quantitative gas chromatographic separation of C_2-C_6 fatty acids, methanol, and ethyl alcohol in aqueous microbial fermentation media. Appl Microbiol 16:285–290

Roitsch T, Stolp H (1985) Distribution of dissimilatory enzymes in methane and methanol oxidizing bacteria. Arch Microbiol 143:233–236

Romesser JA, Balch WE (1980) Coenzyme M: preparation and assay. Meth Enzymol 67:545–556

Salanitro JP, Muirhead PA (1975) Quantitative method for the gas chromatographic analysis of short-chain monocarboxylic and dicarboxylic acids in fermentation media. Appl Microbiol 29:374–381

Simmons JH (1972) The use of gas chromatography to measure organic solvent in factory atmospheres. In: Perry SG (ed) Gas chromatography. Applied Science, England pp 17–24

Smith MR, Lequerica JL (1985) *Methanosarcina* mutant unable to produce methane or assimilate carbon from acetate. J Bacteriol 164:618–625

Smith MR, Mah RA (1980) Acetate as sole carbon and energy source for growth of *Methanosarcina* strain 227. Appl Environ Microbiol 39:992–999

Stanley SH, Prior SH, Leak DJ, Dalton H (1983) Copper stress underlies the fundamental change in intracellular location of methane mono-oxygenase in methane-oxidizing organisms: studies in batch and continuous cultures. Biotech Lett 5:487–492

Taylor GT, Pirt SJ (1977) Nutrition and factors limiting the growth of a methanogenic bacterium (*Methanobacterium thermoautotrophicum*). Arch Microbiol 113:17–22

Tonge GM, Harrison DEF, Knowles CJ, Higgins IJ (1975) Properties and partial purification of the methane-oxidising enzyme system from *Methylosinus trichosporium*. FEBS Lett 58:293–299

Umbreit WW, Burris RW, Stauffer JF (1964) Manometric techniques a manual describing methods applicable to the study of tissue metabolism. Burgess, Minneapolis, pp 5–24

Walther R, Fahlbusch K, Sievert R, Gottschalk G (1981) Formation of trideuteromethane from deuterated trimethylamine or methylamine by *Methanosarcina barkeri*. J Bacteriol 148:371–373

Washburn EW, West CJ, Dorsey NE, Bichowsky FR, Klemene A (eds) (1928) International critical tables of numeric data physics, chemistry and technology, vol 3. McGraw-Hill, New York, pp 254–269

Watson JT (1972) Mass spectrometry instrumentation. In: Waller GR (ed) Biochemical applications of mass spectrometry. Wiley, New York London Sydney Toronto, pp 23–49

Whittenbury R, Dalton H (1981) The methylotrophic bacteria. In: Starr MP, Stolp H, Truper HG, Balows A, Schlegel HG (eds) The prokaryotes a handbook on habitats, isolation and identification of bacteria. Springer, Berlin Heidelberg New York, pp 894–902

Whittenbury R, Phillips KC, Wilkinson JF (1970) Enrichment, isolation and some properties of methane-utilizing bacteria. J Gen Microbiol 61:205–218

Whittenbury R, Dalton H, Eccleston M, Reed HL (1974) The different types of methane oxidizing bacteria and some of their more unusual properties. Proc Int Symp Microbiol growth on C_1-compounds. Soc Ferment Technol, Osaka, Jpn, pp 1–9

Wilhelm E, Battino R, Wilcock RJ (1977) Low pressure solubility of gases in liquid water. Chem Rev 77:219–262

Wolfe RS, Higgins IJ (1979) Microbial biochemistry of methane – a study in contrasts. Int Rev Biochem 21:267–353

Zehnder AJB, Brock TD (1979) Methane formation and methane oxidation by methanogenic bacteria. J Bacteriol 137:420–432

Zehnder AJB, Wuhrmann K (1977) Physiology of a *Methanobacterium* strain AZ. Arch Microbiol 111:199–205

Zehnder AJB, Huser B, Brock TD (1979) Measuring radioactive methane with the liquid scintillation counter. Appl Environ Microbiol 37:897–899

Zinder SH, Mah RA (1979) Isolation and characterization of a thermophilic strain of *Methanosarcina* unable to use H_2-CO_2 for methanogenesis. Appl Environ Microbiol 38:996–1008

Zinder SH, Cardwell SC, Anguish T, Lee M, Koch K (1984) Methanogenesis in a thermophilic (58°) anaerobic digestor: *Methanothrix* sp. as an important aceticlastic methanogen. Appl Environ Microbiol 47:796–807

Methods for the Quantification of Ethylene Produced by Plants

P. K. Bassi and M. S. Spencer

1 Introduction

Ethylene is unique among plant hormones in that it occurs naturally in the gaseous form. Plants produce ethylene in very minute quantities. It is generally agreed that gases in plants are in constant equilibrium with the environment and that the rate of ethylene emanation can be used as an index of the rate of synthesis inside the plant.

The rate of ethylene production has been shown to vary with the species, the organ, and the stage of growth and development. It also varies with the environmental conditions. Thus, it is critical that the quantification of ethylene be done with techniques that keep the alteration of environment, including the gaseous environment, at a minimum during quantification. A continuous flow system to accomplish this is described.

2 Bioassays

Bioassays have been effectively used for the detection of ethylene production and the screening of ethylene-producing compounds. These assays are described in a recent handbook (Yopp et al. 1986).

In general, the focus in bioassays tends to be on the qualitative rather than the quantitative aspects of hormonal analysis. The focus of the present chapter, however, is on the quantification of the minute amounts of ethylene emanating from plant tissues.

3 Gas Chromatographic Analysis of Ethylene

Gas chromatography is the most commonly used technique for the quantitative analysis of ethylene.

3.1 Columns

We have experimented with several different types of solid supports for the chromatography columns. Silica gel, alumina, carbosieve B, and Porapak Q (Supelco

Canada Ltd., Oakville, Ontario) work well. When the column is likely to be exposed to excess moisture and carbon dioxide, the best performance is obtained with Porapak Q. However, ethane and ethylene can have similar retention times on the Porapak Q column. If one of these compounds is prominent it might interfere with integration of the other peak, and in such a case operating parameters must be adjusted to improve peak resolution. Ward et al. (1978) also discuss the choice of chromatography columns.

For routine analysis of ethylene by direct sample injection, Porapak Q (80–100 mesh) in a stainless steel column (3 m × 3.175 mm OD) and a 40 ml min^{-1} flow rate of helium, the carrier gas, serve well. The column is operated iosthermally at 40° C. Samples (1–3 ml, depending on gas concentration) are injected with gas-tight syringes. Disposable plastic syringes are adequate if they are flushed repeatedly (at least three times) with sample gas. They should be used for only one gas mixture since gas absorbed by the plastic may contaminate subsequent samples. Glass gas-tight syringes are more expensive but more reliable.

For larger samples, such as those from the ethylene collection trap described below, a wider column is used (3 m × 6.35 mm OD). The flow rate is increased to 60 ml min^{-1}. With either column, a 1:1 effluent splitter can be attached to direct one-half the flow through the flame ionization detector for quantification of hydrocarbons, and the other half through a thermal conductivity detector for determination of carbon dioxide. An auxiliary flow (30 ml min^{-1}) of carrier gas directly to the thermal conductivity detector is required to improve the stability of the signal. The splitter enables analysis of both hydrocarbons and carbon dioxide in a single injection.

After several runs, columns are regenerated by heating to 120° C for a few minutes. The frequency and length of the heating depend on the amounts of moisture and higher molecular weight hydrocarbons introduced in the column.

3.2 Detectors

3.2.1 Flame Ionization

The most commonly used detector for ethylene analysis is the flame ionization detector. These detectors can be used to analyze ethylene for concentrations as low as 10 $mm^3\ m^{-3}$ in 5-ml gaseous samples (Ward et al. 1978; Bassi and Spencer 1985).

3.2.2 Photoionization

Photoionization detectors can enhance the sensitivity range of gas chromatography by almost an order of magnitude. Thus, photoionization detectors can analyze ethylene levels in the order of 1 $mm^3\ m^{-3}$ (Bassi and Spencer 1985). This permits analysis of ethylene evolution by plants without the use of a collection trap for concentration of the sample.

In selecting a photoionization detector, care should be taken to ensure that the lamp has an ionization potential of near 10.5 eV, required for ethylene analysis. We have used a Photorae Model 10A10 Portable Photoionization Gas Chromatograph, Photovac Incorporated, Canada, with a Poropak Q column, for many years.

4 Continuous Flow Systems

There are three requirements for an efficient flow through system, an air purifier, a sample chamber, and a collection trap. Figure 1 shows such a system.

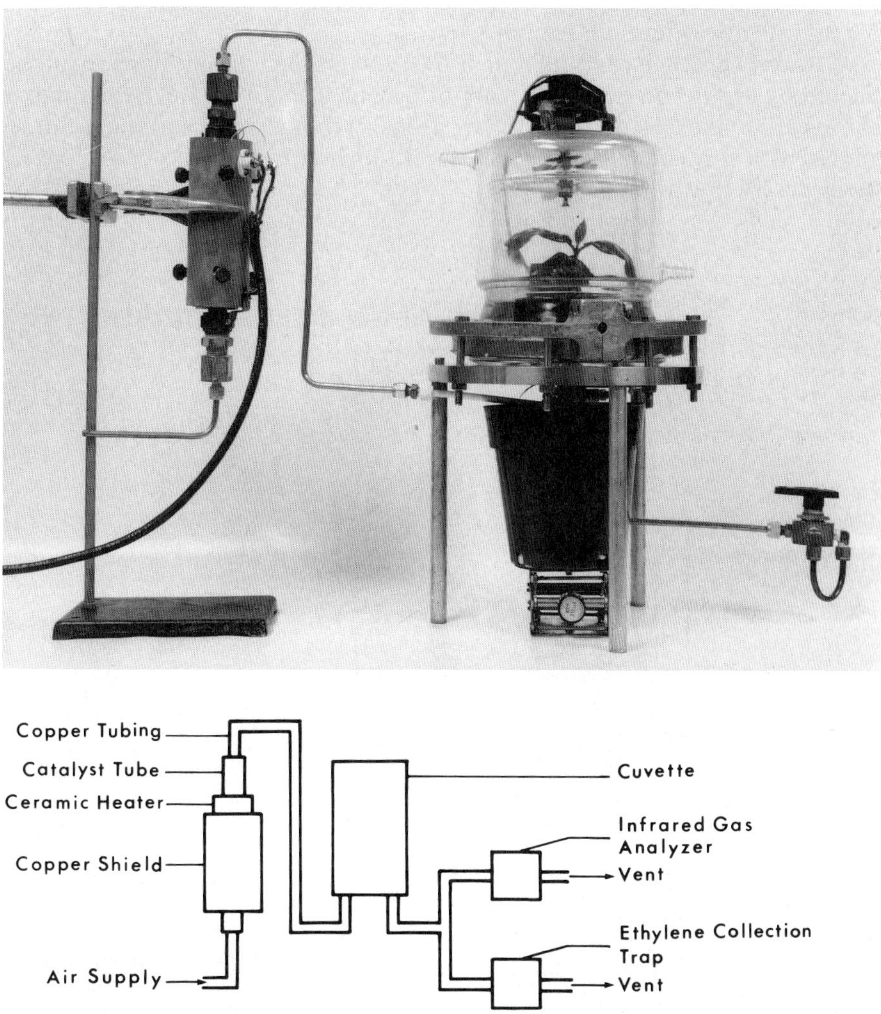

Fig. 1. The complete system for measurement of ethylene production by intact shoots. The individual components are described in the text

All connections between the components should be made with 0.635 cm OD tubing made from materials that do not produce hydrocarbons. The pliability of copper and Teflon tubing makes them ideal for the purpose. If the plant has a high rate of transpiration, water vapors may freeze near the collection trap and plug smaller diameter tubing.

4.1 Purification of Air

As has been indicated above, plants tend to have a very low rate of ethylene emanation. Therefore, the background contaminants in most commercial air sources can make accurate measurement of the rate of ethylene production difficult. Moreover, ethylene in the air can influence plant metabolism and conceivably alter the rate of ethylene production.

We found (Eastwell et al. 1978) that the most efficient air purification can be achieved by heating air in the presence of a metal catalyst to convert hydrocarbons to carbon dioxide and water. The residual carbon dioxide and water can be removed with conventional traps. NO_x species are not by-products of this purification process (Eastwell et al. 1981).

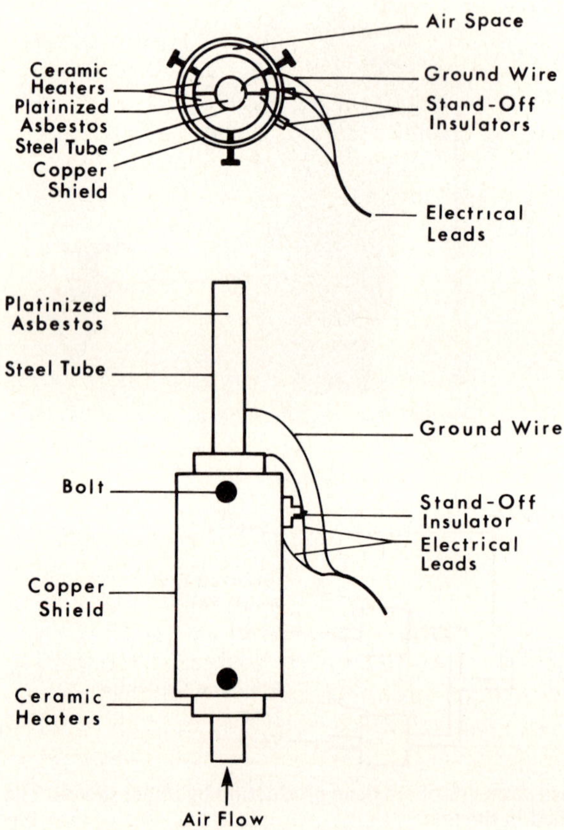

Fig. 2. Purification system for oxidation of hydrocarbons in an air stream. The tube containing platinized asbestos is heated to 650° C. The temperature is regulated by a rheostat in the voltage line (Eastwell et al. 1986)

Figure 2 shows an apparatus that can be assembled inexpensively with commercially available materials. About 4 g of platinized asbestos (5% w/w, K&K Laboratories, Plainsview, N.Y. 11803) is shredded with forceps and packed loosely in a stainless steel tube (1.9 cm diameter, 30 cm long) (other supports for the platinum are also commercially available and may be preferable from the health standpoint). The tube is enclosed in the ceramic core of heating elements, and the assembly is inserted into a galvanized steel pipe (5 cm ID, 13 cm long and thick enough to permit tapping of three holes drilled through the pipe toward each end). Bolts are threaded through the holes to center and secure the heating core. The two leads from the heating element are attached to leads from the power supply with stand-off insulators. A ground wire is attached to the steel tubing and the electrical wires are insulated with ceramic rings. A rheostat controls the temperature of the heater. To obtain the correct operating temperature the voltage is slowly stepped up until no hydrocarbons can be detected in the effluent from the catalyst system, or alternatively, a thermocouple can be used.

An apparatus with the above dimensions, operated at 650° C will remove ethylene at air flow rates of up to 200 ml min^{-1}. Greater flow rates can be accommodated with a larger catalyst bed and/or preheating of the air before it contacts the catalyst. The temperature of the catalyst should not be raised above 650° C as it leads ultimately to the inactivation of the catalyst by formation of platinum oxides and to the deplatinization of the asbestos.

The concentration of carbon dioxide in air varies considerably, depending on the air source. Also, some carbon dioxide will be produced by the oxidation of hydrocarbons in the heated catalyst system. If supplementation of the air with carbon dioxide is necessary, it should be done before air purification. (Commercial carbon dioxide contains hydrocarbons.) On the other hand, carbon dioxide can be removed from the air stream by dispersing the air in a 5% (w/w) solution of sodium hydroxide.

4.2 Sample Chambers

The materials used for the construction of sample chambers for enclosing the plant materials need to be selected with caution. They should not emanate or absorb ethylene under any of a variety of environmental conditions. Over the years, we have constructed several chambers that can be used for different tissues. Figures 3 and 4 give examples of two such units.

The size of the small chamber (Fig. 3) can be customized depending on the individual needs. The inner glass tube, which extends to within 3 mm of the bottom of the vessel, is the gas inlet. It is tapered to provide better dispersion of gases. Springs that hold the glass joint together securely usually ensure an air-tight seal, but if necessary, Teflon sleeves designed for tapered glass joints can be added. The sleeves also prevent the glass joints from seizing. The all-glass construction contributes no hydrocarbons and also permits autoclaving if needed. The sidearm vent may be loosely packed with glass wool to reduce the possibility of microbial contamination of the sample. The vent is connected by Teflon unions to the ethylene collection system, thus protecting the glass from chipping. Use of flexible

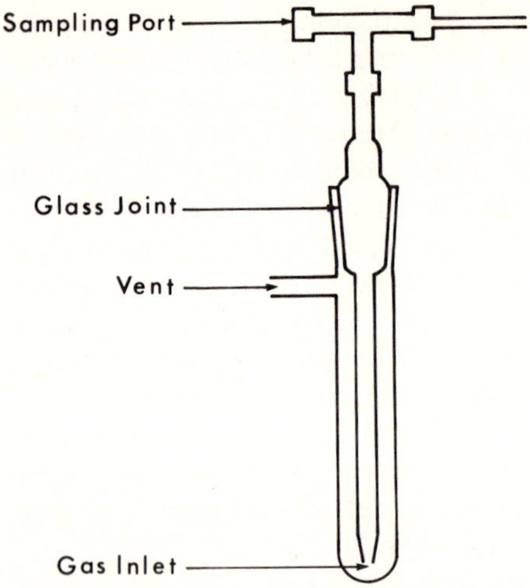

Fig. 3. A culture tube for measuring ethylene production by cell suspensions or small segments of tissue suspended in a small volume of medium. The medium can be maintained at a constant temperature by partial immersion of the culture tube in a constant temperature water bath

Teflon tubing between the culture tube and the collection trap reduces stress on the glass. Eastwell and Spencer (1982) used this open system to study the effect of ethylene on the release of amylase by isolated barley aleurone layers. The same paper also documents the high concentrations of carbon dioxide that accumulate from even small quantities of tissue in a closed system over a short period of time.

Figure 4 illustrates a chamber designed for selective enclosures of plant shoots and allows for precise control of environmental conditions. Similar chambers can be built for roots, individual leaves, etc. of intact plants, or for intact plants. The design permits isolation, if desired, of one part of a plant from the remainder, without wounding (with resultant wound ethylene production). With the exception of the glass chamber (which has to be custom made to suit individual applications), all the other components of this setup can be purchased commercially. The double layered glass chamber with a 1-cm-thick water jacket provides excellent temperature control when a constant temperature water stream is circulated through the chamber.

As shown in Fig. 4 at the bottom of the cuvette a glass collar (15.2 cm diameter) with an "O" ring groove at the base (Corning Glass Works, Cat. No. P1360) is fused with the glass chamber. A Teflon "O" ring is inserted in the groove and a circular aluminum flange (Corning Glass Works, Cat. No. P9450) is mounted around the glass cylinder. The cylinder is pressed against a stainless steel plate by means of eight bolts. An asbestos gasket cushions the metal flange against the glass collar. The plant is inserted in the cuvette through an opening (7 cm diameter) in the base plate and the stem is positioned in a small slit (5 mm wide) in the side of this opening. The opening is then resealed with a metal block with the help of a Teflon "O" ring. The area around the stem must be sealed with a material that does not release or absorb hydrocarbons. For this purpose we have successfully used cellulose based Polyfilla (FMC of Canada Ltd., Burlington, Ontario, Canada).

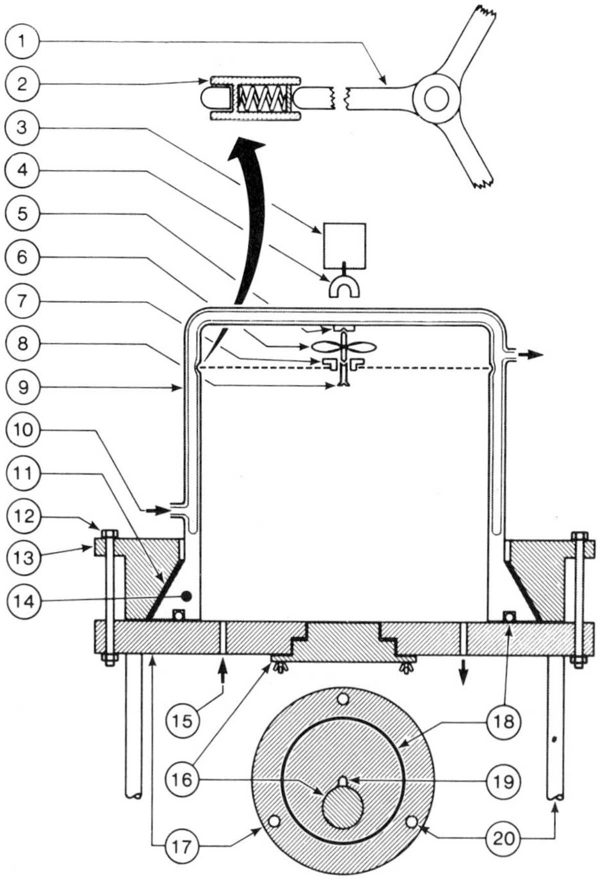

Fig. 4. Cross-sectional view of a cuvette for measurement of ethylene production by intact shoots. *1* Glass ring; *2* spring-loaded aluminum support; *3* motor; *4* magnet; *5* brass disc; *6* fan; *7* aluminum collar; *8* brass screw; *9* glass cylinder; *10* water inlet; *11* asbestos gasket; *12* bolt; *13* aluminum flange; *14* glass collar; *15* air inlet; *16* stainless steel resealing block; *17* base plate; *18* Teflon "O" ring; *19* stem slit; *20* aluminum stand (Bassi and Spencer 1979)

An aluminum fan blade assists air mixing in the cuvette. The stainless steel shaft of the fan is mounted between a brass disk in the top of the cuvette and a brass screw held in place with spring-loaded aluminum supports. Powdered graphite lubricates points of contact between the stainless steel shaft and the brass. To avoid problems associated with hydrocarbons produced by the motor, the fan is driven from outside the cuvette by a rotating magnet.

Immediately prior to assembly, all components of the system are washed with a solvent (methanol : acetone : carbon tetrachloride : hexane, 1 : 1 : 1 : 1), then heated at 250° C for 8 h to remove any solvent residues. During assembly, clean surgical gloves are worn (photolysis of fingerprint residues produces ethylene).

4.3 Collection Trap for Ethylene Analysis

In a continuous flow system, the concentration of ethylene in the effluent is usually below the detection capabilities of flame ionization detectors. This problem can be overcome by selectively collecting ethylene on a solid support such as silica gel (Stinson and Spencer 1969; Eastwell et al. 1986). Figure 5 gives a diagrammatic representation of this method.

The trap consists of a copper U-tube (each arm 4-cm-long) containing 0.5 g of silica gel (30 to 60 mesh). The gel is held in place by glass wool plugs. The amount of silica gel can be increased if the experiment requires it. The U-tube is attached by metal unions to a four-way ball valve (Fig. 5 A). Before beginning collection, all room air is flushed out of the trap by immersing it in a boiling water bath and purging it with sample gas. At this temperature no ethylene will be retained by the trap.

Then the four-way valve is turned so that the gas flow bypasses the collection trap (Fig. 5 A). The U-tube is immersed in a dry ice-acetone slurry for 10 min to equilibrate, while the remainder of the system is being purged with sample gas. At time zero collection is initiated by turning the valve so that the gas flow goes through the trap. After a given length of time, shown (by preliminary experiments) to provide sufficient ethylene for analysis, the valve is turned to the bypass position, isolating the sample collected in the U-tube.

The collection device, including the four-way valve, is disconnected from the sample air line and attached to the side port valve of the gas chromatograph. The

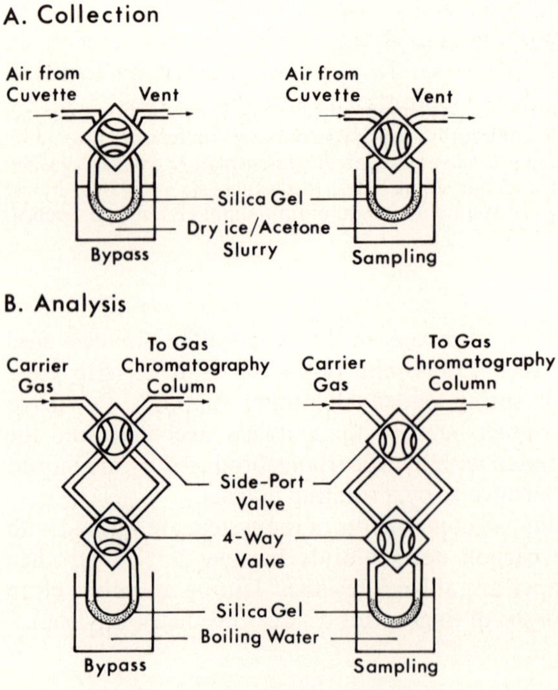

Fig. 5 A, B. Collection **A** and subsequent release **B** of ethylene from a continuous flow system (Eastwell et al. 1986)

trap is heated in a boiling water bath for 10 min to liberate the collected ethylene from the silica gel. During this period the remainder of the tubing and valve is flushed with carrier gas from the gas chromatograph. Then the valve on the trap is turned so that the carrier gas flows through the collection tube and directly onto the gas chromatographic column for analysis (Fig. 5 B). The rate of emanation of ethylene by the plant is calculated from the time for which ethylene collection is made during sampling.

5 Analysis of Ethylene in Aqueous Samples

Since the solubility of ethylene in water is limited, and only small amounts of the gas are produced by most tissues, analysis of ethylene by direct injection of the aqueous sample onto the gas chromatographic columns is not possible. Alternate methods are described and assessed below.

5.1 Head Space Analysis

Estimations of the amount of ethylene dissolved in a liquid medium have most often been made by quantifying the amount of ethylene in the head space above the liquid. This analysis is based on the assumption that ethylene in the gaseous phase above the aqueous solution is in equilibrium with the liquid phase.

These measurements are made either by taking a gaseous sample directly above the liquid phase or by equilibrating a subsample of liquid with an inert gas. Head space analysis, in general, fails to account for gases that remain dissolved in the medium, or in attempting to account for them the medium is treated as pure water for calculation of dissolved ethylene. The fact that changes in amounts of dissolved gases may occur as a result of changes in medium composition during tissue incubation is ignored. In continuous-flow systems, the gaseous phase in equilibrium with the liquid phase becomes negligible.

5.2 Liquid Injection on Gas Chromatographic Columns

McAuliffe (1966) used direct liquid injections on the gas chromatograph to measure the solubility of hydrocarbons in water. The general approach was to absorb excess water on a precolumn packed with firebrick: ascarite (1:2) before the sample reached the chromatographic column. In our experience, this approach has serious lilmitations when used with plants. Most plant tissues produce ethylene at very low rates and this fact, coupled with the low solubility of ethylene in water, make the direct liquid sample injection technique ineffective. The technique also requires frequent repacking of the precolumn and/or extensive heating cycles between runs to purge the excess moisture from the chromatographic column.

5.3 Vacuum Extraction

This technique is based on the use of vacuum to enhance extraction of dissolved gases in liquids. For example, this approach has been used to extract dissolved oxygen from human plasma and fermentation media (Ramsey 1959; Roxburgh 1962, respectively). Vacuum extraction has also been used to extract ethylene from plant tissues (Beyer and Morgan 1970). For a comprehensive review on the procedures for extraction and analysis of internal ethylene from plant tissues, please refer to Saltveit (1982).

We have used vacuum extraction to quantify ethylene dissolved in water and culture media (Bassi et al. 1981). This technique can accommodate large sample volumes and is useful when the ethylene concentration in solution is very low.

Figure 6A shows the apparatus used. Care should be taken to ensure that none of the apparatus components that come in contact with the sample produce and or absorb ethylene. A cylindrical separatory funnel (12 × 3.3 cm OD) is provided with a hollow glass stopper containing a standard injection port to accommodate a Teflon-faced silicone rubber septum. The facing prevents contamination of extracted gases by substances from the septum. The funnel is connected

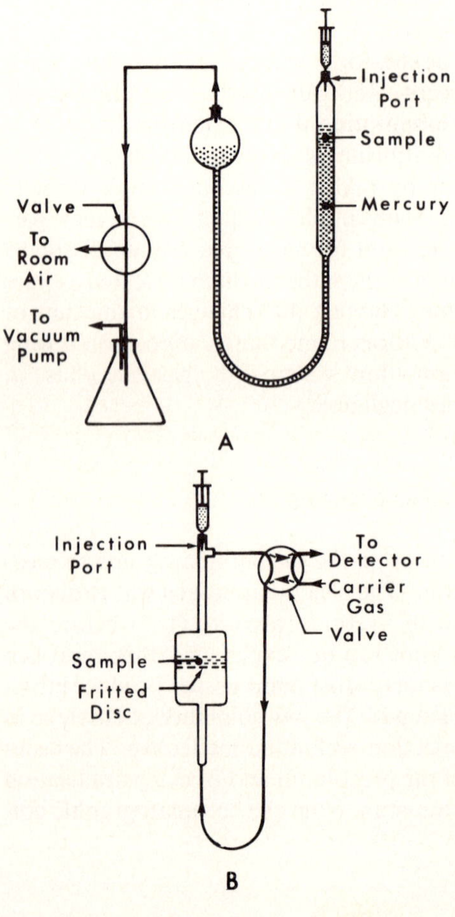

Fig. 6 A, B. Apparatuses used for the extraction of dissolved ethylene from aqueous solutions by: **A** the vacuum extraction method and **B** the gas stripping technique (Bassi et al. 1981)

with tygon tubing to a mercury reservoir. The vacuum source should be such that it allows for fast and reproducible extraction of dissolved gases. We use a portable piston vacuum pump to generate a vacuum of 510 mm mercury.

The most reproducible results are obtained when 3 ml of hydrocarbon-free air are injected preceding the liquid sample to be extracted. This is followed by injection of the sample through the septum into the funnel. For reproducible ethylene recovery the sample volume should be uniform; we generally use 3 ml. Vacuum is applied to the mercury reservoir. The heights of the mercury columns in the reservoir and funnel are adjusted to the same level so that the vacuum in the funnel is not altered by an unsupported column of mercury. Gentle tapping of the mercury column helps dislodge the gas bubbles that form on the interface between glass and mercury and assists the intermixing of the liquid and gaseous phases. For most samples up to 20 ml, a 10-min extraction gives optimum results. Longer periods may be required for viscous samples. After this period, the vacuum is released and the height of the reservoir is again adjusted to equalize the mercury level. The entire gas volume is quickly drawn through the septum with a gas-tight syringe and injected into the gas chromatograph for analysis. As a safety precaution, the vacuum pump should be exhausted in a fume hood to prevent any possible contamination of the laboratory with mercury vapors.

Both this vacuum extraction technique and the gas stripping procedure described below have been standardized (Bassi et al. 1981) and give amounts of ethylene within 8% of the theoretical value at ethylene concentrations from 0 to 5 μl ml^{-1}. Since the fraction of ethylene recovered from solution is reproducible through this concentration range, the methods are readily calibrated.

5.4 Gas Stripping

In this technique, the carrier gas of the gas chromatograph is used to displace the dissolved gases from the solution and to carry theses gases directly onto the analytical column. This approach was first used by Swinnerton et al. (1962) for the extraction of dissolved gases from sea water. The carrier gas is passed through a side chamber containing the liquid to be extracted. The technique is very efficient and requires only minor modifications of the gas chromatograph to accommodate a four-way side-port valve. This enables the carrier gas, at a specified flow rate, to be directed through the sample chamber when desired. A 3 m × 6.3 mm OD stainless steel chromatographic column packed with 80–100 mesh Porpak Q should be used to accommodate the relatively large volumes of gas entering the column.

Figure 6B gives an overview of the apparatus we have standardized for this purpose. The sample chamber can be easily constructed in a glass shop. It is an all-glass cuvette with a fritted glass disk of medium porosity (20–200 μ) across the center. The fritted disk prevents the drainage of the liquid sample without seriously impeding the flow of the carrier gas. The top of the cuvette is fitted with a septum contained in a 0.635×10^{-2} m nut to serve as the injection port. The glass assembly and the four-way valve are installed in the carrier gas line of the gas chromatograph as shown in Fig. 6 B. Heat-shrinkable Teflon tubing provides and excellent way of joining metal to glass.

Before each run, the glass chamber is flushed with the carrier gas for 5 min to remove room air. The side-port valve is turned so that the carrier gas bypasses the sample chamber, and any residual pressure in the cuvette is released by perforating the septum with a fine needle. Then a known volume of sample is injected through the septum. The carrier gas is immediately passed through the sample, taking the eluted gases directly onto the chromatographic column. When Porapak Q is used as the packing material for the chromatographic column, a carrier gas (helium) flow rate of 60 ml min^{-1} is optimum for this technique. It is advisable to have a precolumn for the absorption of excess moisture before the sample enters the chromatographic column. An in-line filter should be installed in the carrier gas line. If foaming occurs, it can be eliminated by the addition of a drop of antifoaming agent.

The gas-stripping technique is limited to a degree by the small sample volumes that can be used with direct passage of the stripped gas onto the chromatographic column. As bigger chambers are used to accommodate larger sample sizes, the resultant gas chromatographic peaks become diffuse, and unsuitable for quantitative measurements. However, the problem can be circumvented by concentration of the stripped gases in a collection trap, such as the one described above, before entry to the gas chromatographic column.

6 Summary

The methods described here have been used to answer a variety of questions pertaining to ethylene physiology in plants. They range from in vivo studies with intact plants to experiments with isolated tissues and subcellular particles. In addition to increasing the overall accuracy of measurements of rates of ethylene production, these techniques allow for precise monitoring of changes in the rate of ethylene production on a temporal basis.

References

Bassi PK, Spencer MS (1979) A cuvette design for measurement of ethylene production and carbon dioxide exchange by intact shoots under controlled environmental conditions. Plant Physiol 64:488–490

Bassi PK, Spencer MS (1985) Comparative evaluation of photoionization and flame ionization detectors for ethylene analysis. Plant Cell Environ 8:161–165

Bassi PK, Eastwell KC, Akalehiywot T, Spencer MS (1981) Methods for quantitative determination of ethylene in aqueous solutions for biological studies. Plant Cell Environ 4:271–274

Beyer EM, Morgan PW (1970) A method for determining the concentration of ethylene in the gas phase of vegetative plant tissues. Plant Physiol 46:352–354

Eastwell KC, Spencer MS (1982) Effect of ethylene on the gibberellic acid-enhanced synthesis and release of amylase by isolated barley aleurone layers. Plant Physiol 69:557–562

Eastwell KC, Bassi PK, Spencer MS (1978) Comparison and evaluation of methods for the removal of ethylene and other hydrocarbons from air for biological studies. Plant Physiol 62:723–726

Eastwell KC, Bassi PK, Spencer MS (1981) NO_x species – not by-products of the purification of air with high temperature combustion devices, for biological studies. Can J Bot 59:1360–1361

Eastwell KC, Bassi PK, Spencer MS (1986) Methods for the determination of ethylene production by plant tissue via gas chromatography. In: Yopp JH, Aung LH, Steffens GL (eds) Bioassays and other special techniques for plant hormones and plant growth regulators. Plant Growth Regul Soc Am, p 152

McAuliffe C (1966) Solubility in water of paraffin, cycloparaffin, olefin, acetylene, cycloolefin, and aromatic hydrocarbons. J Phys Chem 70:1267–1275

Ramsey LH (1959) Analysis of gas in biological fluids by gas chromatography. Science 129:900–901

Roxburgh JM (1962) Determination of oxygen utilization in fermentations by gas chromatography. Can J Microbiol 8:221–227

Saltveit MK Jr. (1982) Procedures for extracting and analyzing internal gas samples from plant tissues by gas chromatography. HortScience 17:878–881

Stinson RA, Spencer MS (1969) β-alanine as an ethylene precursor. Investigations towards preparation, and properties of a soluble enzyme system from a subcellular particulate fraction of bean cotyledons. Plant Physiol 44:1217–1226

Swinnerton JW, Linnenborn VJ (1967) Gaseous hydrocarbons in sea water: determinations. Science 156:1119–1120

Swinnerton JW, Linnenborn VJ, Cheek CH (1962) Determination of dissolved gases in aqueous solutions by gas chromatography. Anal Chem 34:483–485

Ward TM, Wright M, Roberts JA, Self R, Osborne DJ (1978) Analytical procedures for the assay and identification of ethylene. In: Hillman JR (ed) Isolation of plant growth regulators. Cambridge Univ Press, p 135

Yopp JH, Aung LH, Steffens GL (eds) (1986) Bioassays and other special techniques for plant hormones and plant growth regulators. Plant Growth Regul Soc Am

Determination of Extra- and Intracellular pH Values in Relation to the Action of Acidic Gases on Cells

H. Pfanz and U. Heber

1 Introduction

Gaseous air pollutants such as SO_2 or NO_2 are soluble in aqueous media. They react with water to form H_2SO_3, HNO_2 and HNO_3 which increase the concentration of H^+ (or, as H^+ does not really exist, that of the hydrogen-bonded complex $H_3O^+ \cdot 3H_2O$) and thereby decrease pH, which is defined as the negative ^{10}log of the proton concentration $[H^+]$. For living cells the control of intracellular pH is essential for the maintenance of normal metabolic functions. The cytoplasmic pH of plant cells is usually close to 7.5 (Raven and Smith 1981). In chloroplasts, the stroma pH increases from about 7.5 to about 8 on illumination (Heldt et al. 1973; Oja et al. 1986), whereas the pH of the thylakoid compartment may drop to pH 5 owing to the transfer of protons from the stroma to the intrathylakoid space (Schuldiner et al. 1972). The large central vacuole of plant cells is usually acidic, with pH varying rather widely in different plant species (Smith and Raven 1979). In the cytoplasm, protons and hydroxyl ions are produced or consumed in many metabolic reactions (Raven 1985, 1986). Still, the internal pH is altered only within well-defined and rather narrow limits even when external pH values are very different (Langworthy 1978). Different mechanisms are em-

Table 1. pK Value and solubility in water of potentially acidic gases

Gas	Ostwald coefficient at 20° C, 1 atm ratio c_{aq}/C_{gas}		pK$_1$ (of acid)	pK$_2$ (of acid)	Molecular weight
H_2S[f]	2.792[a]	18° C	7.05[b]	11.96[b]	34
SO_2[e]	1.6[a]	18° C	1.79[b]	7.0[b]	64
CO_2[g]	0.039[a, d]	25° C	6.37[b, c]	10.25[b, c]	44
NO_2	Highly soluble, reacts with water to:				46
	HNO_2 and	12.5° C	3.37[b]	–	47
	HNO_3	30° C	−22[b]	–	63
HF[e]	18.0	25° C	3.45[b]	–	20

[a] After Wilhelm et al. (1977).
[b] After Weast et al. (1986) and Perrin (1969).
[c] After Grau (1960).
[d] After Kruis and May (1962).
[e] Does not obey Henry's law.
[f] Obeys Henry's law up to 1 atm.
[g] Obeys Henry's law up to 5 atm (footnotes e–g after Kruis and May 1962).

ployed to control the internal pH. The plasmalemma ATPase can transfer protons into the apoplast and the tonoplast ATPase into the vacuole (Gyenes et al. 1981; Torimitsu et al. 1984; Guern et al. 1986). H^+ generated in the cytoplasm can be consumed by cytoplasmic buffers (Pfanz and Heber 1985, 1986) or it can be compensated by the formation of hydroxyl ions (Davies 1986; Raven 1986; Heber et al. 1987). Excellent reviews on cytoplasmic pH regulation by pH-stat mechanisms are given by Butler et al. (1966), Davies (1973, 1986), Raven and Smith (1974, 1976), Smith and Raven (1979), Böttger et al. (1982), Guern et al. (1983), Raven (1985, 1986), and Booth (1985).

Potentially acidic gases such as CO_2, SO_2 or NO_2 enter leaves by diffusion. The rate of entry is controlled by the aperture of the stomates. Inside the leaves, the gases dissolve in the aqueous phase of the apoplast (which includes the cell walls) before entering the protoplasts. Hydration produces acids from which protons dissociate thereby lowering the pH of the apoplast. Because biomembranes are generally much less permeable to ions than to small neutral solutes, diffusion of dissolved gas through the plasmalemma into the cells dominates over uptake of ions. Inside the cells, the dissolved gas and its reaction products are distributed between different cellular compartments.

We will consider the simple case of the distribution of a weak acid AH which dissociates according to:

$$AH \Leftrightarrow A^- + H^+ . \tag{1}$$

AH (for instance, SO_2) can penetrate biomembranes easily, because it is neutral (cf. Pfanz et al. 1987a). The ions (for instance, HSO_3^-, SO_3^{2-} and H^+) are considered to be impermeable compared with AH (cf. McLaughlin and Dilger 1980). Transport and dissociation equilibrium is then described for the different cellular compartments a, b, c, and i by:

$$\frac{(H^+)_a(A^-)_a}{(AH)_a} = \frac{(H^+)_b(A^-)_b}{(AH)_b} = \frac{(H^+)_c(A^-)_c}{(AH)_c} = \frac{(H^+)_i(A^-)_i}{(AH)_i} = K , \tag{2}$$

where K is the dissociation constant of AH. The negative logarithm of K is termed pK. Table 1 lists solubilities in water and pK values of the acid function of some potentially acidic gases. Because AH is permeable, its concentration must at flux equilibrium (no net flux of AH between the compartments) be identical in the different compartments.

Therefore,

$$(H^+)_a(A^-)_a = (H^+)_b(A^-)_b = (H^+)_c(A^-)_c = (H^+)_i(A^-)_i \tag{3}$$

or,

$$(H^+)_a/(H^+)_b = (A^-)_b/(A^-)_a \tag{4}$$

and

$$(H^+)_c/(H^+)_i = (A^-)_i/(A^-)_c . \tag{5}$$

These relations show that the weak acid is trapped in the anionic form wherever the H^+ concentration is low, i.e. in the cytoplasmic compartments, not where it is high (i.e. in the vacuole). As hydroxyl ions are consumed when AH is trapped as A^-,

$$AH + OH^- \rightarrow A^- + H_2O\,, \tag{6}$$

acidification occurs where trapping occurs, i.e. in the cytoplasmic compartments. This very simplified model permits us to understand a main feature of the action of potentially acidic air pollutants on cells, namely the concentration of the attack on the metabolically active compartments. However, the model does not consider catalyzed transport of ions across biomembranes which is an important aspect of the intracellular distribution of ions (see Hampp and Ziegler 1977; Pfanz et al. 1987a). Also, it does not consider the fact that in real situations flux equilibrium will not be observed. Rather, the removal of reaction products will maintain a steady influx of pollutant into the leaves which is controlled by several flux resistances among which the stomates occupy a dominant position. Protons formed during the dissociation of acids must be compensated metabolically, if the cells are not to suffer damage during prolonged exposure (Heber et al. 1987).

If acidification of the cytoplasm by the steady influx of a potentially acidic gas cannot be prevented by buffering or compensated by OH^- production or H^+ export, metabolism will be affected. For instance, photosynthesis is very sensitive to pH changes (Heldt et al. 1973; Servaites and Ogren 1977; Enser and Heber 1980; Espie and Colman 1981). After light activation, the stroma enzymes sedoheptulose bisphosphatase and fructose bisphosphatase catalyze the hydrolysis of their substrates in a tightly controlled manner close to pH 8. At pH 7, they are inactive and photosynthesis cannot proceed (Garnier and Latzko 1972; Woodrow et al. 1984).

The rate of acid influx into leaves exposed to an atmosphere containing SO_2, NO_2, HF or HCl can be calculated with sufficient accuracy by a simplified form of Fick's law of diffusion:

$$\phi = c_a \cdot R^{-1}\,, \tag{7}$$

where ϕ is the rate of flux, c_a the concentration of a pollutant in the atmosphere and R the sum of the boundary layer and stomatal resistances of the leaf. R can be calculated from transpiration measurements (Nobel 1983). Equation (7) assumes that the intercellular concentration of the pollutant is close to zero. This assumption is justified, when the solubility of the pollutant in aqueous media is high, the biomembrane resistance to penetration low and the conversion to ions fast (Hocking and Hocking 1977; Wilhelm et al. 1977; Mudd 1975; Pfanz et al. 1987a). Thus, knowing pollution levels and flux resistances, potential proton loads on metabolism that must be tolerated or compensated can be calculated (Pfanz et al. 1987b). For SO_2, a computer model has been developed which is capable of simulating SO_2 fluxes into leaves, the intracellular distribution of SO_2 and its reaction products and the acidification of intracellular compartments (Laisk et al. 1988a, b).

In the following we will consider methods useful to measure pH in biological systems.

2 Methods and Applications

2.1 pH-Measurements in Leaf Extracts with Glass Electrodes

A very simple method of measuring pH in tissues is to grind the tissue and to determine pH electrometrically in the homogenate. This yields an average pH of the different cell types of the tissue and of the different compartments of these cells. Since in many differentiated plant tissues the vacuolar compartment occupies a large percentage of the total volume, the measured pH may not be much higher than the pH of the vacuolar content, although cytoplasmic compartments are more strongly buffered than the vacuolar compartment (Pfanz and Heber 1986). Proton concentrations have been determined in expressed fruit juices or leaf saps by Atkins (1922), Hurd-Karrer (1939), Drawert (1955), and Small (1946, 1956) and in *Chara* by Moriyasu et al. (1984), in *Zea mays* and *Avena sativa* by Hager and Moser (1985) and Romani et al. (1983) and in *Acer pseudoplatanus* by Kurkdjian and Guern (1981). When the vacuole is very acidic and well-buffered as, for instance, in the brown alga *Desmarestia* (McClintock et al. 1982), in cells of CAM plants (Lüttge et al. 1982) or in conifer needles (Pfanz and Heber 1986), the pH obtained may be close to the vacuolar pH.

Gracanin and Georgiev (1962) have fumigated different plants with unspecified concentrations of HCl or NH_3 for several minutes. Afterwards the pH of the leaf homogenate was determined. Not surprisingly, HCl treatment of *Hordeum* plants produced a drastic decrease in the pH of the homogenate. Similar experiments have been performed by fumigating alfalfa and dahlias with sulfur dioxide. The maximum decrease in alfalfa was 0.3 in *Dahlia* 1.0 pH units (Thomas et al. 1944). After exposure of detached leaves of spinach to high concentrations of CO_2 (15%) in the dark and the subsequent transfer to normal air, a significant increase was measured in the pH of leaf homogenates (Wagner and Heber, unpublished). The alkalization is thought to reflect the action of the cellular pH-stat mechanism which had been active in compensating the acidification caused by CO_2 (see Wager 1974a, b; Bown 1985). In air, pH values slowly returned to normal levels. This was shown by a decrease in the pH of leaf homogenates which were prepared at different times after the leaves had been transferred from high CO_2 to normal air.

2.1.1 Limitations of the Method

Although this simple method yields only average pH values after cell destruction and is therefore of limited value, it is still necessary to be cautious in the interpretation of results. Dissolved CO_2 can lead to a significant underestimation of pH values around and above neutrality. As the pK_1 of CO_2 is usually given to be 6.38 (Table 1), but may be as low as 6.1 in media of high ionic strength (Yokota and Kitaoka 1985), effects of dissolved CO_2 may be ignored only at pH values well below pH 6.

2.2 Intracellular pH Measurements with Microelectrodes

During the last years sophisticated techniques were developed which allow the conctruction of pH electrodes with a tip diameter of around 1 μm or less which can penetrate into individual cells and measure the cytosolic pH (Thomas 1978; Amman et al. 1981). Felle and Bertl (1986) and Steigner et al. (1988) have optimized and adapted these methods for pH measurements in plant cells which are surrounded by a mechanically resistant cell wall. Excellent introductions into the principles of microelectrode measurements are given by Findlay and Hope (1976) and Thomas (1978).

When the pH electrode punctures the cell so that it is tightly sealed, it measures the intracellular proton activity in relation to a reference which is outside the cell. The electrical signal produced has therefore a ΔpH and a membrane potential component. In order to obtain the intracellular pH, a second electrode must measure the membrane potential alone. Subtraction of the signals yields the intracellular pH. The necessity to use two electrodes restricts application of the method to fairly large cells or requires simultaneous measurements in two cells which are connected by plasmodesmata. Measurements have been reported for algal cells such as *Eremosphaera viridis* (Steigner et al. 1988), the moss *Riccia* (Felle 1981; Bertl et al. 1984), root tissue (Bowling 1974; Felle 1987) and leaf mesophyll tissue of higher plants (Felle and Bertl 1986).

An example of microelectrode measurements is shown in Fig. 1. The lower curve shows the pH response of the cytoplasm of *Eremosphaera viridis* to the ad-

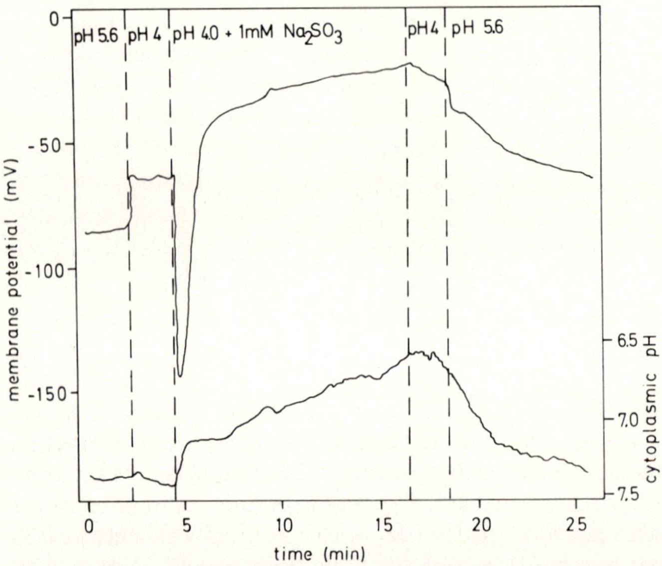

Fig. 1. Original recordings of the membrane potential (*upper curve*) and of the cytoplasmic pH (*lower curve*) of a cell of *Eremosphaera viridis* after addition of 1 m*M* Na_2SO_3 (=6.15 μ*M* SO_2). The external pH was 4, the K^+ concentration 0.1 m*M*. The *dotted lines* indicate the points where solutions were changed (Schnaus, Steigner, Pfanz, Urbach, unpublished)

dition of 1 mM sodium sulfite, the upper curve the membrane potential (which was held by a second inserted electrode). Sulfite dissociates according to:

$$SO_3^{2-} + H_2O \Leftrightarrow SO_2 + 2OH^- . \tag{8}$$

Therefore, the addition of H^+ which removes OH^- must increase the concentration of SO_2 in equilibrium with SO_3^{2-}. Only SO_2 diffuses into the cells. When, with the addition of 1 mM sulfite, the concentration of SO_2 reached 6.15 μM in the external medium, the cytoplasmic pH decreased rapidly from 7.4 to about 7.1 owing to a rapid influx of SO_2 into the cell. Simultaneously, the membrane potential depolarized. Subsequently, it recovered and hyperpolarization was observed. In this period, the cytoplasmic pH decreased slowly but steadily until it was 6.6 after about 12 min exposure to 6.15 μM SO_2. Removal of external bisulfite and SO_2 by washing restored both the membrane potential and the original cytoplasmic pH. Since part of the SO_2 was oxidized inside the cell to sulfuric acid which lowers the cellular pH and cannot be removed by washing, the observations demonstrate that the cell was able to compensate the acidification metabolically.

2.2.1 Limitations of the Method

The preparation and use of microelectrodes requires experience and modern equipment. Cells may be damaged mechanically by the insertion of electrodes. Results are variable, and measurements need to be repeated several times. Still, when used competently, the method gives not only excellent kinetic information, but also records absolute pH values.

2.3 Distribution of Weak Acids: pH in Neutral or Alkaline Cellular Compartments

Intracellular pH can be determined from the equilibrium distribution of weak acids between cells or membrane-surrounded organelles and the external solution [see Eqs. (3)–(6)]. Waddell and Butler (1959) were the first to calculate intracellular pH values from the distribution of ^{14}C-DMO (5,5-dimethyl-oxazolidine-2,4-dione). The method was later used for pH determinations in bacteria, protozoa, erythrocytes (cf. Gillies and Deamer 1979), barley protoplasts (Pfanz et al. 1987b), yeast cells (using propionic acid; Maier et al. 1986) and cells of *Acer* (Kurkdjian and Guern 1978), *Asparagus* (Colman et al. 1979), *Hydrodyction* (De Michelis et al. 1979) and *Chara* (Smith 1986). It was also employed to measure pH in the matrix of mitochondria (Addanki et al. 1968) and in isolated chloroplasts (Heldt et al. 1973; Heldt 1980; Marigo et al. 1982). Other weak acids are also suitable for pH calculations (Table 2). The distribution of CO_2 was used to calculate the stroma pH of isolated chloroplasts (Werdan et al. 1972) and of chloroplasts in situ in intact leaves of sunflower (Oja et al. 1986).

To be useful as an indicator of pH, a weak acid must meet several criteria:

1. It should penetrate biomembranes readily only in the neutral, uncharged form, not after deprotonation. Its pK must be below the pH to be measured. However,

Table 2. pK Values and dissociation constants of weak acids used for pH determinations

Weak acid	Temperature (°C)	Dissociation constant ($mol\,l^{-1}$)	pK
DMO	20	6.31×10^{-7}	6.38
Indole acetic	20	1.78×10^{-5}	4.75
Acetic	25	1.75×10^{-5}	4.76
Propionic	25	1.34×10^{-5}	4.87
Butyric	20	1.54×10^{-5}	4.81

Data from Weast et al. (1986).

Table 3. The pK of DMO in relation to temperature and ionic strength of the solution

Temperature (°C)	H_2O dest.	160 $mol\,m^{-3}$ NaCl
10	6.53	6.44
20	6.38	6.30
30	6.26	6.17
40	6.15	6.06

Data were taken from Fig. 1 in Boron and Roos (1976).

it should be in a range where accumulation in compartments other than that which is of interest is negligible. At the known pH of an external solution, the ratio of the protonated acid AH to the anion A^- can be calculated from the Henderson-Hasselbalch equation:

$$pH = pK + \log[A^-]/[AH]\,. \tag{9}$$

As, at flux equilibrium, [AH] is the same in the external medium and in the compartment of interest, accumulation of $[A^-]$ in that compartment permits calculation of its pH. Table 2 lists dissociation constants and pK values of some ^{14}C- or tritium-labelled weak acids which are available commercially. They must be used at a concentration which minimizes the danger of pH shifts.

2. As the pK of the weak acid is often different in the external medium and in the compartment of interest, correction of published pK values may be required. Dissociation constants are influenced by the ionic environment. Table 3 lists effects of temperature and salt concentration on the pK of DMO. The Debye/Hückel equation is useful to calculate salt effects on pK values (Segel 1976). pK values are changed in the presence of ions by:

$$pK = -{}^{10}\log a_{A^-}\,, \tag{10}$$

where a is the activity coefficient of A^-. The activity coefficient of AH will usually be close to 1. The calculation of a is possible from:

$$\log a = -0.509\,Z^2\sqrt{\Gamma/2}\,, \tag{11}$$

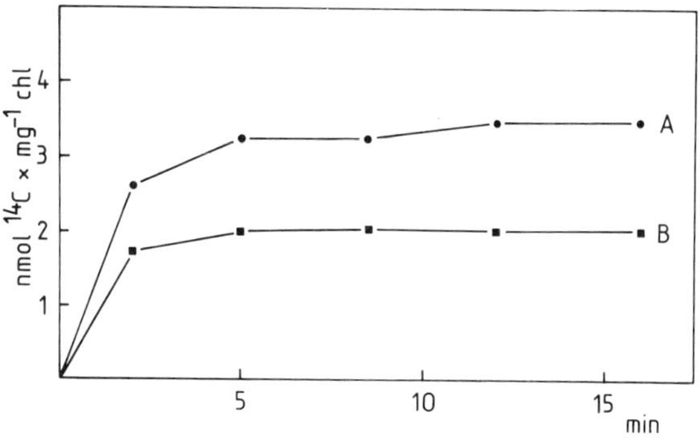

Fig. 2. Kinetics of uptake of DMO by isolated barley mesophyll protoplasts under different conditions. The pH of the incubation medium was 5. The total DMO concentration was 9.3 μ*M*. (*A*) Control without SO_2 being present; (*B*) with 0.62 μ*M* SO_2 (1 m*M* Na_2SO_3) in the solution. Saturation of DMO uptake was reached within 5 to 10 min

where Z ist the charge on A^- and $\Gamma/2$ the ionic strength. Yokota and Kitaoka (1985) have investigated in detail how the pH of carbonic acid changes with the ionic strength of the medium.

3. Flux equilibrium should be reached within a short time span. Figure 2 shows the kinetics of the uptake of DMO by isolated barley mesophyll protoplasts. Within 5 to 10 min, equilibrium between the undissociated form (H-DMO) inside and outside the protoplasts was established (cf. also Gillies and Deamer 1979).
4. The probe should neither be metabolized nor bound to cellular constituents. According to Espie and Colman (1981), DMO was not metabolized in *Asparagus* mesophyll cells, but metabolization was significant in *Acer* cells (Leguay 1977).
5. The probe should not affect metabolism (Leguay 1977; Gillies and Deamer 1979).
6. For the calculation of pH values, information on the volumes of cells or cellular compartments is required. Volumes may be estimated with the double-labelling $^3H_2O/^{14}C$-sorbitol technique of Heldt (1980) and Heldt and Sauer (1971), by the [^{3}H]-inulin method of Kurkdjian and Guern (1978) or by planimetric determinations (Loud et al. 1965; Heldt and Sauer 1971).

Using ^{14}C-DMO as a probe, we have measured pH changes caused in isolated barley mesophyll protoplasts by SO_2 (Pfanz et al. 1987b). Protoplasts were incubated at two different pH values with and without SO_2 present in the suspension. After 30 min ^{14}C-DMO was added. The protoplasts were separated from the incubation medium by a modification of the silicone-oil centrifugation technique of Heldt et al. (1973). Radioactivity was counted in a liquid scintillation counter. The results were in fair agreement with the change in pH expected when information on cellular buffering was used to calculate acidification from SO_2 influx (Pfanz and Heber 1986; Pfanz et al. 1987a, b).

2.3.1 Limitations

The usefulness of the method rests on the assumption that anionic species do not penetrate biomembranes. This is at best an approximation. At very low concentrations of a pH probe, binding to cellular constituents may be a serious source of error, whereas at higher concentrations effects on cellular pH values can become a problem. Volume changes of organelles or cells during the experiment may lead to erroneous results. Guern et al. (1983) state that a ΔpH of 0.1 to 0.2 pH units is the limit of detection by this method.

2.4 Distribution of Weak Bases: pH in Acidic Cellular Compartments

Whereas weak acids are trapped in neutral or alkaline cell compartments, weak bases will accumulate in the protonated cationic form in acidic compartments. Their accumulation can be used to calculate the pH of these compartments in much the same way as it has been described above for the accumulation of anions (Schuldiner et al. 1972). The equal distribution of a membrane-permeable weak base such as ^{14}C-labelled methylamine (CH_3NH_2) between two compartments will lead to the formation of labelled $CH_3NH_3^+$ in these compartments until the condition:

$$(H^+)_a/(H^+)_b = (CH_3NH_3^+)_a/(CH_3NH_3^+)_b \tag{12}$$

is met. Knowing (H^+) and labelled ($CH_3NH_3^+$) in one compartment (or in the medium), it is easy to calculate (H^+) in the other compartment from the measured accumulation of labelled methylamine in that compartment (cf. Rottenberg et al. 1972). Once again, it is necessary for the reliable calculation of concentrations to have information on compartmental volumes. Also, binding of the cation to cellular cation exchangers can lead to serious errors (Fiolet et al. 1974). As in the case of pH determinations in neutral or alkaline compartments with the help of weak acids, it is necessary to find a proper concentration range suitable for the use of weak bases as pH indicators. At very low concentrations of labelled bases, the danger of artifacts by binding may be significant. At higher concentrations, the pH in the compartments to be measured may be decreased by the influx of base. There are many reports on the use of amines for pH determinations in thylakoids (Heldt et al. 1973; Portis and McCarty 1976; Heldt 1980; Köster and Heber 1982; Robinson and Wellburn 1983). The method is also applicable for pH determinations in the vacuole (Kurkdjian and Guern 1981; Martinoia, unpub-

Table 4. pK Values and dissociation constants of weak bases

Weak base	Temperature (°C)	Dissociation constant ($mol\,l^{-1}$)	pK
9-Aminoacridine	20	1.00×10^{-10}	10[b]
Neutral red	20	2.51×10^{-7}	6.6[c]
Benzylamine	25	4.67×10^{-10}	9.33
Hexylamine	25	2.75×10^{-11}	10.56
Methylamine	25	2.24×10^{-11}	10.65[a]
Nicotine (step 1)	25	9.55×10^{-9}	8.02
(step 2)	25	7.59×10^{-4}	3.12

[a] Kurkdjian and Guern (1981).
[b] Schuldiner et al. (1972) and Haraux and de Kouchkovsky (1980).
[c] Junge et al. (1986) and De Wolf et al. (1985); all others from Weast et al. (1986).

lished). Table 4 lists dissociation constants and pK values of some weak bases which can be used for pH determinations.

Of particular interest is the use of fluorescent amines for the determination of pH gradients, as this avoids the necessity of using radioactive tracers and gives easy access to kinetic information. An often used probe is 9-aminoacridine (Schuldiner et al. 1972). In dilute solution it is highly fluorescent. When, in the course of an experiment, the pH of a cellular compartment in contact with a solution containing 9-aminoacridine is decreased, the membrane-permeable base will move into that compartment and accumulate there after protonation. As 9-aminoacridine displays concentration-dependent quenching of fluorescence, the observed fluorescence decrease is a direct measure of the amount of 9-aminoacridine taken up (cf. also Kurkdjian et al. 1984). Schuldiner et al. (1972) have used the fluorescene method to measure the light-dependent proton gradient across thylakoid membranes. In their calculations, they have assumed 9-aminoacridine to behave as an ideal amine. This has later been shown to be incorrect (Fiolet et al. 1974). In a recent report, Vu Van et al. (1987) describe a model which permits the calculation of pH gradients from observed 9-aminoacridine fluorescence quenching even when a considerable part of the protonated amine is membrane-bound. Robinson and Wellburn (1983) have used 9-aminoacridine to measure the influence of NO_2 and SO_2 on the transthylakoid pH gradient.

Neutral red is an amine with a low pK (Table 4). As it changes color with pH, the recording of the absorption of cells stained with neutral red at 548 nm permits kinetic mesurements of pH changes. However, the membrane permeability of the base which makes it suitable for vital staining also causes accumulation in and absorption to membranes. It allows redistribution of the dye and is a mild protonophore (Junge et al. 1986). For these reasons, observed absorption changes are not always easy to interpret. This has led to considerable controversy in the literature about the interpretation of spectrophotometric observations on pH changes in thylakoids (De Wolf et al. 1985; Junge et al. 1986).

2.5 Fluorescent pH Indicators and pH-Sensitive Dyes

Whereas changes in 9-aminoacridine fluorescence indicate changes in the distribution of 9-aminoacridine, other fluorescent dyes change fluorescence in response to protonation or deprotonation (Goodwin and Kavanagh 1950, 1951; Grünhagen and Witt 1970; Graber et al. 1986). Within somewhat more than one pH unit from their pK, they can directly indicate changes in pH. 5-Carboxyfluorescein is non-fluorescent as the diacetylester. After penetrating into cells, it is hydrolyzed in compartments which contain esterases. After hydrolysis, it becomes fluorescent (Graber et al. 1986). The fluorescence excited by blue light [493 nm; filters: Balzers (Liechtenstein) IF 493, Corning (NY, USA) 9782 and 5030] is green. It can be measured at wavelengths above 518 nm [filters: Schott (Mainz, FRG) BG 18, Corning 9782, Balzers K 65] (see also Slavik 1983). As the pK of 5-carboxyfluorescein is 6.4, the dye can be used to record pH changes in the range between pH 5 and 8 (Fig. 3). As a carboxylate, it is anionic at neutral pH and should not be expected to penetrate biomembranes rapidly. In fact, it

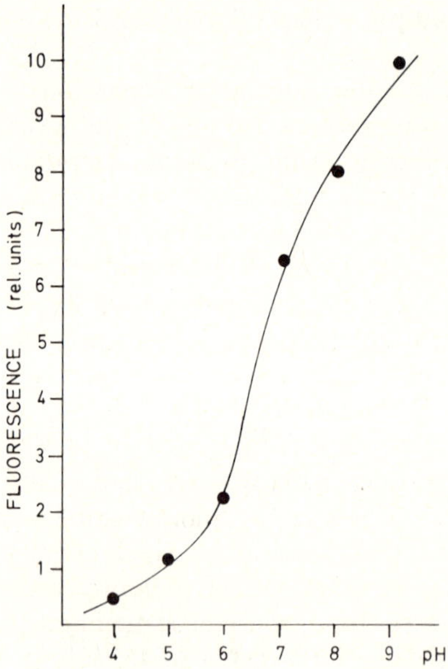

Fig. 3. Relative fluorescence versus pH of a solution containing 5-carboxyfluorescein (10 mmol m^{-3}). Fluorescence was excited at 490 nm and measured at 548 nm in a spectrofluorometer. Half-maximum fluorescence is observed at the pK of the pH-indicating dye

enters mesophyll cells in leaves as readily as it enters isolated mesophyll protoplasts. Inside the cells, it is accumulated in the nucleus which becomes brightly fluorescent, but it also penetrates into the large central vacuole. The chloroplasts are notably weak in emitting green fluorescence, probably because much of it is reabsorbed by chlorophyll. Although, owing to its large volume, a major part of the total green fluorescence emitted by mesophyll cells of barley or spinach originates from the vacuole, 5-carboxyfluorescein is insensitive to record pH changes in the non-acidic vacuoles of other plants. When the vacuolar pH is lower than about 5 [as for vacuoles in conifers or *Rumex* species (Pfanz and Heber 1986)], observed fluorescence changes reveal pH changes in the cytosol only. The fluorescence signal can be calibrated by CO_2. As the solubility of CO_2 and the pK of carbonic acid are known and buffer capacities of cellular systems can been determined by titration (Pfanz and Heber 1986), it is possible to calculate the pH changes caused by CO_2 if it is known from which cellular compartment fluorescence is emitted. Acidic vacuoles do not significantly change pH on addition of CO_2.

Figure 4 shows simultaneous recordings of photosynthetic CO_2 uptake by a spinach leaf and the fluorescence of 5-carboxyfluorescein from the leaf mesophyll. The dye had been fed via the petiole (concentration of the diacetylester 200 μM in water; feeding time 30 min). On illumination with about 200 Wm^{-2} red light, CO_2 was taken up from the air stream passing over the leaf. CO_2 assimilation ceased on darkening. The fluorescence decrease observed as a response to red actinic illumination indicates mesophyll acidification. It was reversed after 5 min photosynthesis. After somewhat more than 20 min photosynthesis, another shift towards acidification occurred. Darkening produced an alkalization reaction which was reversed after about 1 min in the dark. As should be expected, the

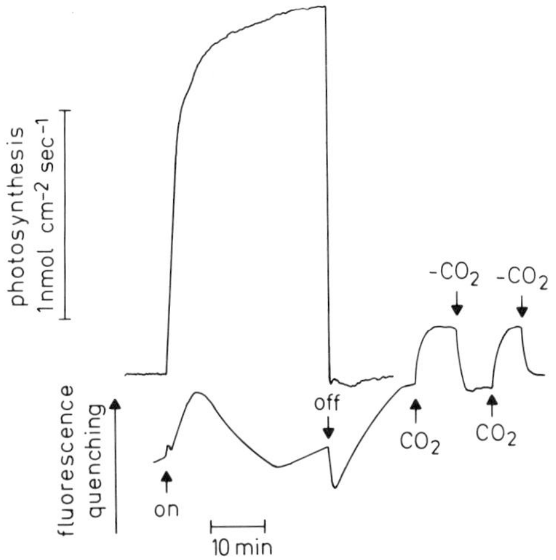

Fig. 4. Simultaneous recording of photosynthesis by a spinach leaf (measured as light-dependent CO_2 uptake from an air stream passing over the leaf) and of pH changes in the leaf mesophyll (measured as changes in 5-carboxyfluorescein fluorescence). 1% CO_2 was used as indicated to acidify cellular compartments. For explanation see text

addition of 1% CO_2 to the air stream caused mesophyll acidification, which was reversed when the CO_2 was removed from the gas stream. The light-dependent pH changes indicated by fluorescence signals are even more complex than Fig. 4 reveals, because fluorescence signals are simultaneously emitted from both the cytoplasm and the vacuole. These signals are opposite in sign (Oja et al. 1986). In contrast to the vacuole, the cytoplasm exhibits a transient alkalization on illumination which is reversed on darkening. This does not become apparent in the fluorescence changes shown in Fig. 4 which are dominated by vacuolar events.

Other pH-sensitive fluorescence or color indicators with pK values different from carboxyfluorescein extend the range of pH values accessible to pH recording by fluorescence or spectrophotometry. A major problem in all cases is uptake of the indicators into the cells. For instance, pyranine (pK 7.2) is not readily taken up by mesophyll protoplasts, but can be fed to mesophyll cells via the transpiration stream. In contrast, neutral red will not enter into the mesophyll when fed to leaves through the petiole. However, it is readily absorbed by isolated mesophyll protoplasts.

A simple way of determining the wavelength range, where recording fluorescence or absorbance changes permits sensitive pH measurements, is to measure excitation, emission and absorption spectra of the dye to be used at pH values corresponding to, below and above the pK of the dye. As absorption of the dye to cellular constituents can alter its pK, such measurements should be performed not only in simple buffer solutions but also in the presence of tissue homogenates so that an impression can be gained as to whether the cellular environment influences the fluorescence or optical properties of the dye.

To measure pH in the extracellular space (i.e. the apoplast) of leaves, non-permeant indicators must be used. Buffered solutions of esculin (6-glucoxy-7-hydroxycoumarin) of known pH are infiltrated in vacuo into leaf discs to fill the intercellular air space and fluorescence is recorded as a function of buffer pH (Pfanz and Dietz 1987). The same procedure is repeated with unbuffered esculin solution

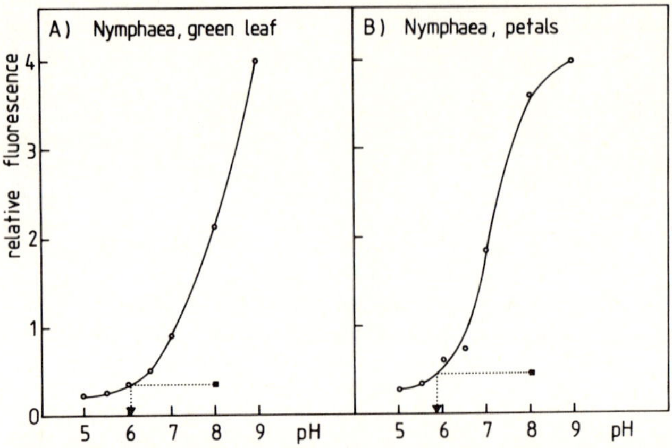

Fig. 5 A, B. Determination of the apoplastic pH in green leaves **A** and white petals **B** of *Nymphaea alba* from the fluorescence of esculin infiltrated into a leaf or a petal (■ = mean value of five measurements). The pH of the apoplastic space was taken from the calibration curves shown in **A** and **B**. They were pH 5.95 and 5.85 respectively. Buffers (50 mol m^{-3}) used were glycylglycine (pH 3.0–4.5), Mes [2-(N-morpholino)-ethanesulfonic acid; pH 5.0–6.5], Hepes (N-2-hydroxyethylpiperazine-N-2-ethanesulfonic acid; pH 7–8) and Epps (N-2-hydroxyethylpiperazine-N′-3-propanesulfonic acid; pH 9–11). The concentration of 6-glucoxy-7-hydroxycoumarin (≡esculin) in the infiltrated solutions was 0.5 mol m^{-3}. The fluorescence is given relative to the maximum fluorescence of the buffered controls at pH 9. The fluorescence was excited at 363 nm and measured at 453 nm (Pfanz and Dietz 1987)

which equilibrates with the apoplastic phase. By comparing the recorded fluorescence with the fluorescence emitted at known pH values from the leaf, the pH of the apoplastic space can be determined in situ (Fig. 5).

2.5.1 Limitations of the Method

Knowledge of the intracellular (or intercellular) distribution of fluorescent dyes or color indicators and of the pH range within which sensitive pH recording is possible is required for competent judgment of kinetic data. Accurate calibration of fluorescence or absorption signals is often difficult to achieve. pH changes can be recorded with a high degree of precision, but the measurement of absolute pH is often difficult or even impossible.

2.6 ^{31}P-Nuclear Magnetic Resonance (^{31}P-NMR)

^{31}P-NMR spectra of biological material can give information on intracellular pH values. Spectral recording is a non-intrusive method of pH determination. It is based on the pH dependence of the chemical shift of phosphate (^{31}P) in solution (Moon and Richards 1973; Roberts 1984). The experimental procedure has been described in several publications (Kime et al. 1982; Roberts 1984; Sianoudis et al. 1987; Kugel et al. 1987). In darkened mesophyll cells of many plants the cytoplasmic phosphate concentration is close to 30 m*M* (Rebeille et al. 1983; Stitt et al.

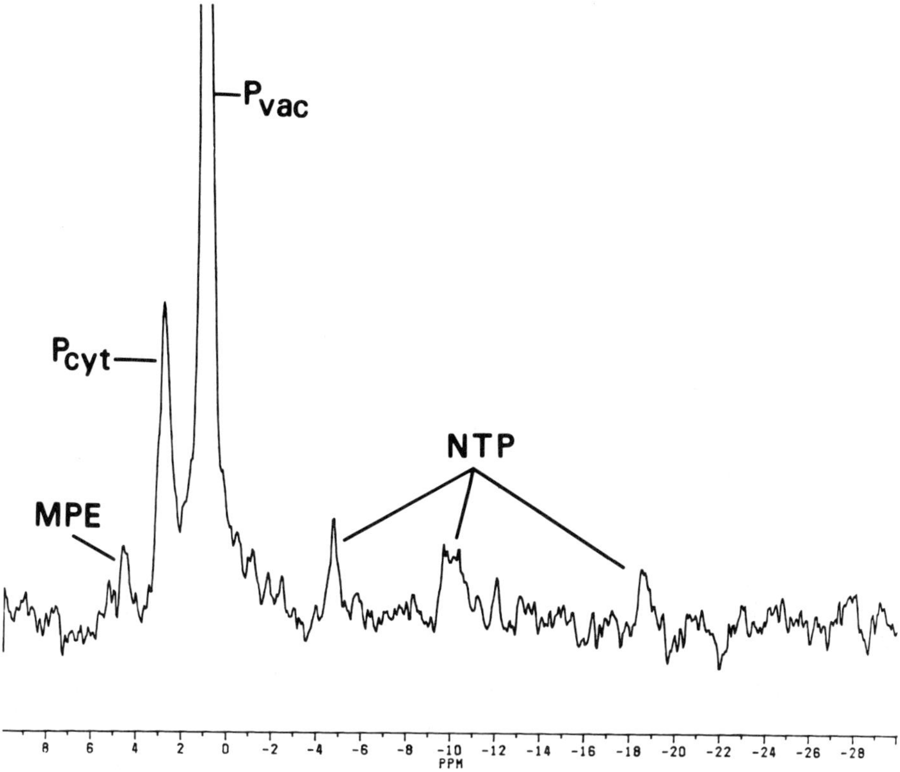

Fig. 6. ^{31}P-NMR spectrum of the unicellular alga *Eremosphaera viridis* cells in solution at an external pH of 7. P_{vac} Vacuolar phosphate; P_{cyt} cytoplasmic phosphate; *MPE* monophosphate esters (e.g. glucose 6-phosphate); *NTP* adenosine nucleotides (Gimmler and Kugel, unpublished)

1985). The vacuolar phosphate level can vary within rather wide limits (Kaiser et al. 1988). From a comparison of chemical shifts of ^{31}P observed in cells or tissues with those measured at different pH values in solution, it is possible to determine cytosolic and vacuolar pH values (see also Mimura and Kirino 1984). According to Roberts and Jardetzky (1981), a careful pH calibration in buffer systems, which in their composition resemble the biological system to be analyzed as closely as possible, is necessary, as in addition to the proton concentration, a great number of plant constituents influence the ^{31}P chemical shift (cf. also Roberts et al. 1980, 1981 a, b, 1982; Reid et al. 1985). Because different cell compartments have different proton concentrations, information on various cell compartments can, in principle, be obtained in a single measurement.

Figure 6 shows an NMR spectrum of cells of the alga *Eremosphaera viridis*. Prominent are two distinct peaks at 1 and 3 ppm. The larger one marks the vacuolar phosphate pool, the smaller one the cytoplasmic phosphate. Adequate calibration allows the determination of cytoplasmic and vacuolar pH values from the phosphate signals (Roberts 1984; Mimura and Kirino 1984). In Fig. 7, the effect

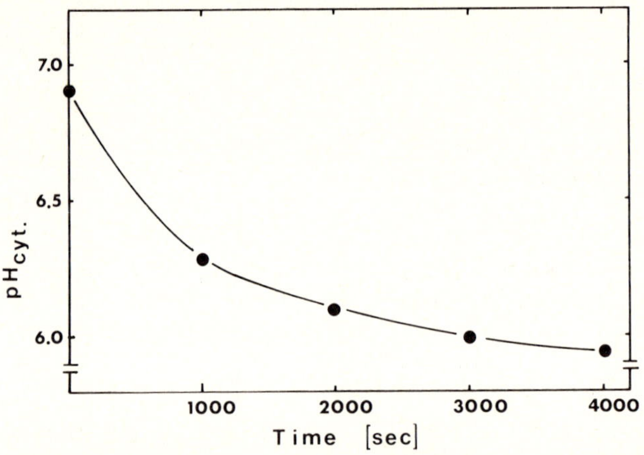

Fig. 7. Acidification of the cytoplasm of the unicellular alga *Dunaliella parva* by 1.85 μ*M* SO_2 (3 m*M* Na_2SO_3 at pH 5). (Gimmler, Kugel, Leibfritz, Mayer, unpublished)

of 1.8 μ*M* SO_2 (3 m*M* bisulfite at pH 5) on the intracellular pH of *Dunaliella parva* is shown. Within a few minutes of exposure, the cytoplasmic pH decreased by 1 pH unit.

2.6.1 Limitations of the Technique

Application of the method requires powerful spectrometers which are very costly and often unavailable. As the method is not very sensitive, high concentrations of biological material must be used. Dense cell suspensions tend to become anaerobic during the measurement owing to respiratory oxygen consumption. This will change intracellular pH. The problem of anaerobiosis can be overcome by bubbling air through the measuring cuvettes (Guern et al. 1986; Mathieu et al. 1986). Densely packed leaves are difficult to illuminate. So far, it has not been possible to resolve the light-dependent pH shift towards alkalization of the chloroplast stroma by ^{31}P-NMR techniques. The sensitivity of the chemical shift of P_i to the ionic environment makes calibration of pH values difficult. According to Kime et al. (1982), the use of NMR for intracellular pH measurements is limited to tissues with high water contents. Leaves of xerophytes or needles of conifers give broad ^{31}P spectra which are difficult to interpret.

2.7 Metabolite Determinations

Protons take part in many enzyme-catalyzed reactions. This permits the calculation of proton concentrations, if the equilibrium constants of the reactions are known and enzyme concentrations are high enough to justify the simplifying assumption that the reactions are very close to thermodynamic equilibrium. For instance, malic dehydrogenase catalyzes the reaction:

$$\text{oxaloacetate}^{2-} + \text{NADH} + \text{H}^{+} \Leftrightarrow \text{malate}^{2-} + \text{NAD}^{+} . \tag{13}$$

Therefore,

$$(\text{H}^{+}) = \text{K} \cdot \frac{(\text{malate}^{2-})(\text{NAD}^{+})}{(\text{oxaloacetate}^{2-})(\text{NADH})} . \tag{14}$$

If the equilibrium constant K is known, (H^+) can be calculated from measured concentrations of malate, oxaloacetate, NAD^+, and NADH.

2.7.1 Limitations of the Technique

In practice, it is not easy to determine oxaloacetate accurately, as its cellular concentration is very low. NADH is also very difficult to measure. Moreover, binding of this pyridine nucleotide to proteins is considerable (Borst 1963). Metabolite compartmentation is also a problem.

3 Conclusions

The use of some of the methods described above for intracellular pH measurements is restricted because the instrumentation required is costly and not available everywhere. Regrettably, this is still the case for high field NMR spectrometers. Still, the further development of non-destructive, intracellular pH determination by ^{31}P-NMR spectroscopy carries considerable promise. The same is true for the use of microelectrodes. It is presently restricted, as the sophisticated instrumentation and the experimental experience required are available only in some specialized laboratories. Widely used are radiotracer and photometric techniques. A combination of measurements of the distribution of labelled, permeable weak acids or weak bases and vital staining of cells with pH-sensitive fluorescent probes or pH-indicating dyes is capable of giving reasonably accurate information on absolute pH values, if the resolution required is not very high, and on pH changes, even if high resolution is required. The reliability of results obtained with one method should be cross-checked by using another, complementary method whereever possible (Boron and Roos 1976; Spanswick and Miller 1977), and interpretation of data requires knowledge and proper consideration of pitfalls.

Acknowledgments. The authors are indebted to Profs. Gimmler and Urbach and to Drs. Martinoia, Dietz, Gsell, Steigner and Kugel, MSc Yin and Dipl.-Biol. Schnaus for helpful comments and for making unpublished data available to us. This work was supported by grants from the Bayerische Forschungsgruppe Forsttoxikologie and the Projektgruppe Bayern zur Erforschung von Umweltschadstoffen (PBWU).

References

Addanki S, Cahill FD, Sotos JF (1968) Determination of intramitochondrial pH and intramitochondrial-extramitochondrial pH gradient of isolated heart mitochondria by the use of 5,5-dimethyl-2,4-oxazolidinedione. J Biol Chem 243:2337–2348

Amman D, Lanter F, Steiner RA, Schulthess P, Shijo Y, Simon W (1981) Neutral carrier-based hydrogen ion selective micro-electrode for extra- and intracellular studies. J Anal Chem 53:2267–2276

Atkins WRG (1922) The hydrogen ion concentration of plant cells. Sci Proc R Dublin Soc N5 16:414–426

Bertl A, Felle H, Bentrup FW (1984) Amine transport in *Riccia fluitans*. Cytoplasmic and vacuolar pH, recorded by a pH-sensitive microelectrode. Plant Physiol 76:75–78

Booth IR (1985) Regulation of cytoplasmic pH in bacteria. Microbiol Rev 49:359–378

Boron WF, Roos A (1976) Comparison of microelectrode, DMO, and methylamine methods for measuring intracellular pH. Am J Physiol 231:799–808

Borst P (1963) Hydrogen transport and transport metabolites. In: Karlson P (ed) Funktionelle und morphologische Organisation der Zelle. Springer, Berlin Göttingen Heidelberg, pp 137–162

Böttger M, Bigdon M, Soll HJ (1982) Regulation of and by pH. In: Marme D, Marre E, Hertel R (eds) Plasmalemma and tonoplast: their function in the plant cell. Elsevier, Amsterdam, pp 103–110

Bowling DJF (1974) Measurement of intracellular pH in roots using a H^+-sensitive microelectrode. In: Zimmermann U, Dainty J (eds) Membrane transport in plants. Springer, Berlin Heidelberg New York, pp 386–390

Bown AW (1985) CO_2 and intracellular pH. Plant Cell Environ 8:459–465

Butler TC, Waddell WJ, Poole DT (1966) The pH of intracellular water. Ann NY Acad Sci 133:73–77

Colman B, Mawson BT, Espie GS (1979) The rapid isolation of photosynthetically active mesophyll cells from *Asparagus* cladophylls. Can J Bot 57:1505–1510

Davies DD (1973) Control of and by pH. Symp Soc Exp Biol 27:513–529

Davies DD (1986) The fine control of cytosolic pH. Physiol Plant 67:702–706

De Michelis MI, Raven JA, Jayasuriya HD (1979) Measurement of cytoplasmic pH by the DMO technique in *Hydrodictyon africanum*. J Exp Bot 30:681–695

De Wolf FA, Groen BH, Houte LPA van, Peters FALJ, Krab K, Kraayenhof R (1985) Studies on well-coupled photosystem I-enriched subchloroplast particles. Neutral red as a probe for external surface charge rather than internal protonation. Biochim Biophys Acta 809:204–214

Drawert H (1955) Der pH-Wert des Zellsaftes. In: Ruhland W (ed) Encyclopedia of plant physiology, vol 1. Springer, Berlin Göttingen Heidelberg, pp 627–648

Enser U, Heber U (1980) Metabolic regulation by pH gradients: inhibition of photosynthesis by induced proton transfer across the chloroplast envelope. Biochim Biophys Acta 592:577–591

Espie GS, Colman B (1981) The intracellular pH of isolated photosynthetically active *Asparagus* mesophyll cells. Planta 153:210–216

Felle H (1981) A study of the current-voltage relationships of electrogenic active and passive elements in *Riccia fluitans*. Biochim Biophys Acta 602:181–195

Felle H (1987) Proton transport and pH control in *Sinapis alba* root hairs: a study carried out with double-barrelled pH micro-electrodes. J Exp Bot 38:340–354

Felle H, Bertl A (1986) The fabrication of H^+-selective liquid-membrane micro-electrodes for use in plant cells. J Exp Bot 37:1416–1428

Findlay GP, Hope AB (1976) What an inserted micro-electrode actually measures. In: Lüttge U, Pitman MG (eds) Transport in plants II. 4. Electrical properties of plant cells: methods and findings. Springer, Berlin Heidelberg New York, pp 57–59

Fiolet JWT, Bakker EP, Dam K van (1974) The fluorescent properties of acridines in the presence of chloroplasts or liposomes on the quantitative relationship between the fluorescence quenching and the transmembrane proton gradient. Biochim Biophys Acta 368:432–445

Garnier RV, Latzko E (1972) Regulation of photosynthetic C-1-fructose diphosphatase. In: Forti G, Avron M, Melandri A (eds) Proc 2nd Int Congr Photosynthesis research. Junk, The Hague, pp 1839–1845

Gillies RJ, Deamer DW (1979) Intracellular pH: methods and applications. In: Sanadi DR (ed) Current topics in bioenergetics, vol 9. Academic Press, New York San Francisco London, pp 63–87

Goodwin RH, Kavanagh F (1950) Fluorescence of coumarin derivatives as a function of pH. Arch Biochem 27:152–173

Goodwin RH, Kavanagh F (1951) Fluorescence of coumarin derivatives as a function of pH, pt II. Arch Biochem Biophys 36:442–455

Graber ML, Dilillo DC, Friedman BL, Pastoriza-Munoz E (1986) Characteristics of fluoroprobes for measuring intracellular pH. Anal Biochem 156:202–212

Gracanin M, Georgiev M (1962) Über den Einfluß der HCl- und NH_3-Dämpfe auf die Reaktion und die Atmung der Pflanzen. Fac Sci Nat Univ Skopje Biol, pp 19–27

Grau GG (1960) Gleichgewichte in elektrochemischen Systemen. Eigenschaften der Materie in ihren Aggregatzuständen. 7. Teil. Elektrische Eigenschaften II (Elektrische Systeme). In: Hellwege KH, Hellwege AM, Schäfer K, Lax E (eds) Landolt-Börnstein. Zahlenwerke und Funktionen aus Physik, Chemie, Astronomie, Geophysik und Technik. Springer, Berlin Göttingen Heidelberg, pp 839–932

Grünhagen HH, Witt HT (1970) Primary ionic events in the functional membrane of photosynthesis. Umbelliferone as indicator for pH changes in one turn-over. Z Naturforsch 25b:373–386

Guern J, Mathieu Y, Kurkdjian A (1983) Phosphoenolpyruvate carboxylase activity and the regulation of intracellular pH in plant cells. Physiol Veg 21:855–866

Guern J, Mathieu Y, Pean M, Pasquier C, Beloeil JC, Lallemand JY (1986) Cytoplasmic pH regulation in *Acer pseudoplatanus* cells. I. A ^{31}P-NMR description of acid-load effects. Plant Physiol 82:840–845

Gyenes M, Bulychev AA, Kurella AG, Perez Alvarez P (1981) Light-activated H^+ transport into the vacuole of *Valonia ventricosa*. J Exp Bot 32:1273–1277

Hager A, Moser J (1985) Acetic acid esters and permeable weak acids induce active proton extrusion and extension growth of coleoptile segments by lowering cytoplasmic pH. Planta 163:391–400

Hampp R, Ziegler I (1977) Sulfate and sulfite translocation via the phosphate translocator of the inner envelope membrane of chloroplasts. Planta 137:309–312

Haraux F, de Kouchkovsky Y (1980) Measurement of chloroplast internal protons with 9-aminoacridine. Probe binding, dark proton gradient, and salt effects. Biochim Biophys Acta 592:153–168

Heber U, Laisk A, Pfanz H, Lange OL (1987) Wann ist SO_2 Nähr- und wann Schadstoff? Ein Beitrag zum Waldschadensproblem. Allg Forstz 27/28/29:700–705

Heldt HW (1980) Measurement of metabolic movement across the envelope and of the pH in the stroma and the thylakoid space in intact chloroplasts. Meth Enzymol 69:604–613

Heldt HW, Sauer F (1971) The inner membrane of the chloroplast envelope as the site of specific metabolite transport. Biochim Biophys Acta 234:83–91

Heldt HW, Werdan W, Milovancev M, Geller G (1973) Alkalization of the chloroplast stroma caused by light-dependent proton flux into the thylakoid space. Biochim Biophys Acta 314:224–241

Hocking D, Hocking MB (1977) Equilibrium solubility of trace atmospheric air pollutants in water and its bearing on air pollution injury to plants. Environ Pollut 13:57–64

Hurd-Karrer AM (1939) Hydrogen-ion concentration of leaf juice in relation to environment and plant species. Am J Bot 26:834–846

Junge W, Schönknecht G, Förster V (1986) Neutral red as an indicator of pH transients in the lumen of thylakoids – some answers to criticism. Biochim Biophys Acta 852:93–99

Kaiser G, Martinoia E, Schröppl-Meier G, Heber U (1988) Active transport of sulfate into the vacuole of plant cells provides halotolerance and can detoxify SO_2. J Plant Physiol (in press)

Kime MJ, Ratcliffe RG, Williams RJP, Loughman BC (1982) The application of ^{31}P nuclear magnetic resonance to higher plant tissue. J Exp Bot 33:656–669
Köster S, Heber U (1982) Light scattering of 9-aminoacridine fluorescence as indicator of the phosphorylation state of the adenylate system in intact spinach chloroplasts. Biochim Biophys Acta 680:88–94
Kruis A, May A (1962) Lösungsgleichgewichte von Gasen in Flüssigkeiten, Bd 2: Eigenschaften der Materie in ihren Aggregatzuständen, 2a. Gleichgewichte außer Schmelzgleichgewichten. Lösungsgleichgewichte I. In: Schäfer K, Lax E (eds) Landolt-Börnstein. Zahlenwerke und Funktionen aus Physik, Chemie, Astronomie, Geophysik und Technik. Springer, Berlin Göttingen Heidelberg, pp 1–210
Kugel H, Mayer A, Kirst GO, Leibfritz D (1987) In vivo ^{31}P-NMR measurements of phosphate metabolism in *Platymonas subcordiformis* as related to external pH. Eur Biophys J 14:461–470
Kurkdjian A, Guern J (1978) Intracellular pH in hihger plant cells. I. Improvements in the use of the 5,5-dimethyloxazolidine-2[^{14}C],4-dione distribution technique. Plant Sci Lett 11:337–344
Kurkdjian A, Guern J (1981) Vacuolar pH measurement in higher plant cells. I. Evaluation of the methylamine method. Plant Physiol 67:953–957
Kurkdjian A, Manigault P, Manigault J, Guern J (1984) Action of fusicoccin on the vacuolar pH of *Acer pseudoplatanus* protoplasts as evidenced by 9-aminoacridine microfluorimetry. Plant Sci Lett 34:1–5
Laisk A, Pfanz H, Schramm MJ, Heber U (1988a) SO_2 fluxes into different cellular compartments of leaves photosynthesizing in a polluted atmosphere. I. Computer analysis. Planta 173:230–240
Laisk A, Pfanz H, Heber U (1988b) SO_2 fluxes into different cellular compartments of leaves photosynthesizing in a polluted atmosphere. II. Consequences of SO_2 uptake as revealed by computer analysis. Planta 173:241–252
Langworthy TA (1978) Microbial life in extreme pH values. In: Kushar DJ (ed) Aerobial life in extreme environments. Academic Press, New York London, pp 279–315
Leguay JJ (1977) The 5,5-dimethyloxazolidine-2[^{14}C]-4-dione distribution technique and the measurement of intracellular pH in *Acer pseudoplatanus* cells. Biochim Biophys Acta 497:329–333
Loud A, Barney JC, Pack BA (1965) Quantitative evaluation of cytoplasmic structures in electron micrographs. Lab Invest 19:996–1008
Lüttge U, Smith JAC, Marigo G (1982) Membrane transport, osmoregulation and the control of CAM. In: Ting P, Gibbs M (eds) Crassulacean acid metabolism. Am Soc Plant Physiol, Rockville, pp 69–91
Maier K, Hinze H, Leuschel L (1986) Mechanisms of sulfite action on the energy metabolism of *Saccharomyces cervisiae*. Biochim Biophys Acta 848:120–130
Marigo G, Ball E, Lüttge U, Smith JAC (1982) Use of the DMO-technique for the study of relative changes of cytoplasmic pH in leaf cells in relation to CAM. Z Pflanzenphysiol 108:223–233
Mathieu Y, Guern J, Pean M, Pasquier C, Beloeil JC, Lallemand JY (1986) Cytoplasmic pH regulation in *Acer pseudoplatanus* cells. II. Possible mechanisms involved in pH regulation during acid-load. Plant Physiol 82:846–852
McClintock M, Higinbotham N, Uribe EG, Cleland RE (1982) Active, irreversible accumulation of extreme level of H_2SO_4 in the brown alga *Desmarestia*. Plant Physiol 70:771–774
McLaughlin SGA, Dilger JP (1980) Transport of protons across membranes by weak acids. Physiol Rev 60:825–863
Mimura T, Kirino Y (1984) Changes in cytoplasmic pH measured by ^{31}P-NMR in cells of *Nitellopsis obtusa*. Plant Cell Physiol 25:813–820
Moon RB, Richards JH (1973) Determination of intracellular pH by ^{31}P magnetic resonance. J Biol Chem 248:7276–7278
Moriyasu Y, Shimmen T, Tazawa M (1984) Vacuolar pH regulation in *Chara australis*. Cell Struct Funct 9:225–234

Mudd JB (1975) Sulfur dioxide. In: Mudd JB, Kozlowski TT (eds) Responses of plants to air pollution. Academic Press, New York London, pp 9–22
Nobel PS (1983) Biophysical plant physiology and ecology, 3rd edn. Freeman, San Francisco
Ohmori M, Oh-hama T, Furihata K, Miyachi S (1986) Effect of ammonia on cellular pH of *Anabaena cylindrica* determined with ^{31}P-NMR spectroscopy. Plant Cell Physiol 27:563–566
Oja V, Laisk A, Heber U (1986) Light induced alkalization of the chloroplast stroma in vivo as estimated from the CO_2 capacity of intact sunflower leaves. Biochim Biophys Acta 849:355–365
Perrin DD (1969) Ionisation constants of inorganic acids and bases in aqueous solutions. IUPAC Chem Data Ser 29, 2nd edn. Pergamon, Oxford New York Toronto Sydney Paris Frankfurt
Pfanz H, Dietz KJ (1987) A fluorescence method for the determination of the apoplastic proton concentration in intact leaf tissues. J Plant Physiol 129:41–48
Pfanz H, Heber U (1985) Protonenflüsse und zelluläre Pufferkapazitäten in Blättern bei SO_2-Belastung. In: PBWU (ed) Proc Int Worksh Physiology and biochemistry of stressed plants. GSF-Ber 44/85, Neuherberg, pp 103–113
Pfanz H, Heber U (1986) Buffer capacities of leaves, leaf cells and leaf cell organelles in relation to fluxes of potentially acidic air pollutants. Plant Physiol 81:597–602
Pfanz H, Martinoia E, Lange OL, Heber U (1987a) Mesophyll resistances to SO_2 fluxes into leaves. Plant Physiol 85:922–927
Pfanz H, Martinoia E, Lange OL, Heber U (1987b) Flux of SO_2 into leaf cells and cellular acidification by SO_2. Plant Physiol 85:928–933
Portis AR, McCarty RE (1976) Quantitative relationships between phosphorylation, electron flow, and internal hydrogen ion concentration in spinach chloroplasts. J Biol Chem 251:1610–1617
Raven JA (1985) pH regulation in plants. Sci Progr 49:495–509
Raven JA (1986) Biochemical disposal of excess H^+ in growing plants. New Phytol 104:175–206
Raven JA, Smith FA (1974) Significance of hydrogen ion transport in plant cells. Can J Bot 52:1035–1048
Raven JA, Smith FA (1976) Nitrogen assimilation and transport in vascular plants in relation to intracellular pH regulation. New Phytol 76:415–431
Raven JA, Smith FA (1981) Cytoplasmic pH regulation and electrogenic H^+ extrusion. In: Smith H (ed) Commentaries in plant science, vol 2. Pergamon, New York Elmsford, pp 27–39
Rebeille F, Bligny R, Martin JB, Douce R (1983) Relationship between the cytoplasm and the vacuole phosphate pool in *Acer pseudoplatanus* cells. Arch Biochim Biophys 225:143–148
Reid RJ, Field LD, Pitman MG (1985) Effects of external pH, fusicoccin and butyrate on the cytoplasmic pH in barley root tips measured by ^{31}P-nuclear magnetic resonance spectroscopy. Planta 166:341–347
Roberts JKM (1984) Study of plant metabolism in vivo using NMR spectroscopy. Annu Rev Plant Physiol 35:375–386
Roberts JKM, Jardetzky O (1981) Monitoring of cellular metabolism by NMR. Biochim Biophys Acta 639:53–76
Roberts JKM, Ray PM, Wade-Jardetzky N, Jardetzky O (1980) Estimation of cytoplasmic and vacuolar pH in higher plant cells by ^{31}P-NMR. Nature 283:870–872
Roberts JKM, Ray PM, Wade-Jardetzky N, Jardetzky O (1981a) Extent of intracellular pH changes during H^+ extrusion. Planta 152:74–78
Roberts JKM, Wade-Jardetzky N, Jardetzky O (1981b) Intracellular pH measurements by ^{31}P-nuclear magnetic resonance. Influence of factors other than pH on ^{31}P chemical shifts. Biochemistry 20:5389–5394
Roberts JKM, Wemmer D, Ray PM, Jardetzky O (1982) Regulation of cytoplasmic and vacuolar pH in maize root tips under different experimental conditions. Plant Physiol 69:1344–1347

Robinson DC, Wellburn A (1983) Light-induced changes in the quenching of 9-aminoacridine fluorescence by photosynthetic membranes due to atmospheric pollutants and their products. Environ Pollut 32:109–120

Romani G, Marrè MT, Marrè E (1983) Effects of permeant weak acids on dark CO_2 fixation and malate level in maize root segments. Physiol Veg 21:867–873

Rottenberg H, Grunwald T, Avron M (1972) Determination of ΔpH in chloroplasts. 1. Distribution of [^{14}C] methylamine. Eur J Biochem 25:54–63

Schuldiner S, Rottenberg H, Avron M (1972) Determination of pH in chloroplasts. 2. Fluorescent amines as a probe for the determination of ΔpH in chloroplasts. Eur J Biochem 25:64–70

Segel JH (1976) Biochemical calculations, 2nd edn. Wiley, New York

Servaites JC, Ogren WL (1977) pH dependence of photosynthesis and photorespiration in soybean leaf cells. Plant Physiol 60:693–696

Sianoudis J, Küsel AC, Mayer A, Grimme LH, Leibfritz D (1987) The cytoplasmic pH in photosynthesizing cells of the green alga *Chlorella fusca* measured by ^{31}P-NMR spectroscopy. Arch Microbiol 147:25–29

Slavik J (1983) Intracellular pH topography: determination by a fluorescent probe. FEBS Lett 156:227–230

Small J (1946) pH and plants. Bailliere, Tindall & Cox, London

Small J (1956) Estimation of pH values (living tissues and saps). In: Paech C, Tracey MV (eds) Modern methods of plant analysis, vol 1. Springer, Berlin Göttingen Heidelberg, pp 375–392

Smith FA (1986) Short-term measurements of the cytoplasmic pH of *Chara corallina* derived from the intracellular equilibration of 5,5-dimethyloxazolidine-2,4-dione (DMO). J Exp Bot 37:1733–1745

Smith FA, Raven JA (1979) Intracellular pH and its regulation. Annu Rev Plant Physiol 30:289–311

Spanswick RM, Miller AG (1977) Measurement of the cytoplasmic pH in *Nitella translucens*. Comparison of values obtained by microelectrode and weak acid methods. Plant Physiol 59:664–666

Steigner W, Köhler K, Simonis W, Urbach W (1988) Transient cytoplasmic pH-changes in correlation with opening of potassium channels in *Eremosphaera*. J Exp Bot 39:23–36

Stitt M, Wirtz W, Gerhardt R, Heldt HW, Spencer C, Walker D, Foyer C (1985) A comparative study of metabolite levels in plant leaf material in the dark. Planta 166:354–364

Thomas MD, Hendricks RH, Hill GR (1944) Some chemical reactions of sulphur dioxide after absorption by alfalfa and sugar beets. Plant Physiol 19:212–226

Thomas RC (1978) Ion-sensitive electrodes. How to make and use them. Academic Press, New York London, pp 32–44

Torimitsu K, Yazaki Y, Nagasuka K, Ohta E, Sakata M (1984) Effect of external pH on the cytoplasmic and vacuolar pHs in mung bean root-tip cells: a ^{31}P nuclear magnetic resonance study. Plant Cell Physiol 25:1403–1409

Vu Van T, Heinze T, Buchholz J, Rumberg B (1987) Quantitative relationships between 9-aminoacridine fluorescence and internal pH in broken chloroplasts. In: Biggins J (ed) Progress in photosynthesis research, vol 3. Nijhoff, Dordrecht, pp 189–192

Waddell WJ, Butler TC (1959) Calculation of intracellular pH from the distribution of DMO. Application to skeletal muscle of the dog. J Clin Invest 38:720–729

Wager HG (1974a) The effect of subjecting peas to air enriched with carbon dioxide. I. The path of gaseous diffusion, the content of CO_2 and the buffering of the tissue. J Exp Bot 25:330–337

Wager HG (1974b) The effect of subjecting peas to air enriched with carbon dioxide. II. Respiration and the metabolism of the major acids. J Exp Bot 25:338–351

Weast RC, Astle MJ, Beyer WJ (1986) Handbook of chemistry and physics. CRC, Boca Raton, Fla

Werdan K, Heldt HW, Geller G (1972) Accumulation of bicarbonate in intact chloroplasts following a pH gradient. Biochim Biophys Acta 283:430–441

Wilhelm E, Battino R, Wilcock RJ (1977) Low-pressure solubility of gases in liquid water. Chem Rev 77:219–262

Woodrow IE, Murphy DJ, Latzko E (1984) Regulation of stromal sedoheptulose-1,7-bisphosphatase activity by pH and Mg^{2+} concentration. J Biol Chem 259:3791–3795

Yokota A, Kitaoka S (1985) Correct pK values for the dissociation constant of carbonic acid lower the reported Km values of ribulose bisphosphate carboxylase to half. Presentation of a nomograph and an equation for determining the pK values. Biochem Biophys Res Commun 131:1075–1079

Subject Index